SCHAUM'S SOLVED PROBLEMS SERIES

3000 SOLVED PROBLEMS IN

BIOLOGY

by

Ruth Bernstein, Ph.D

Stephen Bernstein, Ph.D.

University of Colorado at Boulder

McGRAW-HILL PUBLISHING COMPANY
New York St. Louis San Francisco Auckland Bogotá Caracas
Hamburg Lisbon London Madrid Mexico Milan Montreal
New Delhi Oklahoma City Paris San Juan São Paulo
Singapore Sydney Tokyo Toronto

Ruth Bernstein, Ph.D., *Associate Professor, Department of Environmental, Population, and Organismic Biology, University of Colorado at Boulder*

Dr. Ruth Bernstein currently teaches general biology, ecology, and population dynamics. Previously, she taught general biology at the University of California, Los Angeles. She received her B.S. from the University of Wisconsin and her Ph.D. in biology from UCLA. Her published research is in evolutionary ecology, and she is co-author with Stephen Bernstein of a general biology textbook.

Stephen Bernstein, Ph.D., *Research Associate, Department of Environmental, Population, and Organismic Biology, University of Colorado at Boulder*

Dr. Stephen Bernstein has taught both general biology and biostatistics in his current position. Previously, he taught animal behavior at UCLA. He received his B.A. from Princeton University and his Ph.D. in psychology from the University of Wisconsin. A recipient of various NIMH fellowships and awards, he attended the University of Zürich and the University of Paris for postdoctoral studies. His published research is in animal behavior, neurophysiology, and brain-body allometry. He is co-author with Ruth Bernstein of a general biology textbook.

Project supervision by The Total Book.

Library of Congress Cataloging-in-Publication Data

Bernstein, Ruth.
  Schaum's 3000 solved problems in biology.

  (Schaum's solved problems series)
  1. Biology—Problems, exercises, etc.   I. Bernstein,
Stephen.   II. Title.   III. Title: Schaum's three
thousand solved problems in biology.   IV. Series.
QH316.B47 1988   574′.076   88-1538
ISBN 0-07-005022-8

  3 4 5 6 7 8 9 0 SHP/SHP 8 9 2 1 0 9 ❧

0-07-005022-8

CONTENTS

To the Student

This book provides a complete review of the material covered in a two-semester course in general biology. The review is in the form of questions that range, for each topic, from elementary and basic to advanced and sophisticated. Answers are provided for every question, with essays that integrate the material. By using this book, you can prepare yourself for examinations at many levels: advanced placement tests; college-level biology courses; college-level examination programs; medical-, dental-, and nursing-school admissions tests; graduate record exams; and graduate-school comprehensive exams.

The content of this book is based on our extensive teaching experience and on a survey of eight biology textbooks that are currently best sellers in the field—four for general-background, nonmajors courses and four for professional-level, majors courses. We organized the information into chapters that follow a standard sequence: chemistry of life, cells, genetics, evolution, diversity and history of life, form and function of plants, form and function of animals, and ecology. Each chapter includes the names, facts, concepts, and principles covered in most biology courses and also includes drawings of the most commonly illustrated material. Look in the table of contents to find the topics you want to review.

By encountering here the fundamental biological information isolated from lectures and textbooks, you will be able to rapidly determine which areas you have mastered and which areas require further effort on your part. Each chapter begins with a set of multiple-choice and fill-in-the-blank questions, with answers provided at the end of the chapter. If these objective questions alert you to gaps in your knowlege, read the short-essay questions; the answers to these integrate the chapter details and so may provide the knowledge you lack. Alternatively, if you write your own essay answers and then check them against those given, you will get an idea of your mastery of the material. We hope that, by structuring and guiding your efforts, this form of active review will enable you to use your available review time with maximum efficiency.

Acknowledgments

The authors are indebted to the many people at the McGraw-Hill Book Company who have contributed to this work. In particular, we thank G. Frederick Perkins for suggesting us for this project and encouraging our efforts, and Elizabeth Zayatz, our editor, for enthusiastically guiding and editing our efforts from start to finish.

Ruth Bernstein
Stephen Bernstein

CHAPTER 1
The Science of Biology

WHAT IS SCIENCE*

1.1   Which of the following best describes the scientific method?

(*a*) Doing experiments in laboratories;   (*b*) Collecting all known facts on a subject;   (*c*) Developing and testing hypotheses;   (*d*) Using sensitive electronic measuring instruments

1.2   Which of the following is *not* a characteristic of a hypothesis?

(*a*) A deductive inference;   (*b*) An inductive inference;   (*c*) A guess about cause and effect;   (*d*) A generalization from specific observations

1.3   Which of the following is *not* a characteristic of a theory?

(*a*) It is more comprehensive than a hypothesis;   (*b*) It is limited in scope compared with a hypothesis;   (*c*) It has been repeatedly tested;   (*d*) It is supported by many different lines of evidence

1.4   In 1838, the German botanist Matthis Schleiden, after examining the tissues of many plants under a microscope, concluded: All plant tissues are composed of individual cells. This form of reasoning, from specific observations to a general conclusion, is called _____ logic. The opposite process, going from a general conclusion to a specific consequence, is called _____ logic. Had Schleiden said, "If all plant tissues are composed of individual cells, then the tissues of ferns must be composed of individual cells," he would have been making a _____ using _____ logic.

1.5   Why are observations from the natural world essential to the scientific method?

🐚   The goal of science is to understand the natural, physical world by revealing the cause-and-effect relationships between observable phenomena. This goal is achieved by the development and testing of hypotheses, using a format for asking and answering questions that is known as the scientific method. This powerful method of problem solving involves five steps: (1) observing the natural phenomena; (2) developing a question about cause and effect; (3) formulating a tentative answer to the question (the hypothesis) through inductive generalization from the observations; (4) deriving the consequences (predictions) of the hypothesis through deductive reasoning; and (5) returning to the natural world for new observations in order to test the predictions and, consequently, the hypothesis itself. The scientific method is therefore firmly anchored in the observable, natural world; both questions and hypotheses come from observations and are tested with observations. Furthermore, for the hypothesis to be generally acceptable to the scientific community, the original observations must be repeatable: by using the same methods, other scientists must be able to achieve the same results.

1.6   What is the function of a controlled experiment in the scientific method?

🐚   As discussed in Question 1.5, the scientific method is fundamentally a process of formulating and testing hypotheses, and, for such testing, the technique of controlled experimentation is the most powerful one available.
   To understand controlled experimentation, it will be useful to study an example. Say that a new plant hormone has been discovered, and from a hypothesis about the hormone it is predicted that application of the hormone will greatly accelerate plant growth. To test this prediction, it is necessary to compare growth with and without the hormone. Setting up this test is not simple, because many factors (variables), such as amounts of nutrients, water, and light, are known to influence plant growth. All of the factors that could influence (or cause) growth are called *independent variables*. Measures of growth (the effect produced), such as weight or height, are called *dependent variables*. In experiments, the scientist manipulates (changes) the independent variables to see the effect on the dependent variables. In a controlled experiment, only the independent variable of interest is changed; all other independent variables are held constant (controlled). Thus, in the hypothetical test of the growth-hormone prediction, plants would be grown with and without the hormone, and all other independent variables that could influence growth would be kept the same for both groups.

* Answers to Chapter 1 objective questions appear on page 4.

1.7 In the study of human evolution, it is not known when humans (*Homo sapiens*) first came to the New World. While it is generally accepted that the first humans crossed from Asia to North America (Alaska) along a land bridge through the Bering Sea, scientists differ on when this occurred. The estimates range from 40,000 to 10,000 years ago. How might you test the hypothesis that humans first entered the New World 40,000 years ago?

☗ All hypotheses are tested by verifying their deductively derived predictions—what must also be true if the hypothesis is true. In this case, it would be predicted that if humans did enter the New World 40,000 years ago, then they must have left evidence of this passage along probable migration routes. This evidence, which might include human bone fragments, the remains of campfires, or worked bone or stone tools, must be found in rock layers dated to that earliest time period and associated with plants or animals from that time period.

1.8 What are the limitations of science?

☗ There are four kinds of limitations: (1) the type of question that can be answered; (2) the time it may take to find an answer; (3) the lack of absolute certainty in the answer; and (4) the inability to make moral or value judgments.

Science can answer only certain kinds of questions: those that lead to testable hypotheses. A hypothesis that is not testable, and therefore is outside the realm of science, is one that either: (a) does not have clearly defined predictions or (b) has predictions that cannot be observed, either directly by human sense organs or indirectly by scientific instruments. This is why it is not possible for scientists to investigate the hypothesis that nature is controlled by unpredictable and unobservable supernatural forces.

The scientific process cannot be rushed. Consequently, it can take years to isolate the correct solution. At the start of an investigation there are many possible explanatory hypotheses and it is a matter of skill, imagination, hard work, and luck to eliminate all but the correct hypothesis. It is a common misconception that this laborious and painstaking process can be eliminated if enough money is spent—that severe medical problems like cancer and AIDS could be quickly solved with sufficient resources. Unfortunately, these solutions, like the solutions to all other great scientific mysteries, require an unpredictable amount of time and labor.

Scientists must live with uncertainty; there are no absolute and final truths in science. Every hypothesis or theory, no matter how often it has been tested, can eventually yield a prediction that is found to be false. Because of this, even the most firmly established laws of science are always subject to modification.

Finally, the scientific process cannot answer questions about what is morally correct or what is good or bad; it can only provide predictions about the consequences of our actions. Thus, for example, the scientific process cannot tell us that genetic engineering is moral or that pollution is bad, but it can make predictions about what the future holds if we accept or reject the morality of genetic engineering or if we pollute or do not pollute the environment.

THE SCIENCE OF BIOLOGY

1.9 An argument is made that birds evolved wings in order to fly. This type of argument is described as

(*a*) causal. (*b*) teleological. (*c*) mechanistic. (*d*) circular.

1.10 Which of the following taxonomic categories contains organisms least similar to one another?

(*a*) Class; (*b*) Genus; (*c*) Family; (*d*) Species

1.11 Which of the following taxonomic categories contains organisms belonging to the same class but not to the same family?

(*a*) Species; (*b*) Genus; (*c*) Order; (*d*) Population

1.12 A turning point in the history of biology occurred when the ancient Greek philosophers rejected the vitalistic view that life is controlled by supernatural powers. They accepted instead the view that life is governed entirely by natural laws—those now known to be the laws of physics and chemistry; this is called the _____ view of life.

1.13 All the people listed below made important contributions to biology before the start of the twentieth century. Match each person with his contribution by writing the letter before his name in the space before the contribution. (More names than contributions are listed.)

(*a*) Aristotle	(*e*) Haeckel, Ernst	(*i*) Leeuwenhoeck, Antonie van
(*b*) Cuvier, Georges	(*f*) Harvey, William	(*j*) Linnaeus, Carolus
(*c*) Darwin, Charles Robert	(*g*) Hooke, Robert	(*k*) Lyell, Charles
(*d*) Darwin, Erasmus	(*h*) Lamarck, Jean Baptiste	(*l*) Malthus, Thomas R.

(*m*)	Mendel, Gregor Johann	(*p*)	Schleiden, Matthis	(*s*)	Virchow, Rudolf
(*n*)	Miescher, Friedrich	(*q*)	Schwann, Theodor	(*t*)	Wallace, Alfred Russel
(*o*)	Pasteur, Louis	(*r*)	Vesalius, Andreas		

Contributions are listed in order of contributors' birth dates.

(1) _____ Greek philosopher (384–322 B.C.), whose *scala naturae* (ladder of nature), one of the first theories in biology, places all living things in a hierarchy, with the simplest creatures at the bottom and humans at the top.

(2) _____ English physiologist (1625–1703) who, in his book *Micrographia* (published in 1665), described the tiny, regularly shaped compartments that make up the tissues of cork and other plants and was the first to use the word *cell*.

(3) _____ Dutch naturalist and microscope maker (1632–1723) who, in 1676, was the first to observe living single-celled organisms under a microscope.

(4) _____ Swedish biologist (1707–1778) who developed the binomial system (a two-part Latin name) for naming and classifying organisms that is still in use today.

(5) _____ French naturalist (1744–1829) who proposed a now-rejected theory of evolution in which all species change toward greater complexity and perfection through the inheritance of acquired characteristics.

(6) _____ French naturalist (1769–1832) who, from a study of fossils left in rock layers, developed the catastrophism theory: All species were created at one time, but many species have been destroyed in a series of catastrophes.

(7) _____ English economist (1776–1834), whose idea that human populations grow faster than their food supply, which was presented in his book *Essay on the Principles of Population* (published in 1798), greatly influenced the developers of the theory of evolution by natural selection.

(8) _____ British geologist (1797–1875), whose book *Principles of Geology*, with its evidence for uniformitarianism (natural forces producing continuous change throughout the history of a very ancient earth), had great influence on the developers of the theory of evolution by natural selection.

(9) _____ German botanist (1804–1881) who, in 1838, was the first to state for plants what is now known as the cell theory: All plant tissues are composed of individual cells.

(10) _____ English naturalist (1809–1882), whose studies of plant and animal diversity while serving as ship's naturalist on the *H. M. S. Beagle* (1831–1836) led him to write *On the Origin of Species by Means of Natural Selection* (published in 1859).

(11) _____ German physiologist and zoologist (1810–1882) who, in 1839, extended the cell theory from plants to animals: The tissues of all living things are composed of individual cells.

(12) _____ German pathologist and anthropologist (1821–1902) who, in 1858, was the first to state that all cells can come only from preexisting cells.

(13) _____ Austrian monk (1822–1884) who, with experiments on the common garden pea, discovered many of the basic principles of inheritance.

(14) _____ English naturalist (1823–1913) who, while credited with being the codeveloper of the theory of evolution by natural selection, is much less famous for this than his codeveloper.

1.14 Why is Darwin's theory of evolution still so controversial?

🐚 In 1859, Charles Darwin presented his theory of evolution by natural selection in the book *On the Origin of Species by Means of Natural Selection*. Yet today, over 100 years later, while the theory is universally accepted within the scientific community, it is still highly controversial among nonscientists. This controversy exists for two reasons: (1) the theory conflicts with supernatural explanations of human origins and (2) there is a basic misconception as to the scientific use of the term *theory*.

Darwin's theory proposes that human as well as all other forms of life evolved over a vast period of time through a sequence of ancestral forms that were each subjected to the forces of natural selection. This directly conflicts with the beliefs of most religions that humans were created by supernatural forces at one point in time and have not changed, biologically, since that time.

People who accept the supernatural view of human origins are encouraged by the fact that scientists refer to Darwin's model as a theory. In everyday language, a theory is nothing more than a speculative guess. However, in science a theory is much more than that. It is a group of related hypotheses that have been tested and supported by a great deal of evidence. While Darwin's theory is not, and cannot be, absolutely proven, it has been firmly established by rigorous testing.

WHAT IS LIFE?

1.15 The transformation from a single cell into an adult individual with many different kinds of cells is called

(*a*) development.   (*b*) inheritance.   (*c*) evolution.   (*d*) adaptation.

1.16 Which of the following promotes diversity among living things?

(*a*) Classification of organisms;   (*b*) Natural selection in different environments;   (*c*) Inheritance from a common ancestor;   (*d*) Homeostatic regulation

1.17 Which of the following promotes similarity (unity) among living things?

(*a*) Classification of organisms;   (*b*) Natural selection in different environments;   (*c*) Inheritance from a common ancestor;   (*d*) Homeostatic regulation

1.18 The component parts (units) of the world of life can be placed within a hierarchy of organization with the smallest and simplest units at the bottom and the largest and most complex units at the top. A unit at a particular level of organization in the hierarchy contains components from all lower levels and is in turn a component of higher-level units. Rank the following levels of biologic organization from 1 to 11, in which 1 is the smallest and simplest and 11 is the largest and most complex.

(*a*) _____ atom   (*e*) _____ individual   (*i*) _____ population

(*b*) _____ cell   (*f*) _____ molecule   (*j*) _____ species

(*c*) _____ community   (*g*) _____ organ   (*k*) _____ tissue

(*d*) _____ ecosystem   (*h*) _____ organelle

1.19 Living things are made of the same atoms and chemical energy, and obey the same laws of physics and chemistry, as nonliving things. However, life has many properties that distinguish it from nonlife. What are the distinguishing properties that are unique to living things?

The following properties are used to distinguish living from nonliving things.
1. Compared with nonliving things, organisms have more complexly organized structures and their uses of energy are more controlled and efficient.
2. Every living thing is organized into one or more cells, which are assemblages of large, fragile molecules enclosed within semipermeable membranes.
3. The chemistry of life is governed largely by enzymes, which in turn are controlled by genes.
4. Living things acquire energy and atoms from their surroundings. They then use the energy and atoms to maintain their own structural organization, as well as to grow and reproduce.
5. Each organism has some degree of homeostasis, i.e., is able to make adjustments so that its internal environment remains relatively constant (or appropriate) despite changes in the external environment.
6. Living things reproduce their own kind by forming new cells, which contain copies of their genes.
7. Newly formed individuals go through a process of development; they undergo a series of changes which are characteristic of their kind and which are governed by instructions within their genes.

1.20 Why do biologists need to study chemistry and physics?

Biology is based on the mechanistic view of life: all life forms obey and are completely explained by the laws of physics and chemistry. Life is a chemical phenomenon, and chemistry is based on physics. We understand life through understanding the chemistry of organic molecules and ions, and we understand chemistry by knowing the properties of atoms and how they are influenced by energy, gravity, and other physical phenomena.

Answers to Objective Questions

1.1 *c*

1.2 *a*

1.3 *b*

1.4 inductive; deductive; prediction; deductive

1.9 *b*

1.10 *a*

1.11 *c*

1.12 mechanistic

1.13 (1) *a*;   (2) *g*;   (3) *i*;   (4) *j*;   (5) *h*;   (6) *b*;   (7) *l*;   (8) *k*;   (9) *p*;   (10) *c*;   (11) *q*;   (12) *s*;   (13) *m*;   (14) *t*

1.15 *a*

1.16 *b*

1.17 *c*

1.18 (*a*) 1;   (*b*) 4;   (*c*) 10;   (*d*) 11;   (*e*) 7;   (*f*) 2;   (*g*) 6;   (*h*) 3;   (*i*) 8;   (*j*) 9;   (*k*) 5

CHAPTER 2

Atoms, Bonds, and Molecules

ATOMIC STRUCTURE*

2.1   Which of the following is true of an electron?

(*a*) Neutral in charge;   (*b*) Negative in charge;   (*c*) Heavier than a proton;   (*d*) More fixed in position than a proton

2.2   The different shells in which the electrons of an atom are arranged reflect different

(*a*) sizes of electrons.   (*b*) weights of electrons.   (*c*) levels of energy.   (*d*) isotopes of the atom.

2.3   A filled, or complete, innermost shell of an atom contains _____ electrons, whereas a filled outermost shell of most atoms contains _____ electrons.

2.4   Why do sodium (atomic number = 11) and potassium (atomic number = 19) exhibit similar chemical behaviors?

🐚   The chemical behavior of an atom refers to the way in which it interacts with other atoms. Chemical behavior depends largely on the number of electrons in the atom's outer shell. Both sodium and potassium have just a single electron in their outermost shells. Sodium, with 11 protons, has two electrons in its innermost shell, eight in its next shell, and one in its outermost shell. Potassium, with 19 protons, has two electrons in its innermost shell, eight electrons in each of its next two shells, and a single electron in its outermost shell. Both sodium and potassium tend to lose the single electron in their outermost shell, thereby achieving a stable outer shell of eight electrons.

2.5   Your body is made of atoms.   (*a*) Where did these atoms come from just prior to when they became part of you?   (*b*) What will happen to them after you die?   (*c*) Where were they formed originally?

🐚   (*a*) The atoms of your body came from your environment, in the form of food and water. Most of these atoms traveled from your digestive tract to various parts of your body as components of small molecules.   (*b*) After you die and your body decomposes, your atoms will return to the environment and be recycled—become part of some other living or nonliving thing.   (*c*) All of your atoms (except hydrogen) were formed billions of years ago, when clouds of hydrogen atoms condensed to form stars. Within a star, the nuclei of hydrogen atoms fuse to form helium, the nuclei of helium atoms fuse to form other small atoms, and the nuclei of small atoms fuse to form larger atoms. Hydrogen was formed when the universe itself was formed, approximately 20 billion years ago.

CHEMICAL BONDS AND MOLECULES

2.6   A covalent bond develops when

(*a*) ions collide with each other.   (*b*) electrons are transferred from one atom to another.   (*c*) electrons are shared between two atoms.   (*d*) neutrons of two atoms are attracted to each other.

2.7   Which of the following kinds of bonds requires the most energy to break (when in an aqueous solution)?

(*a*) Covalent;   (*b*) Ionic;   (*c*) Hydrogen;   (*d*) van der Waals

2.8   A molecule that adds hydrogen ions to a solution is known as

(*a*) a buffer.   (*b*) a base.   (*c*) an acid.   (*d*) a hydrophobic substance.

2.9   Solutions with pH values below 7 are called _____. A solution with a pH of 5 has _____ times more _____ in relation to _____ than a solution with a pH of 6.

2.10   (*a*) Draw the sodium atom (atomic number = 11) and its ion.   (*b*) Also draw the chlorine atom (atomic number = 17) and its ion.   (*c*) What kind of a bond causes formation of the sodium chloride molecule?

🐚   For (*a*) and (*b*), see Fig. 2.1.

*Answers to Chapter 2 objective questions appear on page 8.

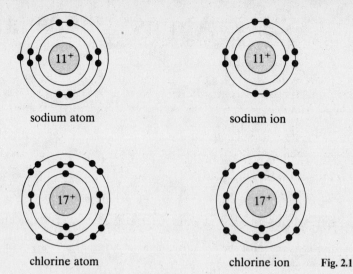

sodium atom   sodium ion

chlorine atom   chlorine ion   Fig. 2.1

(c) In order to achieve stable outermost shells of eight electrons each, the sodium atom loses an electron to become a sodium ion (Na^+) and the chlorine atom gains an electron to become a chloride ion (Cl^-). Because of the attractions of opposite electric charges, these two kinds of ions form *ionic bonds* and so build molecules of sodium chloride (NaCl).

2.11 (a) Draw the methane molecule (CH_4), in which a carbon atom (atomic number = 6) is joined by covalent bonds with the hydrogen atoms (atomic number = 1). (b) Is methane a polar or nonpolar molecule? Why?

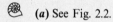 (a) See Fig. 2.2.

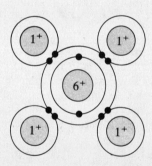

Fig. 2.2. Methane.

(b) A polar molecule has an asymmetrical distribution of electric charges. While the shared electrons of the covalent bonds within methane spend more time near the carbon nucleus (making the center of the molecule more negative) than near the hydrogen nuclei (making the outer parts of the molecule more positive), the symmetrical distribution of the hydrogen atoms around the carbon atom gives an overall symmetry to the distribution of charges. Thus, methane is a nonpolar molecule.

2.12 Acid precipitation has less effect on the pH of lakes on limestone bedrock ($CaCO_3$) than on the pH of lakes on other kinds of bedrock. How does the limestone act to counter the acid?

⚞ Acid precipitation adds hydrogen ions to lakes, thereby lowering the pH of the water. Limestone is $CaCO_3$, which, when dissolved in water, forms Ca^{2+} and CO_3^{2-}. The CO_3^{2-} in the soil and water above limestone bedrock acts as a buffer; it combines with the excess H^+ to form HCO_3^- and H_2CO_3. By removing the H^+ from solution, CO_3^{2-} prevents a decrease in the pH of the lake.

THE WATER MOLECULE

2.13 An unusual property of water is that a large amount of heat energy is required to raise its temperature (i.e., to increase the average speed at which its molecules move). The amount of heat energy needed to raise one gram of a substance 1 °C is called its

(a) heat of vaporization. (b) heat of melting. (c) specific temperature. (d) specific heat.

2.14 In order for water to become a vapor, there must be sufficient heat energy to

(*a*) break its hydrogen bonds. (*b*) break its covalent bonds. (*c*) lower its specific heat. (*d*) raise its specific heat.

2.15 For most substances, the density (weight, or number of molecules, per unit volume) increases as the temperature decreases until the substance reaches its maximum density as a solid. Ice, however, is cooler than liquid water yet floats on it. This unusual property of water occurs because water reaches its greatest density at

(*a*) +4 °C. (*b*) 0 °C. (*c*) −12 °C. (*d*) −32 °C.

2.16 Most of the extraordinary properties of water are caused by the _____ of its molecules.

2.17 Water is an excellent solvent for molecules that have electric charges. Two categories of such hydrophilic (water-loving) molecules are _____ and _____.

2.18 (*a*) Draw a water molecule. (*b*) Is it a polar or nonpolar molecule? Why? (*c*) Draw several more water molecules and show how hydrogen bonds form between the molecules.

(*a*) See Fig. 2.3.

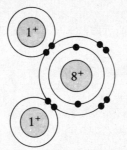

Fig. 2.3. A water molecule.

(*b*) Water is a polar molecule, because its electric charges are distributed asymmetrically. The eight protons in the oxygen nucleus attract electrons more strongly than the single proton in each of the hydrogen nuclei; thus, as the electrons travel around both kinds of nuclei, they spend more time near the oxygen nucleus. The side of the molecule with the two hydrogen atoms, therefore, has a slightly positive charge, and the side without the hydrogen atoms has a slightly negative charge. The two sides of the molecule resemble the two poles of a magnet, which is why the molecule is said to be polar.

(*c*) Hydrogen bonds form between water molecules because the slightly positive end of one molecule is attracted to the slightly negative end of another molecule. Each water molecule can form hydrogen bonds with a maximum of four other water molecules, as shown in Fig. 2.4.

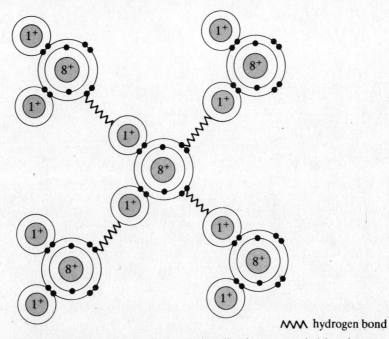

ʌʌʌ hydrogen bond

Fig. 2.4. Diagram showing hydrogen bonding between molecules of water.

2.19   Why is the climate of land near large bodies of water warmer in the winter and cooler in the summer than the climate of areas far from water?

&   Large bodies of water influence the climate of adjacent land because water has a much higher specific heat than land. This is primarily due to the hydrogen (H) bonds of water: the breaking of H bonds requires energy, and their formation releases energy. Because its H bonds must be broken, water requires more heat energy to raise its temperature than does land; conversely, because it forms H bonds upon cooling, water releases more heat energy when its temperature drops. Thus, when the water temperature is rising in summer, a lake or ocean absorbs more heat than the land, causing cooler temperatures near the earth's surface than in areas where no large body of water exists. Conversely, when water temperature is dropping in winter, a lake or ocean releases more heat than the land, causing warmer temperatures near the earth's surface than in areas lacking a large body of water.

2.20   The capacity of soil to hold water against the downward pull of gravity depends largely on the size of the mineral particles in the soil. Discuss the property of water that enables clay soil (tiny particles) to hold more water than sandy soil (large particles).

&   Water is held in soil by *capillary action* and *surface wetting*, both consequences of the adhesive and cohesive properties of water. Capillary action holds water within the pores between mineral particles, just as water is held in a narrow glass tube. It holds more water when the pores are smaller, because then there is more surface area in contact with water—more adhesion—for the volume of water moving through the pores. Clay soils contain smaller pores than sandy soils, because the smaller particles of clay can be more closely packed together than the larger particles of sand. Surface wetting holds water by hydrogen bonds to mineral particles; the amount held is directly proportional to the total surface area of the mineral particles—an area much larger in the smaller particles of clay than the larger particles of sand. Thus, clay soil holds more water by both capillary action and surface wetting than does sandy soil.

Answers to Objective Questions

2.1 *b*	**2.7** *a*	**2.14** *a*
2.2 *c*	**2.8** *c*	**2.15** *a*
2.3 two; eight	**2.9** acids; ten; H^+; OH^-	**2.16** polarity
2.6 *c*	**2.13** *d*	**2.17** ions; polar molecules

CHAPTER 3
The Molecules of Life

ORGANIC CHEMISTRY*

3.1 The six most common atoms in organic molecules are

(*a*) carbon, hydrogen, oxygen, helium, calcium, and sulfur.   (*b*) carbon, hydrogen, oxygen, calcium, magnesium, and sulfur.   (*c*) carbon, oxygen, nitrogen, sulfur, phosphorus, and magnesium.   (*d*) carbon, hydrogen, oxygen, nitrogen, phosphorus, and sulfur.

3.2 Sugars are characterized by having which two functional groups?

(*a*) Carbonyl and hydroxyl;   (*b*) Carbonyl and methyl;   (*c*) Hydroxyl and amino;   (*d*) Sulfhydryl and phosphate

3.3 The functional group with the formula $-NH_2$ is

(*a*) a hydroxyl.   (*b*) an amino.   (*c*) a sulfhydryl.   (*d*) a carbonyl.

3.4 Methane (CH_4) is the simplest

(*a*) alcohol.   (*b*) hydrocarbon.   (*c*) carbonyl.   (*d*) amine.

3.5 All alcohols include at least one _____ group.

3.6 In dehydration synthesis, one monomer loses a _____ and the other loses a _____.

3.7 What are the main differences between inorganic and organic molecules?

Organic molecules are complex molecules containing carbon atoms; they are found in living or once-living things. All other molecules are inorganic. Both types of molecules are essential—without such inorganic molecules as water (H_2O), carbon dioxide (CO_2), and molecular oxygen (O_2), life would not be possible; but it is organic molecules that are responsible for the incredible diversity of living things.

Biologic diversity is a function of the capacity of carbon atoms to form large and complex molecules. Each carbon atom can form as many as four covalent bonds, and this results in organic molecules with large chains, rings, or interconnected rings of carbon atoms (the carbon skeleton) to which other elements are bonded. Thus, the largest organic molecules contain millions of atoms. This size and complexity gives almost unlimited potential for diversity of molecules, but it also makes organic molecules much more fragile and easy to destroy than the smaller and simpler inorganic molecules.

While there are vast numbers of organic molecules (e.g., as many as 5000 different kinds in a single bacterial cell), they can be grouped into two main categories, each with four subcategories: (1) small organic molecules (no more than 20 carbon atoms) classified as simple sugars, fatty acids, amino acids, and nucleotides; and (2) large organic molecules (over 20 carbon atoms) classified as carbohydrates, lipids, proteins, and nucleic acids.

CARBOHYDRATES

3.8 The most common monomer of carbohydrates is a molecule of

(*a*) amino acid.   (*b*) phospholipid.   (*c*) maltose.   (*d*) glucose.

3.9 What kind of reaction is shown by the following diagram?

glucose   fructose   sucrose

(*a*) Hydrolysis;   (*b*) Dehydration synthesis (or condensation reaction);   (*c*) Denaturation;   (*d*) Incorporation synthesis

* Answers to Chapter 3 objective questions appear on page 16.

3.10 Which of the following is a polysaccharide?

(a) Glucose; (b) Glycogen; (c) Maltose; (d) Lactose

3.11 Which of the following is *not* a correct diagram of the molecular formula for glucose?

(a) $C_6H_{12}O_6$ (b) (c)

3.12 The structural polysaccharide found in plant cell walls is _____ , while the storage polysaccharide found in seeds and some plant roots is _____ .

3.13 (a) How are polysaccharides formed from monosaccharides? (b) How are monosaccharides formed from polysaccharides?

☙ (a) *Polysaccharides* are polymers formed by the bonding of more than two molecules—typically hundreds of molecules—of monosaccharides. A *monosaccharide* is the simplest sugar molecule (a monomer), composed of carbon, hydrogen, and oxygen atoms in some multiple of the ratio 1:2:1. There are more than 200 known kinds of monosaccharides, each having carbon skeletons of from three to seven carbon atoms. Two of the most important to biology are glucose and fructose (see Questions 3.9 and 3.11), both having six carbon atoms. Glucose is the primary energy source for most cells.

Monosaccharides are joined to form larger molecules by dehydration synthesis (see Question 3.9). Each monosaccharide has two or more hydroxyl groups ($-OH^-$), which can be replaced by covalent bonds. Dehydration synthesis is a series of reactions in which covalent bonds are formed by the removal of $-OH^-$ from one sugar monomer and H^+ from its bonding partner; i.e., a molecule of water is removed for each covalent bond formed.

When two monosaccharides are joined by dehydration synthesis, the result is a double sugar, or *disaccharide*. The three most important disaccharides for biology are: sucrose (table sugar—glucose and fructose); lactose (milk sugar—glucose and galactose); and maltose (sugar in germinating seeds—glucose and glucose).

When more than two sugar monomers are joined, the result is a polysaccharide. There are storage and structural polysaccharides. Energy is stored in plants as starch and in animals as glycogen; both are polymers of glucose. Cellulose and chitin are the principal structural polysaccharides.

(b) Polysaccharides are broken down into their monosaccharide components by hydrolysis. This process is essentially the reverse of dehydration synthesis: each bond between monomers is broken, and a molecule of water is added to form the original monosaccharides. The process is essential for use of sugars by cells; starch and glycogen must be broken down into monomers (glucose) before their energy is available for cellular work.

LIPIDS

3.14 Each fat molecule is formed from

(a) three glycerol molecules and one fatty acid molecule. (b) one glycerol molecule and three fatty acid molecules. (c) one glycerol molecule and one fatty acid molecule. (d) three glycerol molecules and three fatty acid molecules.

3.15 Cholesterol is a(n)

(a) diglyceride. (b) saturated fat. (c) unsaturated fat. (d) steroid.

3.16   All _____ have the same skeleton of four interlocking carbon rings, as shown below:

3.17   A fat molecule has _____ fatty acids, whereas a phospholipid has _____ fatty acids.

3.18   What is the difference between a saturated and an unsaturated fat?

🐚   Each fat molecule is a polymer made of one glycerol and three fatty acid monomers. Whether a fat is saturated or unsaturated depends on the kinds of covalent bonds in the fatty acid parts of the molecule.

A *saturated* fatty acid has only *single* bonds between its carbon atoms.

Each of its carbon atoms is "saturated" with hydrogen atoms, i.e., no more could possibly be added. By contrast, an *unsaturated* fatty acid has some *double* bonds between its carbon atoms.

Some of its carbon atoms are not "saturated" with hydrogen atoms, i.e., more could be added wherever there is a double bond. An unsaturated fatty acid could be made into a saturated fatty acid by adding more hydrogen atoms, a process that would eliminate double bonds.

All fats are composed of some saturated and some unsaturated fatty acids. A saturated fat contains mostly saturated fatty acids. These kinds of fats, such as butter and lard, are solids at room temperature. An unsaturated fat contains mostly unsaturated fatty acids. There are two kinds of unsaturated fats—mono- and polyunsaturated, depending on whether each of their fatty acids has only one (mono) or more than one (poly) double bond. These kinds of fats, such as olive oil (mono-unsaturated) and corn oil (polyunsaturated), are liquids at room temperature.

PROTEINS

3.19   The enormous diversity of protein molecules is due mostly to the diversity of

(*a*) amino groups on the amino acids.   (*b*) R groups on the amino acids.   (*c*) amino acid sequences within protein molecules.   (*d*) peptide bonds.

3.20   The structure of a protein can be denatured by

(*a*) the polar bonds of water molecules.   (*b*) heat.   (*c*) the presence of oxygen gas.   (*d*) the presence of carbon dioxide gas.

3.21   The unique properties of each amino acid are determined by its particular

(*a*) R group.   (*b*) amino group.   (*c*) kinds of peptide bonds.   (*d*) number of bonds to other amino acids.

3.22   The covalent bond between two amino acids is called a _____ bond, and when three or more amino acids are so joined, they form a _____ chain.

3.23   The two types of secondary structures of proteins are the _____ and the _____.

3.24   What are the molecular shapes and kinds of chemical bonds that characterize the (**a**) primary, (**b**) secondary, (**c**) tertiary, and (**d**) quaternary structures of a protein?

(**a**) The primary structure of a protein is a linear sequence of approximately 40 to 1000 amino acids (a polypeptide chain), in which the amino acids are joined by covalent bonds between as peptide bonds.

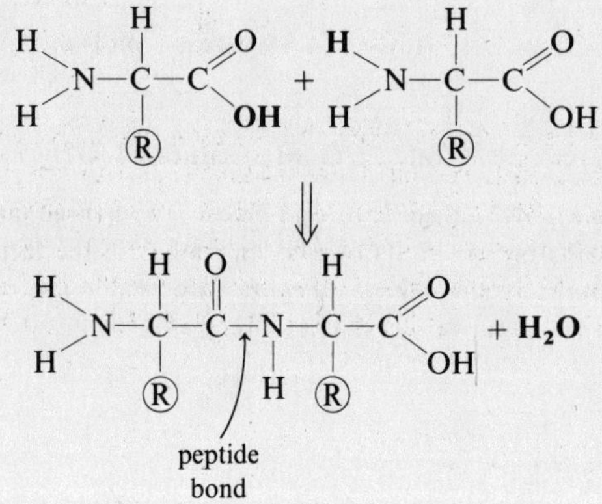

peptide
bond

Because covalent bonds are strong bonds, the primary structure of a protein is its most stable part.
(**b**) The secondary structure of a protein is the bending of the primary structure, caused by movement of the hydrophobic R groups (on some of the amino acids) toward the nonaqueous center of the molecule and of the hydrophilic R groups (on other amino acids) toward the aqueous surface of the molecule. This shape is then held by numerous hydrogen bonds between amino acids that have been brought near each other by the bending. Each hydrogen bond forms when a weakly positive hydrogen atom (which is covalently bonded to the nitrogen of one amino acid) is attracted to a weakly negative oxygen atom (which is covalently bonded to another amino acid).

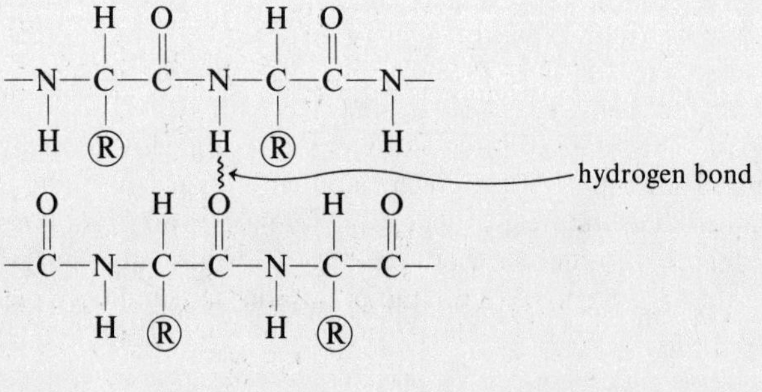

hydrogen bond

Secondary structures are either spirals or folds; the two most common are the *alpha helix* (a spiral) and the *beta pleated sheet* (folds).
(**c**) Many proteins have a tertiary structure superimposed on the primary and secondary structures, and this usually gives the molecule a globular shape. A tertiary structure is the result of numerous bonds between the various R groups of the amino acids in the primary structure. These bonds are of four types: (1) hydrophobic attractions in the center of the molecule, in which the nonpolar R groups are held by van der Waals interactions (weak); (2) hydrogen bonds (weak); (3) ionic bonds (weak); and (4) covalent bonds (strong) between the sulfur of one cysteine monomer and the sulfur of another cysteine monomer. (Cysteine is the only amino acid with an —SH group at the unattached end of its R group.) Tertiary structures with covalent bonds between sulfur atoms are more stable than those with only the three kinds of weak bonds. Usually, proteins with the covalent bonds are the kinds secreted from a cell, whereas those without these strong bonds remain within the cell.
(**d**) Some proteins have quaternary structures, in which two or more polypeptide chains are joined to form one functional molecule. (Each polypeptide chain would be called a protein if it existed alone.) A protein with a quaternary structure may or may not also have a tertiary structure. Quaternary structures, like tertiary structures, may be held together only by numerous weak bonds, or they may have the stronger covalent bonds between sulfur atoms in addition to the weak bonds.

3.25   Why is the primary structure of a protein necessarily a linear (rather than branched) sequence of amino acids?

🐚   Every amino acid has an amino group (—NH$_2$) at one end of its structure and a carboxyl group (—COOH) at the opposite end.

The amino group acts as a base, because the nitrogen atom (with five electrons in its outer shell and three covalent bonds) has a pair of unshared electrons it can share with a hydrogen ion (giving H$^+$ a stable outer shell). When the amino group picks up a hydrogen ion, it takes on a positive charge (—NH$_3^+$). At the other end of the molecule, the carboxyl group releases a hydrogen ion, because the covalent bond between oxygen and hydrogen is very polar (the hydrogen electron spends more time circling the oxygen nucleus than the hydrogen nucleus). This end of the molecule then takes on a negative charge (COO$^-$). At the pH of a cell (around 7), both of these charges are present.

The arrangement of the two weak charges causes amino acids to act as magnets, in which the negative end of one attracts the positive end of another. Consequently, amino acids near one another orient themselves in a linear sequence (a branch is not possible) and are in position to form peptide bonds, during which H$^+$, O$^-$, and H$^+$ (i.e., H$_2$O) are released.

NUCLEIC ACIDS

3.26   The part of a DNA molecule that varies among DNA molecules is its

(*a*) glycerol attachments. (*b*) nitrogenous bases. (*c*) sugars. (*d*) phosphates.

3.27   DNA is unique among molecules in that it can

(*a*) form multipolymer complexes. (*b*) come apart and re-form. (*c*) withstand very high temperatures. (*d*) replicate itself.

3.28   The molecule shown in Fig. 3.1 is a _____. It is a polymer formed of _____ monomers.

3.29   There are two families of nitrogenous bases in nucleotides, the _____ (single rings of atoms) and the _____ (double rings of atoms).

3.30   What are the structural differences between a molecule of DNA and a molecule of RNA?

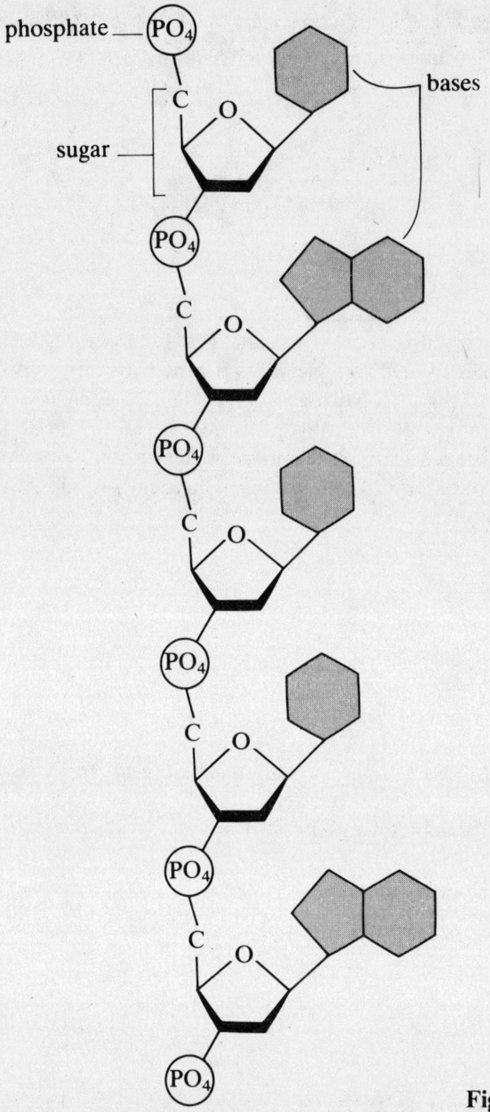

phosphate — PO₄

sugar

bases

Fig. 3.1

⚲ Both DNA and RNA are nucleic acids—polymers made of nucleotide monomers. Each nucleotide, in turn, is made of a five-carbon sugar, a phosphate, and a nitrogenous base. A molecule of DNA differs from a molecule of RNA in (1) the kind of sugar in its nucleotides, (2) the kinds of nitrogenous bases in its nucleotides, and (3) the arrangement of nucleotides within its polymer.

The nucleotide monomers of DNA contain the sugar *deoxyribose*, whereas in RNA the sugar is *ribose* (deoxyribose has one less oxygen atom than ribose does).

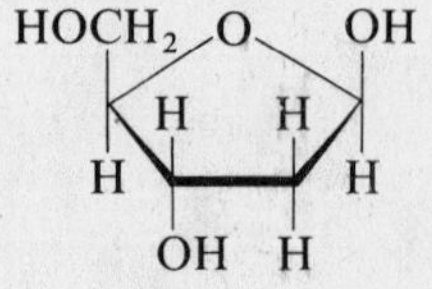

deoxyribose (in DNA) 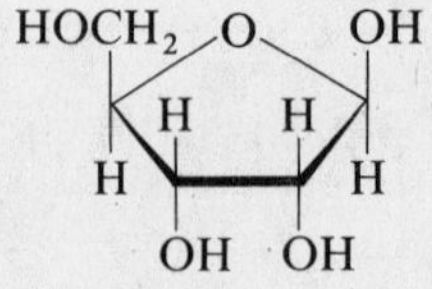   ribose (in RNA)

This difference in the sugar component of the nucleotides has been used to name the two polymers: *deoxyribonucleic acid* (DNA) and *ribonucleic acid* (RNA).

Both DNA and RNA have four different kinds of nitrogenous bases, and consequently four different kinds of nucleotides (the sugar and the phosphate components are the same for all the nucleotides within each molecule).

Three of these four bases—adenine, guanine, and cytosine—are the same in both molecules, but the fourth base is different—DNA has thymine and RNA has uracil. The only difference between these two bases is that thymine has a methyl group and uracil does not.

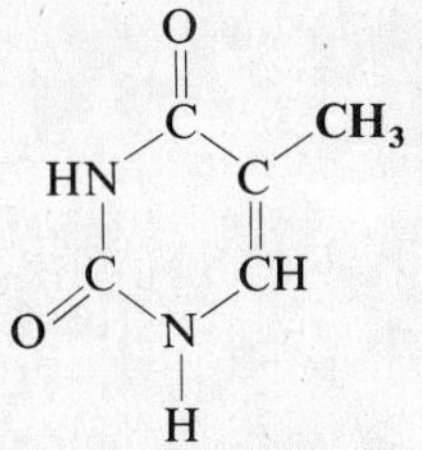

thymine (in DNA) 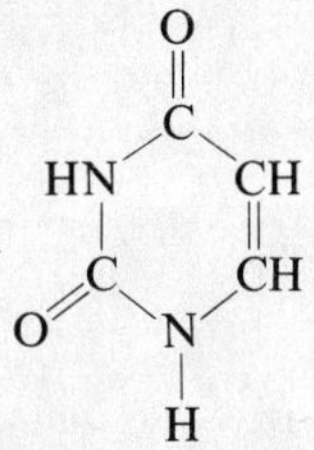   uracil (in RNA)

In both DNA and RNA, the nucleotide monomers are joined by covalent bonds between the sugar of one monomer and the phosphate of another monomer to form long chains (or strands) of nucleotides. In a DNA molecule, there are two strands of nucleotides, joined to each other by hydrogen bonds between the bases of one strand and the bases of the other strand (Fig. 3.2).

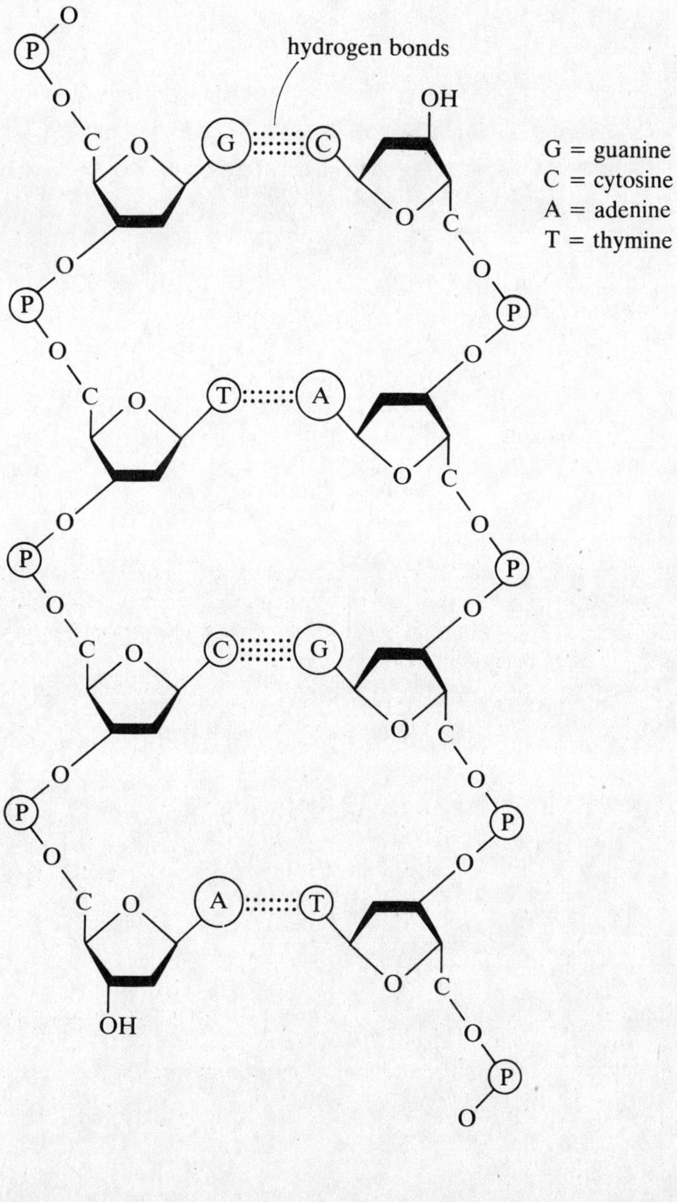

G = guanine
C = cytosine
A = adenine
T = thymine

Fig. 3.2

Thus, the primary structure of DNA resembles a ladder, with the sugar-phosphate strands forming the vertical sides and the base pairs forming the horizontal rungs. In an RNA molecule, by contrast, the nucleotide monomers form just a single strand, like half a ladder (Fig. 3.3).

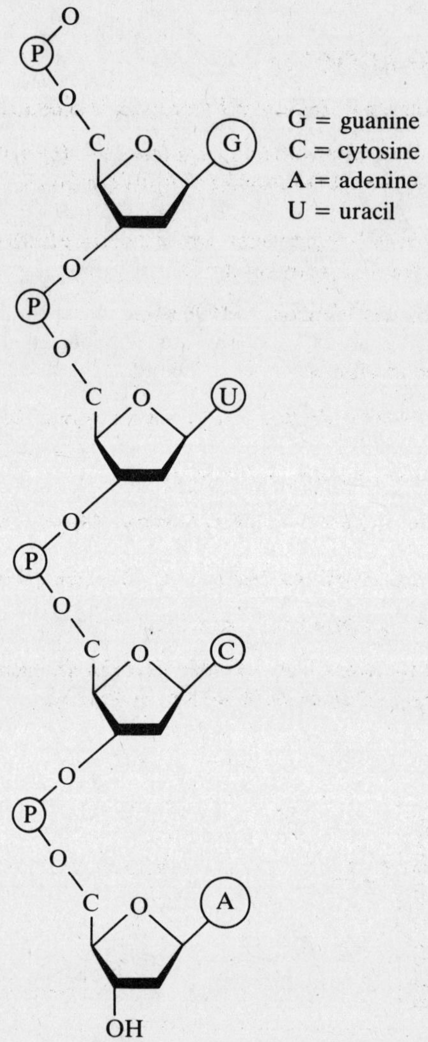

G = guanine
C = cytosine
A = adenine
U = uracil

Fig. 3.3

DNA is said to be double stranded and RNA to be single stranded.

Answers to Objective Questions

3.1 d	**3.11** c: This structural formula depicts fructose, which has the same molecular formula as glucose ($C_6H_{12}O_6$).	**3.19** c
3.2 a		**3.20** b
3.3 b		**3.21** a
3.4 b		**3.22** peptide; polypeptide
3.5 hydroxyl (—OH⁻)	**3.12** cellulose; starch	**3.23** alpha helix; beta pleated sheet
3.6 hydroxyl; hydrogen	**3.14** b	**3.26** b
3.8 d	**3.15** d	**3.27** d
3.9 b	**3.16** steroids	**3.28** nucleic acid; nucleotide
3.10 b	**3.17** three; two	**3.29** pyrimidines; purines

CHAPTER 4

Enzymes and Metabolism

ENERGY AND CHEMICAL REACTIONS*

4.1   When energy is used to promote a biochemical process, it is acquired from the

   (*a*) replacement of one set of covalent bonds by another set.   (*b*) replacement of covalent bonds by ionic bonds.
   (*c*) formation of hydrogen bonds.   (*d*) breaking of hydrogen bonds.

4.2   Many of the energy reactions in living systems are oxidation-reduction (redox) reactions. Which one of the
following is always transferred in a redox reaction?

   (*a*) Hydrogen;   (*b*) Oxygen;   (*c*) Electron;   (*d*) Proton

4.3   When a molecule is reduced, it always

   (*a*) gains an electron.   (*b*) loses an electron.   (*c*) gains a proton.   (*d*) loses a proton.

4.4   In a spontaneous reaction, the free energy of a system

   (*a*) decreases.   (*b*) increases.   (*c*) becomes equal to zero.   (*d*) remains unchanged.

4.5   Energy must be added for a chemical reaction to start. This energy is known as the energy of

   (*a*) entropy.   (*b*) activation.   (*c*) enthalpy.   (*d*) oxidation.

   Questions 4.6 through 4.10 pertain to Fig. 4.1, which depicts the energy changes that take place during the
reaction between molecule A and molecule B to form molecule C.

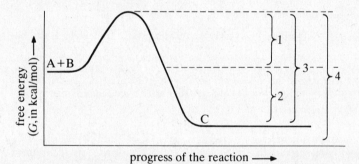

Fig. 4.1. Energy changes for the reaction A + B → C.

4.6   Which segment of the graph represents the usable (net) energy yield?

   (*a*) 1;   (*b*) 2;   (*c*) 3;   (*d*) 4

4.7   Which segment of the graph represents the energy of activation?

   (*a*) 1;   (*b*) 2;   (*c*) 3;   (*d*) 4

4.8   Which segment of the graph would be the same regardless of whether the reaction were catalyzed or not?

   (*a*) 1;   (*b*) 2;   (*c*) 3;   (*d*) 4

4.9   The chemical reaction diagrammed in the graph is

   (*a*) exergonic.   (*b*) enthalpic.   (*c*) energetically neutral.   (*d*) irreversible.

* Answers to Chapter 4 objective questions appear on page 24.

4.10 The chemical reaction diagrammed in the graph would be accelerated by all of the following processes *except*

(*a*) heating A and B together. (*b*) applying pressure to A and B. (*c*) adding an appropriate catalyst. (*d*) increasing the concentration of C.

4.11 Of the two chemical reactions shown in Fig. 4.2, reaction 1 is

(*a*) faster and more endergonic than 2. (*b*) faster and more exergonic than 2. (*c*) slower and more endergonic than 2. (*d*) slower and more exergonic than 2.

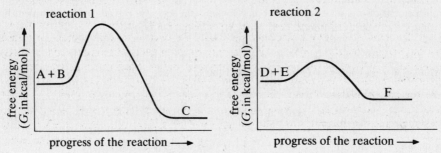

Fig. 4.2. Graphs of free energy for two chemical reactions.

4.12 ATP molecules are especially suitable for transporting energy because they have

(*a*) ionic bonds formed of wavelike movements of electrons. (*b*) very strong, triple covalent bonds. (*c*) bonds that release large amounts of energy when broken. (*d*) a large store of energy in the sugar, ribose.

4.13 A molecule of ATP is structurally most similar to a molecule of

(*a*) RNA nucleotide. (*b*) DNA nucleotide. (*c*) amino acid. (*d*) fatty acid.

4.14 A molecule of ADP differs from a molecule of ATP in that it has

(*a*) diamine instead of thymine. (*b*) fewer phosphate groups. (*c*) more phosphate bonds. (*d*) less electrical activity.

4.15 In an endergonic reaction, the product molecules have _____ chemical energy than the reactant molecules. In a spontaneous reaction, the product molecules usually have _____ chemical energy than the reactant molecules.

4.16 When a molecule is oxidized, it _____ one or more electrons and _____ potential energy. When a molecule is reduced, it _____ one or more electrons and _____ potential energy.

4.17 In order to pedal a bicycle, _____ energy within your leg muscles must be transformed into _____. An unavoidable and generally unusable form of energy that is released during the transformation is _____, as predicted by the _____ Law of Thermodynamics.

4.18 All forms of energy can be categorized as being either _____ or _____.

4.19 Glucose has a large amount of energy within its covalent bonds. The energy available for doing work is called its _____.

4.20 Describe the (*a*) First and (*b*) Second Laws of Thermodynamics.

⊛ (*a*) Our basic understanding of energy can be expressed in the form of two laws. The most powerful and fundamental generalization that can be made about the universe is the First Law of Thermodynamics, which states that energy can be transferred from one place to another or transformed from one form to another but it cannot be created or destroyed. From this generalization, it follows that the total amount of energy in any closed system, including the universe, is constant.

(b) The Second Law of Thermodynamics cannot be as easily stated. The original expression of this law was that heat can never pass spontaneously from a cooler to a warmer body and that a temperature difference can never appear spontaneously in a body that is at uniform temperature. A more general interpretation of the law is that any system, including the universe, naturally tends to increase its *entropy*—to become less ordered. Entropy increases with every energy transformation, because at least some of the energy being transformed is inevitably converted to heat, and heat is the unordered, random movement of molecules. In time, therefore, more and more of the energy in a system becomes randomly distributed, and once this happens, no further energy changes, or work, can take place.

4.21   (a) What is an oxidation-reduction reaction? (b) What is its function in living systems?

🐌   (a) An oxidation-reduction reaction is the transfer of one or more electrons from one atom or molecule to another. Sometimes an entire hydrogen atom—both the electron and the proton—is transferred. Since a substance can lose an electron (become oxidized) only when another substance accepts an electron (becomes reduced), every oxidation is accompanied by a corresponding reduction. Such reactions are referred to as redox reactions. (b) Oxidation-reduction reactions are important to living systems because energy is released during an oxidation; an electron always tends to flow down an energy gradient, from a higher to a lower level of chemical energy, and it releases some free energy as it is doing so. In a cell, energy for doing work is slowly released from energy-rich molecules by passing electrons (or hydrogen atoms) along a series of electron donors and electron acceptors, in which each electron acceptor in turn becomes an electron donor. In this manner, the energy within the molecule is released in very small quantities at each step in the series. This slow release of energy enables it to be used more efficiently and prevents the development of detrimentally high temperatures within the cell.

4.22   (a) Diagram the three main regions of an ATP molecule and of an ADP molecule.   (b) Show and explain how ATP couples exergonic and endergonic reactions.

🐌   (a) The three main regions of an ATP (adenosine triphosphate) molecule are: (1) the nitrogenous base *adenine*; (2) the sugar *ribose*; and (3) a series of three phosphate groups (Fig. 4.3).

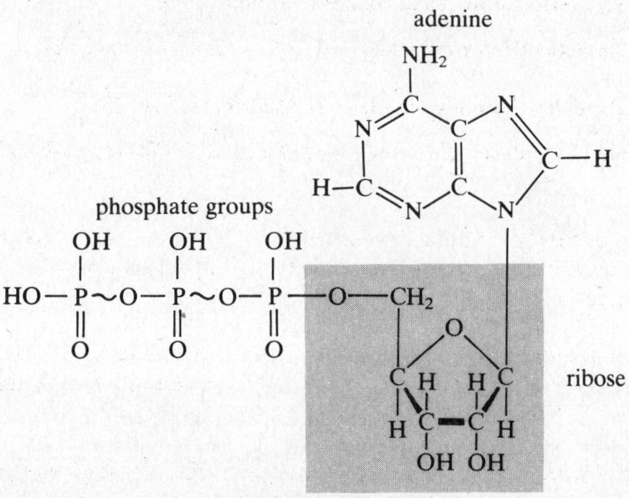

Fig. 4.3. Structure of ATP.

The wavy lines between the P and the O in the phosphate groups indicate bonds that, when broken, cause the release of a relatively large amount of energy. At the normal pH of a cell, most of the hydroxyl groups (OH) on the phosphates are ionized (O^-).

The three main regions of an ADP molecule are the same as of an ATP molecule, except there are two rather than three phosphate groups (Fig. 4.4).

(b) ATP couples exergonic and endergonic chemical reactions by carrying energy from one to the other. Energy is released for endergonic reactions when the terminal phosphate group is split from an ATP molecule. The phosphate group, with the energy, temporarily joins one of the molecules involved in the endergonic reaction while the energy it carries is picked up. The phosphate group then moves to the exergonic reaction, acquires energy again, and rejoins an ADP molecule to re-form ATP. Thus, by converting from ATP to ADP, and from ADP to ATP, the molecule acts as an energy shuttle between exergonic and endergonic chemical reactions (Fig. 4.5).

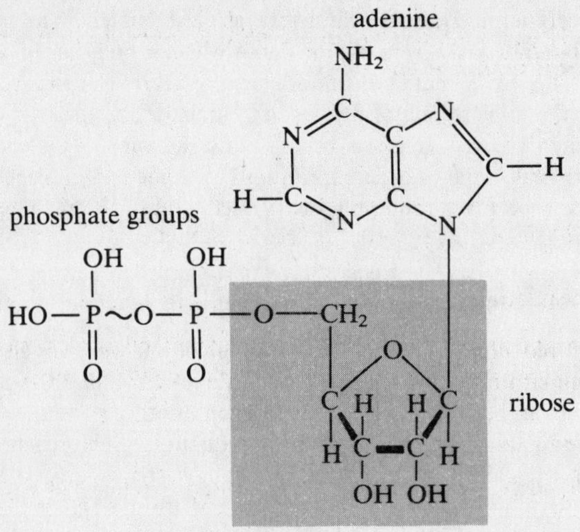

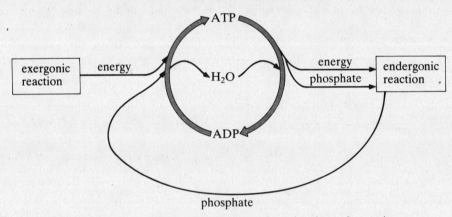

adenine

Fig. 4.4. Structure of ADP.

Fig. 4.5. Diagram of ATP coupling exergonic and endergonic reactions.

4.23 It has been said that life violates the Second Law of Thermodynamics.

(a) What observations led to such a statement? (b) Why is the statement untrue?

💠 (a) The Second Law of Thermodynamics predicts an increase in entropy—a decrease in order or degree of organization within a system. Living things, however, are observed to be more highly ordered than nonliving things and to actually increase their degree of organization (to decrease entropy) during development.
(b) The statement that life violates the Second Law of Thermodynamics is untrue because living things are not closed systems. Their high degree of organization is acquired and maintained by a continuous input of potential energy. Chemical energy is formed continually from light energy, in a process known as *photosynthesis*, and then passed to other organisms in the form of food molecules, which are used by the organisms to maintain and develop molecular organization. Ultimately, all of this chemical energy becomes heat energy—the random energy of molecular motion that is the least ordered form of energy—in compliance with the Second Law of Thermodynamics. Heat is lost eventually to outer space. Thus, energy enters living systems in a more ordered state (light or chemical energy) than it leaves (heat), and in the process of going from more ordered to less ordered, work is done to maintain a high degree of organization. Whenever the input of ordered energy ceases, an organism loses its high degree of organization and dies.

4.24 When ATP and water interact to form ADP and phosphate, a weak bond is broken to form a stronger bond and there is a large decrease in free energy. Why, then, does this reaction proceed very slowly when ATP is kept in an aqueous solution in the laboratory?

💠 The rate at which a chemical reaction proceeds depends on its energy of activation rather than on the amount of energy it releases. The reaction that forms ADP from ATP has a very high energy of activation in the absence of its catalyst. Inside a cell, the reaction proceeds rapidly—10 million molecules of ATP are converted to

ADP and back to ATP every second within a typical cell—because the reaction is catalyzed by an enzyme which acts to lower the energy of activation.

ENZYMES

4.25   An enzyme is a

(*a*) carbohydrate.   (*b*) lipid.   (*c*) protein.   (*d*) nucleic acid.

4.26   The function of an enzyme is to

(*a*) cause chemical reactions that would not otherwise take place.   (*b*) change the rates of chemical reactions. (*c*) control the equilibrium points of reactions.   (*d*) change the directions of reactions.

4.27   The enzyme *sucrase* acts on

(*a*) sucrose only.   (*b*) sucrose and starch.   (*c*) any disaccharide.   (*d*) any organic monomer.

4.28   The shape of an enzyme, and consequently its activity, can be reversibly altered from moment to moment by

(*a*) heat.   (*b*) amino acid substitutions.   (*c*) allosteric subunits.   (*d*) sulfur substitutions.

4.29   The active site of an enzyme is formed by a few of the enzyme's

(*a*) R groups of the amino acids.   (*b*) amino groups of the amino acids.   (*c*) carboxyl groups of the amino acids. (*d*) exposed sulfur bonds.

4.30   Which of the following forms part of a coenzyme?

(*a*) Zn^{2+};   (*b*) Lipase;   (*c*) Vitamin B_2;   (*d*) Lysine

4.31   Hydrogen cyanide binds to the active site of an enzyme that is part of the pathway that forms ATP in cells; in this way, it prevents the enzyme's activity. Hence, hydrogen cyanide can best be described as a

(*a*) coenzyme.   (*b*) cofactor.   (*c*) competitive inhibitor.   (*d*) allosteric modulator.

4.32   An enzyme promotes a chemical reaction by

(*a*) lowering the energy of activation.   (*b*) causing the release of heat, which acts as a primer.   (*c*) increasing molecular motion.   (*d*) changing the free energy difference between substrate and product.

4.33   All of the following terms relate to enzyme activity. Match each term with its function by writing the letter of the term before the function in the space provided.

Term
(*a*)	Active site	(*e*)	Irreversible inhibitor
(*b*)	Allosteric inhibitor	(*f*)	Multienzyme complex
(*c*)	Competitive inhibitor	(*g*)	Substrate
(*d*)	Cooperativity	(*h*)	Tertiary structure

Function

(1) _____ Upon binding the substrate at one site, other sites on an enzyme become more reactive

(2) _____ Increases the efficiency with which metabolic pathways proceed

(3) _____ Molecule acted upon by an enzyme

(4) _____ Holds the substrate during a reaction

(5) _____ Inactivates an enzyme by changing the enzyme's shape

(6) _____ Produces the active site of an enzyme

(7) _____ Inactivates an enzyme by denaturing it

(8) _____ Inactivates an enzyme by occupying its active site

4.34   A substance that accelerates a chemical reaction, but itself is unchanged when the reaction is over, is a _____. In living things, most of these substances are proteins known as _____.

4.35   A high fever is dangerous to a human because enzymes are _____ by heat; without their _____, enzymes can no longer function.

4.36   What is the relation between an enzyme's tertiary structure and its specificity?

🐌   An important characteristic of an enzyme is its specificity for a particular *substrate*—the molecule upon which it acts. This specificity for a particular substrate, and consequently for a particular chemical reaction, is controlled by the three-dimensional shape (the tertiary structure) of the enzyme.

In forming a tertiary structure, bonds develop between certain amino acids in the linear, primary structure. The resulting shape of the molecule provides a (1) spatial fit for the substrate and (2) bonding fit for the substrate.

Spatial fit is the way in which pockets or grooves in the surface of the tertiary structure match the shape of the substrate, just as a key matches a lock or two pieces of a jigsaw puzzle match each other. The spatial fit of an enzyme permits only a substrate with a particular shape to be held by the enzyme.

Bonding fit of an enzyme is the presence of certain chemically active sites within the pockets or grooves in the surface of the tertiary structure. Chemical activity of these sites alters the substrate in a way that promotes the particular chemical reaction. Specificity of the bonding fit for the particular reaction is the consequence of the R groups of the amino acids that constitute the active site—amino acids from several regions of the primary structure that have been brought into close proximity by the folding of the molecule during the formation of its tertiary structure.

4.37   Discuss the statement that the kinds of things a cell can do depend on the kinds of enzymes it can make.

🐌   In the absence of enzymes, the chemical reactions within a cell would proceed so slowly that cellular organization would not be maintained. By accelerating the rate at which chemical reactions proceed, enzymes enable a cell to successfully counter the force of entropy. Each enzyme facilitates a particular chemical reaction, so that a list of the enzymes a cell can make is also a list of the chemical reactions that can take place at effective rates. If one of the enzymes is missing from the cell, then one of its chemical reactions cannot proceed at a reasonable rate and the product of the reaction is missing from the cell.

4.38   Why is heat used to sterilize nonliving objects?

🐌   Proteins are denatured at temperatures above about 60°C; they lose their tertiary and quaternary structures as the bonds that hold these structures are broken by thermal agitation of the atoms within the molecule. Such denaturation is irreversible; the tertiary and quaternary structures will not re-form. Since the chemistry of all life is governed by enzymes, which are proteins, and the activity of enzymes depends on their tertiary and quaternary structures, the denaturation of proteins eliminates the chemical activities of an organism and it dies. Thus, an object is sterilized when heat kills bacteria and other microorganisms on it.

4.39   The chemical reactions that occur when paper is burned are similar to some of the energy-yielding reactions that occur inside cells. How do the enzymes within cells make such reactions more suitable for living things?

🐌   First of all, if the energy-yielding reactions in cells produced a sudden and uncontrolled release of heat, like the burning of paper, the heat would disrupt other activities in the cell. Heat would destroy the organization of some of the molecules (e.g., proteins) and accelerate the rates of other chemical reactions.

Second, the cell would not be able to use the released energy in an efficient manner. More energy would be released than could be used right away, because most cellular work requires energy supplied in small doses.

Third, the use of heat (a flame) to initiate a chemical reaction is nonspecific—all chemical reactions within a cell would proceed rapidly as the heat released from one reaction initiated other reactions. Chaos would prevail inside the cell. The activity of each enzyme, by contrast, is controlled specifically by such mechanisms as feedback inhibition.

4.40   Enzymes are highly specific in the reactions they promote. What is a disadvantage of such specificity?

🐌   A disadvantage is that if one of the enzymes needed by a cell is absent, or nonfunctional, then one of its chemical reactions cannot proceed. No other enzyme can substitute for the missing one.

METABOLISM

4.41   A metabolic pathway is a

(*a*) route taken by chemicals through a solution.   (*b*) sequence of enzyme-facilitated chemical reactions.   (*c*) route taken by a particular enzyme from one chemical reaction to another.   (*d*) diagram of how organic molecules evolved.

4.42   Which of the following biochemical reactions is a catabolic reaction?

(*a*) The construction of a protein from amino acids;   (*b*) ADP + phosphate + energy $\longrightarrow$ ATP + H_2O;   (*c*) $C_6H_{12}O_6 + 6O_2 \longrightarrow 6CO_2 + 6H_2O$ + energy;   (*d*) $6CO_2 + 12H_2O$ + energy $\longrightarrow C_6H_{12}O_6 + 6O_2 + 6H_2O$

4.43   In most metabolic pathways, all needed enzymes are arranged together, in a multienzyme complex, within a

(*a*) solution of ATP.   (*b*) membrane.   (*c*) quaternary protein.   (*d*) coenzyme.

4.44   In feedback inhibition, a metabolic pathway is switched off by

(*a*) a rise in temperature.   (*b*) lack of a substrate.   (*c*) accumulation of the end product.   (*d*) competitive inhibition.

4.45   A metabolic pathway is a sequence of _____, in which each step is controlled by its own specific _____.

4.46   Metabolism involves two kinds of processes: _____, in which larger molecules are broken down into smaller ones, and _____, in which larger molecules are built from smaller ones. During growth, the rate of the _____ processes exceeds the rate of the _____ processes.

4.47   In coupled reactions, _____ reactions are linked with such _____ reactions as the synthesis of polymers.

4.48   Describe feedback inhibition of a metabolic pathway.

   Feedback inhibition occurs when the high concentrations of the end product of a metabolic pathway act to slow down or switch off enzymes that facilitate earlier steps in the pathway.

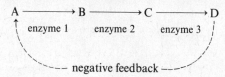

In this negative feedback, the higher the concentration of product D, the less active is enzyme 1 in promoting the conversion of substrate A to B. Feedback inhibition often involves allosteric inhibition, in which the product (e.g., D) binds to an enzyme (e.g., enzyme 1) at a site other than the enzyme's active site and, by doing so, changes the shape of the enzyme, which inactivates it. Allosteric inhibition is readily reversible, since when the product is rare, the enzyme is free of its inhibitory action and the metabolic pathway then proceeds at its normal rate.

4.49   An experiment was done to determine the effect of compound *y* on the biochemical reaction: A + B $\longrightarrow$ C. It was found that in the presence of *y*, very little of the product C was formed, but if the concentration of A and B was greatly increased, then C formed at an almost normal rate. Explain how *y* is acting upon this reaction.

   Compound *y* appears to be acting as a competitive inhibitor of the reaction, by binding to the active sites of the enzyme that facilitates the reaction. In this way it prevents the enzyme's normal substrates—molecules A and B—from gaining access to the active sites. With the enzyme inactivated in this way, the reaction proceeds very slowly and very little of product C is formed. When the system is flooded with molecules A and B, however, they occupy the active sites of the enzyme more often than compound *y* does, and the reaction proceeds and C is rapidly formed. If the effect were noncompetitive inhibition, rather than competitive, then *y* would not occupy active sites of the enzyme and an increase in the concentration of molecules A and B would have no effect on the inhibitory action of compound *y*.

4.50   The cells of a very sick baby were analyzed and found to contain abnormally large amounts of molecule C. Analyze this medical condition in terms of the following metabolic pathway:

$$A \xrightarrow[\text{enzyme 1}]{} B \xrightarrow[\text{enzyme 2}]{} C \xrightarrow[\text{enzyme 3}]{} D + F$$

   The cells of the baby do not have a functional enzyme 3. C is formed, but it cannot be broken down into D and F. Apparently, C does not act as a feedback inhibitor on earlier steps in the pathway, so these reactions proceed at normal rates and too much C accumulates in the cells. Products D and F may be waste products—forms in which excess C is normally eliminated from the cells.

Answers to Objective Questions

4.1 *a*

4.2 *c*

4.3 *a*

4.4 *a*

4.5 *b*

4.6 *b*

4.7 *a*

4.8 *b*

4.9 *a*

4.10 *d*

4.11 *d*

4.12 *c*

4.13 *a*

4.14 *b*

4.15 more; less

4.16 loses; liberates; gains; stores

4.17 chemical; work; heat; Second

4.18 potential; kinetic

4.19 free energy

4.25 *c*

4.26 *b*

4.27 *a*

4.28 *c*

4.29 *a*

4.30 *c*

4.31 *c*

4.32 *a*

4.33 (1) *d*; (2) *f*; (3) *g*; (4) *a*; (5) *b*; (6) *h*; (7) *e*; (8) *c*

4.34 catalyst; enzymes

4.35 denatured; tertiary and quaternary structures

4.41 *b*

4.42 *c*

4.43 *b*

4.44 *c*

4.45 chemical reactions; enzyme

4.46 catabolism; anabolism; anabolic; catabolic

4.47 exergonic; endergonic

🐚 Phosphorylation is the addition of a phosphate group to an organic molecule. In the formation of ATP from ADP and phosphate during glycolysis, an enzyme facilitates the direct transfer of a phosphate group from an enzyme substrate to ADP (Fig. 7.1).

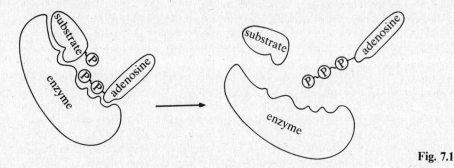

Fig. 7.1

The reaction proceeds because more energy is released when phosphate is removed from the substrate (an exergonic reaction) than is used to add phosphate to ADP (an endergonic reaction). Substrate-level phosphorylation occurs twice during glycolysis: first when the substrate is 1,3-diphosphoglyceric acid and then again when the substrate is phosphoenolpyruvic acid.

7.19   Describe what is used, what is produced, and what is accomplished in glycolysis.

🐚 The word *glycolysis* means "splitting of glucose," which is in essence what happens during the process. The six-carbon molecule of glucose is split into two three-carbon molecules of pyruvic acid.

Glycolysis involves a series of nine reactions, each catalyzed by a specific enzyme. All of the materials used and produced during these reactions are listed in Table 7.1.

TABLE 7.1 Glycolysis: Reactants and Products

used	produced
1 glucose ($C_6H_{12}O_6$)	2 pyruvic acids ($C_3H_4O_3$)*
4ADP	4ATP
4 phosphate groups	2 phosphate groups
2ATP	2ADP
2NAD$^+$	2NADH
	2H$^+$
	2H$_2$O

* The four hydrogen atoms removed from glucose and not part of pyruvic acid are now present as 2NADH and 2H$^+$.

Two things are accomplished in glycolysis. First, there is an immediate net yield of two ATP molecules—four are formed and two are used. Second, some of the energy in glucose is transferred to four hydrogen atoms, which become part of two molecules of NADH and form two hydrogen ions. Eventually, the energy within the NADH is released in the electron transport system and forms six molecules of ATP.

FERMENTATION

7.20 When oxygen is not available to a muscle cell, NADH formed during glycolysis does not pass electrons to the electron transport system. Instead, it passes hydrogen atoms to

(*a*) acetyl coenzyme A. (*b*) pyruvic acid. (*c*) fructose. (*d*) ADP.

7.21 Which one of the following processes releases a carbon dioxide molecule?

(*a*) Glycolysis; (*b*) Lactic acid fermentation; (*c*) Alcohol fermentation; (*d*) Hydrolysis of glycogen

7.22 When a yeast is producing wine, which of the following is not formed?

(*a*) Pyruvic acid; (*b*) Ethanol; (*c*) Carbon dioxide; (*d*) Acetyl coenzyme A

7.23 In fermentation, the hydrogen atoms removed from glucose end up as part of _____ or _____, depending on the type of cell.

7.24 In the production of wine, the glucose in fruit juice is converted by yeast to _____. This process is called _____.

7.25 When not enough oxygen gets to muscle cells during a sprint, energy is provided by glycolysis of glucose to _____ and then conversion of these molecules to _____.

7.26 In the fermentation of one glucose molecule, there is a net gain of _____ molecules of ATP.

7.27 Match the following names with their molecular structures.

(*a*) pyruvic acid (*b*) lactic acid (*c*) ethanol

_____ 1.
$$
\begin{array}{c}
OH \\
| \\
C{=}O \\
| \\
H{-}C{-}OH \\
| \\
H{-}C{-}H \\
| \\
H
\end{array}
$$

_____ 2.
$$
\begin{array}{c}
OH \\
| \\
C{=}O \\
| \\
C{=}O \\
| \\
H{-}C{-}H \\
| \\
H
\end{array}
$$

_____ 3.
$$
\begin{array}{c}
H \\
| \\
H{-}C{-}OH \\
| \\
H{-}C{-}H \\
| \\
H
\end{array}
$$

7.28 Describe what is used, what is produced, and what is accomplished in anaerobic cellular respiration (fermentation).

☙ Anaerobic cellular respiration, or fermentation, is the incomplete breakdown of glucose in the absence of oxygen gas. The end product is either lactic acid or alcohol, depending on the type of cell, and still contains a lot of energy. The first set of reactions—glycolysis—is the same for either lactic acid fermentation or alcohol fermentation. Table 7.2 shows what is used, produced, and accomplished by fermentation (see also Question 7.19).

TABLE 7.2 Fermentation: Major Reactants and Products

used	produced	accomplished
1 glucose	2 pyruvic acids	Energy is transferred from the
4ADP	4ATP	glucose molecule to 4ATP molecules.
4 phosphates	2 phosphates	Since 2ATP molecules were used to prime
2ATP	2ADP	the reaction, the net yield is 2ATP.
$2NAD^+$	2NADH	Energy is transferred also from glucose
	$2H^+$	to 2NADH.
	$2H_2O$	

In *lactic acid fermentation*, the next and final step after glycolysis is simply conversion of the two molecules of pyruvic acid to two molecules of lactic acid. This conversion uses the four hydrogen atoms removed from glucose during glycolysis and now present in the two NADH and two H^+ ions.

$$
\begin{array}{c}
\text{OH} \quad\quad \text{OH} \\
| \quad\quad\quad | \\
\text{C}=\text{O} \quad\ \text{C}=\text{O} \\
| \quad\quad\quad | \\
\text{C}=\text{O} \quad\ \text{C}=\text{O} \\
| \quad\quad\quad | \\
\text{H}-\text{C}-\text{H} \quad \text{H}-\text{C}-\text{H} \\
| \quad\quad\quad | \\
\text{H} \quad\quad\quad \text{H}
\end{array}
+ 2\text{NADH} + 2\text{H}^+ \longrightarrow
\begin{array}{c}
\text{OH} \quad\quad \text{OH} \\
| \quad\quad\quad | \\
\text{C}=\text{O} \quad\ \text{C}=\text{O} \\
| \quad\quad\quad | \\
\text{H}-\text{C}-\text{OH} \quad \text{H}-\text{C}-\text{OH} \\
| \quad\quad\quad | \\
\text{H}-\text{C}-\text{H} \quad \text{H}-\text{C}-\text{H} \\
| \quad\quad\quad | \\
\text{H} \quad\quad\quad \text{H}
\end{array}
+ 2\text{NAD}^+
$$

pyruvic   pyruvic   lactic   lactic
acid   acid   acid   acid

Lactic acid is a waste product of lactic acid fermentation. In human muscles, it is removed from the cells, carried to the liver, and there converted back into pyruvic acid (a process that requires oxygen). Some anaerobic yeasts and bacteria which produce lactic acid are used to make cheese and yogurt.

What is accomplished in the last step of lactic acid fermentation is the retrieval of NAD^+, which is now free to be used again. Had anaerobic cellular respiration ended with pyruvic acid, then NAD^+ would be tied up as NADH and unavailable for use in glycolysis.

In *alcohol fermentation* there are *two* steps after glycolysis is completed. First, both pyruvic acid molecules are converted into two-carbon molecules of acetaldehyde, with the release of one molecule of carbon dioxide for each pyruvic acid converted.

$$
\begin{array}{c}
\text{OH} \quad\quad \text{OH} \\
| \quad\quad\quad | \\
\text{C}=\text{O} \quad\ \text{C}=\text{O} \\
| \quad\quad\quad | \\
\text{C}=\text{O} \quad\ \text{C}=\text{O} \\
| \quad\quad\quad | \\
\text{H}-\text{C}-\text{H} \quad \text{H}-\text{C}-\text{H} \\
| \quad\quad\quad | \\
\text{H} \quad\quad\quad \text{H}
\end{array}
\longrightarrow
\begin{array}{c}
\text{H} \quad\quad\quad \text{H} \\
| \quad\quad\quad | \\
\text{C}=\text{O} \quad\ \text{C}=\text{O} \\
| \quad\quad\quad | \\
\text{H}-\text{C}-\text{H} \quad \text{H}-\text{C}-\text{H} \\
| \quad\quad\quad | \\
\text{H} \quad\quad\quad \text{H}
\end{array}
+ 2\text{CO}_2
$$

pyruvic   pyruvic   acetaldehyde   acetaldehyde
acid   acid

Second, the four hydrogen atoms removed from glucose during glycolysis (now part of the two NADH and two H^+) are added to the two acetaldehyde molecules to form two molecules of ethanol.

$$
\begin{array}{c}
\text{H} \quad\quad\quad \text{H} \\
| \quad\quad\quad | \\
\text{C}=\text{O} \quad\ \text{C}=\text{O} \\
| \quad\quad\quad | \\
\text{H}-\text{C}-\text{H} \quad \text{H}-\text{C}-\text{H} \\
| \quad\quad\quad | \\
\text{H} \quad\quad\quad \text{H}
\end{array}
+ 2\text{NADH} + 2\text{H}^+ \longrightarrow
\begin{array}{c}
\text{H} \quad\quad\quad \text{H} \\
| \quad\quad\quad | \\
\text{H}-\text{C}-\text{OH} \quad \text{H}-\text{C}-\text{OH} \\
| \quad\quad\quad | \\
\text{H}-\text{C}-\text{H} \quad \text{H}-\text{C}-\text{H} \\
| \quad\quad\quad | \\
\text{H} \quad\quad\quad \text{H}
\end{array}
+ 2\text{NAD}^+
$$

acetaldehyde   acetaldehyde   ethanol   ethanol

The production of bread, beer, and wine involves alcohol fermentation by yeasts. When bread is made, the alcohol evaporates and the carbon dioxide causes the bread to rise. When beer or wine is made, the carbon dioxide evaporates and the alcohol is retained.

As with lactic acid fermentation, there is no further energy release after formation of pyruvic acid during glycolysis. What is accomplished by the last two steps of alcohol fermentation is the freeing of NAD^+ so it can be used again in glycolysis.

FORMATION OF ACETYL COENZYME A

7.29 In the conversion of pyruvic acid to acetyl coenzyme A, pyruvic acid is

(**a**) oxidized. (**b**) reduced. (**c**) broken into one-carbon fragments. (**d**) isomerized.

7.30 In the conversion of pyruvic acid to acetyl coenzyme A, NAD^+ is

(**a**) oxidized. (**b**) reduced. (**c**) broken into one-carbon units. (**d**) isomerized.

7.31 The function of coenzyme A is to

(*a*) isomerize pyruvic acid. (*b*) isomerize NAD^+. (*c*) activate the acetyl group. (*d*) facilitate oxidative phosphorylation.

7.32 The chemical formula of the acetyl group is

(*a*)
$$
\begin{array}{c}
| \\
C=O \\
| \\
C=O \\
| \\
H-C-H \\
| \\
H
\end{array}
$$

(*b*)
$$
\begin{array}{c}
H-C-OH \\
| \\
H-C-H \\
| \\
H
\end{array}
$$

(*c*)
$$
\begin{array}{c}
C=O \\
| \\
H-C-H \\
| \\
H
\end{array}
$$

(*d*)
$$
\begin{array}{c}
| \\
H-C-H \\
| \\
H
\end{array}
$$

7.33 Coenzyme A, which combines with the acetyl group, is formed in part from

(*a*) zinc. (*b*) iron. (*c*) vitamin A. (*d*) one of the B vitamins.

7.34 Glucose has _____ carbon atoms, pyruvic acid has _____ carbon atoms, and the acetyl group has _____ carbon atoms.

7.35 The formation of acetyl coenzyme A from pyruvic acid produces (in addition to acetyl coenzyme A): one molecule of _____, one molecule of _____, and one molecule (ion) of _____.

7.36 Describe what is used, what is produced, and what is accomplished in the conversion of pyruvic acid to acetyl coenzyme A.

Pyruvic acid is transported into a mitochondrion and converted into acetyl coenzyme A, which enters the Krebs citric acid cycle. The conversion of pyruvic acid to acetyl coenzyme A takes place on a multienzyme complex, which is made of many copies of the three enzymes needed as well as of their coenzymes. This complex, somewhat larger than a ribosome, is located in the matrix of the mitochondrion. There, the carboxyl group (COOH) of pyruvic acid is removed and the remaining two-carbon molecule (an acetyl group) is attached to coenzyme A by a high-energy sulfur bond (one end of coenzyme A is an —SH group). One molecule of carbon dioxide (from COOH) and two hydrogen atoms (from COOH and from coenzyme A) are released during the reaction. The carbon dioxide diffuses out of the cell and the two hydrogen atoms combine with NAD^+ to form $NADH + H^+$.

$$
\begin{array}{c}
OH \\
| \\
C=O \\
| \\
C=O \\
| \\
H-C-H \\
| \\
H
\end{array}
+ H-S-CoA + NAD^+ \longrightarrow
\begin{array}{c}
S-CoA \\
C=O \\
| \\
H-C-H \\
| \\
H
\end{array}
+ NADH + H^+ + CO_2
$$

Table 7.3 lists the molecules used and produced during formation of acetyl coenzyme A.

TABLE 7.3 Formation of Acetyl Co-A: Reactants and Products

used	produced
1 pyruvic acid ($C_3H_4O_3$)	1 acetyl coenzyme A ($C_2H_3O \sim S-CoA$)
1 coenzyme A (H—S—CoA)	$1H^+$
$1NAD^+$	1NADH
	$1CO_2$

Since two molecules of pyruvic acid are produced from each glucose molecule, the energy gain from the reaction, per glucose molecule, is two NADH.

Three things are accomplished by this conversion: (1) pyruvic acid is oxidized, and some of its energy transferred, via electrons, to NADH for later use in the electron transport system; (2) a three-carbon molecule is converted into a two-carbon molecule, for use in the Krebs citric acid cycle; and (3) the two-carbon molecule (acetyl group) is attached to coenzyme A by a high-energy sulfur bond, which activates the acetyl group and prepares it for participation in the Krebs citric acid cycle.

KREBS CITRIC ACID CYCLE

7.37 How many carbon atoms are in an oxaloacetic acid molecule, which joins with an acetyl group during step 1 of the Krebs citric acid cycle?

(a) 2; (b) 3; (c) 4; (d) 6

7.38 How many carbon atoms are in a citric acid molecule?

(a) 2; (b) 3; (c) 4; (d) 6

7.39 Oxidative decarboxylation, which occurs during steps 3 and 4 of the Krebs citric acid cycle, is the removal of both _____ and _____ from a substrate at the same time.

7.40 FAD and $FADH_2$ are functionally most similar to _____ and _____, also in the Krebs citric acid cycle.

7.41 A single turn of the Krebs citric acid cycle produces one molecule of _____, one molecule of _____, two molecules of _____, and three molecules of _____. For each glucose molecule processed, there are _____ turns of the cycle.

7.42 Describe what is used, what is produced, and what is accomplished by the Krebs citric acid cycle.

🐚 In the Krebs citric acid cycle, a two-carbon fragment of the original glucose molecule, present as acetyl coenzyme A, is joined with water and a four-carbon molecule (oxaloacetic acid) to form the six-carbon molecule, citric acid. This molecule ($C_6H_8O_7$) is then stripped of two carbons, four oxygens, and eight hydrogens, and joined with two water molecules to form again the four-carbon molecule present at the start of the cycle.

$$C_2H_3O \sim S\text{---}CoA + C_4H_4O_5 + H_2O \longrightarrow C_6H_8O_7 + H\text{---}S\text{---}CoA$$

acetyl coenzyme A   oxaloacetic acid   citric acid   coenzyme A

$$C_6H_8O_7 + 2H_2O \longrightarrow C_4H_4O_5 + 2CO_2 + 8H^+ + energy$$

citric acid   oxaloacetic acid

Energy is released in the breakdown of citric acid. Some is used immediately to form ATP from ADP and phosphate, by the process of substrate-level phosphorylation (see Question 7.18). The rest, released by oxidation (removal of H^+), is transferred to NAD^+ and FAD.

$$8H^+ + 3NAD^+ + 1FAD \longrightarrow 3NADH + 3H^+ + 1FADH_2$$

The complete cycle is shown in Fig. 7.2. All reactions take place in the matrix of the mitrochondrion, except the reduction of FAD, which occurs on the inner membrane of the mitrochondrion. As with other biochemical pathways, each reaction is facilitated by a specific enzyme.

Materials used and produced during the Krebs citric acid cycle are listed in Table 7.4.

TABLE 7.4 Krebs Cycle: Reactants and Products

used	produced
$1C_2H_3O \sim S\text{---}CoA$ (acetyl coenzyme A)	1 coenzyme A
$1C_4H_4O_5$ (oxaloacetic acid)	$2CO_2$
1ADP	$1C_4H_4O_5$ (oxaloacetic acid)
1 phosphate group	1ATP
$3NAD^+$	3NADH
1FAD	$3H^+$
$2H_2O$	$1FADH_2$

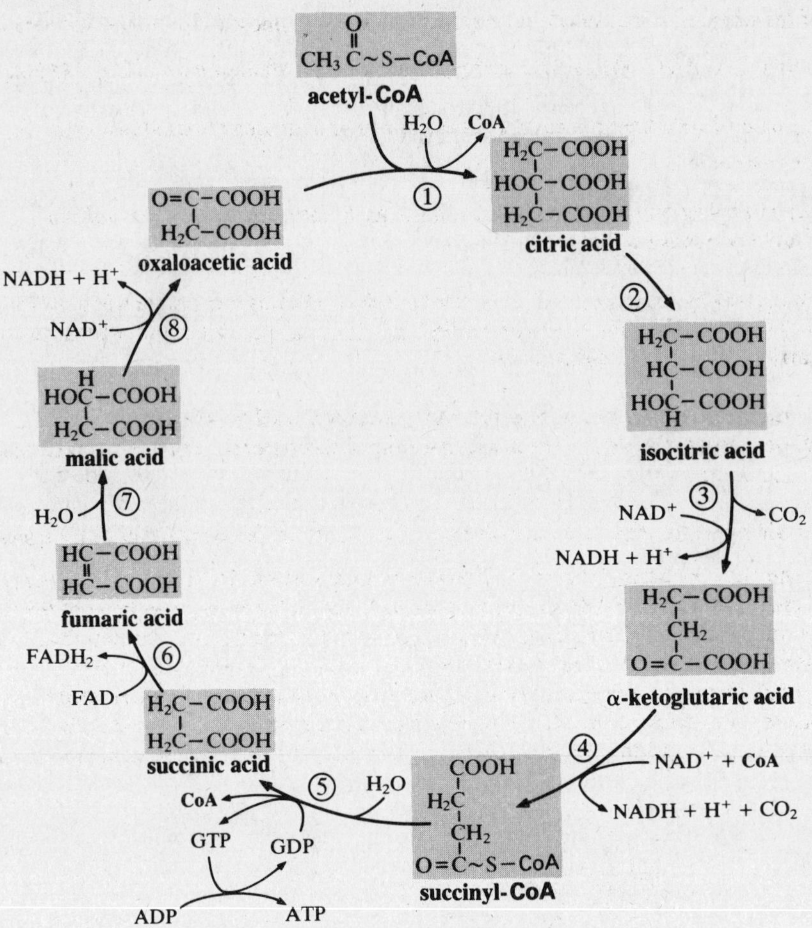

Fig. 7.2. The Krebs citric acid cycle.

What has been accomplished is the transfer of energy from the newly formed citric acid molecule to one molecule of ATP, three molecules of NADH, and one molecule of $FADH_2$. Energy stored in NADH and $FADH_2$ is used to form ATP in the electron transport system.

ELECTRON TRANSPORT SYSTEM (RESPIRATORY CHAIN)

7.43   At the end of the Krebs citric acid cycle, most of the energy removed from the glucose molecule has been transferred to

(a) NADH and $FADH_2$.   (b) ATP.   (c) oxaloacetic acid.   (d) citric acid.

7.44   In the electron transport system, the final acceptor of electrons is

(a) cytochrome b.   (b) cytochrome a_3.   (c) oxygen.   (d) ubiquinone (substance Q).

7.45   In the electron transport system, the final acceptor of protons is

(a) cytochrome b.   (b) cytochrome a_3.   (c) oxygen.   (d) ubiquinone (substance Q).

7.46   The atom within each cytochrome molecule that actually accepts and releases electrons is

(a) carbon.   (b) iron.   (c) zinc.   (d) oxygen.

7.47   The production of ATP by oxidative phosphorylation is driven by energy from

(a) coenzyme A.   (b) isomerization of the cytochromes.   (c) the formation of NADH.   (d) the diffusion of protons from the intermembrane space to the matrix of the mitochondrion.

7.48   Oxygen, which forms part of the electron transport system, enters the mitochondrion as an atom in

(a) glucose ($C_6H_{12}O_6$).   (b) pyruvic acid ($C_3H_4O_3$).   (c) carbon dioxide (CO_2).   (d) oxygen gas (O_2).

7.49 Most of the protons, which play a crucial role in oxidative phosphorylation, enter the mitochondrion as
(*a*) glucose ($C_6H_{12}O_6$). (*b*) pyruvic acid ($C_3H_4O_3$). (*c*) carbon dioxide (CO_2). (*d*) oxygen gas (O_2).

7.50 Electrons enter the electron transport system as parts of hydrogen atoms attached to _____ and _____.

7.51 In an electron transport system, each electron carrier in the series holds electrons at a _____ energy level than the previous carrier.

7.52 Electrons carried by _____ enter the electron transport system when they are transferred to flavin mononucleotide (FMN). Electrons carried by _____ enter the chain at the next level down the line, at the carrier ubiquinone (substance Q).

7.53 Energy released from electrons during electron transport is used to move _____ out of the matrix into the intermembrane space of the mitochondrion. Energy stored in this way is then used to build _____.

7.54 Describe what is used, what is produced, and what is accomplished by the electron transport system.

🐚 In the electron transport system, high-energy electrons are converted to low-energy electrons (Fig. 7.3). The released energy is used to establish a *proton gradient* across the inner membrane of the mitochondrion, in which there are more protons in the intermembrane space than in the matrix. As protons flow down this gradient (i.e., move through the inner membrane), the energy released is used to form ATP from ADP and inorganic phosphate. The use of electrons, originally part of the glucose molecule and transferred to NAD^+ and FAD by oxidation and reduction, to attach phosphate to ADP is called *oxidative phosphorylation*. The transfer of electron energy to a proton gradient prior to its use in phosphorylation is known as the *chemiosmotic mechanism*.

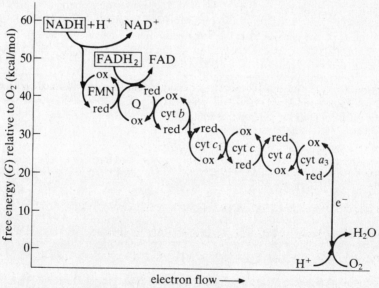

Fig. 7.3. Controlled release of energy in the electron transport system. cyt = cytochrome; red = reduced; ox = oxidized.

Electrons in NADH and $FADH_2$, taken from glucose during earlier stages of cellular respiration, enter the electron transport system, which is a series of molecules embedded within the inner membrane of the mitochondrion. Each molecule in the series is an electron carrier; it receives electrons (is reduced) and then passes them (is oxidized) to the next molecule in the series. Energy carried by the electrons is released in small amounts at each transfer, since each molecule in the series holds electrons with lower free energy than the preceding molecule. Electrons from NADH enter the system at a protein called *flavin mononucleotide* (FMN), whereas electrons from $FADH_2$ enter one step lower, at a molecule called *ubiquinone* (carrier Q). All five cytochrome molecules, which follow ubiquinone in the series, are proteins that contain iron—the atom within the cytochrome molecule that is oxidized and reduced. The final carrier in the system—cytochrome a_3—transfers the electron to an oxygen atom.

The two electrons carried in NADH are released in the form of H^- (one proton with two electrons), which picks up another proton from the matrix of the mitochondrion and then releases the two protons to the proton pump and the two electrons to their electron acceptor, FMN. The two protons, as well as the two released when the two electrons in $FADH_2$ join the electron transport chain, are pumped from the matrix to the intermembrane space of the mitochondrion. Energy released from the transport of electrons is used to pump these protons, which establishes a gradient of protons across the inner membrane. Then, when ATP is made from ADP and phosphate, the energy needed is acquired by allowing the protons to flow down the gradient; the protons move through an enzyme, ATPase (also called ATP synthetase), situated within the membrane (Fig. 7.4).

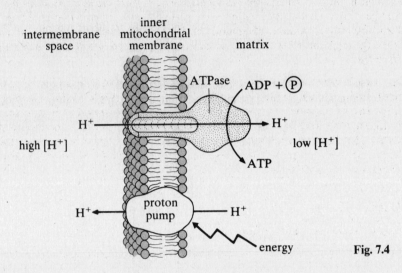

Fig. 7.4

Energy released by the flow of protons is used to attach a phosphate to ADP. Each NADH releases enough energy to form three molecules of ATP. Each $FADH_2$ releases only enough to form two molecules of ATP, since it joins the electron transport chain at a lower energy level (ubiquinone) than NADH does. Table 7.5 summarizes, for the catabolism of one glucose molecule, what is used and what is produced in the electron transport system.

TABLE 7.5 Electron Transport System: Reactants and Products

used	produced
10NADH (2 from glycolysis; 2 from oxidation of pyruvic acid; 6 from the Krebs cycle)	10NAD$^+$
10H$^+$ (from the matrix, 1 for each NADH)	
2FADH$_2$ (from the Krebs cycle)	2FAD
34ADP	34ATP
34 phosphate groups	
6O$_2$	12H$_2$O (24 electrons: 20 from the 10NADH, 4 from the 2FADH$_2$; 24 protons: 10 from the 10NADH, 10 from the 10H$^+$, and 4 from the 2FADH$_2$; 12 oxygen atoms: from the 6O$_2$)

What is accomplished is the use of energy, transferred from glucose to NADH and $FADH_2$ earlier in cellular respiration, to form ATP from ADP and phosphate. In a eukaryotic cell, the aerobic catabolism of glucose yields approximately 40 molecules of ATP, most of which (34) are formed by the electron transport system.

7.55 Cyanide is a deadly poison. It forms a complex with cytochrome a_3, preventing the transfer of electrons from this carrier to oxygen. What effect does this action have on cellular respiration?

☙ The electron transport system will cease to function: no electrons will be transported, no proton gradient will be established, and no ATP will be formed from this phase of cellular respiration.

Since NADH and $FADH_2$ in the mitochondrion will no longer be reduced by the electron transport system, there will be no NAD$^+$ or FAD for oxidation in the Krebs citric acid cycle or oxidation of pyruvic acid to acetyl coenzyme A. Thus, all cellular respiration in the mitochondria will come to a halt, as there are no molecules available to accept electrons.

What about fermentation in the cytosol? Cells vary in their ability to switch from aerobic to anaerobic cellular respiration. Skeletal muscle cells, for example, do this very well; nerve cells, hardly at all. Thus, with no aerobic cellular respiration in the mitochondria, some cells will switch to lactic acid fermentation, thereby freeing NAD^+ for glycolysis, and there will be some energy production (only a net of two ATP molecules per glucose molecule). But soon the accumulation of lactic acid and depletion of glucose supplies will cause these cells to die. Other cells will die immediately, unable to produce lactic acid from pyruvic acid, and therefore unable to continue glycolysis because all the NAD^+ in the cytosol is tied up as NADH.

7.56   Brown fat is found in hibernating mammals, where it functions as a fuel when the animal's body temperature is raised back to normal after the hibernation period is over. In cells that are using brown fat instead of glucose for cellular respiration, the inner membranes of the mitochondria are permeable to hydrogen ions. What effect does this change in permeability have on cellular respiration, and how does it enable an animal to raise its body temperature?

🐚   A membrane that is permeable to hydrogen ions cannot form a proton gradient, i.e., more protons on one side than on the other. Without a proton gradient, no ATP is formed by the electron transport system. Energy is still released by the system, and this uncaptured energy is converted entirely to heat. Heat produced in this fashion is crucial to a hibernating animal, since the central nervous system is too cool to stimulate muscle contractions for shivering, the normal method that a mammal's body uses to raise its temperature. By providing fuel for cellular respiration yet preventing transfer of the energy to ATP, brown fat greatly increases heat production and rapidly raises the body temperature of a hibernating mammal.

YIELD OF ATP

7.57   In aerobic cellular respiration, most of the ATP is synthesized during

(**a**) glycolysis.   (**b**) oxidation of pyruvic acid.   (**c**) the Krebs citric acid cycle.   (**d**) electron transport.

7.58   The free energy change ΔG from the conversion of one molecule of glucose to six molecules of carbon dioxide is -686 kcal/mol, yet only about 266 kcal/mol of this is captured within ATP molecules. The rest is

(**a**) converted to heat.   (**b**) lost within carbon dioxide.   (**c**) used to form lactic acid.   (**d**) transferred to water molecules.

7.59   In a eukaryotic cell, the breakdown of one molecule of glucose to six molecules of carbon dioxide causes formation of a total of _____ molecules of ATP, of which _____ are formed in the mitochondrion.

7.60   During electron transport, each molecule of NADH produces a maximum of _____ molecules of ATP and each molecule of $FADH_2$ produces a maximum of _____ molecules of ATP.

7.61   Compare what is accomplished in the various phases of aerobic cellular respiration.

    See Table 7.6.

TABLE 7.6 Comparison of the Four Phases of Aerobic Cellular Respiration

phase	molecular changes	cost, per glucose	gain, per glucose
Glycolysis	Converts glucose (6C) to 2 pyruvic acids (3C each)	2ATP (to prime)	4ATP + 2NADH
Oxidation of pyruvic acid	Converts pyruvic acid (3C) to an acetyl group (2C)	None	2NADH
Krebs citric acid cycle	Converts citric acid (6C, formed from an acetyl group and oxaloacetic acid) to oxaloacetic acid (4C)	None	$2ATP + 6NADH + 2FADH_2$
Electron transport	Converts NADH and $FADH_2$ to NAD^+, FAD, electrons, and protons; released energy is used to build ATP; electrons and protons join oxygen to form water	2ATP (to carry 2 electrons in NADH into mitochondrion)	34ATP

7.62 A total of 40ATP molecules are formed in the conversion of glucose to carbon dioxide and water. The estimated net yield is 36 molecules of ATP. (*a*) Account for the difference of four ATP molecules between the number formed and the net yield. (*b*) Why is the net yield only an estimate?

(*a*) Four molecules of ATP are spent during cellular respiration; they are converted to ADP and phosphate, and the released energy is used to do work. Two molecules of ATP initiate glycolysis. One of the molecules phosphorylates glucose during step 1 and the other phosphorylates fructose 6-phosphate during step 2 of glycolysis. In each of the phosphorylations, an enzyme transfers a phosphate from ATP to the sugar and, by doing so, makes the sugar more chemically active and more easily split into two three-carbon molecules. Another two molecules of ATP are used in eukaryotic cells to carry the two electrons in NADH, produced in the cytosol during glycolysis, across the membranes of the mitochondrion, where they join NAD$^+$ to reform NADH. The mitochondrial membranes are not permeable to NADH.

(*b*) A net yield of 36ATP molecules is only an estimate for two reasons. First, *prokaryotic* cells can have a net yield of 38ATP molecules per glucose molecule because they do not have to spend two ATP molecules to transport electrons from NADH into a mitochondrion. They have no mitochondria, and their electron transport system is embedded within the plasma membrane and available directly to the NADH produced during glycolysis. Second, the amount of ATP formed in the electron transport system varies according to how permeable the mitochondrial membrane is to protons (see Question 7.56) and how much of the energy in the proton gradient is used to transport materials across the mitochondrial membranes. The energy may be used to drive other reactions within the mitochondrion.

OTHER MOLECULES AS FUEL

7.63 Fatty acids enter cellular respiration as

(*a*) one-carbon fragments.   (*b*) two-carbon fragments.   (*c*) three-carbon fragments.   (*d*) long chains of 16 to 20 carbon atoms.

7.64 The point in cellular respiration at which a particular amino acid enters depends on the

(*a*) temperature of the cell.   (*b*) phase of cellular respiration that needs fuel.   (*c*) pH of the cell.   (*d*) particular R group of the amino acid.

7.65 A disadvantage of using amino acids as fuels for cellular respiration is that the waste product _____ is formed, and it must be removed from the human body by the _____, which may become stressed from the overwork.

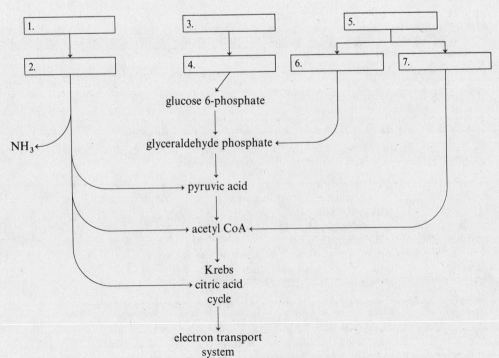

Fig. 7.5

7.66 Refer to the diagram of cellular respiration and its fuels shown in Fig. 7.5 on p. 52. Fill in the empty boxes with the names of the appropriate polymers and monomers.

7.67 Aerobic exercise is physical activity in which all ATP used by the muscle cells comes from aerobic cellular respiration; anaerobic cellular respiration is not used. One cannot run, aerobically, as fast when fats replace glucose as the main fuel for aerobic cellular respiration. This decline in performance is known by marathoners as "hitting the wall." What is the chemical basis for this difference in muscle function?

🐚 Most of the energy from fats comes from their fatty acid monomers rather than from glycerol. Conversion of a fatty acid to carbon dioxide and water releases a great deal of energy, yet the rate of ATP production is slower than when glucose is used. This is because the catabolism of fatty acids requires more oxygen for a given energy yield than the catabolism of glucose, and it is the rate of oxygen delivery to muscle cells that sets an upper limit to aerobic running speed.

A fatty acid contains much less oxygen in relation to carbon and hydrogen than glucose does. For example, the formula for palmitic acid, a typical fatty acid, is $C_{16}H_{32}O_2$. As with other fatty acids, palmitic acid is a long chain of carbon atoms attached to hydrogen atoms, except at one end.

$$H-\underset{\underset{H}{|}}{\overset{\overset{H}{|}}{C}}-\underset{\underset{H}{|}}{\overset{\overset{H}{|}}{C}}-\underset{\underset{H}{|}}{\overset{\overset{H}{|}}{C}}-\underset{\underset{H}{|}}{\overset{\overset{H}{|}}{C}}-\underset{\underset{H}{|}}{\overset{\overset{H}{|}}{C}}-\underset{\underset{H}{|}}{\overset{\overset{H}{|}}{C}}-\underset{\underset{H}{|}}{\overset{\overset{H}{|}}{C}}-\underset{\underset{H}{|}}{\overset{\overset{H}{|}}{C}}-\underset{\underset{H}{|}}{\overset{\overset{H}{|}}{C}}-\underset{\underset{H}{|}}{\overset{\overset{H}{|}}{C}}-\underset{\underset{H}{|}}{\overset{\overset{H}{|}}{C}}-\underset{\underset{H}{|}}{\overset{\overset{H}{|}}{C}}-\underset{\underset{H}{|}}{\overset{\overset{H}{|}}{C}}-\underset{\underset{H}{|}}{\overset{\overset{H}{|}}{C}}-\underset{\underset{H}{|}}{\overset{\overset{H}{|}}{C}}-C\overset{O}{\underset{OH}{}}$$

A fatty acid enters cellular respiration as acetyl coenzyme A. Carbon atoms in the chain are broken off, two at a time, to form an acetyl group, which then joins with coenzyme A. An acetyl group contains an oxygen atom, whereas the two-carbon fragment of a fatty acid does not. Thus, an oxygen atom has to be added to each two-carbon fragment before it can be used in cellular respiration. This addition makes a greater demand for oxygen when fatty acids are used than when glucose is used to fuel muscular activity. Since the maximum ability to transport oxygen gas to muscle cells is fixed for a particular person at a particular time, the more oxygen needed to produce each ATP molecule, the slower a person will run.

THE MITOCHONDRIA: SITES OF BIOCHEMICAL PATHWAYS

7.68 In a eukaryotic cell, glycolysis takes place

(*a*) within the nucleus. (*b*) on the rough endoplasmic reticulum. (*c*) in the cytoplasm, but outside the organelles. (*d*) within the mitochondria.

7.69 In a eukaryotic cell, the Krebs citric acid cycle and terminal electron transport take place

(*a*) within the nucleus. (*b*) on the rough endoplasmic reticulum. (*c*) in the cytoplasm, but outside the organelles. (*d*) within the mitochondria.

7.70 The inner membrane of the mitochondrion is very selective about what it normally allows to enter the organelle. One molecule it regularly allows in is

(*a*) citric acid. (*b*) ATP. (*c*) pyruvic acid. (*d*) glucose.

7.71 The inner membrane of a mitochondrion is very selective about what it allows to leave the organelle. One molecule that regularly passes out of a mitochondrion is

(*a*) citric acid. (*b*) ATP. (*c*) pyruvic acid. (*d*) glucose.

7.72 The electron transport chain is a group of molecules located in the

(*a*) inner membrane of the mitochondrion. (*b*) outer membrane of the mitochondrion. (*c*) intermembrane space of the mitochondrion. (*d*) matrix of the mitochondrion.

7.73 Within the mitochondrion, the proton gradient develops across the

(*a*) inner membrane. (*b*) outer membrane. (*c*) intermembrane space. (*d*) matrix.

7.74 The place in the mitochondrion where the pH is lowest is the

(*a*) ribosomal complex. (*b*) intermembrane space. (*c*) cytosol. (*d*) matrix.

7.75 The function of the mitochondrial cristae is to

(*a*) prevent escape of oxygen gas. (*b*) store coenzyme A. (*c*) increase the surface area of the inner membrane. (*d*) increase the availability of phospholipids.

7.76 Seven of the eight steps of the Krebs citric acid cycle take place within the _____ of the mitochondrion. Only the production of _____ occurs elsewhere.

7.77 Label the lettered parts of the mitochondrion shown in Fig. 7.6.

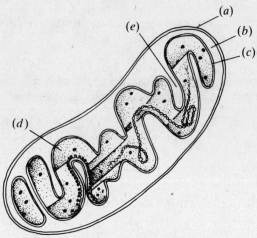

Fig. 7.6. Mitochondrion.

METABOLIC RATES

7.78 When metabolic rates are low, the production of ATP is slow. The main control over ATP production is allosteric inhibition, by ATP and citric acid, of the enzyme that facilitates formation of

(*a*) glucose from glycogen. (*b*) fructose 1,6-diphosphate from fructose 6-phosphate. (*c*) acetyl coenzyme A from pyruvic acid. (*d*) citric acid from acetyl coenzyme A and oxaloacetic acid.

7.79 For an animal cell, the main advantage of aerobic cellular respiration over lactic acid fermentation is that

(*a*) more energy is released from each glucose molecule. (*b*) less carbon dioxide is released. (*c*) more carbon dioxide is released. (*d*) fats and proteins are not used as fuel.

7.80 What is the relation between body temperature and metabolic rate?

⚲ Metabolism is all of the chemical processes going on within the organism. Metabolic rate—the rate of biochemical reactions—is increased by an increase in temperature, and, also, body temperature is increased by an increase in metabolic rate.

Most chemical reactions are exceedingly sensitive to temperature. In general, the rate of a biochemical reaction doubles with each 10 °C rise in temperature up to about 45 °C, at which point enzymes begin to denature. Birds and mammals are able to be very active because they maintain body temperatures near 40 °C.

While heat increases the rate of chemical reactions, it is also true that chemical reactions release heat. In the catabolism of glucose, for example, about 60 percent of the energy released from glucose becomes heat; the rest becomes ATP. Thus, the higher the metabolic rate, the higher the body temperature. During physical exercise, for example, the metabolic rate increases abruptly, as does the body temperature. All organisms have some way of getting rid of body heat when it nears the lethal temperature. Humans, for example, sweat.

Answers to Objective Questions

7.1 *a*	**7.9** *d*	**7.16** two; two
7.2 *d*	**7.10** *a*	**7.17** allosteric inhibitor
7.3 *b*	**7.11** *a*	**7.20** *b*
7.4 *d*	**7.12** *a*	**7.21** *c*
7.5 *d*	**7.13** *d*	**7.22** *d*
7.6 glycolysis; Krebs citric acid cycle; electron transport (oxidative phosphorylation)	**7.14** *b* **7.15** hydrogen atoms; electrons; NAD$^+$	**7.23** ethanol; lactic acid **7.24** ethanol; alcohol fermentation **7.25** pyruvic acid; lactic acid

7.26 two

7.27 1(*b*); 2(*a*); 3(*c*)

7.29 *a*

7.30 *b*

7.31 *c*

7.32 *c*

7.33 *d*

7.34 six; three; two

7.35 CO_2; NADH; H^+

7.37 *c*

7.38 *d*

7.39 CO_2; electrons (or hydrogen atoms)

7.40 NAD^+; NADH

7.41 $FADH_2$; ATP; CO_2; NADH; two

7.43 *a*

7.44 *c*

7.45 *c*

7.46 *b*

7.47 *d*

7.48 *d*

7.49 *b*

7.50 NADH; $FADH_2$

7.51 lower

7.52 NADH; $FADH_2$

7.53 protons; ATP

7.57 *d*

7.58 *a*

7.59 40; 36

7.60 three; two

7.63 *b*

7.64 *d*

7.65 ammonia; kidneys

7.66 (1) proteins; (2) amino acids; (3) carbohydrates (glycogen); (4) glucose; (5) fats; (6) glycerol; (7) fatty acids

7.68 *c*

7.69 *d*

7.70 *c*

7.71 *b*

7.72 *a*

7.73 *a*

7.74 *b*

7.75 *c*

7.76 matrix; $FADH_2$

7.77 (*a*) outer membrane; (*b*) intermembrane space; (*c*) inner membrane; (*d*) matrix; (*e*) crista

7.78 *b*

7.79 *a*

CHAPTER 8
Photosynthesis

OVERVIEW*

8.1   An autotroph is an organism that

(*a*) requires no input of materials from its environment.   (*b*) sustains itself without eating other organisms.
(*c*) sustains itself without aerobic cellular respiration.   (*d*) uses ammonia instead of water as a solvent.

8.2   An autotroph gets its carbon from

(*a*) carbon dioxide.   (*b*) methane.   (*c*) soil.   (*d*) organic molecules.

8.3   Which one of the following organisms is *not* an autotroph?

(*a*) Moss;   (*b*) Grass;   (*c*) Mushroom;   (*d*) Fern

8.4   A heterotroph is an organism that gets its energy from

(*a*) heat.   (*b*) light.   (*c*) inorganic molecules.   (*d*) organic molecules.

8.5   A heterotroph gets its carbon from

(*a*) carbon dioxide.   (*b*) methane.   (*c*) soil.   (*d*) organic molecules.

8.6   Which of the following organisms is *not* a heterotroph?

(*a*) Grass;   (*b*) Mushroom;   (*c*) Wine-producing yeast;   (*d*) Human

8.7   The first photosynthetic organisms appeared about how long ago?

(*a*) 7 billion years;   (*b*) 3 billion years;   (*c*) 1 billion years;   (*d*) 500 million years

8.8   Chemosynthetic autotrophs get their energy from

(*a*) heat.   (*b*) light.   (*c*) inorganic molecules.   (*d*) organic molecules.

8.9   Photosynthetic autotrophs get their energy from

(*a*) heat.   (*b*) light.   (*c*) inorganic molecules.   (*d*) organic molecules.

8.10   One of the earliest experiments on photosynthesis was done in 1772 by Joseph Priestley. He demonstrated that

(*a*) sunlight is the energy source.   (*b*) water is required.   (*c*) plants and animals "restore" the air for each other.
(*d*) chlorophyll captures light energy.

8.11   Which of the following equations is the correct summary of photosynthesis?

(*a*) $6CO_2 + 12H_2O + light \longrightarrow C_6H_{12}O_6 + 6O_2 + 6H_2O$;
(*b*) $6CO_2 + 12NH_3 + light \longrightarrow C_6H_{12}O_6 + 6H_2O + 6H_2N_2$;
(*c*) $C_6H_{12}O_6 + 6O_2 + 6H_2O + light \longrightarrow 6CO_2 + 12H_2O$;
(*d*) $3CO_2 + 6H_2O + light \longrightarrow C_3H_6O_3 + 3O_2 + 3H_2O$

8.12   In the 1930s, C. B. van Niel correctly hypothesized that oxygen atoms in the oxygen gas released by plants come from

(*a*) H_2O.   (*b*) CO_2.   (*c*) $C_6H_{12}O_6$.   (*d*) O_3.

* Answers to Chapter 8 objective questions appear on page 67.

8.13 In a plant cell, the light reactions of photosynthesis take place in the

(*a*) cytosol.   (*b*) endoplasmic reticulum.   (*c*) leucoplasts.   (*d*) chloroplasts.

8.14 If there were no pollution by humans, the concentration of carbon dioxide in the atmosphere would remain relatively constant, because

(*a*) in photoautotrophs, the rate of photosynthesis is equal to the rate of their cellular respiration.   (*b*) in plants, photosynthesis occurs during the day and cellular respiration at night.   (*c*) during photosynthesis, carbon dioxide is consumed and oxygen gas is released.   (*d*) the rate of photosynthesis by photoautotrophs is about equal to the rate of cellular respiration by all organisms.

8.15 In a plant cell, the dark reactions of photosynthesis take place in the

(*a*) cytosol.   (*b*) endoplasmic reticulum.   (*c*) leucoplasts.   (*d*) chloroplasts.

8.16 Identify the indicated structures of the chloroplast shown in Fig. 8.1.

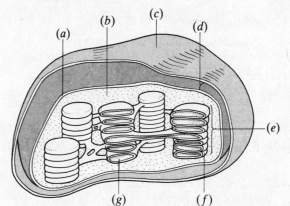

Fig. 8.1

8.17 Photosynthesis is the transformation of _____ energy to _____ energy.

8.18 A light-absorbing organic molecule is called a _____. In plants, the main kind of light-absorbing molecule is _____.

8.19 A chloroplast has three membrane-enclosed spaces: the _____; the _____; and the _____.

8.20 (*a*) Give the overall equation for photosynthesis, showing the sources of the atoms in the product molecules. (*b*) Why is water present as both reactant and product molecules?

🐚   (*a*) The overall equation for photosynthesis is

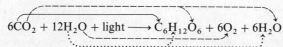

$$6CO_2 + 12H_2O + light \longrightarrow C_6H_{12}O_6 + 6O_2 + 6H_2O$$

(*b*) Water molecules appear on both sides of the equation because the molecules that enter the reaction are not the same molecules that emerge from the reaction; water molecules do not move intact through the process. The six water molecules formed during photosynthesis have carbon dioxide as their source of oxygen and water as their source of hydrogen atoms.

8.21 Why is the term *carbohydrate* a misnomer?

🐚   The term *carbohydrate* means "hydrated carbon." It is used for all molecules with a $n(CH_2O)$ formula [e.g., glucose $= 6(CH_2O)$], because it originally was believed that in the synthesis of such molecules a water molecule is simply attached to each carbon atom: $C + H_2O \longrightarrow CH_2O$. We now know that water molecules are not attached to carbon atoms in the formation of glucose and other carbohydrates. While the hydrogen atoms of a carbohydrate do come from water, the oxygen atoms originate in carbon dioxide rather than in water. In fact, each water molecule is entirely dismantled during photosynthesis to form two electrons, two protons, and an oxygen atom; it does not move intact to join with carbon, as originally believed and implied in the term "carbohydrate."

THE LIGHT REACTIONS

8.22 A wavelength of light is the distance

(*a*) traveled each millisecond by a wave of light. (*b*) from one wave peak to the next of an electromagnetic wave. (*c*) from crest to valley of an electromagnetic wave. (*d*) the wave penetrates within a pigment.

8.23 The wavelengths of visible light are longer than the wavelengths of

(*a*) infrared. (*b*) ultraviolet. (*c*) microwaves. (*d*) radio waves.

8.24 The wavelengths of visible light are shorter than the wavelengths of

(*a*) infrared. (*b*) ultraviolet. (*c*) x-rays. (*d*) gamma rays.

8.25 Which of the following colors of light work(s) best for photosynthesis?

(*a*) Green; (*b*) Yellow; (*c*) Blue and red; (*d*) Violet and yellow

8.26 Which of the following colors of light work(s) least well for photosynthesis?

(*a*) Green; (*b*) Yellow; (*c*) Blue and red; (*d*) Violet and yellow

8.27 A description of the wavelengths absorbed by a pigment is called its

(*a*) electromagnetic properties. (*b*) electromagnetic spectrum. (*c*) absorption spectrum. (*d*) action spectrum.

8.28 In a plant cell, which of the following pigments participates directly in the light reactions of photosynthesis?

(*a*) Chlorophyll *a*; (*b*) Chlorophyll *b*; (*c*) Chlorophyll *d*; (*d*) Carotenoids

8.29 The red, orange, and yellow colors of autumn leaves are caused by light reflected from

(*a*) chlorophyll *a*. (*b*) chlorophyll *b*. (*c*) chlorophyll *d*. (*d*) carotenoids.

8.30 The pigment molecules of a chloroplast are located

(*a*) within its thylakoid membranes. (*b*) within its intrathylakoid spaces. (*c*) within its inner membrane. (*d*) within the space between its inner and outer membranes.

8.31 The electron carriers of a chloroplast are located

(*a*) within its thylakoid membranes. (*b*) within its intrathylakoid spaces. (*c*) within its inner membrane. (*d*) within the space between its inner and outer membranes.

8.32 The primary electron acceptor in cyclic photophosphorylation is

(*a*) a protein that contains iron and sulfur. (*b*) carbon dioxide. (*c*) FAD. (*d*) $NADP^+$.

8.33 During photosynthesis in a green plant, chlorophyll *b* differs from chlorophyll *a* in that chlorophyll *b* does not

(*a*) absorb photons. (*b*) produce excited electrons. (*c*) become oxidized. (*d*) function within a membrane.

8.34 A source of protons for the proton gradient within a chloroplast is

(*a*) phospholipids within the thylakoid membranes. (*b*) water. (*c*) CH_2O. (*d*) chlorophyll.

8.35 When sunlight is on the chloroplast, pH is lowest in the

(*a*) stroma. (*b*) space enclosed by the inner and outer membranes. (*c*) spaces enclosed by the thylakoid membranes. (*d*) cytosol.

8.36 Production of NADPH in a chloroplast takes place during

(*a*) cyclic photophosphorylation. (*b*) noncyclic photophosphorylation. (*c*) series photophosphorylation. (*d*) substrate-level photophosphorylation.

8.37 In photosynthesis, energy for attaching phosphate to ADP in photosystem II comes directly from

(*a*) oxidation of glucose. (*b*) reduction of glucose. (*c*) a proton gradient. (*d*) substrate-level phosphorylation.

8.38 Oxygen gas released during photosynthesis is formed during

(*a*) oxidative phosphorylation. (*b*) cyclic photophosphorylation. (*c*) noncyclic photophosphorylation.
(*d*) carbon fixation during the dark reaction.

8.39 Photophosphorylation in a chloroplast is most similar to which of the following mitochondrial reactions?

(*a*) Oxidative phosphorylation; (*b*) Substrate-level phosphorylation; (*c*) Oxidative decarboxylation;
(*d*) Hydrolysis

8.40 When light meets an object, it may be _____, _____, or _____.

8.41 If an object appears black, it _____ all wavelengths of light; if it appears white, it _____ all wavelengths of light.

8.42 When a photon of light is absorbed by a pigment, one of the pigment's _____ is elevated to a state in which it has more _____.

8.43 The function of accessory pigments is to _____ light and pass _____ to the reaction center.

8.44 In the light reactions, _____ energy is absorbed and briefly stored in _____ and _____.

8.45 In cyclic photophosphorylation, the electrons donated by the reaction center are ultimately accepted by the _____, whereas in noncyclic photophosphorylation, the ultimate acceptor of electrons is _____.

8.46 To generate one molecule of NADPH, _____ photons must be absorbed: _____ from photosystem I and _____ from photosystem II.

8.47 In photosystem II, the electrons lost by the reaction center are replaced by electrons from _____.

8.48 Three forms of energy play a vital role in photosynthesis. They are: _____; _____; and _____.

8.49 Three minerals are needed for photosystem II: _____ in chlorophyll; _____ in cytochrome *f*; and _____ in plastocyanin.

8.50 When the light reactions are proceeding in a chloroplast, there is a continuous flow of electrons from _____ to _____ in photosystem I, and from _____ to _____ in photosystem II.

8.51 The products of the light reaction are _____ and _____. They are used in the _____.

8.52 (*a*) Which wavelengths of solar energy are used in photosynthesis by a green plant? (*b*) Why only these wavelengths?

& (*a*) Photosynthesis in green plants uses solar energy of intermediate wavelengths (380–750 nm) known as light, which is the tiny portion of the electromagnetic spectrum that a human can see. Most effective are violet, blue, orange, and red light; least effective is green light. Each chloroplast has several kinds of pigments, with each kind absorbing best at wavelengths different from the others.
(*b*) The wavelengths of solar energy used in photosynthesis have just the right amount of energy per wave to raise an electron within a pigment from one orbital to another (a quantum jump). All other wavelengths are ineffective. Waves shorter than light have too much energy: if absorbed, they disrupt the molecular organization of the cell. For example, waves only slightly shorter than violet (380 nm) break weak bonds, such as the hydrogen bonds, and

waves shorter than 200 nm cause all atoms in the cell to lose electrons. At the opposite end of the spectrum, waves that are longer than light do not pack enough energy to raise an electron to a higher orbital; they cause molecular motion (heat) but not changes in the configuration of electrons within the atoms.

8.53   Describe photosystem I and photosystem II in green plants.

⬡   A photosystem is an assemblage of 200 to 400 pigment molecules together with a primary electron acceptor and a series of electron carriers. Located within the thylakoid membrane, its function is to capture light energy for photosynthesis. Plants use two types of photosystems for photosynthesis: photosystem I, which was discovered first, and photosystem II.

A pigment is an organic molecule that absorbs solar energy in the region of the electromagnetic spectrum known as light. All pigment molecules of a photosystem absorb light, but only one—the reaction center—passes electrons to the primary electron acceptor of the system. The other pigment molecules funnel light energy, but not electrons, to the reaction center. From the primary electron acceptor, electrons are passed through the series of electron carriers.

Photosystem I has three kinds of pigments: chlorophyll *a* (the most abundant); chlorophyll *b*; and carotenoids. One of the chlorophyll *a* molecules—called P700 because it absorbs light waves that are 700 nm (far-red) and less in length—is the reaction center; it receives energy from the other pigment molecules of the system. Energy received by P700 causes electrons to move out of it and into a protein known as FeS, so called because it contains both iron (Fe) and sulfur (S). FeS, the primary electron acceptor of photosystem I, is positioned adjacent to P700 in the thylakoid membrane. The other electron carriers in photosystem I, in order of decreasing free energy, are: ferredoxin (Fd); flavoprotein (FAD); and nicotinamide dinucleotide phosphate ($NADP^+$). Electron flow through photosystem I is, therefore, as follows.

$$P700 \longrightarrow FeS \longrightarrow Fd \longrightarrow FAD \longrightarrow NADP^+$$

Photosystem II consists of three kinds of pigments: chlorophyll *a*; chlorophyll *b* (or *c*, or *d*, depending on the species of plant); and carotenoids. Chlorophyll *b* (or *c*, or *d*) is more abundant than chlorophyll *a* in this photosystem; it absorbs best at slightly different wavelengths than chlorophyll *a* and appears more yellow-green than green. The reaction center is a molecule of chlorophyll *a*, called P680 because it absorbs wavelengths that are 680 nm (red) and less. (All chlorophyll *a* molecules are structurally identical, but they are distorted by adjacent proteins and, consequently, absorb best at slightly different wavelengths.) The primary electron acceptor of photosystem II is substance Q (of unknown molecular structure). The other carriers, in order of decreasing free energy, are: plastoquinone (Pq); cytochrome *f*; and plastocyanin (Pc). Electron flow through photosystem II is, therefore, as follows.

$$P680 \longrightarrow Q \longrightarrow Pq \longrightarrow Cyt\ f \longrightarrow Pc$$

8.54   Describe what happens to a water molecule during noncyclic photophosphorylation.

⬡   During noncyclic photophosphorylation, a water molecule is broken down into its components: two electrons; two protons; and one oxygen atom.

$$H_2O \longrightarrow 2e^- + 2H^+ + O$$

The two electrons from water replace the two electrons that have left the reaction center (P680) of photosystem II. The P680 molecule itself is responsible for splitting water. When this molecule is missing electrons, it has such a strong affinity for them that it pulls electrons out of a water molecule, causing it to split into its components. The oxygen atom of water combines with another oxygen atom (split from another water molecule) to form oxygen gas (O_2), which diffuses out of the chloroplast and either is used in cellular respiration or diffuses out of the cell into the atmosphere. The two protons from water remain inside the intrathylakoid space (water is split on the side of the membrane facing the intrathylakoid space), where they eventually contribute to the proton gradient that releases energy for ATP production.

8.55   Describe the flow of electrons in noncyclic photophosphorylation.

⬡   Noncyclic photophosphorylation is the main way in which plants harvest light energy. In it, electrons flow from reaction centers of both photosystem I and photosystem II (see Question 8.54). In order to keep photosynthesis going, both systems must continuously absorb light.

Photosystem I (Fig. 8.2) provides both energy and hydrogen atoms for the dark reactions, in which glucose is assembled. Excited electrons leave the P700 reaction center, join FeS, and are then passed to carriers Fd, FAD, and $NADP^+$. As two electrons are passed to $NADP^+$, they are joined by a proton and form NADPH, which moves into the stroma of the chloroplast, where NADPH serves as a source of hydrogen and energy for the dark reactions.

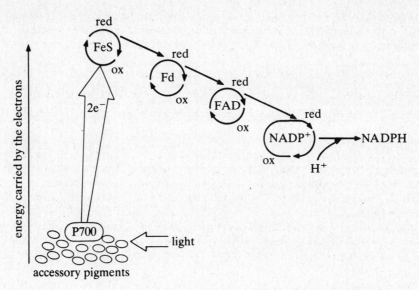

Fig. 8.2

Meanwhile, photosystem II (Fig. 8.3) provides both energy for the dark reactions and electrons to replace those lost from P700 in photosystem I. Electrons in the P680 reaction center receive energy from other pigment molecules and move to molecule Q (the primary electron acceptor). From Q they pass through the chain of carriers—Pq, cytochrome f, and Pc. As they pass from Pq to cytochrome f, the released energy pumps protons from the stroma to the intrathylakoid space, forming a proton gradient that provides energy for the chemiosmotic phosphorylation of ADP to ATP. From Pc, low-energy electrons move to the reaction center (P700) of photosystem I to replace the electrons lost from that molecule.

Electrons lost from P680, the reaction center of photosystem II, are replaced by electrons from a water molecule (see Question 8.54). Without some of its electrons, P680 is a strong oxidizer and pulls electrons out of a water molecule.

In summary, the flow of electrons is as follows.

$$H_2O \longrightarrow P680 \longrightarrow \begin{array}{c}\text{transport chain of}\\ \text{photosystem II}\end{array} \longrightarrow P700 \longrightarrow \begin{array}{c}\text{transport chain of}\\ \text{photosystem I}\end{array}$$

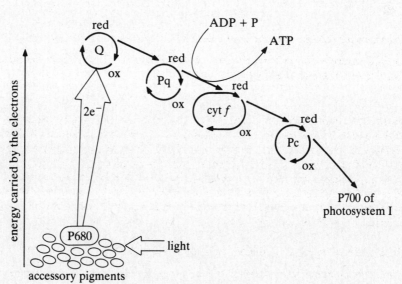

Fig. 8.3

8.56 Compare what is used, what is produced, and what is accomplished by cyclic and noncyclic photophosphorylation.

Cyclic photophosphorylation uses the energy of light to build ATP from ADP and phosphate. It cannot lead to the synthesis of sugar because it provides no NADPH for reducing carbon dioxide. Cyclic photophosphorylation is an inefficient way of harvesting light and was probably the first to evolve. Among modern photoautotrophs, only certain photosynthetic bacteria rely on this form of phosphorylation. Other photo-autotrophs use it only as a backup for times when no $NADP^+$ is available for synthesizing NADPH or no CO_2 is available for synthesizing sugars.

Noncyclic photophosphorylation uses the energy of light to build both ATP and NADPH. It is the main way in which photoautotrophs harvest energy for the synthesis of sugars.

A summary of what is used, produced, and accomplished by these two pathways is given in Table 8.1.

TABLE 8.1 Summary of Cyclic and Noncyclic Photophosphorylation

	cyclic	noncyclic
Used	2 photons 1ADP 1 phosphate group	4 photons 1ADP 1 phosphate group $1H_2O$ $1NADP^+$
Produced	1ATP	1ATP $1NADPH + H^+$ $\frac{1}{2}O_2$
Accomplished	Captured energy in the form of ATP	Captured energy in the form of ATP and NADPH; transfers hydrogen (as NADPH) to the dark reactions

THE DARK REACTIONS

8.57   The molecule in the Calvin-Benson cycle that combines with carbon dioxide is

(**a**) glyceraldehyde phosphate.   (**b**) ribulose biphosphate.   (**c**) phosphoenol pyruvic acid.   (**d**) citric acid.

8.58   In an experiment, the carbon dioxide available to a C_3 plant was labeled with a radioactive isotope and the amount of radioactivity in the chloroplast was measured. As photosynthesis proceeded, in which of the following molecules did the radioactivity first appear?

(**a**) PGAL;   (**b**) PEP;   (**c**) PGA;   (**d**) RuBP

8.59   How many carbon atoms are there in a molecule of glyceraldehyde phosphate?

(**a**) 2;   (**b**) 3;   (**c**) 4;   (**d**) 6

8.60   How many carbon atoms are there in a molecule of ribulose biphosphate?

(**a**) 2;   (**b**) 3;   (**c**) 5;   (**d**) 6

8.61   The molecule in the C_4 pathway that combines with carbon dioxide is

(**a**) glyceraldehyde phosphate.   (**b**) ribulose biphosphate.   (**c**) phosphoenol pyruvic acid.   (**d**) citric acid.

8.62   In an experiment, the carbon dioxide available to a C_4 plant was labeled with a radioactive isotope, and the amount of radioactivity in the chloroplast was measured. As photosynthesis proceeded, in which of the following molecules did the radioactivity first appear?

(**a**) Oxaloacetic acid;   (**b**) PEP;   (**c**) Malic acid;   (**d**) RuBP

8.63   The source of hydrogen atoms for the synthesis of glucose is

(**a**) H_2O.   (**b**) NADPH.   (**c**) $FADH_2$.   (**d**) $n(CH_2O)$.

8.64   Which of the following kinds of plant fixes carbon dioxide by way of crassulacean acid metabolism?

(**a**) Oak tree;   (**b**) Cactus;   (**c**) Grass;   (**d**) Red alga

8.65   In the dark reactions of photosynthesis, the energy stored in _____ and _____ is used to build _____.

8.66 In a eukaryotic cell, the dark reactions take place in the _____ of the chloroplasts.

8.67 Carbon dioxide reaches the photosynthetic cells of a plant by way of specialized openings in the leaves known as _____.

8.68 For every three molecules of carbon dioxide that enter the Calvin-Benson cycle, a total of _____ molecules of glyceraldehyde phosphate are made at a cost of _____ molecules of ATP and _____ molecules of NADPH. It takes _____ turns of the Calvin-Benson cycle to make one molecule of glucose.

8.69 Photorespiration is the catabolism of _____ to form _____ and _____, with the synthesis of _____ molecules of ATP.

8.70 In a C_3 plant, carbon fixation takes place in the _____ cells, whereas in a C_4 plant it takes place in the _____ cells.

8.71 What is used, produced, and accomplished by the Calvin-Benson cycle?

🐚 Glyceraldehyde phosphate (also called phosphoglyceraldehyde or PGAL), a three-carbon sugar, is built from carbon dioxide in the Calvin-Benson cycle (Fig. 8.4). In addition to carbon dioxide, the cycle uses ATP, NADPH, and ribulose biphosphate (RuBP).

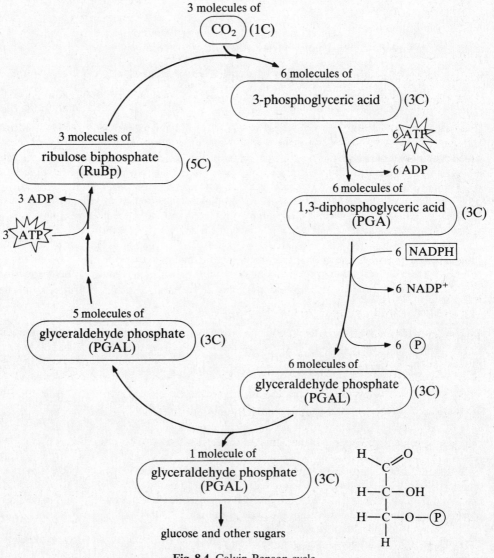

Fig. 8.4. Calvin-Benson cycle.

The cycle is initiated when a molecule of carbon dioxide combines with RuBP, a five-carbon sugar, to form a six-carbon sugar that immediately breaks into two three-carbon molecules of phosphoglyceric acid (PGA). Each PGA is phosphorylated by ATP and reduced by NADPH to form PGAL.

Once formed, a PGAL molecule follows one of two possible pathways: five out of every six molecules of this sugar combine with three ATP molecules to form three molecules of RuBP (used to pick up more carbon dioxide), and one out of every six becomes half of a glucose molecule. Since each turn of the Calvin-Benson cycle yields two PGAL molecules, it takes six turns to produce the two PGAL molecules that form one glucose molecule. Table 8.2 summarizes the reactants and products of the Calvin-Benson cycle upon synthesis of one glucose molecule.

TABLE 8.2 Calvin-Benson Cycle: Reactants and Products per Glucose Molecule Produced

used	produced
$6CO_2$	12PGAL (two become one glucose)
6RuBP	18 phosphates (return to light reactions)
18ATP (from light reactions)	18ADP (return to light reactions)
12NADPH (from light reactions)	$12NADP^+$ (return to light reactions)
	$12H^+$ (return to light reactions)
	$6H_2O$

What is accomplished is the production of a glucose molecule, which is an energy-rich fuel for cellular respiration and a carbon skeleton for building other organic molecules.

8.72   Ribulose biphosphate (RuBP) can combine with either carbon dioxide or oxygen gas.   (*a*) What determines which of these two gases combines with RuBP?   (*b*) Is there any advantage in having RuBP combine with oxygen rather than with carbon dioxide?

🐚   (*a*) An enzyme, RuBP carboxylase, catalyzes both the joining of carbon dioxide with RuBP and the joining of oxygen gas with RuBP. The two molecules are alternative substrates that compete with each other for the same active site on the enzyme. The more abundant of the two molecules gets to occupy the active site and subsequently joins with RuBP. When the concentration of carbon dioxide in the stroma of the chloroplast is high compared with the concentration of oxygen, then carbon dioxide joins with RuBP and the Calvin-Benson cycle is initiated. When the concentration of carbon dioxide is low relative to oxygen gas, then oxygen joins with RuBP and a pathway known as *photorespiration* is initiated. A high concentration of oxygen relative to carbon dioxide occurs whenever the stomata of a leaf remain closed while photosynthesis continues.
(*b*) In photorespiration, oxygen gas combines with RuBP to form an unstable molecule that breaks down into glyceraldehyde phosphate and glycolic acid, a two-carbon molecule that is further catabolized into carbon dioxide. Although this is a form of respiration, no ATP is produced and much of the energy within RuBP is lost as heat. Photorespiration has no known function and is detrimental to a cell: RuBP is destroyed and glucose production by the Calvin-Benson cycle is inhibited.

8.73   (*a*) How does the C_4 pathway differ from the C_3 pathway of carbon fixation?   (*b*) What are the advantages and disadvantages of each pathway?

🐚   (*a*) The C_4 (or Hatch-Slack) pathway differs from the C_3 pathway in that carbon dioxide combines first with phosphoenol pyruvic acid (PEP) to form a four-carbon molecule, oxaloacetic acid, whereas in the C_3 pathway carbon dioxide combines first with ribulose diphosphate to form two three-carbon molecules of phosphoglyceric acid. In a C_4 plant, this initial fixation of carbon takes place in a mesophyll cell, and the Calvin-Benson cycle occurs in a different kind of cell, called a *bundle sheath cell* (Fig. 8.5). In a C_3 plant, by contrast, both the initial carbon fixation and the Calvin-Benson cycle occur in the same cell, called a *mesophyll cell*.

Oxaloacetic acid, formed by the addition of carbon dioxide to PEP in a C_4 plant, is converted to another four-carbon acid, usually malic acid, and then transported from the mesophyll cell to a bundle sheath cell for entry into the Calvin-Benson cycle. Once inside this cell, malic acid is converted back into PEP and carbon dioxide. The carbon dioxide then joins the cycle in the same manner as in the C_3 pathway (see Fig. 8.4), and the PEP returns to the mesophyll cell for reuse.

The enzyme that catalyzes attachment of carbon dioxide to PEP in the C_4 pathway—PEP carboxylase—has a strong affinity for carbon dioxide and no affinity for oxygen gas. Thus, carbon fixation takes place, and the

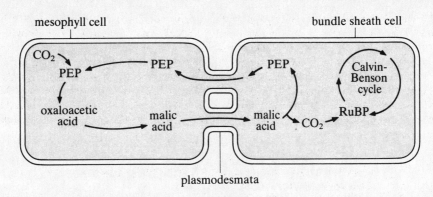

mesophyll cell   bundle sheath cell

Fig. 8.5

plasmodesmata

Calvin-Benson cycle proceeds rapidly even when carbon dioxide concentration is low, because the bundle sheath cells are flooded with carbon dioxide from the mesophyll cells.

(b) A plant with the C_4 pathway has a tremendous advantage over a plant with the C_3 pathway when the weather is hot and dry, since then the leaves close their stomata to eliminate water loss. In a C_3 plant, this closure results in low carbon dioxide concentrations and, ultimately, both loss of RuBP and inhibition of the Calvin-Benson cycle by photorespiration. There are no such disadvantages in a C_4 plant during hot, dry weather: even with its stomata closed, carbon dioxide is fixed because of the efficiency of PEP carboxylase in trapping and concentrating carbon dioxide. Consequently, the Calvin-Benson cycle continues to produce glucose and there is no loss of chemical energy (as RuBP) through photorespiration.

The C_3 pathway has an advantage over the C_4 pathway, however, under cooler and wetter conditions, since then the stomata remain open and there is always sufficient carbon dioxide to combine directly with RuBP and drive the Calvin-Benson cycle. About half as much energy is needed to pump carbon dioxide directly into the cycle as is needed to pump it in the roundabout way used in the C_4 pathway. Since less energy is expended, each day a C_3 plant can use more ATP to synthesize glucose than a C_4 plant can under these conditions.

8.74   Other than by a detailed biochemical study, how could you distinguish between a C_3 and a C_4 plant?

🐚   Plants with the C_4 pathway have several unique anatomical features, known as the *Kranz anatomy* (in German, *Kranz* = wreath).

There are two distinct kinds of photosynthetic cells in a C_4 plant: (1) bundle sheath cells, which provide the Calvin-Benson cycle, have many large chloroplasts with large starch grains, but have poorly developed grana; and (2) mesophyll cells, which provide the carbon-fixing reactions, have just a few small chloroplasts with no starch grains, but have well-developed grana. Plants with the C_3 pathway, by contrast, have just a single type of photosynthetic cell: the mesophyll cell. Their bundle sheath cells do not contain chloroplasts.

Most striking is the different arrangements of the photosynthetic cells in the two kinds of plants (Fig. 8.6). The columnar mesophyll cells (i.e., the palisade mesophyll) of a C_3 plant form a row of closely packed cells just beneath the upper epidermis of the leaf, whereas in a C_4 plant, these cells form a ring, or wreath (*Kranz*), around the bundle sheath cells and the vein of the leaf. The two arrangements can be distinguished easily by examination through a light microscope.

8.75   (a) What is meant by CAM?   (b) Why are CAM plants also succulents?

🐚   (a) The term CAM means *crassulacean acid metabolism*, named after one of the plant families—Crassulaceae—in which this kind of metabolism is found. The CAM pathway is an alternative to the C_3 and C_4 pathways of carbon fixation and is found in plants that live in dry, hot climates. All CAM plants are succulents; water is stored within cells in their stems or fleshy leaves. Examples of such plants are the cacti, stonecrops, and ice plants.

The CAM pathway is similar to the C_4 pathway in that carbon dioxide is trapped by the highly efficient PEP carboxylase, which combines carbon dioxide with phosphoenol pyruvic acid (PEP) to form a four-carbon acid. Where CAM differs from C_4 is that instead of having two kinds of photosynthetic cells—one for carbon fixation and the other for the Calvin-Benson cycle—a CAM plant has just one kind of photosynthetic cell, in which carbon is fixed during the night and used during the day to make glucose. In the C_4 plant, carbon fixation and the Calvin-Benson cycle are separated in space; in the CAM plant they are separated in time.

A CAM plant opens its stomata only at night, when lower temperatures and higher humidities cause less water loss. The carbon dioxide that diffuses into each mesophyll cell is stored as a four-carbon acid, usually malic acid. A CAM plant closes its stomata during the day, and the stored acid is used as a source of carbon for the Calvin-Benson cycle.

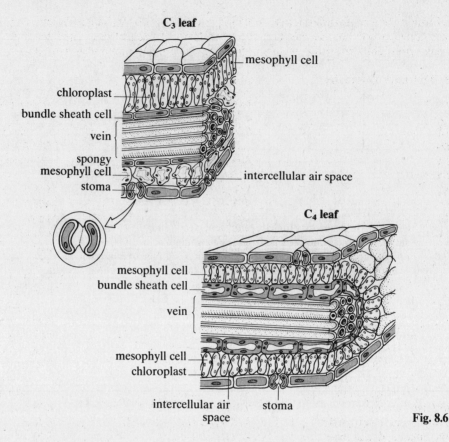

C₃ leaf

mesophyll cell
chloroplast
bundle sheath cell
vein
spongy mesophyll cell
stoma
intercellular air space

C₄ leaf

mesophyll cell
bundle sheath cell
vein
mesophyll cell
chloroplast
intercellular air space   stoma

Fig. 8.6

(*b*) A CAM plant is a succulent, because the large water vacuoles within the mesophyll cells of such a plant serve as places for storing the four-carbon acid (e.g., malic acid) prior to use. If not isolated from the rest of the cell, such acids would so lower the pH as to interfere with cellular metabolism.

FATES OF PHOTOSYNTHETIC PRODUCTS

8.76   About how much of the sugar formed in a plant is used by the plant itself during cellular respiration?

(*a*) 1%;   (*b*) 10%;   (*c*) 50%;   (*d*) 98%

8.77   In most plants, carbohydrate is transported from the leaves, where it is synthesized, to other parts, where it is used, in the form of

(*a*) sucrose.   (*b*) fructose.   (*c*) maltose.   (*d*) starch.

8.78   Plants store glucose as

(*a*) monosaccharides.   (*b*) cellulose.   (*c*) starch.   (*d*) glycogen.

8.79   Plants do not store carbohydrates as glucose, because it

(*a*) dissolves in water, thereby altering the osmotic balance.   (*b*) attracts insect herbivores.   (*c*) is an unstable molecule.   (*d*) would replace ribose in DNA synthesis.

8.80   What happens to a glyceraldehyde phosphate molecule produced by the Calvin-Benson cycle?

🐚   While glyceraldehyde phosphate (PGAL) is the end product of the Calvin-Benson cycle, glucose is usually listed as the end product of photosynthesis. Most of the PGAL does become glucose, by two of these three-carbon molecules being combined with each other. The rest of the PGAL molecules are converted to lipids, amino acids, and nucleotides, which are easier to synthesize directly from PGAL than from glucose.

Of the glucose produced, approximately half is used by the autotroph in cellular respiration to provide energy for maintaining its molecular organization. After cellular respiration, the remainder of the glucose is used to build polysaccharides, such as cellulose for cell walls and starch for energy storage.

Most of the new molecules formed—lipids, proteins, nucleic acids, and polysaccharides—become part of new cells during growth and reproduction of the autotroph. These molecules ultimately end up in organisms that eat living autotrophs (herbivores) and organisms that eat dead autotrophs (detritivores).

Answers to Objective Questions

8.1 *b*
8.2 *a*
8.3 *c*
8.4 *d*
8.5 *d*
8.6 *a*
8.7 *b*
8.8 *c*
8.9 *b*
8.10 *c*
8.11 *a*
8.12 *a*
8.13 *d*
8.14 *d*
8.15 *d*
8.16 (*a*) inner membrane; (*b*) stroma; (*c*) outer membrane; (*d*) intermembrane space; (*e*) granum; (*f*) thylakoid; (*g*) intrathylakoid space
8.17 light; chemical
8.18 pigment; chlorophyll
8.19 intermembrane space; stroma; intrathylakoid space
8.22 *b*
8.23 *b*

8.24 *a*
8.25 *c*
8.26 *a*
8.27 *c*
8.28 *a*
8.29 *d*
8.30 *a*
8.31 *a*
8.32 *a*
8.33 *c*
8.34 *b*
8.35 *c*
8.36 *b*
8.37 *c*
8.38 *c*
8.39 *a*
8.40 absorbed; reflected; transmitted
8.41 absorbs; reflects
8.42 electrons; energy
8.43 absorb; energy
8.44 light; ATP; NADPH
8.45 reaction center; $NADP^+$
8.46 four; two; two
8.47 water
8.48 light; electrical; chemical

8.49 magnesium; iron; copper
8.50 P700; $NADP^+$; P680; plastocyanin
8.51 ATP; NADPH; dark reactions
8.57 *b*
8.58 *c*
8.59 *b*
8.60 *c*
8.61 *c*
8.62 *a*
8.63 *b*
8.64 *b*
8.65 ATP; NADPH; glucose (or glyceraldehyde phosphate)
8.66 stroma
8.67 stomata
8.68 one; nine; six; six
8.69 ribulose biphosphate; glyceraldehyde phosphate; carbon dioxide; zero
8.70 mesophyll; bundle sheath
8.76 *c*
8.77 *a*
8.78 *c*
8.79 *a*

CHAPTER 9
Mitosis and the Cell Cycle

CELL DIVISION AND THE CELL CYCLE*

9.1   In mitosis, the number of chromosome sets in daughter cells will be

(*a*) half the number in the parent cell.   (*b*) twice the number in the parent cell.   (*c*) the same as in the parent cell.   (*d*) one fourth the number in the parent cell.

9.2   The process in prokaryotic cell division where the DNA and its copy are divided through attachment and then growth of the plasma membrane is called

(*a*) cytokinesis.   (*b*) fusion.   (*c*) fission.   (*d*) meiosis.

9.3   Mitosis is the process by which eukaryotic cells

(*a*) grow.   (*b*) multiply.   (*c*) become specialized in structure and function.   (*d*) expose the genes for protein synthesis.

9.4   In eukaryotic cell division, the process of cytoplasmic division is called

(*a*) cytokinesis.   (*b*) cytomeiosis.   (*c*) cytoplasmosis.   (*d*) cytomitosis.

9.5   As mitosis begins, a condensed chromosome consists of two

(*a*) centromeres.   (*b*) centrioles.   (*c*) kinetochores.   (*d*) chromatids.

9.6   DNA replication occurs in which phase of the cell cycle?

(*a*) Prophase;   (*b*) Interphase;   (*c*) Anaphase;   (*d*) Telophase

9.7   During which phase of the cell cycle does the cell grow?

(*a*) Interphase;   (*b*) Metaphase;   (*c*) Anaphase;   (*d*) Prophase

9.8   The cell doubles in size during which phase of the cell cycle?

(*a*) G_1;   (*b*) S;   (*c*) G_2;   (*d*) M

9.9   When a cell stops growing, say due to a shortage of nutrients, this will occur in which phase of the cell cycle?

(*a*) G_1;   (*b*) S;   (*c*) G_2;   (*d*) M

9.10   Normal cellular activities, such as protein synthesis, occur primarily during

(*a*) prophase.   (*b*) metaphase.   (*c*) anaphase.   (*d*) interphase.

9.11   The division of a prokaryotic cell into two parts is called _____ fission.

9.12   The nuclear division mechanism used in multicellular growth is _____. The nuclear division mechanism used in the reproduction of a single-celled protist such as an amoeba is _____. The nuclear division mechanism used in the formation of gametes is _____.

9.13   If a parent cell has 30 chromosomes, then after mitosis the daughter cells will each have _____ chromosomes.

9.14   In eukaryotic cells, cell division has two components: the process by which the nucleus divides, called _____, and the process by which the cytoplasm is divided, called _____.

* Answers to Chapter 9 objective questions appear on page 72.

9.15   In the normal cell cycle, a cell spends roughly 90 percent of its time in _____.

9.16   Human body cells have _____ chromosomes, while human gametes (sperm or egg) have _____ chromosomes.

9.17   In mitosis, just after duplication, the two sister _____ remain attached at the _____.

9.18   A diagram of a typical cell cycle of higher plants and animals is shown in Fig. 9.1. Identify each stage of the cycle and explain what happens during that stage.

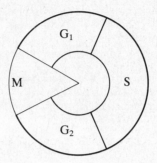

Fig. 9.1. The cell cycle.

🐚   The M stage of the cycle occurs when the cell is dividing to form two cells. It includes both mitosis, in which the nucleus and its contents divide, and cytokinesis, in which the cytoplasm divides to form two separate daughter cells. The M stage is the shortest stage of the cell cycle.

The G_1, S, and G_2 stages are all part of interphase, so named because at these times the cell is not dividing. The G_1 stage, or first-gap stage, is the period after cytokinesis but before DNA synthesis. It is a time of cell growth, high metabolic activity, and synthesis of enzymes needed for DNA replication. The length of this stage is the most variable of all the stages in the cell cycle.

The S stage, or synthesis stage, is the period when DNA synthesis takes place. The single, long molecule of DNA within a chromosome is precisely copied to yield two identical molecules, called sister chromatids. They are held together at one point—the centromere, which consists of DNA that was not replicated along with the rest of the molecule. All chromosomes of the cell are replicated during the S phase.

The G_2 stage, or second-gap stage, begins as soon as all the chromosomes are completely replicated. As with the G_1 stage, normal metabolic activity and growth occur, in addition to the synthesis of proteins needed for mitosis. The G_2 stage is followed by mitosis of the M stage to complete the cycle.

9.19   How does mitosis function differently in humans and amoebas?

🐚   Mitosis in a human functions to increase the number of cells in the individual, and consequently the size of the body, during development from a single fertilized egg to a multicellular adult. It also functions to replace worn-out cells and to maintain the vitality of adult tissues.

Mitosis in an amoeba, by contrast, functions as a way of reproducing rather than of increasing the size of or maintaining the individual. Each amoeba is a single cell. After it grows to a certain size, it divides by mitosis to form two identical cells that go their separate ways rather than remaining together. Amoebas do not deteriorate with age; the process of cell division produces two youthful cells from one aged cell.

9.20   How does mitosis in a cancer cell differ from mitosis in a normal somatic cell?

🐚   Cancer is uncontrolled mitosis of somatic cells. It is abnormal in three ways: (1) cancer cells do not exhibit contact inhibition; (2) they stop dividing at random points in the cell cycle; and (3) they are immortal.

Normal cells, when grown in a laboratory culture, divide by mitosis until there are so many cells that they contact one another, filling the container with a single layer of cells. Mitosis then ceases in all the cells. This phenomenon is known as *contact inhibition*. If some of the cells are removed, those remaining in the vacated area will begin to divide again, until the vessel is full of cells and contact inhibits further cell division. Cancer cells do not show such contact inhibition. Instead, they continue to divide by mitosis after contacting one another, and they pile up within the container.

When a normal cell stops dividing to enter a nondividing period, it stops late in the G_1 stage of the cell cycle. If it passes this specific point, called *the restriction point*, another complete cell cycle is inevitable, regardless of environmental conditions. Cancer cells do sometimes stop dividing, but when this happens, mitosis can be halted at any point in the cell cycle.

Normal somatic cells do not live forever when grown in laboratory cultures. They divide a certain number of times—20 to 50 times for mammalian cells—and then die. This phenomenon has been named the *Hayflick limit* for the man who first described it. Cancer cells do not show the Hayflick limit; they continue to divide indefinitely. One line of cancer cells—the so-called HeLa cells, named after Henrietta Lacks, from whom they were taken—have been reproducing continuously since 1951. Cancer cells in laboratory cultures appear to be immortal.

PHASES OF MITOSIS

9.21 Which of the following is the correct sequence of phases in mitosis?

(*a*) Telophase–metaphase–anaphase–prophase; (*b*) Metaphase–telophase–prophase–anaphase; (*c*) Prophase–metaphase–anaphase–telophase; (*d*) Anaphase–metaphase–prophase–telophase

9.22 The threadlike structures that begin to radiate from each centromere by the end of prophase are

(*a*) kinetochore microtubules. (*b*) polar microtubules. (*c*) aster microtubules. (*d*) spindle microtubules.

9.23 It is important that the centromere not divide until the end of metaphase because it

(*a*) contains the genes that control prophase. (*b*) holds the replicated DNA molecules together. (*c*) is connected to the nuclear membrane. (*d*) produces the spindle fibers.

9.24 The spindle fibers formed during mitosis connect to the

(*a*) nucleoli. (*b*) sugar-phosphate strands. (*c*) kinetochores. (*d*) nuclear membrane.

9.25 In mitosis, the chromosomes are distributed to the daughter cells by many thin parallel fibers called _____, which together form a _____. The ends of the fibers come together on opposite sides of the cell and form _____.

9.26 In mitosis, all chromosomes become aligned at the spindle equator at the end of _____, and the sister chromosomes are moved to opposite poles during _____.

9.27 The radial arrangement of microtubules around a centriole pair at the start of prophase in animal cells is called an _____.

9.28 In metaphase, the plane equidistant between the spindle's two poles where the chromosomes are aligned is called the _____.

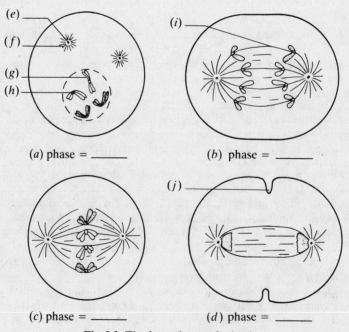

(*a*) phase = _____   (*b*) phase = _____

(*c*) phase = _____   (*d*) phase = _____

Fig. 9.2. The four phases of mitosis.

9.29   From the drawing in Fig. 9.2, identify the four phases of mitosis and the different contributing structures.

9.30   What are the basic achievements of each phase of mitosis?

🐚   Prophase sets the stage for migrations of the chromosomes in later phases of mitosis. Disintegration of the nuclear envelope during prophase allows the spindle apparatus to form between the two poles of the cell. The spindle apparatus, a structure comprised of all the spindle microtubules and formed during prophase, organizes later chromosomal movements. The nucleoli disintegrate and the chromosomes become condensed during prophase; these changes facilitate travel from place to place without entanglement.

Metaphase ensures equal division of the chromosomes. All of the chromosomes, each composed of two sister chromatids held together by a mutual centromere, line up in a row along an area midway between the two poles, an area known as the metaphase plate or the equatorial plane. Such alignment guarantees that when the centromeres later divide and the spindles shorten, one copy of each chromosome (i.e., one sister chromatid of each pair) will move to each of the two poles of the cell. Each pole—and ultimately each daughter cell—will then receive a complete copy of all the genetic material within the parental cell.

Equal division of the chromosomes takes place during anaphase. The centromeres divide, separating each pair of sister chromatids. Once a chromatid has its own centromere, it is a chromosome. Each chromosome of a pair begins to migrate along the spindle apparatus to one of the two poles.

Chromosomal migrations are completed during telophase, so that after this phase of mitosis there are two identical sets of chromosomes, one set at each of the two poles. Disappearance of the spindle, uncoiling of the chromosomes, and re-formation of the nuclear membrane and nucleolus prepare the daughter nuclei for normal activities during the G_1 stage of the cell cycle, which follows immediately after cytokinesis.

CYTOKINESIS

9.31   At what stage does cytokinesis typically begin?

(*a*) Anaphase;   (*b*) Prophase;   (*c*) Metaphase;   (*d*) Interphase

9.32   Which of the following is part of mitosis in the cells of seed plants?

(*a*) Centrioles;   (*b*) Asters;   (*c*) Spindles;   (*d*) Cleavage furrows

9.33   In animal cells, the visible part of cytokinesis, called _____, usually begins during _____.

9.34   _____, called cytokinesis, is accomplished in animal cells by the formation of a depression around the midsection, called a _____, and in plant cells by the formation of a disklike layer of vesicles, at the spindle equator, whose contents produce the _____.

9.35   How do animal and plant cells differ in the way they divide?

🐚   Cell division in plant and animal cells differs in two ways: (1) animal cells have centrioles and asters, whereas plant cells do not, and (2) animal cells have cleavage furrows, whereas plant cells have cell plates.

Centrioles are the centers of spindle formation in animal cells. During prophase, two pairs of centrioles appear and become surrounded by rays of microtubules known as asters. The two pairs separate, one of each pair moving to one of the two poles of the cell. They leave behind them a trail of microtubules that becomes the spindle apparatus. Centrioles and their asters are not, however, essential to spindle formation, since plant cells without these structures and animal cells in which they have been destroyed (by lasers) form normal spindles.

Cytokinesis in animal cells is effected by cleavage. It begins as a constriction in the plasma membrane midway between the two poles of the cell. A furrow, or groove, then develops from the constriction as a contracting ring of microtubules (made of actin) forms in the cell just beneath the constriction. This phenomenon is comparable to pulling the strings around the opening of a sack. As the ring of microtubules becomes very small, the cell is pinched in two. Plant cells cannot divide in this way, because of their rigid cell walls. Instead, they divide by developing a cell plate midway between the two poles of the cell. The cell plate forms from vesicles within the Golgi complex, which migrate to the area and combine to form a series of elongated, membrane-bound spaces. These structures join with one another to form a cell plate that bisects the cell. Pectins secreted into the intermembrane spaces of the cell plate form the middle lamella of the developing cell wall. Eventually, each daughter cell constructs its own cell wall by secreting cellulose and other polysaccharides into the intermembrane spaces.

Answers to Objective Questions

9.1 *c*

9.2 *c*

9.3 *b*

9.4 *a*

9.5 *d*

9.6 *b*

9.7 *a*

9.8 *a*

9.9 *a*

9.10 *d*

9.11 binary

9.12 mitosis; mitosis; meiosis

9.13 30

9.14 mitosis; cytokinesis

9.15 interphase

9.16 46; 23

9.17 chromatids; centromere

9.21 *c*

9.22 *a*

9.23 *b*

9.24 *c*

9.25 microtubules; spindle; poles

9.26 metaphase; anaphase

9.27 aster

9.28 metaphase plate

9.29 (*a*) prophase; (*b*) anaphase;
(*c*) metaphase; (*d*) telophase;
(*e*) centriole; (*f*) aster;
(*g*) chromatid; (*h*) centromere;
(*i*) spindle microtubule;
(*j*) cleavage furrow

9.31 *a*

9.32 *c*

9.33 cleavage; telophase

9.34 cytoplasm division; cleavage
furrow; cell plate

CHAPTER 10
DNA: Molecular Basis of Inheritance

DISCOVERY OF THE GENETIC MATERIAL*

10.1 The Swiss biochemist who in 1868 discovered DNA was

(*a*) Friedrich Miescher.   (*b*) Robert Feulgen.   (*c*) Alfred Mirsky.   (*d*) Max Delbrück.

10.2 The experiment in which it was shown that DNA is the genetic material in bacteriophages is the

(*a*) Meselson-Stahl experiment.   (*b*) Franklin-Wilkins experiment.   (*c*) Hershey-Chase experiment.
(*d*) Delbrück-Luria experiment.

10.3 The x-ray crystallography studies of Rosalind Franklin and Maurice H. F. Wilkins showed that

(*a*) DNA contains only four kinds of nucleotides.   (*b*) DNA is a helix of uniform diameter.
(*c*) the amount of adenine found in DNA equals the amount of thymine.   (*d*) the same base-pairing rules
apply to all species.

10.4 The scientist who discovered that the proportion of nitrogenous bases is the same in all cells of a given
species was _____.

10.5 In 1928, the bacteriologist Frederick Griffith, in attempting to develop a vaccine against pneumonia, discovered
that the hereditary material moved from _____ bacteria to _____ bacteria. This
phenomenon is now called _____. In 1944, Oswald Avery showed that the assimilated material
was _____.

10.6 Alfred Hershey and Martha Chase, in 1952, concluded from their experiments that the _____
of the _____ is injected into the bacterium, while most of the _____ remain outside.

10.7 In 1928, the bacteriologist Frederick Griffith discovered transformation and the transforming factor. What are
these, and how did their discovery contribute to the history of molecular genetics?

In the 1920s, Frederick Griffith, an English medical bacteriologist, worked to develop a vaccine against
pneumococcus, which is a strain of bacteria that can produce a form of pneumonia in humans. In 1928, he published the results of a series of experiments in which living and dead, virulent and nonvirulent pneumococci were
injected into mice. One of these experiments, in which a mixture of dead-virulent and live-nonvirulent bacteria
were injected, produced startling and puzzling results: Within the host mouse, some of the living nonvirulent
bacteria were transformed into the virulent form. It was as if some sort of transforming factor, carrying hereditary
material, had moved from a dead to a living bacterium. We now know that this is indeed what happened and
that the transforming factor is DNA. This routine experiment in immunology is now considered one of the classic
and pioneering studies in molecular genetics.

The two strains of pneumococci that Griffith used in this experiment were called S and R. The S-strain was
so-named because it formed shiny, smooth colonies when artificially cultured. This smoothness, it is now established, is produced by polysaccharide capsules that form around the bacteria. The R-strain, lacking these
capsules, form rough-looking colonies. The S-strain is virulent because its capsules protect it from mammalian
immunologic defenses—phagocytosis by white blood cells. The nonencapsulated R-strain is harmless because it
can be inactivated by these defense mechanisms.

Griffith did four experiments with these two strains. Mice injected with living S-strain were dead within
24 hours, and an autopsy showed them to be massively infected with S-strain bacteria. Injecting live R-strain,
or heat-killed S-strain, had no effect on the mice. It was the final experiment that was so surprising: When a
mixture of heat-killed S-strain and live R-strain was injected, the mice died of pneumonia and living S-strain
bacteria were found in their blood.

By the early 1930s, it had been shown that a rodent host was not essential for bacterial transformation. It also
occurred when living R-strain and heat-killed S-strain were incubated together in a test tube. Then, in 1933,

---

* Answers to Chapter 10 objective questions appear on page 81.

James L. Alloway of the Rockefeller Institute showed that it was not even necessary to have intact S-strain cells, for transformation in a test tube took place when a cell-free extract from S-strain cells was incubated with live R-strain. Finally, in 1944, after 10 years of work, Oswald T. Avery and his colleagues (L. M. MacLeod and M. J. McCarty) conclusively demonstrated that the extracted transforming factor was *deoxyribonucleic acid*, or *DNA*. This was a significant, but not conclusive, step in showing that DNA is the genetic material in cells.

10.8   What properties of the bacteriophages made them ideal material for solving the controversy of which is the genetic material, protein or DNA?

🐌   Up to 1952, many biologists, despite the earlier experiments of Griffith, Alloway, Avery, and others (discussed in Question 10.7), were still convinced that protein, and not DNA, was the hereditary material in cells. It was known that eukaryotic chromosomes consist of roughly equal amounts of both protein and DNA, and it was said that only protein had sufficient chemical diversity and complexity to encode the information required for genetic material. In 1952, however, the results of the Hershey-Chase experiment finally convinced most scientists that DNA is the genetic material.

In that year, Alfred D. Hershey and Martha Chase of the Carnegie Laboratory of Genetics published their studies on viruses (called bacteriophages or phages) that attack bacteria. They concentrated on the T2 (type 2) bacteriophage that attacks a common bacterium—*Escherichia coli*—in the human digestive tract. This bacteriophage (Fig. 10.1) has only two components: protein and DNA. Protein forms the complex external structures (head, sheath, and tail fibers), and a DNA molecule is confined within the head. The phage attacks *E. coli* by attaching its tail fibers to the bacterial wall and injecting genetic material that takes over the bacterial metabolic machinery, forcing it to produce new bacteriophages. At the appropriate time, the bacterium is instructed to produce an enzyme (lysozyme) that ruptures the bacterial cell wall to release hundreds of new bacteriophages.

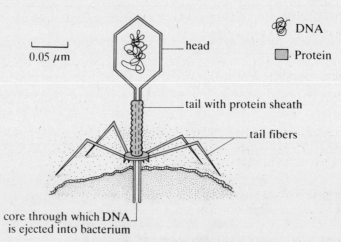

Fig. 10.1. The T2 bacteriophage.

Hershey and Chase realized that this bacteriophage-bacterium system was the ideal material for solving the DNA versus protein controversy. Their plan was to separately label the protein and DNA components of the bacteriophages with specific radioactive tracers and then follow these components through the phages' life cycles.

First, they developed two strains of viruses, one with labeled proteins and the other with labeled DNA. Almost all proteins contain sulfur, an atom not found in DNA, whereas all DNA molecules contain phosphorus, an atom not found in proteins. Therefore, bacteriophages parasitizing bacteria grown in the presence of radioactive sulfur (^{35}S) will have labeled proteins, and bacteriophages parasitizing bacteria grown in the presence of radioactive phosphorus (^{32}P) will have labeled DNA.

After developing these two strains, Hershey and Chase combined each strain with nonradioactive bacteria and gave the bacteriophages time to attach and inject their genetic material. The experimenters then analyzed the external bacteriophage shells and the contents of the bacteria. By these means, they determined that the labeled DNA was injected into the bacteria, while most of the labeled protein remained outside the cell walls. The Hershey-Chase results finally solved the controversy: It is DNA, not protein, that carries the hereditary information.

MOLECULAR STRUCTURE OF DNA: THE DOUBLE HELIX

10.9   Genetic information in a DNA molecule is coded in the

(*a*) sequence of nucleotides. (*b*) base pairings. (*c*) proportion of each base present. (*d*) the turning pattern of the helix.

10.10   The two strands of a double-helix model of DNA are held together by hydrogen bonds between

(*a*) sugar and phosphate groups. (*b*) sugars and nitrogenous bases. (*c*) phosphate groups and nitrogenous bases. (*d*) nitrogenous bases.

10.11   In the double-helix model of DNA, each base pair is how far from the next base pair?

(*a*) 0.034 nm; (*b*) 0.34 nm; (*c*) 3.4 nm; (*d*) 34 nm

10.12   In a single strand from a DNA molecule, nucleotides are linked by covalent bonds between

(*a*) sugar and phosphate groups. (*b*) sugars and nitrogenous bases. (*c*) phosphate groups and nitrogenous bases. (*d*) nitrogenous bases.

10.13   The American James D. Watson and the Englishman Francis Crick published their first paper on the double-helix model of DNA in

(*a*) 1923. (*b*) 1937. (*c*) 1953. (*d*) 1978.

10.14   The number of cytosine bases in a DNA molecule

(*a*) is equal to the number of uracil bases. (*b*) is equal to the number of guanine bases. (*c*) is equal to the number of adenine bases. (*d*) cannot be predicted.

10.15   If the sequence of bases along one side of a DNA molecule is AAGCT, then the complementary sequence of bases on the other side of the DNA molecule is

(*a*) AAGCT. (*b*) GGTAC. (*c*) UUCGA. (*d*) TTCGA.

10.16   DNA molecules are composed of three units: _____, _____, and a nitrogen-containing base. There are four possible bases: the two double-ring purines _____ and _____; and the two single-ring pyrimidines _____ and _____.

10.17   Adenine and thymine are held together by _____ hydrogen bonds, while guanine and cytosine are linked by _____ hydrogen bonds.

10.18   The sugar molecule in each DNA nucleotide is bound to a _____ at its 5′ carbon position and to a _____ at its 3′ carbon position. Because of this, the polynucleotide chain has a _____ end and a _____ end.

10.19   What are Chargaff's rules?

☘   It was known since the 1920s, from the work of biochemist P. A. Levene, that DNA is constructed of four types of molecules. These molecules, called *nucleotides*, each contain three different parts: a five-carbon sugar (with carbon positions labeled 1′, 2′, 3′, 4′, and 5′), a phosphate group, and one of four different nitrogen-containing (nitrogenous) bases (Fig. 10.2)—the two double-ring purines (adenine and guanine) and the two single-ring pyrimidines (thymine and cytosine). From a limited sample, however, Levene had mistakenly concluded that the four types of nucleotides are present in equal amounts in all DNA and that they are grouped in repeating units of four nucleotides, which he called tetranucleotides. In 1950, Erwin Chargaff and his colleagues at Columbia University published the results of a study that both eliminated Levene's tetranucleotide theory and made it possible for Watson and Crick, in 1953, to develop the true molecular model of DNA: the double helix.

From studies of DNA found in different types of cells from (1) the same organism, (2) different organisms within a species, and (3) organisms from different species, Chargaff and his colleagues developed the following

purine-containing nucleotides   pyrimidine-containing nucleotides

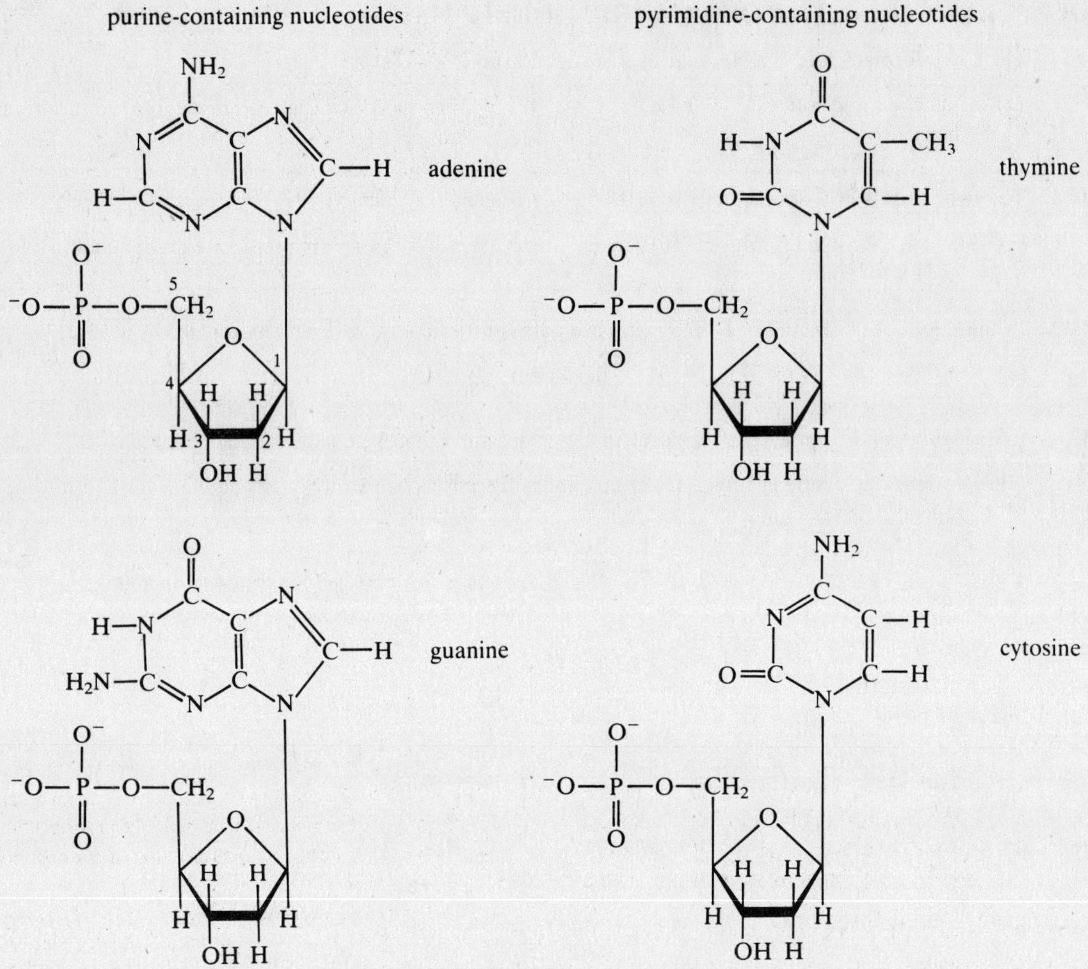

adenine

thymine

guanine

cytosine

Fig. 10.2. The four nucleotides of DNA.

conclusions, now known as Chargaff's rules:

1. The relative amounts of each nitrogenous base present in a sample of DNA differ from species to species, but these relative amounts are always the same within a species. Thus, for example, in all humans there is (approximately) 30% adenine, 30% thymine, 20% guanine, and 20% cytosine, while in all *Escherichia coli* bacteria there is (approximately) 24% adenine, 24% thymine, 26% guanine, and 26% cytosine.
2. As with humans and *E. coli*, it is true for all DNA that the amount of adenine present always equals the amount of thymine, and the amount of guanine always equals the amount of cytosine.
3. It follows from rule 2 that the amount of combined purines always equals the amount of combined pyrimidines.

10.20   How did the discovery that the DNA molecule is helical with a uniform 2-nm diameter lead Watson and Crick to propose the pairing rules for the double-helix model?

☘   The American geneticist James D. Watson and the English physicist Francis Crick, working together at the Cavendish Laboratory of Cambridge University, developed the definitive model of the molecular structure of DNA: the double helix. In 1953, they published their now classic first report on the model in the British journal *Nature*. This model integrated the work of many previous scientists, such as Levene and Chargaff (see Question 10.19), but the critical, final element came from the x-ray crystallography studies done by the English scientists Maurice H. F. Wilkins and Rosalind Franklin of Kings College, London.

In x-ray crystallography, a substance is made into a crystal (crystallized) and an x-ray beam is passed through the crystal onto a photographic plate. The atoms of the crystallized substance form planes that disperse (or diffract) the x-ray beam, producing patterns of dots and streaks on the film. By measuring these diffraction patterns, investigators can determine the size and position of atoms, as well as the distances between atoms. Such

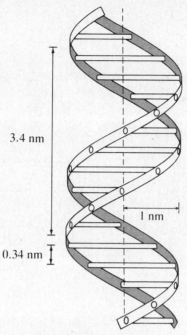

Fig. 10.3. Features of the DNA molecule revealed by x-ray diffraction.

x-ray diffraction pictures of DNA, made by Franklin and Wilkins, revealed many important features of DNA to Watson and Crick: (1) It has a helical structure like the bannister of a spiral staircase; (2) it is long and thin with a uniform diameter of 2 nm; (3) the distance between successive nucleotides is 0.34 nm; and (4) the distance between turns of the helix is 3.4 nm (or 10 nucleotides; see Fig. 10.3).

With this precise information, plus Chargaff's rules, Watson and Crick developed scale models of all plausible structures of the DNA molecule. They quickly realized that if DNA were a single coiled chain of nucleotides positioned 0.34 nm apart, with a uniform 2.0-nm diameter, then the molecule would have only half the known density of DNA. This discrepancy was solved by making the molecule a double helix, with two polynucleotide chains in a curving ladderlike configuration. Each chain was constructed by linking the sugar-phosphate components of the nucleotides, and the chains were held together by cross-rungs formed by the nitrogenous bases of parallel nucleotides (Fig. 10.4). Hydrogen bonds between the two bases on each rung loosely bound the two chains together.

It was next apparent to Watson and Crick that the helix could only have a uniform 2-nm diameter throughout if each rung of the helix always consisted of a double-ringed purine paired with a single-ringed pyrimidine. This is so because the pairing of two purines would produce a bulge larger than 2 nm and the pairing of two pyrimidines would produce a constriction smaller than 2 nm. Furthermore, they found that it was not physically possible to bond each purine with both pyrimidines; the only possible bonding was adenine (A) with thymine (T) and guanine (G) with cytosine (C). When this was done, there were two hydrogen bonds between T and A and three hydrogen bonds between G and C. These rules (A with T; G with C) are the base-pairing rules of DNA, and it can be seen that they agree with Chargaff's empirical rules.

Finally, Watson and Crick realized that the two chains were antiparallel, i.e., they ran in opposite directions (see Fig. 10.4). Because the phosphate groups are each attached to the 3' carbon of one sugar and the 5' carbon of the next sugar, the ends of each chain are hydroxyl (OH) groups attached to a 3' or a 5' carbon. Therefore, it is said that one strand of the helix runs from 3' to 5', while the other, antiparallel, strand runs from 5' to 3'.

DNA REPLICATION

10.21   Which of the following is characteristic of DNA replication?

(*a*) Each of the two newly formed molecules contains one newly constructed sugar-phosphate strand and one sugar-phosphate strand from the original molecule;   (*b*) One of the newly formed molecules contains two newly constructed sugar-phosphate strands, and the other contains both sugar-phosphate strands from the original molecule;   (*c*) Both of the newly formed molecules contain newly constructed sugar-phosphate strands;   (*d*) Both of the newly formed molecules contain uracil instead of thymine.

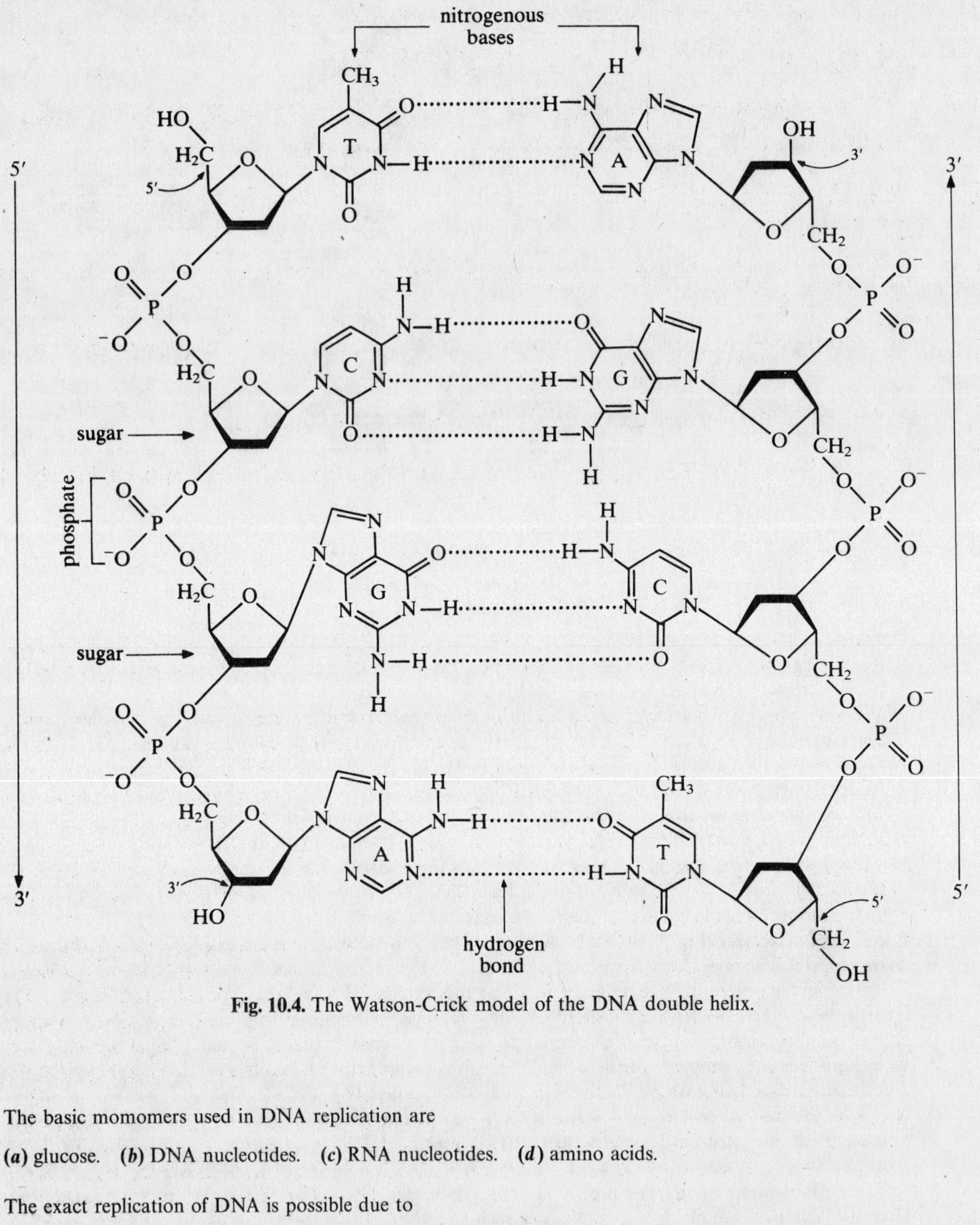

Fig. 10.4. The Watson-Crick model of the DNA double helix.

10.22 The basic momomers used in DNA replication are

(*a*) glucose. (*b*) DNA nucleotides. (*c*) RNA nucleotides. (*d*) amino acids.

10.23 The exact replication of DNA is possible due to

(*a*) the genetic code. (*b*) mitosis. (*c*) the base-pairing rules. (*d*) the fact that the DNA molecules are enclosed within a nuclear membrane.

10.24 Which enzyme catalyzes the synthesis of a new strand for a DNA molecule, by linking nucleotides to the developing strand?

(*a*) DNA ligase; (*b*) DNA polymerase; (*c*) Single-strand binding proteins; (*d*) Topoisomerase

10.25 In DNA replication, the helix is unwound by which type of enzyme?

(*a*) Topoisomerase; (*b*) Primase; (*c*) DNA polymerase; (*d*) Helicase

10.26 In DNA replication, the Okazaki fragments on the lagging strand are joined together by

(*a*) DNA ligase. (*b*) DNA polymerase. (*c*) primase. (*d*) helicase.

10.27 In the formation of base pairs in *E. coli* DNA replication, on the average one mistake occurs for every

(*a*) 100 pairs. (*b*) 1000 pairs. (*c*) 1,000,000 pairs. (*d*) 1,000,000,000 pairs.

10.28 In DNA replication, when two adjacent bases along one strand become linked together, they form a
_____.

10.29 In the Meselson-Stahl experiment, it was confirmed that DNA replication is _____, as was predicted by the Watson and Crick double-helix model.

10.30 In replication, the two strands of a DNA molecule unzip as _____ bonds between the _____ are broken.

10.31 In bacteria, errors in base-pairings are corrected by _____.

10.32 In _____ repair of a DNA molecule, the damaged section is cut out by a nuclease enzyme and the gap is then filled by _____ and sealed by _____.

10.33 In postreplication repair of a DNA molecule, there is first _____ and then _____.

10.34 How did the Meselson-Stahl experiment confirm that DNA replication is semiconservative?

🐚　By 1953, it had been established that DNA is the genetic material (see Questions 10.7 and 10.8) and that its molecular structure is a double helix (see Question 10.20). However, a fundamental question remained: How does the DNA molecule make identical copies of itself?

Watson and Crick had proposed complementary, semiconservative replication. This hypothesis is based on the fact that the two strands of a DNA molecule are complementary, i.e., that because of the base-pairing rules, the sequence of nitrogenous bases on one strand is bonded to a complementary sequence on the other strand. Thus, for example, the sequence ATTCG would be bonded to the complementary sequence TAAGC. Because of this complementarity, Watson and Crick reasoned that if the hydrogen bonds between the paired bases were broken and the strands pulled apart (unzipped), then each strand could serve as a *template* (or mold) upon which a complementary strand could be synthesized. DNA replication was said to be *semiconservative* because in each of the resulting molecules one strand from the original DNA molecule would be kept (conserved), and this strand would be bonded to a newly synthesized complementary strand.

In 1956, the biophysicists Gunther Stent and Max Delbrück, while accepting the complementary template aspects of the Watson-Crick hypothesis, suggested that there were actually three possibilities for replication: semiconservative (as proposed by Watson and Crick); conservative; and dispersive. In *conservative* replication, the original double helix serves as a template, but then, somehow, the original molecule is preserved intact and an entirely new double-stranded molecule is synthesized. In *dispersive* replication, the original molecule is broken into fragments, each fragment serves as a template for the synthesis of complementary fragments, and finally two new molecules are formed both of which consist of old and new fragments.

In 1957, Matthew Meselson and Franklin Stahl, at the California Institute of Technology, did an experiment that confirmed the Watson-Crick hypothesis: DNA replication is semiconservative. In this experiment, they first grew two cultures of *E. coli* bacteria for many generations in separate media: the "heavy" culture was grown in a medium in which the nitrogen source (ammonium chloride) contained the heavy isotope ^{15}N, and the "light" culture was grown in a medium in which the nitrogen was the more common, light isotope ^{14}N. At the end of this growth, they reasoned, the bacterial DNA in the heavy culture would contain only ^{15}N and the DNA in the light culture would contain only ^{14}N.

They next analyzed the two types of bacterial DNA with a technique called *density gradient centrifugation*. In this technique DNA is dissolved in a solution of cesium chloride in a test tube, and the solution is whirled around in an ultracentrifuge. The force generated by centrifugation separates the particles in the solution to produce a density gradient extending from the heaviest concentrations at one end of the tube to the lightest concentrations at the other. Heavy and light DNA, extracted from cells in the two cultures and subjected to this technique, settled into two distinct and separate bands in the cesium chloride density gradient.

Meselson and Stahl next transferred the heavy culture (containing ^{15}N) into a medium that had only ^{14}N, leaving the bacteria in this light medium long enough to allow two replications of the DNA (two generations of bacteria). After the first replication, they extracted DNA and subjected it to density gradient centrifugation. The DNA settled into a band that was intermediate in position between the previously determined heavy and light bands. After the second replication, they again extracted DNA samples, and this time found the DNA settling into two bands, one at the light band position and one at the intermediate position.

These results confirm Watson and Crick's semiconservative replication hypothesis. After the first replication, there were only intermediate molecules containing both ^{14}N and ^{15}N. This could have happened with either semiconservative or dispersive replication; it could *not* have happened with conservative replication, which would have produced light and heavy molecules but no intermediate molecules. The results for the second replication again agreed with semiconservative replication, but this time eliminated the possibility of dispersive replication, which predicts lighter and lighter molecules with each successive generation.

10.35   How are errors that occur during DNA replication repaired?

🐚   The replication of a DNA molecule is a complex, multistep process, with each step precisely controlled by a specific enzyme. First, the hydrogen bonds that both maintain the helix and link the polynucleotide chains are broken. Next, the unbonded chains are separated and unwound, and then complementary nucleotides are paired with each nucleotide on the parent chains. Finally, the newly positioned nucleotides are covalently bonded together to form their own chains. This is all done rapidly and with very few errors. In eukaryotic cells, 50 base pairs are formed per second, while in prokaryotic cells the rate is 500 base pairs per second. In both types, only about one error appears in every one billion base pairs replicated. As with the steps in replication, the repair of errors is controlled by specific enzymes.

Replication begins at an initiation site, called the *origin*, on a chromosome. In the circular prokaryotic chromosome, there is one origin, while in the larger, linear eukaryotic chromosomes there can be hundreds or thousands. At the origin, enzymes relax (facilitated by DNA gyrase), unwind (facilitated by helicase), and pull apart the strands, forming a Y-shaped structure called a *replication fork* (Fig. 10.5). There are two such forks at each origin, and as they move away from the origin in both directions, newly synthesized complementary nucleotides are paired with existing nucleotides on the parent strands and covalently bonded together by a complex of enzymes called DNA polymerases. The energy used by the DNA polymerases for the covalent bonding comes from the

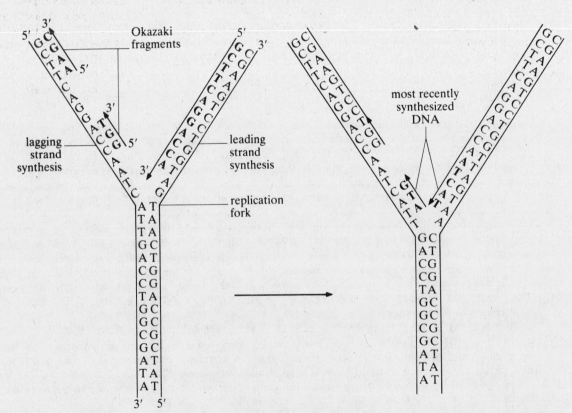

Fig. 10.5. Replication of DNA, showing a replication fork, where the two sugar-phosphate strands have been pulled apart, and Okazaki fragments, where the polynucleotide is synthesized backward in short fragments that are later pieced together.

newly synthesized nucleotides, which are assembled as triphosphates (rather than monophosphates). As each of these nucleotides is bonded, it supplies energy for the reaction by releasing two of its phosphates. Finally, when all of the nucleotides are in position, gaps are sealed by another enzyme, DNA ligase.

Because the two strands of a DNA helix have an antiparallel orientation—one going in the 5'-to-3' direction and the other in the 3'-to-5' direction—as the two strands come apart at the replication fork, they require different treatment by the DNA polymerase. This enzyme can only catalyze the addition of a nucleotide to the new strands in the 5'-to-3' direction, because it can only add nucleotides to the 3' carbon position. For one of the parental strands (the 5'-to-3' strand) this means there is always a 3' position at the replication fork, and, therefore, that its new complementary strand (the leading strand) can be synthesized continuously in the 5'-to-3' direction. For the other parental strand (the 3'-to-5' strand), however, there is always a 5' carbon at the replication fork, so its new strand of nucleotides (called the *lagging strand*) must be synthesized backward, in pieces (*Okazaki fragments*) that are later joined together.

While the final error rate for DNA replication is one error in every one billion base pairs formed, the initial error rate is much greater, roughly three errors in every 100,000 base pairs. If this were not corrected, it would mean a mistake in 3 percent of the cell's proteins. Fortunately, almost all replication errors are immediately corrected by repair enzymes within the DNA polymerase complex, which proofread each base pair as it is formed and then remove and replace mistakes.

Damage to DNA that occurs between replications is also repaired by specialized enzymes. One example of such damage is the formation of dimers; these are linkages between adjacent pyrimidine bases on the same strand, produced by environmental conditions such as exposure to ultraviolet light. Such dimers are removed and re-placed, in a process called *excision repair*, by a series of enzymes.

Answers to Objective Questions

10.1 *a*

10.2 *c*

10.3 *b*

10.4 Erwin Chargaff

10.5 dead virulent (S); live nonvirulent (R); transformation; DNA

10.6 DNA; bacteriophage; proteins

10.9 *a*

10.10 *d*

10.11 *b*

10.12 *a*

10.13 *c*

10.14 *b*

10.15 *d*

10.16 phosphate group; deoxyribose; adenine; guanine; thymine; cytosine

10.17 two; three

10.18 phosphate group; phosphate group; 3'; 5'

10.21 *a*

10.22 *b*

10.23 *c*

10.24 *b*

10.25 *d*

10.26 *a*

10.27 *d*

10.28 dimer

10.29 semiconservative

10.30 hydrogen; paired bases

10.31 DNA polymerase

10.32 excision; DNA polymerase; DNA ligase

10.33 cross-strand exchange; excision repair

CHAPTER 11
Protein Synthesis

GENES AND METABOLISM*

11.1 The "recipe" for constructing each enzyme is located within the

(*a*) DNA molecules.   (*b*) ribosomes.   (*c*) polysomes.   (*d*) ribosomal RNA molecules.

11.2 The metabolic activity of the different cell types within an organism varies because of differences in the kinds of

(*a*) genes in each cell.   (*b*) ribosomes in each cell.   (*c*) enzymes in each cell.   (*d*) nucleoli in each cell.

11.3 According to the central dogma of molecular biology, the sequence of _____ in a DNA molecule determines the sequence of _____ in an mRNA molecule, which in turn dictates the sequence of _____ in a protein. The first process is called _____, because it involves the same "language," and the second process is called _____, because it involves two different "languages."

11.4 The experiments by George Beadle and Edward Tatum in the early 1940s on *Neurospora crassa* (the red bread mold) led them to the hypothesis that each gene controls the production of an enzyme. This one-gene one-enzyme hypothesis was later extended to include all polymers made of amino acids and was called the _____ hypothesis. Now we recognize that genes provide instructions for building _____ as well as polymers from amino acids, and so the modern statement of what a gene does is the _____ hypothesis.

11.5 The phrase "inborn errors of metabolism" was coined, in the early 1900s, by Archibald Garrod to describe some human diseases. One of the metabolic pathways he studied was the conversion of phenylalanine to other molecules.

$$\text{phenylalanine} \longrightarrow \text{tyrosine} \longrightarrow \text{homogentisic acid}$$

$$\text{melanin} \quad \text{fumaric acid} \quad \text{acetoacetic acid}$$

Three human diseases are caused by failures within this pathway. Phenylketonuria (PKU) develops when the amino acid phenylalanine is not converted to the amino acid tyrosine, and the excess phenylalanine that accumulates damages brain and other body cells. (The disease is effectively treated by reducing the amount of phenylalanine in the diet.) Albinism is a condition in which melanin is not formed, and people with this disease have no pigment in their skin, hair, and eyes. Alkaptonuria develops when homogentisic acid is not broken down into fumaric acid and acetoacetic acid. Homogentisic acid is then excreted in the urine, rather than metabolized; its presence causes urine to turn black.

What causes failures, such as those described above, in a metabolic pathway? Why did Garrod call these diseases "inborn" errors of metabolism?

Each of the diseases studied by Garrod is caused by the failure of an enzyme to catalyze a reaction in a metabolic pathway. In phenylketonuria, the enzyme that converts phenylalanine to tyrosine is not functioning; in albinism there is failure of the enzyme that converts tyrosine to melanin; and in alkaptonuria the enzyme that catabolizes homogentisic acid is not working.

Garrod, who was a physician, speculated that the cells of a patient with one of these diseases are unable to synthesize an enzyme needed for the metabolic pathway. The enzyme is not made, or not made correctly, because of a defect in the genetic material of that patient. Thus, the error in metabolism is an "inborn" (i.e., inherited) error.

---

*Answers to Chapter 11 objective questions appear on page 89.

TRANSCRIPTION

11.6 Transcription is the transfer of the genetic code from a DNA molecule to a

(*a*) RNA molecule.   (*b*) sequence of amino acids in a protein molecule.   (*c*) second DNA molecule.
(*d*) ribosomal subunit.

11.7 After transcription takes place, the DNA molecule

(*a*) disintegrates into its component nucleotides.   (*b*) moves to a ribosome.   (*c*) replicates itself.   (*d*) reassociates
to form its original structure.

11.8 The number of cytosine bases in an mRNA molecule

(*a*) is equal to the number of uracil bases.   (*b*) is equal to the number of thymine bases.   (*c*) is equal to the
number of guanine bases.   (*d*) cannot be predicted without knowing what the mRNA codes for.

11.9 Transcription is most similar to

(*a*) amino-acid synthetase.   (*b*) RNA decarboxylase.   (*c*) RNA polymerase.   (*d*) DNA polymerase.

11.10 Transcription is most similar to

(*a*) chemiosmosis.   (*b*) DNA replication.   (*c*) translation.   (*d*) facilitated transport.

11.11 During RNA processing, the RNA transcript is

(*a*) altered by removal and addition of nucleotides.   (*b*) wrapped in protein.   (*c*) combined with the DNA
transcript.   (*d*) joined with its complementary sugar-phosphate strand.

11.12 Genes that have been artificially synthesized without noncoding sequences often fail to yield proteins when placed
inside a cell, because

(*a*) they curl up.   (*b*) their mRNA molecules fail to move through the pores in the nuclear envelope.   (*c*) they
bond to the DNA.   (*d*) they are not transcribed.

11.13 During transcription, temporary hydrogen bonds form between the nitrogenous bases of the _____
molecule and the newly forming _____ molecule. These bonds form according to the Watson-Crick
base-pairing rules, in which adenine pairs with _____ or _____, and cytosine pairs
with _____.

11.14 Transcription is initiated when RNA polymerase binds to a promotor, located in the _____.
Transcription then proceeds until the enzyme reaches the terminator, located in the _____.

11.15 Most genes of eukaryotic cells have both introns and exons. The _____ are noncoding sequences
that are not expressed as polypeptides.

11.16 The three major types of RNA transcribed from DNA are _____, _____, and
_____.

11.17 After RNA processing, an mRNA molecule travels from the _____ to the _____, where
it joins with a _____.

11.18 How does RNA polymerase know when it has reached the end of a gene and that transcription should stop?

🐚   A stop signal, called the *terminator*, is built into the DNA molecule at the end of each gene. The terminator
has been described for prokaryotic cells, but not yet for eukaryotic cells.
   The terminator of a prokaryotic cell has two components. The first is the hairpin loop. It is a base sequence
in the DNA that causes the mRNA (the RNA transcript) to pair with itself (Fig. 11.1*a*) to form a loop (Fig. 11.1*b*).
   The hairpin loop displaces both the RNA transcript and the RNA polymerase from the DNA molecule, enabling
the two strands of DNA to re-form hydrogen bonds between their bases.
   The second component of the terminator, which follows the hairpin loop, is a sequence of four to eight adenines
along the DNA strand being copied, causing a sequence of uracils at the tail end of the RNA transcript (Fig. 11.2).

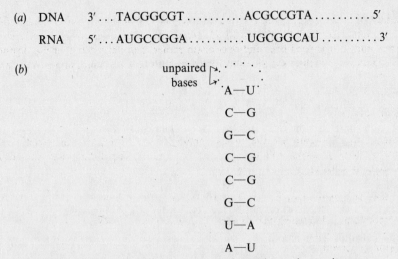

Figure 11.1. The hairpin loop component of a prokaryotic terminator.
(a) The nucleotide sequence. (b) The resulting loop in the RNA molecule.

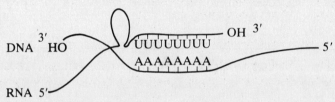

Fig. 11.2. The tail component of a prokaryotic terminator.

11.19   How does a primary transcript differ from a functional mRNA in a eukaryotic cell?

🐚   RNA processing, or RNA splicing, converts a primary transcript (the RNA molecule synthesized on the DNA molecule) to a functional mRNA (the RNA that is translated). The main function of RNA processing is to remove regions of the primary transcript. The nucleotides removed are referred to as *introns*, and the regions that remain are *exons*—and are expressed as polypeptides. After excision of the introns, the exons are spliced back together to make a single mRNA molecule.

Phillip Sharp discovered RNA processing, in 1977, when he noticed that primary transcripts of the genes he was working with were about 6000 bases long, whereas the mRNA that was translated was only about 2000 bases long. Large segments had been removed between transcription and translation.

In addition to removing introns, a eukaryotic mRNA is capped at both ends. A cap of modified guanosine triphosphate is added to the 5′ end, and a cap of between 20 and 250 adenine nucleotides (the poly-A tail) is added to the 3′ end.

$$\text{guanosine} - \text{P} - \text{P} - \text{P} - ^{5'}\underline{\hspace{3cm}}^{3'}\text{A} - \text{A} - \ldots \text{A}$$

The cap at the 5′ end helps initiate translation, and both caps protect the codons of the mRNA from disintegration.

11.20   The DNA code is transcribed into mRNA, rRNA, and tRNA. The rate of mRNA synthesis is much faster than the rate of rRNA and tRNA synthesis, yet the amount of mRNA in a cell is much less than the amount of the other two kinds of RNA. Account for this pattern.

🐚   While mRNA is more rapidly produced, it exists in a cell for a much shorter period of time than either rRNA or tRNA. A molecule of mRNA carries a temporary message, in response to the need for a particular protein; however a cell's need for each protein varies from time to time. For this reason, an mRNA molecule is dismantled immediately after it has been used to construct its protein. Since each mRNA is so short-lived, the total amount of mRNA present at any one time is very low in spite of the rapid rate of mRNA synthesis. By contrast, the function of an rRNA or a tRNA molecule is always the same, regardless of the type of protein being synthesized, and so it is used over and over again rather than degraded after use. Although the rate of rRNA or tRNA synthesis is slow, their long lives in the cell make them abundant at any one time.

TRANSLATION

11.21 Translation is the

(**a**) movement of mRNA through the nuclear membrane. (**b**) transfer of the genetic code to an mRNA molecule. (**c**) transfer of the genetic code to a tRNA molecule. (**d**) transfer of the genetic code from an mRNA to a sequence of amino acids in a polypeptide.

11.22 A polypeptide is assembled on a

(**a**) DNA molecule. (**b**) nuclear membrane. (**c**) nuclear pore. (**d**) ribosome.

11.23 The function of mRNA is to

(**a**) provide specific binding sites for a series of specific tRNA molecules. (**b**) hold a group of ribosomes together. (**c**) transfer the genetic code to ribosomal RNA. (**d**) transfer the genetic code to DNA.

11.24 The function of tRNA is to

(**a**) form a site for protein synthesis. (**b**) transcribe the genetic code. (**c**) transport specific amino acids to specific sites on the mRNA. (**d**) synthesize amino acids.

11.25 Which one of the following statements is true about tRNA?

(**a**) It binds to DNA, initiating translation; (**b**) It has a greater molecular weight than mRNA; (**c**) It transfers the code from the nucleus to the cytoplasm; (**d**) There is at least one form for each kind of amino acid.

11.26 The first event in translation is the binding of the mRNA leader to the

(**a**) smaller ribosomal subunit. (**b**) larger ribosomal subunit. (**c**) polysomal core. (**d**) tRNA.

11.27 The signal to start translation is the initiator codon, usually AUG, the codon for

(**a**) tyrosine. (**b**) methionine. (**c**) leucine. (**d**) no amino acid.

11.28 The second event in translation, after mRNA binding, is

(**a**) synthesis of amino acids from glucose and ammonia. • (**b**) translocation of the nuclear envelope. (**c**) joining together of the two ribosomal subunits. (**d**) rotation of the polysomal unit.

11.29 The enzyme that catalyzes peptide bonding is located in the

(**a**) smaller subunit of the ribosome. (**b**) larger subunit of the ribosome. (**c**) leader region of the mRNA. (**d**) central part of the tRNA.

11.30 The ribosomes of a polysome are the same in that all

(**a**) contain the essential amino acids. (**b**) carry the genetic code within their core. (**c**) are involved in translating the same genetic code. (**d**) contain the nitrogen for synthesizing amino acids.

11.31 A ribosome is made of two polymers: 40 percent is _____ and 60 percent is _____.

11.32 Each functioning ribosome is composed of _____ subunits.

11.33 Translation has three stages: _____, _____, and _____.

11.34 Translation always begins at the _____ end of an mRNA molecule.

11.35 The smaller subunit of a ribosome has a binding site for _____, and the larger subunit has two binding sites for two _____.

11.36 An amino-acid activating enzyme, or aminoacyl-tRNA synthetase, binds a specific _____ with a specific _____. There are at least _____ such enzymes in each cell. Once these two substrates are joined, the product molecule is called _____.

11.37 The synthesis of a protein terminates when a ribosome encounters one or more terminator codons in the

_____.

11.38 After reaching the terminator codons, no more amino acids are added to the newly formed polypeptide. Instead, a molecule of _____ is added.

11.39 After an mRNA has been translated and leaves the ribosome or polysome, it is _____.

11.40 How do a code, codon, and anticodon differ?

☢ A *code* is a sequence of nitrogenous bases (parts of nucleotides) along one sugar-phosphate strand of a DNA molecule. The sequence, which involves the bases adenine, guanine, cytosine, and thymine, specifies the way in which amino acids are to be bonded together within polypeptides. The code, or genetic code, within all of the DNA molecules of a cell determines the kinds of polypeptides the cell can synthesize.

A *codon* is a sequence of just three successive nitrogenous bases within either a DNA molecule or an mRNA molecule. In a DNA molecule, the bases are adenine, guanine, cytosine, and thymine. In an mRNA molecule, the bases involved are adenine, guanine, cytosine, and uracil. The codon, or *base triplet*, specifies a particular amino acid or is a signal to start or stop transcription or translation; it is the basic unit of the genetic code. If we think of the genetic code as being a language, then the codons are the words of the language, with all words being made of three letters, and the letters of the alphabet are adenine, guanine, cytosine, and thymine (or uracil).

An *anticodon* is a sequence of three successive nitrogenous bases at one end of a tRNA molecule. The bases involved are adenine, guanine, cytosine, and uracil. The base triplet constituting the anticodon recognizes and binds (according to the base-pairing rules) with a particular complementary triplet (codon) on an mRNA molecule.

11.41 A tRNA molecule has four active sites. Where are these sites and what does each do?

☢ The transfer RNA molecules of a cell act as vehicles that pick up amino acids scattered throughout the cytosol and transport them to specific codons of mRNA molecules on ribosomes.

The tRNA molecule is a small structure, only about 80 nucleotides long. It is held in a cloverleaf shape by hydrogen bonds between some of its nitrogenous bases (Fig. 11.3).

At one end of the molecule, three unpaired bases form the anticodon; they bind with a complementary codon on an mRNA molecule. An anticodon of GAA, for example, forms bonds with a codon of CUU. At the opposite

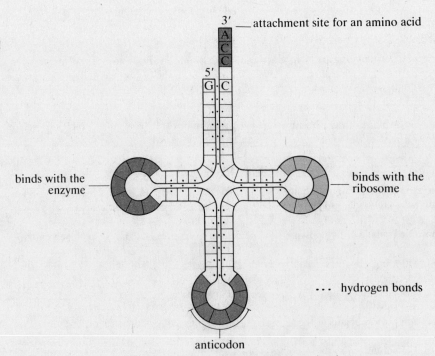

Fig. 11.3. The four active sites of a tRNA molecule.

end of the tRNA molecule, its protruding 3′ end carries the bases CCA. This is an active site that bonds with the particular kind of amino acid dictated by the anticodon. A tRNA with the anticodon GAA, for example, bonds with and carries only the amino acid leucine. The matching of anticodon with amino acid is done by an enzyme—the amino-acid activating enzyme, or aminoacyl-tRNA synthetase. There are at least 20 such enzymes in a cell, one for each kind of amino acid.

On one side of a tRNA molecule, there is an active site that binds with the appropriate amino-acid activating enzyme, which then facilitates attachment of the appropriate amino acid to the tRNA. The fourth active site is on the side opposite the one that binds with the enzyme; its function is to recognize a ribosome and by doing so to hold the tRNA to the ribosome in a manner that facilitates codon-anticodon pairing.

11.42 What is the difference between the P site and the A site of a ribosome?

Both active sites on the larger ribosomal subunit hold tRNA molecules. The P site, or peptide site, is the region of the ribosome that binds with the tRNA carrying the growing polypeptide chain. The A site, or amino acid site, binds with the tRNA carrying the next amino acid to be added to the polypeptide chain. The two sites are diagramed in Fig. 11.4.

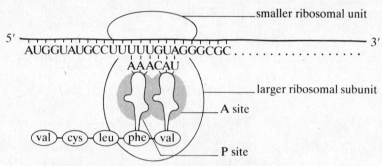

Fig. 11.4. The P site and A site of a ribosome.

While the two tRNA molecules are held, a peptide bond forms between the last amino acid in the polypeptide chain and the amino acid held by the tRNA at the A site. The tRNA at the P site then releases the polypeptide chain and leaves the ribosome. At this point, the ribosome shifts so that the remaining tRNA (formerly at the A site) is moved to the P site, which leaves the A site free to bind with the tRNA carrying the next amino acid for the chain.

THE GENETIC CODE

11.43 All 64 codons of the genetic code were deciphered during the

(a) 1850s. (b) 1880s. (c) early 1900s. (d) 1960s.

11.44 Of the 64 codons, how many code for amino acids?

(a) 20; (b) 22; (c) 43; (d) 61

11.45 Codons that do not code for amino acids code for

(a) phosphates. (b) start and stop signals. (c) nonsense. (d) sugars.

11.46 The wobble effect is the

(a) lack of precision with regard to the third base in the codon and anticodon. (b) instability of the DNA molecule when unwound. (c) instability of pairing when a purine pairs with another purine. (d) undulating movements of mRNA.

11.47 The genetic code that directs protein synthesis in humans is found in

(a) no other kind of organism. (b) virtually all organisms. (c) all animals, but not in plants. (d) all multicellular organisms but not in unicellular ones.

11.48 The genetic code is a sequence of _____ along a sugar-phosphate strand of a DNA molecule.

11.49 A gene contains the following sequence: AAATGCGCGATA. The complementary sequence in mRNA is _____, and the sequence of anticodons is _____.

11.50   A particular gene consists of 600 DNA nucleotides. Ignoring introns, and stop and start signals, how many tRNA molecules are needed to synthesize the polypeptide coded for by this gene? _____. How many amino acids is the polypeptide made of? _____.

11.51   Why are there 64 different codons for 20 different amino acids?

   🐚   There are 64 different codons, because each codon consists of three bases, and there are four different kinds of bases in a nucleic acid. With this setup, there are 64 different ways in which the four bases can be combined in groups of three: $4^3 = 64$.

   We do not know how this particular arrangement first developed, but given that there were initially just four bases in nucleic acids, then groups of three are the smallest units of uniform length that provide enough codons for all 20 amino acids. If each of the four bases coded for an amino acid (a codon of one), then only four amino acids (4^1) could be coded for, and that is not enough. If the codon were a doublet, rather than a triplet, then 16 amino acids (4^2) would be coded for, which is close to the number needed but not quite enough. While a triplet provides more than enough ($4^3 = 64$) codons, it is the minimum number of bases in a codon when four different kinds of bases are used.

   Having 64 codons for 20 amino acids means that some codons can be reserved for start and stop signals, and many can be synonyms of one another. Usually, it is substitutions in the third base of a codon that produce synonyms. For example, CAA, CAG, CAT, and CAC all code for valine. This flexibility with regard to the third base in a codon is known as the *wobble effect*.

11.52   How were the first codons deciphered?

   🐚   The first codon was deciphered by Marshall Nirenberg in 1961. He synthesized an artificial mRNA made entirely of uracil nucleotides: UUUUUUUUUU.... This molecule was added to each of 20 test tubes. All of the test tubes contained ribosomes, tRNA, ATP, appropriate enzymes, and all 20 kinds of amino acids, but differed in that each test tube contained just one of the amino acids in radioactive form. Thus, one of the test tubes contained radioactive tyrosine, another contained radioactive leucine, and so on. After allowing time for protein synthesis, Nirenberg found that in 19 of the test tubes, no radioactive polypeptide had formed; in other words, 19 of the amino acids were not incorporated into a polypeptide. In just one of the test tubes—the one containing radioactive phenylalanine—a radioactive polypeptide had formed. He concluded that this polypeptide was made entirely of phenylalanine and, consequently, that the mRNA codon for phenylalanine was UUU. Soon the amino acids specified by mRNA codons AAA, GGG, and CCC were also determined by using the same experimental procedure. Within a few years, the remaining 60, more difficult, codons were deciphered.

11.53   When an mRNA molecule made only of a random combination of uracil and adenine nucleotides is added to a test tube containing ribosomes, tRNA, ATP, enzymes, and all 20 kinds of amino acids, no long polypeptide forms. Why not?

   🐚   When a polypeptide is synthesized within a cell, the signal to stop translation is a nucleotide sequence of UAA, UAG, or UGA within the mRNA molecule. If the mRNA molecule consists of a random combination of uracil and adenine nucleotides, then the UAA sequence will appear here and there throughout the molecule, and wherever the sequence appears it will cause translation to stop. Thus, only short polypeptide chains will form from this mRNA molecule.

11.54   The genetic code is said to be a universal code. What does this mean, and what does it imply about the history of life?

   🐚   A universal genetic code means that all known living systems use nucleic acids and even the same three-base codons to direct the synthesis of proteins from amino acids. The mRNA codon UUU, for example, codes for phenylalanine in all cells of all organisms. Recently, however, some slight variations in the code have been discovered. In several types of unicellular eukaryotes, the mRNA codons UAA and UAG code for glutamine rather than for the usual stop signals, and the DNA in mitochondria (remnants of when these organelles were unicellular organisms) contains slight variations from the usual code.

   The fact that the code is universal, or nearly so, implies that all life has a common ancestor, in which the code first appeared. From that ancestor the code must have been faithfully reproduced again and again in all of its descendants. A universal genetic code is strong evidence that all organisms evolved from a common ancestor.

REGULATION OF PROTEIN SYNTHESIS IN EUKARYOTES

11.55   All the body cells of an animal contain the same genes. The cells are different in structure and function because they synthesize different

   (*a*) tRNA molecules.   (*b*) mRNA molecules.   (*c*) histones.   (*d*) ribosomes.

11.56 If a cell were treated with a chemical that blocked nucleic acid synthesis, which of the following processes would most likely be affected first?

(*a*) DNA replication; (*b*) tRNA synthesis; (*c*) mRNA synthesis; (*d*) protein synthesis

11.57 About how much of the DNA in a eukaryotic cell is expressed at any one time?
(*a*) 1 percent; (*b*) 20 percent; (*c*) 50 percent; (*d*) 80 percent

11.58 Genes that are inactive for long periods of time tend to be bonded to

(*a*) each other. (*b*) methyl groups. (*c*) actin and myosin. (*d*) the nucleolus.

11.59 Genes that code for polypeptides are called _____ genes, whereas genes that activate or inactive other genes are called _____ genes.

11.60 If all the body cells of an animal are genetically identical, how do they become functionally different from one another?

🐚 Cells that perform different functions must manufacture different enzymes, since these molecules control the chemical activities of a cell. The fact that enzymes are produced according to information stored within the DNA molecules implies that each cell of a multicellular organism expresses only a limited amount of its full genetic potential in the form of enzymes and other proteins. A human cell, for example, contains approximately 100,000 genes, but only about 1000 are used in protein synthesis at any one time, and those used in one type of cell are different from those used in another type of cell.

Expression of genes occurs when DNA directs the synthesis of mRNA (transcription); mRNA, in turn, directs the assembly of proteins (translation). Gene expression may be halted at any point during protein synthesis: transcription, posttranscription, translation, or posttranslation (e.g., by degradation of unwanted polypeptides). Most important, perhaps, is control over transcription by regulatory genes—segments of DNA that turn on or off the other segments, called structural genes, that code for polypeptides. Quite likely much of the genetic information within the cells of more complex organisms is involved in the control of gene expression rather than in the actual synthesis of proteins.

Although we know that gene expression is controlled within the cells of multicellular organisms, the precise mechanisms by which it is brought about have not yet been described.

Answers to Objective Questions

11.1 *a*

11.2 *c*

11.3 nucleotides; nucleotides; amino acids; transcription; translation

11.4 one-gene, one-polypeptide; nucleic acids (rRNA and tRNA); one-gene, one-functional-product

11.6 *a*

11.7 *d*

11.8 *d*

11.9 *c*

11.10 *b*

11.11 *a*

11.12 *b*

11.13 DNA; mRNA; thymine; uracil; guanine

11.14 DNA; DNA

11.15 introns

11.16 mRNA; rRNA; tRNA

11.17 nucleus; cytoplasm; ribosome

11.21 *d*

11.22 *d*

11.23 *a*

11.24 *c*

11.25 *d*

11.26 *a*

11.27 *b*

11.28 *c*

11.29 *b*

11.30 *c*

11.31 protein; RNA

11.32 two

11.33 initiation; elongation; termination

11.34 5′

11.35 mRNA; tRNA molecules

11.36 tRNA; amino acid; twenty; aminoacyl-tRNA

11.37 mRNA

11.38 water

11.39 degraded

11.43 *d*

11.44 *d*

11.45 *b*

11.46 *a*

11.47 *b*

11.48 nitrogenous bases

11.49 UUUACGCGCUAU; AAAUGCGCGAUA

11.50 200 (The number of tRNA, each with a specific anti-codon, will equal the number of codons on mRNA. Since a codon is composed of 3 nucleotides, the number of tRNA is 600/3.); 200 (Each tRNA inserts one amino acid into the polypeptide chain.)

11.55 *b*

11.56 *c*

11.57 *a*

11.58 *b*

11.59 structural; regulatory

CHAPTER 12
Genetics of Viruses and Bacteria

VIRAL REPRODUCTION*

12.1   A virus consists of a

(*a*) cell membrane and chromosome. (*b*) protein coat and nucleic acid molecules.
(*c*) lipid coat (the capsid), genes, and ribosomes. (*d*) protein coat, genes, and mitochondria.

12.2   A virion is a

(*a*) virus. (*b*) viral ribosome. (*c*) viral lysosome. (*d*) viral gene.

12.3   Viral genes are made of

(*a*) RNA only. (*b*) DNA only. (*c*) either RNA or DNA. (*d*) either proteins or nucleic acids.

12.4   An isolated virus is not considered living, since it

(*a*) separates into two inert parts. (*b*) cannot metabolize. (*c*) is coated with an air-tight, chemically inert shield.
(*d*) rapidly loses its genome.

12.5   The enzymes involved in viral replication are synthesized

(*a*) on the viral ribosomes. (*b*) on the interior surface of the viral membrane.
(*c*) on the interior surface of the viral coat. (*d*) by the host cell.

12.6   Most RNA viruses carry a gene for an enzyme that uses viral RNA as a template in the synthesis of more viral RNA. This enzyme is

(*a*) RNA replicase. (*b*) reverse transcriptase. (*c*) RNA polymerase. (*d*) viral nuclease.

12.7   Some RNA viruses carry a gene for an enzyme that uses viral RNA as a template in the synthesis of DNA. This enzyme is

(*a*) RNA replicase. (*b*) reverse transcriptase. (*c*) RNA polymerase. (*d*) viral nuclease.

12.8   The assembly of a virus from already formed polymers occurs

(*a*) outside the cell. (*b*) by a series of enzyme-catalyzed reactions. (*c*) spontaneously.
(*d*) rapidly, consuming a large amount of energy from the host cell's carbohydrates.

12.9   The protein coat that encloses the viral genes is called a _____.

12.10   Viruses are obligate parasites of _____.

12.11   Gene replication in a virus may proceed from DNA to _____, from RNA to _____, or from RNA to _____ to _____.

12.12   A virus reproduces by using the metabolic machinery of a _____.

12.13   A virus recognizes its host by the reaction of specific binding sites on the _____ with those on the _____ or _____ of the host.

12.14   A viroid consists only of _____.

---

* Answers to Chapter 12 objective questions appear on page 97.

12.15 In 1952, Alfred D. Hershey and Martha Chase prepared two groups of viruses, one that incorporated radioactive sulfur and the other that incorporated radioactive phosphorus into its molecules. Each group was allowed to infect its host cells. On later examination of the host cells, Hershey and Chase found that the radioactive _____ was in the cells, whereas the radioactive _____ was not. This experiment demonstrated that the genetic material of a virus is _____ rather than _____.

12.16 The virus that causes acquired immune deficiency syndrome (AIDS) is a retrovirus. How does a retrovirus differ from other kinds of viruses?

🐚 A *retrovirus* (*retro* = turning back) has its genes in the form of single-stranded RNA. One of the genes codes for reverse transcriptase, an enzyme (carried in the viral coat) that causes synthesis of a double-stranded DNA molecule from the single-stranded RNA template. Thus, the direction of transcription is the reverse of the usual pattern.

The newly formed DNA, coding for viral proteins, becomes integrated into one of the cell's chromosomes. It is then known as a *provirus* and may remain dormant for a long time, which means that it is not expressed as proteins, but is replicated along with the rest of the chromosome during mitosis. When stimulated to become active, the provirus initiates transcription of its genes into mRNA molecules, which are then translated into viral proteins. Multiplication of the virus during these active intervals usually causes death of the host cell—a white blood cell in the case of AIDS.

12.17 Why are antibiotics ineffective in treating a viral infection?

🐚 Antibiotics interfere with the normal activities of ribosomes in prokaryotic cells (see Question 5.39) by preventing translation of the cell's genetic code into proteins. Without proteins, the cell has no enzymes and no chemical reactions. A prokaryotic cell treated with an antibiotic soon dies. The ribosomes of eukaryotic cells, on the other hand, are not adversely affected by antibiotics.

A virus has no ribosomes of its own. During a viral infection, the virus uses the ribosomes within its host cell—a human body cell, for example—for translation of its genes into viral proteins. Consequently, an antibiotic (e.g., penicillin, streptomycin, tetracycline) has no effect on the progress of a viral infection in human cells.

BACTERIOPHAGES

12.18 A bacteriophage is a

(*a*) virus that parasitizes a bacterium. (*b*) bacterium with a lysed membrane. (*c*) tiny bacterium. (*d*) unusually large bacterium.

12.19 In the lytic cycle of a bacteriophage, the host DNA is

(*a*) replicated. (*b*) turned off by a protein coat. (*c*) turned on by removal of a protein coat. (*d*) digested into its nucleotides.

12.20 A T4 bacteriophage has a gene for the enzyme lysozyme. The function of this enzyme is to digest the bacterial

(*a*) cell wall. (*b*) cell membrane. (*c*) enzymes. (*d*) glycogen.

12.21 A bacterial cell swells and bursts during the lytic cycle, because it

(*a*) can no longer synthesize proteins. (*b*) no longer has an intact cell wall to counter osmosis. (*c*) no longer has an intact chromosome. (*d*) has greater osmotic pressure due to the catabolism of glycogen.

12.22 A virus that can reproduce without killing its host is called a

(*a*) lytic virus. (*b*) retroactive virus. (*c*) temperate virus. (*d*) virion.

12.23 In the lysogenic cycle, the DNA of a bacteriophage

(*a*) joins the bacterial chromosome. (*b*) attaches to the inner surface of the host membrane. (*c*) goes directly to the host's ribosomes for translation. (*d*) is immediately degraded when it enters the host.

12.24 Some bacteriophages cause serious human diseases (e.g., diphtheria) while in their lysogenic phase in bacteria within the human body. Humans become sick, because the prophage possesses genes that produce, or cause bacterial production of,

(*a*) mutations. (*b*) lysogenic enzymes. (*c*) lytic enzymes. (*d*) toxins.

12.25 A bacteriophage with a lysogenic cycle must have genes that are

(*a*) made of RNA. (*b*) made of double-stranded DNA. (*c*) made of single-stranded RNA or DNA. (*d*) within a circular nucleic acid molecule.

12.26 A virus with genes made of double-stranded DNA can reproduce by two alternative methods: the _____ cycle (discovered in the 1940s by Max Delbrück) or the _____ cycle (discovered in 1953 by André Lwoff).

12.27 Bacteria defend themselves against viruses by making restriction enzymes, which recognize and degrade foreign _____.

12.28 A viral genome incorporated into the DNA molecule of a bacterium is called a _____.

12.29 A virus in its lysogenic phase reproduces during _____, when the host cell makes copies of the viral _____ along with its own _____.

12.30 Where does a T phage get the energy it needs to penetrate its host cell?

🐾 A T phage penetrates the cell wall and plasma membrane of its host bacterium by first attaching its tail to specific receptor sites on the cell wall and then, by contracting the sheath of its tail, drilling a hole through both the wall and plasma membrane of the cell. Its DNA is then injected into the cell. It costs the virus 140 molecules of ATP to carry out these activities.

A virus has no metabolic machinery of its own for making ATP. These high-energy molecules were synthesized in the host cell from which the virus was formed and were stored in the tailpiece prior to the virus's release from the host cell.

12.31 Herpes is a human disease caused by a virus with genes of double-stranded DNA molecules. What is a likely explanation for the periodic eruptions of symptoms in a person infected with the herpes virus?

🐾 The herpes virus, being made of double-stranded DNA, behaves like a lysogenic bacteriophage: It has long periods of dormancy interrupted by short periods of activity. Furthermore, the herpes virus is known to reproduce within the nucleus of its host cell and, like a bacteriophage, is stimulated to enter its active phase by various sorts of stress, such as ultraviolet radiation and mutagenic chemicals.

The facial herpes virus (*Herpes simplex* I), which causes cold sores, resides during its dormant period inside a facial neuron. If it is indeed similar to a lysogenic bacteriophage, then its DNA is part of a chromosome (i.e., a provirus) within the neuron during this time. At regular intervals, or during times of stress (e.g., physical exhaustion, emotional upset, or exposure to intense ultraviolet radiation), the virus leaves the neuron and invades skin cells. As it reproduces within skin cells on or near the lips, it destroys the cells and sores appear. After a week to 10 days of such activity, the virus returns to a neuron and becomes dormant again.

THE BACTERIAL GENOME

12.32 The process (discovered in 1928 by F. Griffith) by which a bacterium acquires new genes by taking up parts of a "naked" DNA molecule from its surroundings is called

(*a*) transformation. (*b*) general transduction. (*c*) restricted transduction. (*d*) conjugation.

12.33 When a temperate bacteriophage breaks loose from its host's chromosome and carries some of the chromosome with it to another host cell, the process is called

(*a*) transformation. (*b*) general transduction. (*c*) restricted transduction. (*d*) conjugation.

12.34 When a bacteriophage, in its lytic phase, carries some of the bacterium's partially digested chromosome with it to another host cell, the process is called

(*a*) transformation. (*b*) general transduction. (*c*) restricted transduction. (*d*) conjugation.

12.35 Restricted transduction differs from general transduction in that

(*a*) it only happens at certain times of the reproductive cycle. (*b*) it only happens in certain kinds of bacteria. (*c*) only certain segments of bacterial chromosomes—segments adjacent to the viral DNA during its lytic phase—are transduced. (*d*) it restricts the virus to only certain routes out of its host.

12.36 When DNA is exchanged, via cytoplasmic bridges, between two bacteria, the process is called

(*a*) transformation.　(*b*) general transduction.　(*c*) restricted transduction.　(*d*) conjugation.

12.37 In the 1940s, Barbara McClintock described "jumping genes" in maize. Such mobile segments of DNA, now called transposons (transposable elements), can insert themselves into

(*a*) virtually any part of any DNA molecule.　(*b*) start and stop signals, only.　(*c*) only DNA molecules where there are complementary base pairs with unfilled active sites.　(*d*) plasmid molecules only.

12.38 The fertility, or F$^+$, factor that plays a role in conjugation is a

(*a*) retrovirus.　(*b*) plasmid.　(*c*) viroid.　(*d*) lysogenic phage.

12.39 Most of a bacterium's genes are in a single, _____, double-stranded DNA molecule usually called a chromosome. Many bacteria also have small rings of DNA called _____, which carry accessory genes.

12.40 A bacterial cell reproduces by _____ rather than by mitosis.

12.41 Bacteria have three ways of transferring genes from one individual to another: _____, _____, and _____.

12.42 Plasmids that can integrate into the bacterial DNA are called _____.

12.43 How did Joshua Lederberg and Edward Tatum discover, in 1946, that bacteria have sexual reproduction?

🐌 Lederberg and Tatum developed two genetic strains of the bacterium *Escherichia coli*. Strain 1 needed, but was unable to synthesize, the amino acid methionine and the vitamin biotin. Strain 2 lacked the ability to make threonine and leucine, both amino acids that it needed for making its proteins. The bacterial populations were grown by providing, as food, the nutrients they needed but could not synthesize.

In the crucial experiment, the two strains of bacteria were grown together in an environment that lacked all four of the nutrients (methionine, biotin, threonine, and leucine). One would expect all bacteria of both strains to die under such conditions, since each individual lacked two nutrients that it needed for survival. Surprisingly, some bacteria survived and flourished in the nutrient-deficient condition; they apparently were able to synthesize methionine, biotin, threonine, and leucine.

Lederberg and Tatum concluded from this experiment that the surviving bacteria had inherited genes for making methionine and biotin from strain 2, and genes for making threonine and leucine from strain 1. Later experiments showed that a bacterium can inherit genes from two "parents" when a narrow cytoplasmic bridge, or *pilus*, connects the two parental bacteria and pieces of DNA move from one cell to the other. In the Lederberg-Tatum experiment, DNA must have moved from a bacterium of strain 1 to a bacterium of strain 2, or vice versa, so that at least one bacterium inherited genes for making all four nutrients. This bacterium then reproduced by binary fission to start a new strain of cells with characteristics of both strains 1 and 2.

Exchange of genetic material by direct cell-to-cell contact in bacteria is known as *conjugation*. It occurs only between cells of different mating types: F$^+$ and F$^-$, or Hfr and F$^-$. The F$^+$ bacteria differ from the F$^-$ bacteria in having small amounts of DNA (i.e., a plasmid), known as the sex factor, in their cytoplasm and separate from their larger chromosome. The sex factor codes for genes that control formation of the cytoplasmic bridge and other aspects of conjugation. The Hfr bacteria also carry this sex factor, but as an episome integrated into their chromosome.

As a plasmid, the sex factor can self-replicate, and its replicates can move from an F$^+$ bacterium to an F$^-$ bacterium during conjugation, thereby converting an F$^-$ individual to an F$^+$ individual. Hfr bacteria, by contrast, rarely transfer their sex factor, because of its position within the chromosome. During conjugation, a copy of the Hfr chromosome moves into an F$^-$ bacterium, but the mating is usually disrupted before the entire chromosome is transferred, and so the sex factor, which is positioned at the end of the chromosome, rarely moves from one cell into the other. Bacteria that transfer copies of their chromosomes are called *high-frequency recombination* (*Hfr*) bacteria, because of their capacity to transfer, and so recombine, genes within their chromosomes.

12.44 How is conjugation used to map a bacterial chromosome?

🐌 The single, circular chromosome of a bacterium is mapped (i.e., the positions of its genes are located) by interrupting conjugation between Hfr and F$^-$ bacteria at various points and observing which genes have been transferred.

The rate at which the Hfr chromosome moves into the F⁻ bacterium is always the same (about 90 minutes for the entire chromosome at 37 °C), and transfer always begins at the same point in the chromosome, for each strain of bacteria.

A strain of F⁻ bacteria is used that cannot synthesize a molecule, say methionine, that it needs. The Hfr bacteria in these experiments do have the ability to synthesize the molecule. The F⁻ and Hfr bacteria are grown together in several separate containers, and conjugation is stopped (by shaking and chilling) at different time periods in the different containers. Thus, in one of the containers conjugation is allowed to continue until just 50 percent of the chromosome is transferred, while in another container it may continue longer, until 60 percent of the chromosome is transferred.

When the gene for methionine is transferred, the recipient group can grow in a methionine-deficient environment. Therefore, if the groups allowed to conjugate until 60 percent or more of the chromosome has been transferred are able to grow in a methionine-deficient environment but groups interrupted in their conjugation at 50 percent or less of chromosome transfer cannot grow in such an environment, then we can conclude that the gene for methionine is positioned somewhere between 50 and 60 percent of the way down the chromosome. The experiment can then be repeated examining finer time periods between the 50 and 60 percent transfer intervals.

CONTROL OF GENE EXPRESSION IN BACTERIA

12.45 Much of the research on gene expression has been done with *Escherichia coli*, which inhabits the human intestine. This organism is a

(*a*) plasmid.   (*b*) virus.   (*c*) bacterium.   (*d*) protozoan.

12.46 In general, bacterial genes are regulated at the time of

(*a*) transcription.   (*b*) posttranscription.   (*c*) translation.   (*d*) posttranslation.

12.47 An operon is a

(*a*) protein that suppresses gene expression.   (*b*) protein that accelerates gene expression.   (*c*) gene that switches other genes on or off.   (*d*) cluster of structural genes with related functions.

12.48 The *lac* operon, described in 1961 by Francois Jacob and Jacques Monod, is transcribed when

(*a*) lactose is needed by the cell.   (*b*) lactose is available to the cell.   (*c*) lactic acid is needed by the cell.
(*d*) lactic acid is available to the cell.

12.49 The *lac* operon needs a "helper" protein that, by binding to the promotor and facilitating attachment of RNA polymerase, accelerates the rate of transcription. This protein is called the

(*a*) catabolite activator protein.   (*b*) inactive repressor protein.   (*c*) essential metabolite.   (*d*) amino-acid activating enzyme.

12.50 The *trp* operon is regulated in a different way from the *lac* operon; it is transcribed when

(*a*) trypsin is needed by the cell.   (*b*) trypsinogen is available to the cell.   (*c*) there is not much tryptophan in the cell.   (*d*) there is a lot of tryptophan in the cell.

12.51 When the substrate for an enzyme (i.e., the substance with which an enzyme reacts) stimulates synthesis (or inactivates the repressor) of that enzyme, it is called a gene

(*a*) repressor.   (*b*) inducer.   (*c*) activator.   (*d*) excitant.

12.52 The activity of a repressor depends on whether

(*a*) the repressor is positioned next to the operon.   (*b*) the repressor is positioned next to the promoter.   (*c*) a key substance in the metabolic pathway is present.   (*d*) there is enough RNA polymerase present.

12.53 When an end product of a metabolic pathway activates the repressor of the operon that produces enzymes for the pathway, it is called a

(*a*) corepressor.   (*b*) operator.   (*c*) promoter.   (*d*) suppressor.

12.54 A _____ operon has its transcription turned off by a specific metabolite; an _____ operon has its transcription turned on by a specific metabolite.

12.55 Unregulated genes, which are _____ continually, are called constitutive genes. The products of these genes are always needed.

12.56 A promoter in the DNA controls the rate at which constitutive genes are _____.

12.57 The *trp* operon is turned off when its repressor protein bonds with the corepressor, which is a molecule of _____. The repressor-corepressor complex then bonds with the operator region and blocks attachment of _____.

12.58 How is the following pathway turned on in *Escherichia coli*?

$$\text{lactose} \xrightarrow[\text{permease}]{} \text{lactose} \xrightarrow[\beta\text{-galactosidase}]{} \text{glucose} + \text{galactose}$$
$$\text{outside} \qquad\qquad \text{inside}$$
$$\text{the cell} \qquad\qquad \text{the cell}$$

🐌 Enzymes that control this pathway in *E. coli* are coded for by genes in the *lac* operon. This operon consists of three structural genes, which code for permease (carries lactose into the cell), β-galactosidase (converts lactose into glucose and galactose), and transacetylase (of unknown function in this pathway). All three genes are transcribed as a unit. Transcription of the operon is controlled by two promoters (P_1 and P_2), an operator (O), and a regulator (R), all composed of nucleotide sequences within the DNA. The regulator gene codes for a repressor that binds to the operator, blocking attachment of RNA polymerase so that transcription of the operon is not possible (Fig. 12.1).

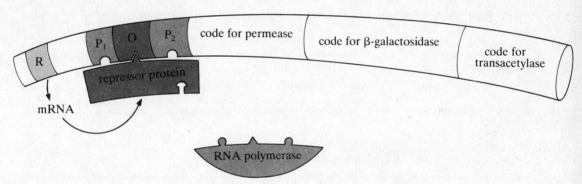

Fig. 12.1. Repression of *lac* operon transcription.

The repressor protein is dislodged from the operator when allolactose (an isomer of lactose) binds to it. The two promoter regions are then free to bind with RNA polymerase and transcription can proceed (Fig. 12.2).

Transcription of the *lac* operon proceeds very slowly unless a second event also takes place: attachment of a catabolic activator protein to the chromosome adjacent to the RNA polymerase. It appears that RNA polymerase does not fit well onto the two promoters and that the binding of a catabolic activator protein (CAP) to both the

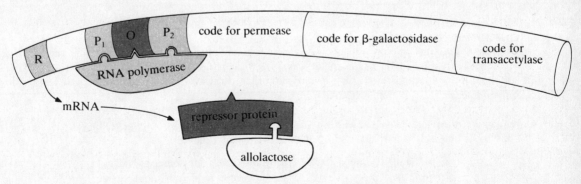

Fig. 12.2. Activation of *lac* operon transcription.

polymerase and the DNA molecule improves the fit and greatly increases the rate of transcription. CAP is activated by an intracellular messenger known as cyclic AMP (adenosine monophosphate), which, in turn, responds to the cell's need for the enzymes coded for by the *lac* operon.

12.59 What are two ways in which the following pathway, in an *E. coli*, can be turned off?

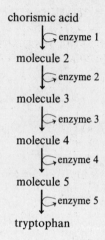

chorismic acid

↳ enzyme 1

molecule 2

↳ enzyme 2

molecule 3

↳ enzyme 3

molecule 4

↳ enzyme 4

molecule 5

↳ enzyme 5

tryptophan

🐚 A pathway can be turned off (1) by inhibiting the activity of one or more of the enzymes involved or (2) by inhibiting the synthesis of one or more of the enzymes.

In this particular pathway, activity of the first enzyme is inhibited by binding of this enzyme to the end product, tryptophan. Such binding so alters the enzyme's shape that it can no longer join with its substrate, chorismic acid. The pathway then ceases to function.

The operon that codes for all five of the enzymes involved in this pathway—the *trp* operon—does not synthesize the enzymes when its repressor protein is bonded to its operator, thereby blocking attachment of mRNA polymerase to the promoters. This particular repressor, however, cannot bind to the operator unless it is also bonded to tryptophan, the corepressor and end product of the pathway. Such control of transcription is diagrammed in Fig. 12.3.

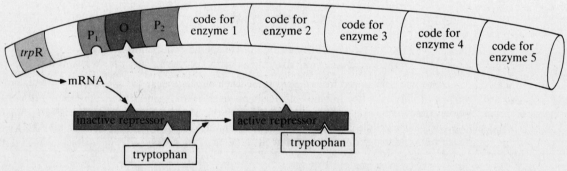

Fig. 12.3. Repression of enzyme synthesis in the *trp* operon.

Thus, the synthesis of tryptophan stops when there is plenty of tryptophan available in the cell. In some cases, the presence of tryptophan inactivates the first enzyme in the pathway, whereas in other cases the presence of tryptophan turns off the operon so that the enzymes of the pathway are no longer synthesized. Both cases are examples of feedback inhibition, or negative feedback.

12.60 A population of *E. coli* is provided with both lactose and glucose in a single, large feeding. What happens to the *lac* operon as time passes and the amounts of these two sugars decline?

🐚 The repressor of the *lac* operon is inactivated by allolactose, an isomer of lactose, as soon as lactose is in the environment of the bacteria. Transcription of the *lac* operon then proceeds, but too slowly to be of any consequence. Rapid transcription requires not only the presence of lactose, but also the absence of glucose. This second requirement ensures that *E. coli* will use the more efficient fuel—glucose—whenever it is available.

A population of *E. coli*, given both glucose and lactose, will use all the glucose first. The presence of glucose causes a drop in cellular levels of cyclic AMP (adenosine monophosphate), an intracellular messenger with many functions. Low levels of cyclic AMP, in turn, inactivate the catabolite activator protein (CAP), which is needed for rapid transcription of the *lac* operon. Glucose is then used as the cells' source of energy and carbon. Lactose is not used, since the enzymes needed for its transport into the cell and its conversion into monomers are produced too slowly to be effective.

When the glucose is all used up, cyclic AMP levels in the bacterial cells increase dramatically, and this change stimulates the CAP to attach itself to the chromosome. Once this happens, there is rapid transcription of the *lac* operon and rapid synthesis of the enzymes that transport and catabolize lactose. After the lactose has been used up, it can no longer form allolactose, and the repressor protein is free to bind with the operator and turn the operon off.

Answers to Objective Questions

12.1 *b*

12.2 *a*

12.3 *c*

12.4 *b*

12.5 *d*

12.6 *a*

12.7 *b*

12.8 *c*

12.9 capsid

12.10 cells

12.11 DNA; RNA; DNA; RNA

12.12 host cell

12.13 viral coat; cell membrane; wall

12.14 RNA

12.15 phosphorus; sulfur; nucleic acid; protein

12.18 *a*

12.19 *d*

12.20 *a*

12.21 *b*

12.22 *c*

12.23 *a*

12.24 *d*

12.25 *b*

12.26 lytic; lysogenic

12.27 DNA

12.28 prophage

12.29 mitosis; DNA; DNA

12.32 *a*

12.33 *c*

12.34 *b*

12.35 *c*

12.36 *d*

12.37 *a*

12.38 *b*

12.39 circular; plasmids

12.40 binary fission

12.41 transformation; transduction; conjugation

12.42 episomes

12.45 *c*

12.46 *a*

12.47 *d*

12.48 *b*

12.49 *a*

12.50 *c*

12.51 *b*

12.52 *c*

12.53 *a*

12.54 repressible; inducible

12.55 transcribed

12.56 transcribed

12.57 tryptophan; RNA polymerase

CHAPTER 13
Recombinant DNA Technology

METHODS*

13.1 Using recombinant DNA technology, genes from a donor cell can be implanted into a bacterium for DNA replication and protein synthesis. The kinds of cells that can be used as gene donors in this technology are

(*a*) bacteria, only.　(*b*) either yeast or bacteria, only.　(*c*) eukaryotic cells, only.　(*d*) any kind of cell.

13.2 The technique of recombinant DNA first became available in the

(*a*) 1880s.　(*b*) 1930s.　(*c*) 1950s.　(*d*) 1970s.

13.3 A gene carried by recombinant DNA is cloned when

(*a*) its host bacterium divides by binary fission.　(*b*) it is transcribed.　(*c*) it is fragmented by restriction enzymes. (*d*) it is hybridized.

13.4 A piece of nucleic acid used to find a gene, by forming a hybrid with it, is called a

(*a*) probe.　(*b*) vector.　(*c*) restriction sequence.　(*d*) retrovirus.

13.5 In DNA hybridization, the hybrid is formed of

(*a*) one double-stranded DNA and one single-stranded RNA molecule.　(*b*) two double-stranded DNA molecules. (*c*) two single-stranded DNA molecules.　(*d*) one single-stranded DNA and one single-stranded RNA molecule.

13.6 In situ hybridization is used to

(*a*) remove mutations from a chromosome.　(*b*) remove plasmids from a cell.　(*c*) clone a gene.　(*d*) locate a gene on a chromosome.

13.7 A restriction enzyme breaks bonds between the

(*a*) base pairs of a DNA molecule.　(*b*) base pairs of a DNA-RNA hybrid molecule.　(*c*) sugar and phosphate components of a nucleic acid molecule.　(*d*) exons and introns of a DNA molecule.

13.8 Restriction enzymes are synthesized by

(*a*) bacteria, only.　(*b*) yeast and bacteria, only.　(*c*) eukaryotic cells, only.　(*d*) all kinds of cells.

13.9 The natural function of a restriction enzyme is to

(*a*) cut up foreign DNA.　(*b*) remove introns from the RNA transcript.　(*c*) remove exons from the RNA transcript. (*d*) facilitate mRNA formation from nucleotides.

13.10 A bacterium adds methyl groups to its DNA, by a process known as modification, in order to

(*a*) clone its DNA.　(*b*) turn its genes on.　(*c*) transcribe many genes simultaneously.　(*d*) protect its DNA from its own restriction enzymes.

13.11 An advantage of using yeasts rather than bacteria as recipient cells for recombination of eukaryotic DNA is that yeast can

(*a*) produce restriction enzymes.　(*b*) excise introns from the RNA transcript.　(*c*) remove methyl groups. (*d*) reproduce more rapidly.

13.12 The "sticky" ends of a fragmented DNA molecule are made of

(*a*) calcium salts.　(*b*) endonuclease.　(*c*) unpaired bases.　(*d*) methyl groups.

* Answers to Chapter 13 objective questions appear on page 102.

98

13.13 A fragment of DNA, cut by a restriction enzyme, forms bonds with other DNA molecules that have

(*a*) been fragmented by the same restriction enzyme. (*b*) sticky ends. (*c*) plasmid components. (*d*) attached methyl groups.

13.14 One way in which a eukaryotic chromosome differs from a bacterial chromosome is in having

(*a*) reverse transcriptase. (*b*) introns. (*c*) start and stop signals. (*d*) thymine instead of uracil.

13.15 The formation of covalent bonds between deoxyribose of one DNA fragment and phosphate of another DNA fragment (i.e., phosphodiester bonds) is facilitated by

(*a*) DNA ligase. (*b*) permease. (*c*) DNA phosphodiesterase. (*d*) endonuclease.

13.16 Each restriction enzyme cleaves a molecule only at

(*a*) methyl groups. (*b*) the ends of genes. (*c*) a particular nucleotide sequence. (*d*) the time of DNA replication.

13.17 Hybridization of mRNA with DNA can reveal which segments of the DNA are introns and which segments are exons. When the magnification is high enough to see the molecules, the introns appear as

(*a*) single-stranded loops in a double-stranded molecule. (*b*) separate fragments. (*c*) triple-stranded nucleic acid molecules. (*d*) Barr bodies.

13.18 In recombinant DNA technology, a plasmid vector must be cleaved by

(*a*) four separate enzymes. (*b*) modified DNA ligase. (*c*) a heated alkaline solution. (*d*) the same enzyme that cleaves the donor gene.

13.19 Bacterial resistance to antibiotics is a genetic trait carried in the bacterial

(*a*) intron. (*b*) chromosome. (*c*) plasmid. (*d*) centromere.

13.20 Recombinant DNA is a DNA molecule carrying a new combination of _____.

13.21 The two main vectors used in genetic engineering to carry genes into bacteria are _____ and _____.

13.22 A laboratory technique for separating molecules on the basis of size and electric charge, by measuring their rate of movement through an electric field, is _____.

13.23 Recombinant DNA research uses mostly prokaryotic _____ and eukaryotic _____ as recipient cells, because they reproduce rapidly under laboratory conditions.

13.24 Copy DNA is synthesized in the laboratory from a template of _____, in which the _____ have been removed.

13.25 The enzyme that facilitates synthesis of copy DNA is _____, made naturally by _____.

13.26 The position of a probe on a chromosome is easily detected by marking the probe with _____.

13.27 A strain of bacteria is known to synthesize protein A. How can one isolate the gene that codes for this protein?

🐚 The gene for protein A can be isolated by means of a "shotgun" experiment, in which the genetic material of the bacteria is cut up, each fragment is inserted into a recipient bacterium that does not itself produce protein A, and the proteins synthesized after fragment incorporation are examined. Any recipient bacterium with a newly acquired ability to produce protein A carries a DNA fragment with the gene for protein A. Details of the experimental procedure are described below.

All the genetic material within the bacteria that make protein A is cut into pieces by one of the 500 or so known restriction enzymes, each of which cleaves DNA at a certain base sequence where there is symmetry (see Fig. 13.1*a*). Plasmids taken from other bacteria are purified and cut by the same restriction enzyme as was used to fragment the donor DNA (Fig. 13.1*b*). Thus, the donor fragment has unpaired bases that are complementary to unpaired bases in the plasmid. Hydrogen bonds form between these bases (Fig. 13.1*c*) and, after addition of DNA ligase, covalent bonds form between the sugar and phosphate components of the fragment and plasmid. The result is a set of plasmid vectors—circular DNA molecules composed of plasmids and donor fragments. One of the vectors contains the gene for protein A.

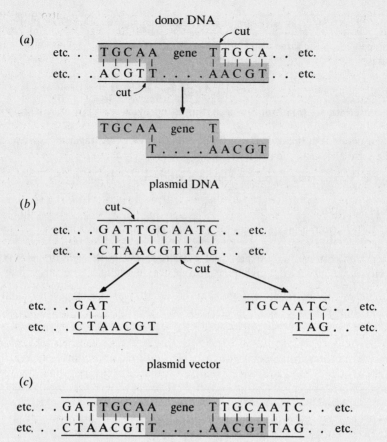

donor DNA

(a)

etc. . . TGCAA   gene   TTGCA . . etc.

etc. . . ACGTT . . . . AACGT . . etc.

cut

plasmid DNA

(b)

cut

etc. . . GATTGCAATC . . etc.

etc. . . CTAACGTTAG . . etc.

cut

etc. . . GAT   TGCAATC . . etc.

etc. . . CTAACGT   TAG . . etc.

plasmid vector

(c)

etc. . . GATTGCAA   gene   TTGCAATC . . etc.

etc. . . CTAACGTT . . . . AACGTTAG . . etc.

Fig. 13.1. Construction of the plasmid vector. (*a*) The donor DNA is fragmented into genes by a restriction enzyme, which cuts the molecule at a particular symmetrical sequence. The enzyme used here cuts after the sequence ACGT which appears reading right-to-left on the top strand and left-to-right on the bottom strand of the donor DNA. (*b*) The plasmid is cleaved by using the same restriction enzyme, which cuts after the same sequence. (*c*) The donor DNA is joined with the plasmid as complementary bases form bonds with each other.

Recipient bacteria, with no plasmids of their own and without the ability to make protein A, are immersed in a weak solution of calcium chloride to make their membranes more permeable to plasmids. Each kind of plasmid vector is mixed with recipient bacteria in a separate container, and the bacteria are allowed time to incorporate the plasmids and to reproduce. A clone of identical bacteria, carrying copies of the same fragment of donor DNA, grows in each container, and the clone's proteins are examined. The clone that produces protein A carries plasmids with the gene for protein A. This gene can then be chemically isolated and its properties analyzed.

13.28   How can one find out whether human cells have a particular gene known to occur in reptiles?

☙   Human cells that produce the protein coded for by the gene have, of course, the gene for it. But if the gene is turned off (i.e., not expressed) in the cells, then its presence is more difficult to detect. A DNA probe can be used to test for the presence of an unexpressed gene.

The DNA probe is prepared by first isolating messenger RNA, complementary to the particular gene, from reptilian cells that produce the protein coded for by the gene. The mRNA, placed in a solution with reverse transcriptase (obtained from retroviruses) and radioactive (^{32}P) nucleotides, serves as a template for synthesis of copy DNA—a single-stranded, radioactive molecule of DNA with a nucleotide sequence complementary to the mRNA sequence, and therefore identical (except for the lack of introns, which were removed during RNA processing in the reptilian cell) to the gene under study. Ribonuclease is added to the solution to digest the mRNA, leaving only the newly synthesized strand of radioactive DNA. This molecule is the DNA probe.

The probe is added to a solution of human chromosomes that have been heat-treated to split the double-stranded DNA molecules into single-stranded molecules. If the reptilian gene is present, then the DNA probe will bond with its complementary sequence of bases to form a double-stranded hybrid molecule. (The introns in the human

DNA will form loops; they will not pair with the probe, since there are no introns in the processed mRNA.) Radioactive material within the human chromosomes is evidence that human cells carry the reptilian gene.

13.29   In the recombination DNA experiments, how are clones of bacteria that have incorporated the donor gene isolated from clones without the donor gene?

     Three methods are used to isolate bacteria that have taken up the donor gene. First, the bacterial clones can be tested for the gene product. An enzyme is detected by its activity; a structural protein is detected by its adherence to a specific antibody. Second, a nucleic acid probe, as described in Question 13.28, can be used to detect the gene in the bacteria. Third, a plasmid vector can be used that carries genes for obvious traits in the bacteria. This third method, which is simple and often used, is described below.

     Plasmids used in recombinant DNA experiments to carry donor genes often carry, in addition, one or more genes that produce conspicuous traits in bacteria. A recipient bacterium that exhibits one of these traits must have the plasmid that carries the gene for the trait and, most likely, the donor gene as well.

     Resistance to antibiotics, a trait conferred by genes in a type of plasmid called the R plasmid, is often used to screen for recombinant clones. The donor gene is placed into an R plasmid, say the one carrying a gene for resistance to the antibiotic ampicillin. After exposure of the bacterial population to this plasmid, ampicillin is added to the culture; all bacteria without the plasmid die, leaving only those that have incorporated the plasmid with genes for ampicillin resistance and, presumably, the donor gene.

     To be certain that the remaining bacteria actually carry the donor gene, a plasmid can be used that confers resistance to both ampicillin and a second antibiotic—tetracycline, for example. The plasmid is treated with a restriction enzyme that cuts through nucleotides within the tetracycline-resistant gene, and the donor gene is inserted there. Then, after removing from the culture all bacteria without the plasmid (by adding ampicillin), the remaining bacteria that have the donor gene in their plasmids are isolated by adding tetracycline to the culture. A bacterium resistant to tetracycline has an intact gene—one not interrupted by insertion of the donor gene—for this trait, whereas a bacterium that is not resistant has the donor gene and does not grow well in the presence of tetracycline. Its colonies can be identified, removed, and grown in a tetracycline-free environment.

13.30   A cell is known to carry five genes that code for enzymes of the same metabolic pathway. How can one find out if all five genes are located next to one another on the same chromosome?

     DNA probes, consisting of single-stranded copy DNA, are made from mRNA transcripts of the five genes, as described in Question 13.28. When these radioactive probes are added to a solution of heat-treated (denatured) DNA from the cell under study, they will pair with complementary base sequences in the cell's chromosomes. The distribution of radioactivity in the chromosomes reflects the distribution of the five genes. If all of the radioactivity appears in a single location, then one can conclude that all five of the genes are positioned next to one another on the same chromosome.

APPLICATIONS AND ETHICS OF GENETIC ENGINEERING

13.31   The first human hormone produced by recombinant DNA technology was

     (*a*) estrogen.   (*b*) testosterone.   (*c*) thyroxin.   (*d*) insulin.

13.32   Human growth hormone is now produced in large quantities by recombinant DNA technology. The previous source of this hormone, for treating pituitary dwarfs, was

     (*a*) chemical laboratories.   (*b*) mutant mice.   (*c*) human cadavers.   (*d*) pig cadavers.

13.33   Resistance to antibiotics is a genetic trait that spreads naturally from one type of bacterium to

     (*a*) almost any other type of bacterium.   (*b*) another bacterium of the same strain.   (*c*) eukaryotic cells of all types. (*d*) any other cell containing copy DNA.

13.34   In gene therapy, DNA is inserted into a cell to compensate for

     (*a*) the absence of plasmids.   (*b*) mutant alleles.   (*c*) holes in the DNA made by viruses.   (*d*) the lack of copy DNA.

13.35   The science of improving physical and mental qualities of humans, through control of the factors influencing heredity, is called _____.

13.36   Under laboratory conditions, bacteria that are not resistant to antibiotics can be made resistant by placing them in a solution containing _____ from dead, resistant bacteria.

13.37 Strains of bacteria now used in gene-splicing experiments cannot invade natural environments, because they are _____ forms that can only _____ under laboratory conditions.

13.38 How is recombinant DNA technology used to map eukaryotic chromosomes?

⊛ Eukaryotic chromosomes are mapped by in situ hybridization. Radioactive DNA probes are made from the mRNA of a cell, and the probes allowed to form hybrids with denatured DNA in the eukaryotic chromosomes (see Question 13.28). Radioactivity, detected by autoradiography and staining, on the chromosomes reflects the position of the gene that codes for the mRNA.

13.39 Suppose your hypothesis is that a particular kind of cell makes a particular protein, but in very small quantities. How can you confirm your hypothesis?

⊛ The first step is to harvest all of the messenger RNA made by the cell type. Copy DNA is then made from all of the mRNA molecules, as described in Question 13.28, and the single-stranded DNA molecules are allowed to replicate (in the presence of DNA polymerase) into double-stranded DNA molecules. Finally, these newly formed DNA molecules are inserted into bacteria, via plasmids, and their protein products are analyzed. If the particular protein under study is produced, then your hypothesis is confirmed.

13.40 Antibiotics are given to pigs and other domestic animals to help them grow better under crowded conditions. Why does such nonmedical use of antibiotics concern many people?

⊛ Any use of antibiotics increases the abundance of bacteria that are resistant to antibiotics and decreases our chances of controlling bacterial infections with these medicines.

Resistance to antibiotics is a bacterial trait coded for by genes within plasmids (the R plasmids). The trait is passed from bacterium to bacterium during conjugation, transformation, and transduction. A bacterium with such a plasmid is not killed by one or more forms of antibiotics, and so it multiplies in the presence of the antibiotic while the nonresistant forms die. As we have used these "miracle" drugs during the past 50 years, we have selected for strains of bacteria that carry the resistant genes.

When domestic animals are fed antibiotics, bacteria within these animals are killed if they do not have the plasmid with genes for resistance to antibiotics and flourish if they do have the plasmids. In time, large populations of antibiotic-resistant bacteria develop within these animals and their environments. Their plasmids, which carry the genes for resistance, are transferred to other kinds of bacteria, including those that live within humans. As more and more of our bacteria have these genes, it becomes increasingly more difficult to treat the diseases they cause. We have to continue to discover new antibiotics as our old ones become ineffective. Antibiotics are our main weapon against bacterial diseases, and many people feel it is unwise to jeopardize human health by feeding antibiotics to domestic animals just to make them grow faster.

Answers to Objective Questions

13.1 *d*	**13.13** *a*	**13.24** mRNA; introns
13.2 *d*	**13.14** *b*	**13.25** reverse transcriptase;
13.3 *a*	**13.15** *a*	retroviruses
13.4 *a*	**13.16** *c*	**13.26** radioactive atoms
13.5 *c*	**13.17** *a*	**13.31** *d*
13.6 *d*	**13.18** *d*	**13.32** *c*
13.7 *c*	**13.19** *c*	**13.33** *a*
13.8 *a*	**13.20** genes	**13.34** *b*
13.9 *a*	**13.21** plasmids; bacteriophages	**13.35** eugenics
13.10 *d*	**13.22** electrophoresis	**13.36** plasmids
13.11 *b*	**13.23** bacteria; yeasts	**13.37** mutant; survive
13.12 *c*		

CHAPTER 14
Meiosis and Life Cycles

ASEXUAL AND SEXUAL REPRODUCTION*

14.1 Fertilization is the

(*a*) storage of nutrients for the offspring.   (*b*) union of an egg and a sperm.   (*c*) process by which a gamete is formed.   (*d*) division of cells during development.

14.2 The number of chromosomes in a fertilized egg is

(*a*) half as many as in an unfertilized egg.   (*b*) the same as in a sperm.   (*c*) twice the number as in a sperm.   (*d*) twice the number as in a skin cell.

14.3 The somatic cells of each diploid organism all originated from a single

(*a*) gamete.   (*b*) autosome.   (*c*) chiasma.   (*d*) zygote.

14.4 If at the end of meiosis, the four daughter cells have four chromosomes, how many chromosomes were in the mother cell?

(*a*) 2;   (*b*) 4;   (*c*) 8;   (*d*) 16

14.5 The multicellular organism *Hydra* reproduces by budding. This is an example of

(*a*) asexual reproduction.   (*b*) sexual reproduction.   (*c*) syngamy.   (*d*) meiosis.

14.6 When a cell has two sets of chromosomes, one inherited from each parent, the cell is _____. When the cell has half the number of chromosomes of the parent cell, it is _____.

14.7 When a single parent supplies all its offspring's DNA, this is _____.

14.8 Chromosomes that are similar in size and shape and contain genes for the same traits are called homologous chromosomes, or _____.

14.9 In humans, meiosis occurs during the production of _____.

14.10 Asexual reproduction takes place when an organism reproduces by _____.

14.11 What are the advantages and disadvantages of asexual reproduction?

Asexual reproduction takes place when a single parent produces offspring that are genetically the same as itself. By contrast, in sexual reproduction there are two parents and both contribute genes to each of their offspring. These offspring, then, carry sets of genes that are different from the sets carried by every other offspring and from the sets carried by either parent.

When biologists speak of advantages or disadvantages of any trait, such as type of reproduction, they are referring to its contribution to reproductive success, which is evaluated by the number of surviving offspring an individual organism produces in its lifetime. By this criterion, it can be said that asexual reproduction is an advantage to populations living in uniform, stable, and thus predictable environments and, obversely, a disadvantage to populations living in changing, unstable, and thus less predictable environments.

Asexual reproduction is an advantage in stable environments because each offspring receives a copy of a set of successful genes—genes from a parent who has survived and reproduced under the same conditions. Also, with each member of a population being a potential parent, the population can reproduce very rapidly when it encounters ideal conditions for its genes. This is why bacteria are able to rapidly spoil meat or produce infections. Reproducing asexually by binary fission, bacteria in an ideal environment can reproduce roughly once every 20

* Answers to Chapter 14 objective questions appear on page 110.

minutes. Thus, within six hours, a single original bacterium in a suitable medium will have become the progenitor of 500,000 new, identical bacteria.

Asexual reproduction, which utilizes binary fission or mitosis, is found in a large variety of forms at all levels of biologic organization: cell division in unicellular bacteria and protista; vegetative reproduction in multicellular forms, such as the budding of *Hydra* or the development of new strawberry plants from runners; and partheno-genesis in multicellular organisms, in which a female produces a diploid egg that develops without being fertilized by a sperm. In multicellular forms, asexual reproduction can be an advantage if the individuals of a population are not likely to find mates easily, say in aquatic, sessile (i.e., attached to the bottom) forms or where the population density is low.

The same feature, genetic uniformity, that makes asexual reproduction an advantage in stable environments makes it a disadvantage in unpredictable environments. Under such conditions, the genetic variation produced by the recombination processes of sexual reproduction (see Question 14.12) is advantageous, because such recombination makes it more likely that some members of the population will have the combination of genes needed to survive and reproduce under the new conditions.

14.12 Why is it true for all sexually reproducing organisms that there is always an alternation between meiosis and fertilization?

⚉ In sexually reproducing organisms, there is always an alternation between meiosis and fertilization, i.e., between the separation of homologous chromosomes by meiosis to produce haploid gametes and their joining by fertilization (or *syngamy*) to produce diploid zygotes. The timing of these critical events differs in different life cycles (see Question 14.40), but the alternation is always there.

As was indicated in Question 14.11, the advantage of sexual reproduction is the genetic variation it provides for a population being challenged by an unpredictable environment. Genetic variation is produced by both meiosis and fertilization. During meiosis, variation is produced by the random placement of the homologous chromosomes (a process called *independent assortment*) at the spindle equator during metaphase I and by the random exchange of genetic material between homologous chromosomes (called *crossing-over*) during prophase I. This variation is then greatly increased by fertilization, when new pairings of homologues occur. Thus, in humans there are roughly eight million possible gametes for each meiosis from independent assortment alone, and with each mating there are roughly 70 trillion possible zygotes. Beyond this, the random and unpredictable outcomes of crossing-over tremendously increase the amount of genetic variation possible with each mating.

Another function of meiosis in sexual reproduction is to keep the number of chromosomes constant for the species. Without meiosis, in which the number of chromosomes is halved, each successive fertilization would *double* the number of chromosomes, until finally a cell would have little room for anything but chromosomes. In humans, for example, starting with the diploid number of 46, the next zygote would have 92 chromosomes, the next 184, and so on.

PHASES OF MEIOSIS

14.13 In meiosis, the chromosomes are replicated during

(*a*) interkinesis. (*b*) prophase II. (*c*) interphase. (*d*) prophase I.

14.14 At what phase of meiosis are there two cells, each with sister chromatids aligned at the spindle equator?

(*a*) Metaphase II; (*b*) Metaphase I; (*c*) Anaphase I; (*d*) Anaphase II

14.15 At what phase of meiosis are there two cells, each with separated sister chromatids that have been moved to opposite spindle poles?

(*a*) Anaphase II; (*b*) Anaphase I; (*c*) Telophase I; (*d*) Telophase II

14.16 At what phase of meiosis are homologous chromosomes separated?

(*a*) Prophase I; (*b*) Prophase II; (*c*) Anaphase I; (*d*) Anaphase II

14.17 The meiotic process by which homologues are paired during prophase I is called

(*a*) chiasma. (*b*) interkinesis. (*c*) crossing-over. (*d*) synapsis.

14.18 Crossing-over occurs during

(*a*) prophase II. (*b*) prophase I. (*c*) interphase. (*d*) interkinesis.

14.19 If there were four chromosomes present during prophase I, how many chromosomes are there in each cell at the end of anaphase II?

(*a*) 2; (*b*) 4; (*c*) 8; (*d*) 16

14.20 The points at which crossing-over has taken place between homologous chromosomes are called

(*a*) chiasmata. (*b*) synaptonemal complexes. (*c*) centromeres. (*d*) protein axes.

14.21 During what phase of meiosis do tetrads form?

(*a*) Anaphase I; (*b*) Prophase II; (*c*) Prophase I; (*d*) Anaphase II

14.22 Refer to Fig. 14.1 and identify the four phases of meiosis that are diagramed for a cell with four chromosomes.

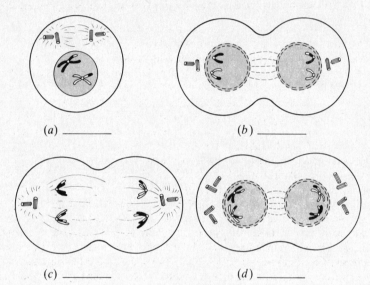

(*a*) _____   (*b*) _____

(*c*) _____   (*d*) _____   **Fig. 14.1**

14.23 Meiosis consists of _____ nuclear divisions, producing _____ haploid cells.

14.24 Genetic recombination results from crossing-over between _____ chromatids of _____ chromosomes.

14.25 The function of meiosis I is to separate _____. The function of meiosis II is to separate _____.

14.26 Meiosis I produces two _____ cells, each with _____ chromosomes. Meiosis II produces four _____ cells, each with _____ chromosomes.

14.27 The transition between meiosis I and meiosis II is called _____.

14.28 What is accomplished in each phase of meiosis in animal cells?

🐚 Meiosis, a process involving two consecutive cell divisions (Fig. 14.2), is an essential component of sexual reproduction. It produces haploid gametes from diploid parental cells, with each gamete containing a unique mixture of the parental genes. Each of the two cell divisions has phases that superficially resemble the phases of mitosis, but actually quite different events are occurring.

Before the first cell division (meiosis I), there is an interphase period comparable to the interphase prior to mitosis. And, as with mitosis, chromosome replication occurs only during this phase.

Many things happen in the first phase of meiosis I, called prophase I, which is why this phase usually lasts for over 90 percent of the total time required for meiosis. During this time, homologous chromosomes (each consisting

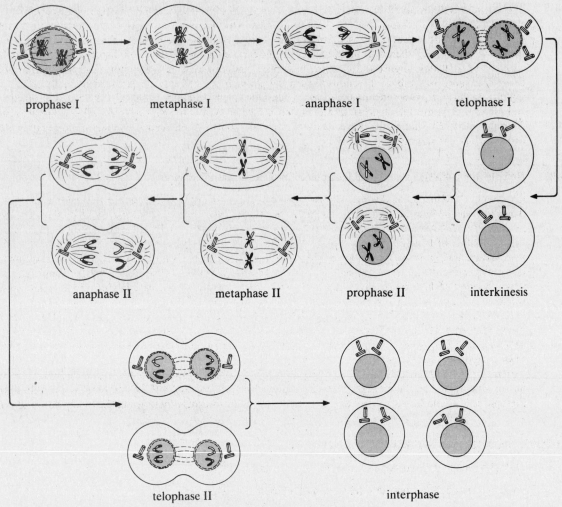

prophase I   metaphase I   anaphase I   telophase I

anaphase II   metaphase II   prophase II   interkinesis

telophase II   interphase

Fig. 14.2. Phases of meiosis.

of two sister chromatids) come together as pairs, in a process called *synapsis*, to form a four-chromatid structure called a *tetrad*. This structure is precisely aligned so that homologous genes are opposite each other. At this point, *crossing-over* takes place; this is a process in which genetic information is exchanged between nonsister chromatids of homologous pairs of chromosomes. The X-shaped sites of such crossovers are called *chiasmata*. As crossing-over takes place, the cell is preparing for nuclear division. The nuclear envelope and nucleoli disperse; centriole pairs separate and spindles form between them; and kinetochore microtubules develop from each centromere.

In the next phase of meiosis I—metaphase I—the tetrads move to the equator of the cell (the *metaphase plate*). At the equator, a process known as *independent assortment* randomly positions the homologues from the maternal and paternal lines relative to the two poles of the cell, one on each side of the equator. At this point, the kinetochore microtubules expand from each chromosome in opposite directions toward the nearest pole.

Next, in anaphase I of meiosis I, the spindle and the kinetochore microtubules interact to separate the homologous chromosomes. The centromeres joining sister chromatids do not split, but instead entire double-chromatid chromosomes are moved toward the two poles. At this point, *cytokinesis* begins, which will eventually result in two haploid cells, each with either the maternal or paternal homologue of each type of chromosome.

The final phase of meiosis I—telophase I—differs among species. In some, after the separation of homologous chromosomes is complete and the two new cells form, nuclear membranes develop around the chromosomes and a short interim period, called *interkinesis*, ensues between meiosis I and meiosis II. In other species meiosis II begins immediately.

Whether or not there is interkinesis, the result of meiosis I is two haploid cells from the original diploid cell, with each haploid cell containing one of the original pair of homologous chromosomes. The chromosomes in each haploid cell are in the replicated form, with two chromatids attached at a centromere. The two chromatids are actually no longer sister chromatids, since crossing-over has made them unique hybrids.

If the function of meiosis I is to separate homologous chromosomes, then the function of meiosis II is to separate the sister (now hybrid) chromatids of each chromosome. The phases of meiosis II, the second cell division, are much more similar to the phases of mitosis. In prophase II in each of the two cells, the centrioles separate, the spindle begins to form, and, if there was interkinesis, the nuclear membrane and nucleoli disperse. In metaphase II, the chromosomes become aligned on the metaphase plate, and now kinetochore microtubules from each centromere move simultaneously in both directions toward the poles. In anaphase II, the centromeres split and the sister (hybrid) chromatids, now individual chromosomes, move toward the two poles. Cytokinesis is completed by the end of the final phase, telophase II, and the result is four haploid daughter cells from a single parental diploid cell. Each daughter cell has a complete set of chromosomes, and each set is unique because of independent assortment and crossing-over during prophase of meiosis I.

14.29   How does metaphase of mitosis differ from the two metaphases of meiosis?

In mitosis (Chapter 9) there is a single nuclear division forming two exact copies of a parent cell, with each of the cells receiving exact duplicates of the parental chromosomes. In meiosis (Question 14.28) there are two consecutive cell divisions forming four haploid cells from a diploid parent cell, and each of the four new cells has a unique mixture of parental genes.

In metaphase of mitosis, the replicated chromosomes line up one by one on the metaphase plate, with kinetochore microtubules extending from each centromere in both directions toward the poles. Then, in anaphase, the centromeres of each chromosome split and the spindle pulls identical, single-chromatid chromosomes toward the two poles.

In metaphase I of meiosis I, by contrast, the replicated homologous chromosomes line up as pairs on the metaphase plate, and kinetochore microtubules extend from each centromere in one direction only—toward the nearest pole. Then, in anaphase I, the homologous chromosomes are separated, being moved by the spindle toward the two poles.

In metaphase II of meiosis II, in each of the two cells produced by meiosis I, the double-chromatid chromosomes line up one by one on the metaphase plate in preparation for separation of the chromatids in anaphase II. Metaphase II of meiosis II looks just like metaphase of mitosis except there are half as many chromosomes.

MEIOSIS IN DIFFERENT LIFE CYCLES

14.30   In oogenesis, the haploid egg that is fertilized by a sperm is the

(*a*) ootid.   (*b*) primary oocyte.   (*c*) secondary oocyte.   (*d*) ovum.

14.31   In oogenesis, when a diploid cell in the ovary undergoes meiosis, how many ova result?

(*a*) 1;   (*b*) 2;   (*c*) 3;   (*d*) 4

14.32   In oogenesis, the second meiotic division does not occur until after _____.

14.33   In the plant life cycle, the multicellular diploid stage is called a _____ and the multicellular haploid stage is called a _____.

14.34   Meiosis in the sporophyte stage of the plant life cycle provides _____ cells called _____.

14.35   In diploid male animals, the process of gamete formation is called _____, whereas in diploid females, the process is called _____.

14.36   Refer to Fig. 14.3 and identify the labeled structures in the stages of spermatogenesis.

14.37   Refer to Fig. 14.4 and identify the labeled structures in the stages of oogenesis.

14.38   In plants such as ferns, meiosis produces _____ spores, which divide mitotically and then develop into _____ multicellular plants.

14.39   In all vertebrates, meiosis takes place in the _____ of the male and the _____ of the female.

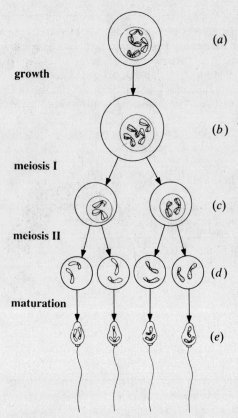

growth

meiosis I

meiosis II

maturation

Fig. 14.3. Spermatogenesis.

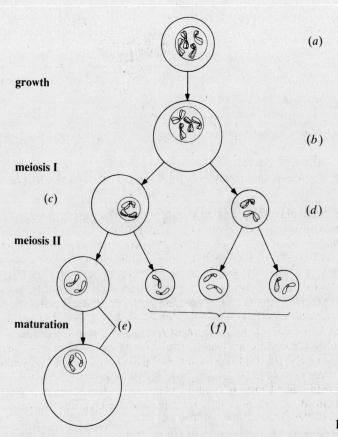

growth

meiosis I

meiosis II

maturation

Fig. 14.4. Oogenesis.

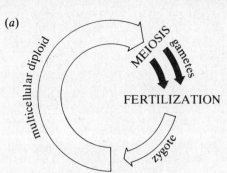

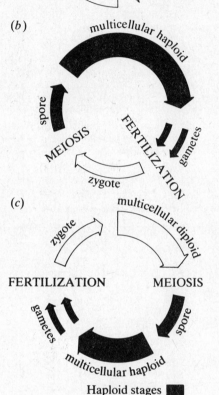

Haploid stages ■
Diploid stages □

Fig. 14.5. The life cycles of (a) an animal,
(b) an alga or fungus, and (c) a plant.

14.40 Discuss life cycles in which the multicellular forms are: (a) always diploid; (b) always haploid; and, (c) both haploid and diploid.

🐚 (a) The pattern of alternation between diploid and haploid cells varies among multicellular organisms. In all animals, the diploid zygote undergoes a series of mitotic divisions right after fertilization to produce an adult multicellular organism composed of diploid cells. Prior to reproduction by the adult, the number of chromosomes within the reproductive cells is halved by meiosis to yield haploid gametes—sperm or eggs—which unite to form a diploid zygote. This familiar life cycle, in which haploid cells occur very briefly as gametes, is diagramed in Fig. 14.5a. (b) Some algae and fungi have an opposite type of life cycle, as diagramed in Fig. 14.5b, with adults being composed of haploid cells. The adult haploid organism produces gametes by mitosis, rather than by meiosis, and two gametes unite at fertilization to form a diploid zygote. Immediately after it is formed, the zygote undergoes meiosis to produce haploid cells, called spores rather than gametes because they divide by mitosis to develop a multicellular individual, the haploid adult in this case. Diploid cells appear very briefly, as zygotes, in the life cycle. (c) Most plants have life cycles in which both haploid and diploid multicellular individuals are present, as diagramed in Fig. 14.5c. In ferns, the two types appear as separate individuals—a large, conspicuous diploid plant alternating with a small, inconspicuous haploid plant. Meiosis occurs within certain cells of the diploid fern to produce haploid spores that drop to the ground and, after a series of mitotic divisions, develop into tiny haploid individuals—the gametophytes—which live in the soil beneath the larger diploid parent. Each gametophyte produces sperm and/or eggs by mitosis and releases them into the moist soil. A sperm from one plant fertilizes an egg from another; the resulting zygote divides repeatedly by mitosis to form an adult diploid fern—the sporophyte. Mosses also appear in both haploid and diploid multicellular forms, but, in contrast with ferns, the more conspicuous part of the life cycle of a moss is a plant formed of haploid cells.

Flowering plants and conifers have life cycles similar to ferns and mosses, except that the haploid spores remain on the adult diploid plant and, after multiplying by mitosis, develop into tiny multicellular haploid gametophytes (the pollen grains and embryo sacs), which remain as parts of the adult diploid plant. The gametophytes produce gametes—the sperm nucleus and egg—by mitosis, and a diploid zygote forms when a sperm nucleus fertilizes an egg. The zygote divides repeatedly by mitosis, and at some point leaves the adult plant as a seed to complete its development into a diploid adult.

Answers to Objective Questions

14.1 b

14.2 c

14.3 d

14.4 c

14.5 a

14.6 diploid; haploid

14.7 asexual reproduction

14.8 homologues

14.9 gametes

14.10 binary fission or mitosis

14.13 c

14.14 a

14.15 a

14.16 c

14.17 d

14.18 b

14.19 b

14.20 a

14.21 c

14.22 (a) prophase II; (b) telophase II; (c) anaphase I; (d) telophase I

14.23 two; four

14.24 nonsister; homologous

14.25 homologous chromosomes; sister chromatids

14.26 haploid; double-chromatid; haploid; single-chromatid

14.27 interkinesis

14.30 d

14.31 a

14.32 fertilization

14.33 sporophyte; gametophyte

14.34 haploid; spores

14.35 spermatogenesis; oogenesis

14.36 (a) spermatogonium; (b) primary spermatocyte; (c) secondary spermatocyte; (d) spermatid; (e) sperm

14.37 (a) oogonium; (b) primary oocyte; (c) secondary oocyte; (d) first polar body; (e) ovum; (f) polar bodies

14.38 haploid; haploid

14.39 testes; ovaries

CHAPTER 15

Mendelian Inheritance

IDEAS PRIOR TO MENDEL*

15.1   Both Jean-Baptiste de Lamarck and Charles Darwin believed in the idea that particles come together from all parts of the body to form eggs and semen. This theory is called

(*a*) pangenesis.   (*b*) spontaneous generation.   (*c*) Mendelian inheritance.   (*d*) sexual inheritance.

15.2   Some people thought they could see in a human sperm a homunculus or

(*a*) set of genes.   (*b*) set of homologous chromosomes.   (*c*) miniature human.   (*d*) Y chromosome.

15.3   Advocates of the homunculus idea believed characteristics of a child were transferred from

(*a*) the mother only.   (*b*) the father only.   (*c*) both mother and father.   (*d*) nonliving things.

15.4   Followers of Régnier de Graaf (discoverer of the ovarian follicle, in the 1670s) believed characteristics of a child were transferred from

(*a*) the mother only.   (*b*) the father only.   (*c*) both mother and father.   (*d*) nonliving things.

15.5   Biologists first understood that both parents contribute to the characteristics of offspring in the

(*a*) 12th century.   (*b*) 15th century.   (*c*) early 1800s.   (*d*) early 1900s.

15.6   In the 19th century, prior to Mendel's work, many people believed in the blending theory of inheritance. According to this theory,

(*a*) genes from somatic cells mix with genes from gametes.   (*b*) hereditary materials from both parents become permanently mixed in their offspring.   (*c*) somatic cells blend into sperm or eggs.   (*d*) nonliving things blend to form living things.

15.7   Aristotle believed that traits are inherited by virtue of particles called pangenes coming together from all parts of the body to form male and female "semen." This theory is known as _____.

15.8   Prior to the 16th century, many people believed that parents were not essential to the development of some forms of life. This belief, disproved in 1668 by F. Redi, is called _____.

15.9   According to the blending theory, matings between black animals and white animals would produce _____ offspring, and when these offspring mated with each other their progeny would be _____.

MENDEL'S WORK

15.10   Mendel published the results of his experiments in

(*a*) 1568.   (*b*) 1773.   (*c*) 1866.   (*d*) 1921.

15.11   Mendel started his experiments with pure strains of peas. A pure strain was developed by removing all

(*a*) female plants.   (*b*) male plants.   (*c*) atypical plants in each generation.   (*d*) weak plants.

15.12   The offspring of matings between two pure strains are called

(*a*) hybrids.   (*b*) mutants.   (*c*) the P generation.   (*d*) the F_2 generation.

15.13   One of Mendel's pure strains of pea plants had green peas. How many different kinds of *eggs* could such a plant produce with regard to pea color?

(*a*) 1;   (*b*) 2;   (*c*) 4;   (*d*) 8

* Answers to Chapter 15 objective questions appear on page 118.

15.14 One pure strain of pea plants developed by Mendel had yellow peas and another strain had green peas. All the offspring from crosses between these two parental (P) strains of plants had yellow peas. In these plants, the allele for yellow pea color is

(*a*) recessive to the allele for green color. (*b*) dominant over the allele for green color. (*c*) epistatic over other alleles. (*d*) expressed only in gametes.

15.15 How many different kinds of *eggs* are produced by the F_1 offspring from a cross between a pure strain of plants with yellow peas and a pure strain of plants with green peas?

(*a*) 1; (*b*) 2; (*c*) 4; (*d*) 8

15.16 If the P, or parental, generation was a pure strain with green peas crossed with a pure strain with yellow peas, and their offspring (the F_1 generation) were self-pollinated, then the F_2 generation would be

(*a*) all plants with green peas. (*b*) all plants with yellow peas. (*c*) half plants with green peas and half plants with yellow peas. (*d*) $\frac{3}{4}$ plants with yellow peas and $\frac{1}{4}$ plants with green peas.

15.17 An organism with two copies of the same allele is

(*a*) homozygous for that trait. (*b*) homologous for the allele. (*c*) heterozygous for that trait. (*d*) heterologous for the allele.

15.18 An organism with two different alleles is

(*a*) homozygous for that trait. (*b*) homologous for the allele. (*c*) heterozygous for that trait. (*d*) heterologous for the allele.

15.19 A woman without dimples mates with a man who has dimples and who is known to be heterozygous for the trait. What is the chance their first child will have dimples?

(*a*) One in four; (*b*) One in two; (*c*) Three out of four; (*d*) It is certain

15.20 If the first child of the couple described in Question 15.19 had dimples, then what is the chance that their second child will have dimples?

(*a*) No chance; (*b*) One in four; (*c*) One in two; (*d*) Three out of four

15.21 A testcross is done to find out

(*a*) the genotype of an individual by examining the phenotypes of its offspring from a particular mating. (*b*) the genotype of an individual by testing for its DNA content (electrophoresis). (*c*) whether a mating is fertile. (*d*) whether two species can interbreed.

15.22 In Mendel's crosses beginning with two pure strains of pea plants, one with yellow peas (Y/Y) and the other with green peas (y/y), the test cross was done between F_2 offspring with yellow peas and a pure strain of plants with the genotype

(*a*) Y/Y. (*b*) y/y. (*c*) Y/y. (*d*) YG.

15.23 A testcross distinguishes between

(*a*) two homozygous forms. (*b*) a homozygous dominant and the heterozygous form. (*c*) two heterozygous forms. (*d*) a homozygous recessive and a heterozygous form.

15.24 The allele for black hair color (B) is dominant over the allele for white hair color (b) in guinea pigs. A test cross between a black male and a white female produced a litter of five black and one white guinea pigs. The genotype of the father is

(*a*) unknown, due to the small sample size. (*b*) B/B. (*c*) B/b. (*d*) b/b.

15.25 The allele for black hair color (B) is dominant over the allele for white hair color (b) in guinea pigs. A test cross between a black female and a white male produced a litter of six black guinea pigs. The genotype of the mother is

(*a*) unknown, due to the small sample size. (*b*) B/B. (*c*) B/b. (*d*) b/b.

15.26 In Mendel's experiments, there are two alleles of the gene that causes pea shape—R (round) and r (wrinkled)—and two alleles of the gene that causes plant height—T (tall) and t (short). How many different kinds of *eggs* are produced by a short plant with wrinkled peas?

(*a*) 1; (*b*) 2; (*c*) 4; (*d*) 8

15.27 When a pure strain of tall plants with round peas is crossed with a pure strain of short plants with wrinkled peas (see Question 15.26), what proportion of the F_1 generation will be short with wrinkled peas?

(*a*) 0; (*b*) $\frac{1}{16}$; (*c*) $\frac{1}{2}$; (*d*) $\frac{9}{16}$

15.28 When a pure strain of tall plants with round peas is crossed with a pure strain of short plants with wrinkled peas (see Question 15.26), how many different kinds of *eggs* can their offspring (the F_1 generation) produce?

(*a*) 1; (*b*) 2; (*c*) 4; (*d*) 8

15.29 When a pure strain of tall plants (T/T) with round peas (R/R) is crossed with a pure strain of short plants (t/t) with wrinkled peas (r/r), an F_1 generation is produced. When these F_1 plants self-pollinate, how many *genotypes* (with regard to the genes for height and pea shape) are produced in the F_2 generation?

(*a*) 4; (*b*) 6; (*c*) 9; (*d*) 16

15.30 When a pure strain of tall plants (T/T) with round peas (R/R) is crossed with a pure strain of short plants (t/t) with wrinkled peas (r/r), an F_1 generation is produced. When these F_1 plants self-pollinate, how many *phenotypes* (with regard to plant height and pea shape) are produced in the F_2 generation?

(*a*) 4; (*b*) 6; (*c*) 9; (*d*) 16

15.31 When a pure strain of tall plants (T/T) with round peas (R/R) is crossed with a pure strain of short plants (t/t) with wrinkled peas (r/r), an F_1 generation is produced. The alleles for short and wrinkled are recessive to those for tall and round, respectively. When these F_1 plants self-pollinate, what proportion of the F_2 generation is short with wrinkled peas?

(*a*) 0; (*b*) $\frac{1}{16}$; (*c*) $\frac{1}{2}$; (*d*) $\frac{9}{16}$

15.32 In watermelons, the allele for green color (G) is dominant over the allele for striped color (g) and the allele for short shape (S) is dominant over the allele for long shape (s). When long, striped watermelons are crossed with watermelons heterozygous for both traits, what proportion of the offspring are striped and short?

(*a*) 0; (*b*) $\frac{1}{4}$; (*c*) $\frac{1}{2}$; (*d*) $\frac{9}{16}$

15.33 How many different kinds of *gametes* can an organism of genotype A/a; B/B; C/c produce?

(*a*) 3; (*b*) 4; (*c*) 9; (*d*) 16

15.34 A trihybrid cross is made between two yeasts, both with genotypes A/a; B/b; C/c. What proportion of the offspring will be of genotype a/a; b/b; c/c?

(*a*) 0; (*b*) $\frac{1}{4}$; (*c*) $\frac{1}{16}$; (*d*) $\frac{1}{64}$

15.35 Now that we know the physical basis of inheritance, what is it that assorts independently, in keeping with the Law of Independent Assortment?

(*a*) Sister chromatids; (*b*) Homologous chromosomes; (*c*) Heterologous chromosomes; (*d*) Different genes on the same chromosome

15.36 Mendel studied a total of _____ traits in peas, each trait occurring in _____ different forms.

15.37 When parental plants (the P generation) are crossed, their hybrid offspring are the _____ generation. When hybrid plants self-fertilize, their offspring are the _____ generation.

15.38 Mendel concluded that each organism has _____ hereditary "factors" for each trait. They are now called _____ if different.

15.39 A plant with green peas has _____ dominant allele(s) and _____ recessive allele(s). A plant with yellow peas has either _____ dominant allele(s) and _____ recessive allele(s) or _____ dominant allele(s) and _____ recessive allele(s).

15.40 An organism's expressed traits is its _____, whereas its genetic makeup is its _____.

15.41 You can find out whether an organism is homozygous or heterozygous for a trait by carrying out a _____.

15.42 An event that is certain to occur has a probability of _____. An event that is certain not to occur has a probability of _____. The probability of getting a head when a two-sided coin is flipped is _____. A coin has been flipped four times and has come up heads every time. The probability it will come up tails on the fifth flip is _____. The probability of rolling a six with a six-sided die is _____. The probability of drawing an ace of spades from a deck of 52 cards is _____. The probability of drawing a card other than the ace of spades is _____.

15.43 When Mendel cross-pollinated plants of two purebred strains, all the offspring were _____ in their phenotypes.

15.44 A trait present in the P generation, absent in the F_1 generation, and present in the F_2 generation is caused by a gene that is _____ to its allele. A trait present in every generation (does not skip generations) is caused by a gene that is _____ to its allele.

15.45 Two or more forms of a gene are called _____. A diploid cell can have only _____ of these forms.

15.46 In the abbreviation A/a, the slash indicates that the two copies of a gene are on _____.

15.47 From the Punnett square given below, the genotype of the mother must be _____ and the genotype of the father must be _____.

		male gametes			
		$A B$	$A b$	$a B$	$a b$
female gametes	?	$A/a; B/B$	$A/a; B/b$	$a/a; B/B$	$a/a; B/b$

15.48 How did Mendel control the parentage of his experimental plants?

⚛ Mendel controlled the parentage of his pea plants by controlling the flow of pollen (which contains the sperm nuclei) to the eggs. The flower of a pea contains both male and female sex organs, as shown in Fig. 15.1a. The male organ, or *stamen*, produces the pollen. Under natural conditions, the pollen either moves a short distance from the stamen to the female parts of the same flower or is carried by an insect vector (e.g., bee) from the stamen of one flower to the female organ of another flower on another plant. The female organ, or *pistil*, produces the egg, which remains in the pistil during fertilization and seed development.

The petals of a pea flower are folded over the stamen and pistil (Fig. 15.1b), so that entry into the flower is difficult for all insects except a few kinds of bees especially adapted for moving the petals out of their way. Most often pea plants fertilize themselves—the egg of a flower is fertilized by pollen from the same flower. Seeds of a self-fertilized pea plant develop into normal, reproducing adults.

Mendel guaranteed self-fertilization in some of his experiments (development of pure strains; reproduction of the F_1 generation) by placing bags over the flowers to make sure no insects got into the flowers and deposited pollen from another plant. When he wanted cross-pollination—to have two parents rather than one (for matings between two pure strains)—he cut off the immature stamens of one flower (restricting it to a female role) and carried pollen to this flower from the flower of another plant (making it the male parent).

15.49 Under what conditions does Mendel's Law of Segregation apply?

⚛ Mendel's Law of Segregation states: (1) An organism has a pair of discrete factors (genes) for each inherited trait; (2) the pair of factors is segregated during the formation of gametes when copies of one factor go to half the gametes and copies of the other factor go to the rest, so that the fertilized egg has a pair of factors, one from each parental gamete; and (3) when the two factors of a pair are different, one is dominant (fully expressed) and the other is recessive (not expressed). The Law of Segregation is Mendel's most important contribution to biology, because it introduced the concept of hereditary factors as discrete, physical entities that do not become blended or altered

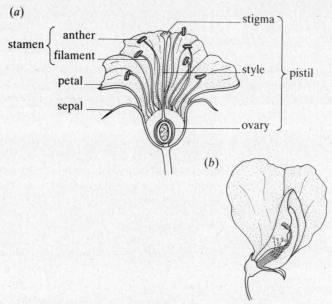

Fig. 15.1. (*a*) The male and female parts of a flower. (*b*) Side view of a pea flower. This flower usually self-pollinates because the stigma lies above the anthers and traps the pollen.

when present together in the same individual. He disproved the blending theory by showing that although traits caused by recessive alleles disappear in the F_1 generation, they reappear unchanged in the F_2 generation.

The Law of Segregation applies only to diploid organisms (two copies of each chromosome) that form haploid gametes to reproduce sexually. Moreover, it applies only to traits controlled exclusively by a single gene pair in which one of the two alleles is dominant over the other. The law does not, therefore, apply to (1) alleles that are incompletely dominant or codominant; (2) genes that collaborate or vary in their expressivity or penetrance; (3) genes that are *pleiotropic* (i.e., each gene having two or more phenotypic effects), complementary, or influenced by *epistasis* (suppression of one gene's effects by another) or modifiers; (4) traits caused by many gene pairs. In fact, very few inherited traits conform to the Law of Segregation, because very few are controlled exclusively by a single gene pair.

15.50   Under what conditions does Mendel's Law of Independent Assortment apply?

   Mendel's Law of Independent Assortment states that the way in which one pair of factors segregates (assorts) is independent of (i.e., has no influence on) the way in which another pair of factors segregates during gamete formation. Thus, if the two pairs of factors were A/a and B/b, whether or not a gamete received a copy of A, for example, would have no influence over whether it also received a copy of B or b, and so four kinds of gametes would be formed in equal frequency: $A B$, $A b$, $a B$, $a b$.

This law applies only to gene pairs on different pairs of homologous chromosomes—one gene pair on one pair of homologous chromosomes and the other gene pair on another pair of homologous chromosomes. Mendel did not know about chromosomes, but all of the traits he studied were on different pairs of homologous chromosomes (or assorted as though they were), which is why he concluded the gene pairs segregate independently of one another. Had he studied gene pairs located together on the *same* pair of homologous chromosomes, he would have found that the way in which one gene pair segregates usually determines the way in which the other gene pair segregates during gamete formation, because they would be linked on the same chromosome and move together into gametes (except when crossovers occur). Thus, if gene A were right next to gene B on one chromosome, and genes a and b were next to each other on the other chromosome of the homologous pair, then only two kinds of gametes would form: one kind carrying A and B and the other kind carrying a and b.

FROM GENOTYPE TO PHENOTYPE

15.51   In all of Mendel's experiments, the two alleles causing a trait were

(**a**) dominant-recessive.   (**b**) codominant.   (**c**) incompletely dominant.   (**d**) corecessive.

15.52   When red-flowered snapdragons are crossed with white-flowered snapdragons, their offspring have pink flowers. This type of genotypic expression is called

(**a**) dominant-recessive.   (**b**) codominance.   (**c**) incomplete dominance.   (**d**) corecessive.

15.53 The A and B carbohydrates on the surfaces of human red blood cells are synthesized by way of enzymes produced by codominant alleles. A person of blood group A has a different sequence of sugars in the carbohydrates than a person of blood group B. A heterozygote with both the I^A and I^B alleles has both the A carbohydrate and the B carbohydrate on his or her red blood cells. A third allele at this locus, symbolized by i, is recessive to both the I^A and I^B alleles; it codes for a nonfunctioning enzyme and so produces no carbohydrate. The letter I is used for this locus because its products are important isoagglutinins—molecules that cause a response by the immune system. How many possible *genotypes* are there for the ABO blood groups?

(*a*) 4; (*b*) 6; (*c*) 8; (*d*) 16

15.54 How many possible *phenotypes* are there for the ABO blood groups?

(*a*) 4; (*b*) 6; (*c*) 8; (*d*) 16

15.55 The genotypic expression seen in a person of blood group AB is called

(*a*) dominant-recessive. (*b*) codominance. (*c*) incomplete dominance. (*d*) corecession.

15.56 A child with blood-group genotype I^A/I^B is born of a woman with genotype I^B/I^B. The father could *not* be a man of genotype

(*a*) I^A/I^A. (*b*) I^B/I^B. (*c*) I^A/I^B. (*d*) I^A/i.

15.57 Genes that exist in more than two forms are called _____.

15.58 An individual can have at most _____ forms of a gene, whereas a population can have

_____.

15.59 In light-skinned people, straight hair is incompletely dominant over curly hair. A man with curly hair mates with a woman with straight hair. The chance their daughter will have wavy hair is _____.

15.60 How can one demonstrate that the inheritance of incompletely dominant alleles is not the same as inheritance according to the blending theory?

∰   The two genes of a pair blend, rather than remain discrete physical entities, according to the blending theory. Thus, matings between two pure strains produce F_1 individuals with traits intermediate between the traits of their parents.

An observation that fits the blending theory is: A pure strain of sweet peas with red flowers and a pure strain of sweet peas with white flowers produce progeny (the F_1 generation) with pink flowers. The allele for red color and the allele for white color seem to become blended in the fertilized egg to form a new gene with properties of both alleles and coding for pink color. This observation on sweet-pea reproduction is also in accordance with the inheritance of two alleles in which one is incompletely dominant over the other; when present together, they produce an intermediate phenotype, but each allele is retained as a discrete entity rather than being blended.

Whether the formation of pink flowers in sweet peas is the consequence of two discrete alleles or of a newly formed blend of two previous alleles can be determined by self-pollinating the F_1, pink-flowered plants. Their progeny will all be pink if the allele for red and the allele for white blend when in the F_1 plant. By contrast, if the two alleles remain discrete and segregate during gamete formation in the F_1 plants, some of the plants from F_1 selfings will be red, some will be pink, and some will be white (a 1:2:1 ratio if the sample is large). This is, in fact, what happens.

MENDELIAN INHERITANCE IN HUMANS

15.61 The genetic basis of hemophilia, so common within European royal families, was revealed by studies of

(*a*) DNA sequences. (*b*) chromosomes in gametes. (*c*) family pedigrees. (*d*) prenatal gene products.

15.62 Consanguineous matings often result in deformed children because a child is likely to inherit

(*a*) two copies of the same recessive allele. (*b*) two incompletely dominant alleles. (*c*) only one allele for a trait. (*d*) broken chromosomes.

15.63 A man and a woman each carry the allele for phenylketonuria, an inborn error of metabolism. While neither of them has this disease themselves, what is the probability that their child will have the disease?

(*a*) 0.25; (*b*) 0.50; (*c*) 0.75; (*d*) 1.00

15.64 If the couple described in Question 15.63 has a normal child, without phenylketonuria, what is the probability this child is a carrier of the disease?

(*a*) 0.33; (*b*) 0.50; (*c*) 0.67; (*d*) 1.00

15.65 Cystic fibrosis is a disease characterized by unusually viscous mucus. It develops in people who inherit two copies of a recessive allele. If a man with cystic fibrosis marries a woman without the disease, and for whom there is no family history of the disease, what is the probability that their child will be a carrier?

(*a*) 0.33; (*b*) 0.50; (*c*) 0.67; (*d*) 1.00

15.66 A person with sickle-cell anemia is _____ for the alleles at that locus.

15.67 A person heterozygous for the sickle-cell allele is more resistant to _____ than a person without the trait.

15.68 A person who is heterozygous at the gene locus of a disorder, but shows no signs of the disorder, is a _____ of the disorder.

15.69 An inborn error of metabolism is a genetic disease in which a defective _____ is synthesized.

15.70 Whether one's earlobes are attached or unattached (i.e., somewhat dangling) is an inherited trait in humans. How can one find out whether the attached form is caused by a dominant or a recessive allele?

Construct a pedigree of a large family, consisting of several generations (the trait can be observed from photographs), in which some members have attached and others have unattached earlobes. One might find, for example, the pedigree shown in Fig. 15.2.

A trait caused by a dominant allele appears in every generation, whereas a trait caused by a recessive allele appears sporadically, skipping generations when present in a family along with the dominant allele. According to

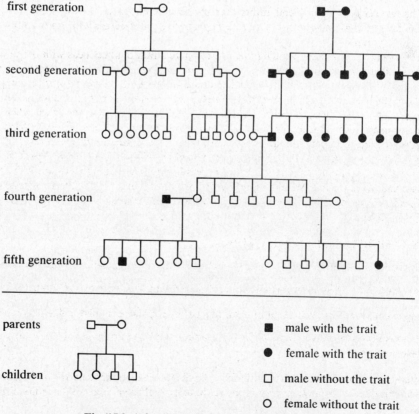

Fig. 15.2. A family pedigree for attached earlobes.

the pedigree in Fig. 15.2, the allele causing attached earlobes must be caused by a recessive allele. The main clue, here, is that one family had only unattached earlobes and the other family had only attached earlobes for at least three generations. These two families, therefore, are the equivalent of Mendel's two pure strains in his parental (P_1) generation. If one allele is dominant over the other, then offspring from crosses between the two families will all be heterozygotes and the trait they exhibit will be caused by the dominant allele. In the pedigree, all the heterozygotes (4th generation) have unattached earlobes. One can conclude, then, that unattached is dominant over attached earlobes. This conclusion can be tested by seeing what happens when such heterozygotes reproduce to form a fifth generation.

Answers to Objective Questions

15.1 *a*

15.2 *c*

15.3 *b*

15.4 *a*

15.5 *c*

15.6 *b*

15.7 pangenesis

15.8 spontaneous generation

15.9 gray; gray

15.10 *c*

15.11 *c*

15.12 *a*

15.13 *a*

15.14 *b*

15.15 *b*

15.16 *d*

15.17 *a*

15.18 *c*

15.19 *b*

15.20 *c*

15.21 *a*

15.22 *b*

15.23 *b*

15.24 *c*

15.25 *a*

15.26 *a* (The genotype of the plant would be *t/t*; *r/r*. Its eggs can have only one genotype: *t r*.)

15.27 *a* (All of the F_1 plants will be heterozygous, whereas a short plant with wrinkled peas is homozygous at both loci.)

15.28 *c* (F_1 genotype is *T/t*; *R/r*. The possible genotypes for the eggs are: *T R*, *T r*, *t R*, and *t r*.)

15.29 *c* (See Punnett square in answer to Question 15.31.)

15.30 *a* (tall, round; tall, wrinkled; short, round; and short, wrinkled)

15.31 *b* (F_1 gametes can be of four genotypes: *T R*, *T r*, *t R*, and *t r*. The Punnett square is:

15.32 *b*

	S g	*S G*	*s g*	*s G*
s g	*S/s*; *g/g*	*S/s*; *G/g*	*s/s*; *g/g*	*s/s*; *G/g*

15.33 *b*

15.34 *d* (The frequency of getting *a/a*, *b/b*, or *c/c* separately is $\frac{1}{4}$. Therefore, the probability of offspring having all three of these homozygous pairs is $\frac{1}{4} \times \frac{1}{4} \times \frac{1}{4} = \frac{1}{64}$.)

15.35 *b*

15.36 seven; two

15.37 F_1, or first filial; F_2, or second filial

15.38 two; alleles

15.39 zero; two; two; zero; one; one

15.40 phenotype; genotype

15.41 test cross

15.42 1; 0; 0.5; 0.5; $\frac{1}{6}$; $\frac{1}{52}$; $\frac{51}{52}$

15.43 alike

15.44 recessive; dominant

15.45 alleles; two

15.46 separate chromosomes of a homologous pair

15.47 *a/a*, *B/B*; *A/a*, *B/b*

15.51 *a*

15.52 *c*

15.53 *b*

Genotype	Blood group
I^A/I^A and I^A/i	A
I^B/I^B and I^B/i	B
I^A/I^B	AB
i/i	O

15.54 *a*

15.55 *b*

15.56 *b*

15.57 multiple alleles

15.58 two; many

15.59 100%

15.61 *c*

15.62 *a*

15.63 *a*

15.64 *c* (Parents are heterozygous for the trait, say *B/b*. Then

	♂	
	B	b
♀ B	*B/B*	*B/b*
b	*B/b*	*b/b*

The child is normal, so *b/b* is not a possibility. That leaves a $\frac{2}{3}$ chance that the child is a carrier, i.e., *B/b*.)

15.65 *d*

15.66 homozygous

15.67 malaria

15.68 carrier

15.69 enzyme

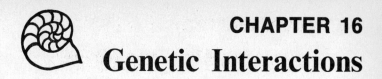

CHAPTER 16
Genetic Interactions

NONADDITIVE INTERACTIONS*

16.1 An interaction between nonallelic genes in which an allele at one locus prevents expression of an allele at another locus, but not vice versa, is called

(*a*) collaboration.   (*b*) complementation.   (*c*) epistasis.   (*d*) modification.

16.2 When two nonallelic gene pairs on the same homologous chromosomes are each defective but together give a normal phenotype, this is called

(*a*) collaboration.   (*b*) complementation.   (*c*) epistasis.   (*d*) modification.

16.3 When two nonallelic gene pairs influencing the same character interact to produce a novel phenotype which neither gene pair could produce by itself, this is called

(*a*) collaboration.   (*b*) complementation.   (*c*) epistasis.   (*d*) modification.

16.4 If an animal's coat color depends on two separate gene pairs, in which pair A codes for the pigment protein and pair B codes for the control mechanism that turns on pigment production, then a cross between two albinos (no pigments), one with defects at locus A and the other with defects at locus B, will produce offspring that are all

(*a*) albinos.   (*b*) streaked, in which pigmented areas are mixed with unpigmented areas.   (*c*) pink-eyed and blind. (*d*) normally pigmented.

16.5 If the offspring described in Question 16.4 mate with each other, what kind(s) of pigmentation are expected in their offspring?

(*a*) Some will have normal pigmentation; some will not.   (*b*) All will have normal pigmentation.   (*c*) All will be albinos.   (*d*) All will be streaked.

16.6 Epistasis differs from dominance in that in epistasis one _____ masks the effects of another, whereas in dominance one _____ masks the effects of another.

16.7 The color of human skin depends in part on how much melanin is synthesized, the quantity being controlled by several gene pairs. Yet another gene pair codes for tyrosinase, the first enzyme needed for synthesizing melanin; without tyrosinase, no melanin is produced regardless of the kinds of genes present at the other loci. The gene for tyrosinase is said to be _____ to the others; it interferes with the _____ of the other genes.

16.8 In chickens, gene R produces a rose-shaped comb, gene r produces a single comb, gene P produces a pea-shaped comb, and gene p produces a single comb. Genotypes R/r P/p, R/R P/p, R/R P/P, and R/r P/P produce a walnut-shaped comb. This type of gene interaction is known as _____.

16.9 There are two forms of abnormal albino finches. One form is completely white and the other is all white except for a tiny blotch of pale brown near its eyes. When these two forms are crossed, all the offspring are normal, with slate-gray bodies and colorful markings. This result indicates that each form of albinism is produced by a _____ gene pair. Reversion to the normal phenotype in birds heterozygous at both loci is known as _____.

16.10 How is it possible for two blue-eyed people to have a brown-eyed child?

Eye color is the product of several gene pairs, which interact in a nonadditive fashion. At least three loci control the amount, tone, and distribution of pigments in the iris. The contributions of these three qualities to eye color are shown in Table 16.1

* Answers to Chapter 16 objective questions appear on page 123.

TABLE 16.1 The Contributions of Various Gene Products to Eye Color

amount of melanin	tone of melanin	distribution of melanin	eye color
large	brown	even throughout iris	brown
large	brown	back of iris	dark blue
small	brown	back of iris	light blue
intermediate	brown or yellow	scattered in flecks throughout iris	hazel

Heavy deposits of brown melanin throughout the iris give brown eyes. True blue eyes develop when there is no melanin deposited in the front part of the iris, but there is some in the deeper layers; thus, most of the light entering the iris is scattered (as it is in a clear sky) and perceived as a blue color. Hazel eyes appear in a variety of colors and patterns; they have scattered deposits of yellow or brown melanin throughout the iris. In general, genes for darker eyes are dominant over genes for blue. It is possible, however, for two blue-eyed parents to have a brown-eyed child. One of the parents may have true blue eyes, with genes for no melanin in the front part of the iris (b/b) and genes for an even distribution of melanin when present (C/C). The other parent may have blue eyes with brown flecks, e.g., have genes for melanin in the iris (B/B) and genes that cause the melanin to be scattered in a flecked pattern (C/c). If their child inherits a B/b; C/C genotype, it will have an even distribution of melanin throughout its irises and so have brown eyes.

ADDITIVE INTERACTIONS

16.11 When two or more nonallelic gene pairs affect the same character in the same way, this is called

(a) polygenic inheritance. (b) pleiotropy. (c) total penetrance. (d) additive expressivity.

16.12 Human skin color is controlled by several gene pairs. Let us assume here that there are just three gene pairs on different chromosomes and that for each pair there are two alleles—an incompletely dominant one that codes for melanin deposition and an incompletely recessive one that codes for no melanin deposition. If a very dark-skinned person mates with a very light-skinned person, what is the chance that their offspring will have very dark skin?

(a) 0; (b) $\frac{1}{4}$; (c) $\frac{5}{8}$; (d) $\frac{9}{64}$

16.13 In a mating between two people of intermediate skin color, each heterozygous at all three gene loci for skin color, what is the chance their child will have very light skin?

(a) $\frac{1}{64}$; (b) $\frac{1}{4}$; (c) $\frac{5}{8}$; (d) $\frac{9}{64}$

16.14 In polygenic inheritance, a cross between two extreme phenotypes (similar to Mendel's P generation) produces a range of phenotypes that is usually broader in the _____ generation than in the _____ generation.

16.15 When phenotypes fall into a few clear-cut categories, the variation is _____; when there is a gradation of small differences among the phenotypes, with no clear-cut categories, the variation is _____.

16.16 The greater the number of _____ determining a trait in an additive fashion, the more _____ the variation.

16.17 Why are the frequency distributions of most traits smooth, bell-shaped curves?

⎘ Most traits cannot be placed into two or three distinct categories, but rather they vary continuously over a broad range. Humans, for example, are not either short or tall, but rather there is a broad range of heights within which all possible dimensions are represented within the population. The same is true of skin color, hair color, body build, heart rate, and so on. Traits that vary continuously are under the influence of many gene pairs, each contributing its product to the development of the trait. The passage of such traits from one generation to the next is called *polygenic inheritance*.

A polygenic trait exhibits a greater variety of phenotypes than a Mendelian trait because there are more loci within each individual for the trait and the alleles at the different loci can combine in more ways than the alleles of a single gene pair of one locus. Consider the inheritance of melanin production. Melanin is a dark pigment that contributes (along with melanoid and carotenoid pigments in the skin and hemoglobin in the blood) to the color of human skin. Approximately four gene pairs code for the distribution and amount of melanin in the skin. Each of the four loci has a pair of alleles with one showing incomplete dominance over the other; the heterozygote is intermediate in color to the two homozygotes. In dark-skinned people, all eight genes (four loci) code for the synthesis of large amounts of melanin and its distribution throughout the outer layers of skin. In light-skinned people, all eight genes code for the synthesis of small amounts of melanin and its deposition chiefly in the deeper layers of the skin. People who have some of each type of allele have skin of intermediate color.

If just a single gene pair (locus A), rather than four, controlled all production and deposition of melanin, then there would be just three skin colors in the population: dark (A^1/A^1), one intermediate shade (A^1/A^2), and light (A^2/A^2). Matings between two individuals with the intermediate skin color would produce children of all three categories, with a 25% chance of being dark, a 25% chance of being light, and a 50% chance of being intermediate. The three categories would be a form of discontinuous variation, as three distinct shades would be seen rather than all possible shades within the range of dark to light. Such a frequency distribution is shown in Fig. 16.1a.

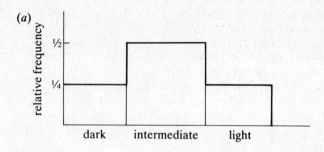

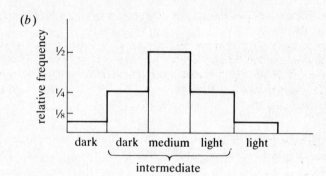

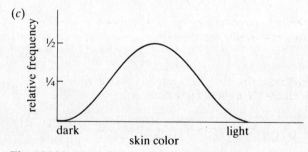

Fig. 16.1 Number of categories of skin color in relation to number of genes involved: (a) one gene pair; (b) two gene pairs; (c) many gene pairs.

If two gene pairs (loci A and B) determined the amount and distribution of melanin and if the loci were not on the same chromosomes, then there would be five distinct categories of skin color in the population. Each person would inherit four codes (two gene pairs) for skin color and each code would either contribute to a dark color (A^1 or B^1) or to a light color (A^2 or B^2). The five phenotypes would be produced by the genotypes shown in Table 16.2. Matings between double heterozygotes would produce children with any of the five categories of skin color. A frequency distribution of many children from such matings would still be one of discontinuous variation, as shown in Fig. 16.1b.

TABLE 16.2

genotypes	phenotypes	
$A^1/A^1; B^1/B^1$	dark	
$A^1/A^1; B^1/B^2$	medium dark	
$A^1/A^2; B^1/B^1$	medium dark	
$A^1/A^2; B^1/B^2$	medium	
$A^1/A^1; B^2/B^2$	medium	intermediate
$A^2/A^2; B^1/B^1$	medium	
$A^1/A^2; B^2/B^2$	medium light	
$A^2/A^2; B^1/B^2$	medium light	
$A^2/A^2; B^2/B^2$	light	

Increasing the number of gene pairs to three would produce seven categories of skin color; four gene pairs would yield nine categories; and so on. As the number of categories increases, each category becomes less distinct from the others, since the range remains the same, until distinctions can no longer be made and there is continuous variation—a smooth curve (Fig. 16.1c)—rather than discontinuous variation of phenotypes. Human skin color varies continuously from dark to light, in part because of the many genes involved and in part because of the effect of sunlight, which darkens the color produced by the genotype and so gives additional shades.

The frequency distribution curve is bell-shaped, with the largest proportion of individuals exhibiting the average phenotype and the smallest proportion exhibiting either extreme, because the number of ways in which the genes can combine to give an average phenotype is much greater than the number of ways they can combine to give an extreme phenotype. In the example above involving two gene pairs, the four genes combine in three ways to give the average skin color (intermediate), but only a single combination gives dark and a single combination gives light skin color.

PLEIOTROPY

16.18 Pleiotropy occurs when a gene has

(*a*) a complementary gene elsewhere. (*b*) a small effect on one trait. (*c*) reversible effects on the phenotype, depending on age. (*d*) many effects on the phenotype.

16.19 Diseases caused by pleiotropic genes are

(*a*) syndromes. (*b*) reversible by diet therapy. (*c*) reversible by gene therapy. (*d*) extremely rare.

16.20 In Siamese cats, a single _____, when present in both homologous chromosomes, causes crossed eyes and abnormal pigmentation. It is said to be a _____ gene.

16.21 With regard to frequency, pleiotropic genes are very _____, whereas genes with a single effect on the phenotype are very _____.

16.22 Sickle-cell anemia is a disease syndrome. How can a single mutation have so many effects on the phenotype?

@ Sickle-cell anemia is a genetic disease caused by a codominant allele that, when present in the homozygous state, causes a change in just one amino acid at two of the 574 amino acid sites of hemoglobin. (The allele contains the base sequence CAT, the DNA code for valine, instead of the base sequence CTT, the code for glutamic acid.) This change so alters hemoglobin that the red blood cells carrying it take on a sickle shape, rather than the normal disk shape.

Sickle-shaped red blood cells not only transport oxygen poorly, resulting in anemia, but also tend to clump together and clog small arteries. As less blood gets through these arteries, the tissues and organs they nourish become impaired in their functions. Many phenotypic changes occur as parts of the body fail to function in an optimal manner. Lethargy, susceptibility to disease, edema, and shortness of breath develop from inadequate blood flow to the heart, kidneys, and spleen. Jaundice and weight loss occur from liver disfunction. Slow reflexes, forgetfulness, speech defects, and personality changes become a consequence of insufficient blood flow to the brain. Thus, a tiny change in the DNA—really just a single base substitution—causes poor circulation and thereby significant changes in both the body and mind of the affected person.

While the homozygous state endangers the life of the individual, the heterozygous state confers protection against the most dangerous form of malaria. Heterozygous individuals (said to have the *trait* rather than exhibit the *syndrome*) rarely suffer sickling episodes under normal conditions, but if they contract malaria, any red blood cells infected with the causative organism (a protozoan) become sickle-shaped and, being defective, are removed by the spleen.

PENETRANCE AND EXPRESSIVITY

16.23 One individual from a pair of identical twins developed a hare lip, whereas the other did not. This is an example of

(*a*) variable pleiotropy. (*b*) incomplete penetrance. (*c*) variable expressivity. (*d*) reversible expressivity.

16.24 A person with polydactyly (many digits) may have 11 fingers, 12 fingers, 11 toes, 12 toes, 5 fingers on one hand and 6 on the other, or 5 toes on one foot and 6 on the other. This inherited trait is an example of

(*a*) variable pleiotropy. (*b*) incomplete penetrance. (*c*) variable expressivity. (*d*) reversible expressivity.

16.25 All children homozygous for an allele that causes Tay-Sachs disease develop symptoms of this disease. This allele has a penetrance that is

(*a*) deep. (*b*) shallow. (*c*) 0%. (*d*) 100%.

16.26 The darker hair on the paws, ears, and tail of a Siamese cat develops in response to an enzyme that is less active when in a warmer environment. Temperature influences the _____ of the gene for this enzyme.

16.27 A gene in humans causes blue sclera, in which the whites of the eyes appear blue. Only 9 out of 10 people with this gene have blue sclera; one in 10 have normal, white sclera. Thus, the _____ of the gene is 90 percent. Among those with blue sclera, some have very dark and others very pale blue sclera. This variability is called variable _____.

16.28 Two factors that can influence expression of a gene are: _____ and _____.

16.29 Phenylketonuria (PKU) is an inborn error of metabolism caused by a faulty enzyme in metabolic pathways that begin with the amino acid phenylalanine. A person with PKU whose disease goes untreated becomes mentally retarded. A person with the disease but who has had diet therapy (no dietary phenylalanine) since birth develops a normal intellect. Diet therapy changes the phenylketonuria-causing gene from _____ expressivity to _____ expressivity.

16.30 "Stiff little finger" is an inherited trait, caused by a dominant allele, in which the little fingers are permanently rigid and bent. A woman is seen to have this trait, her only child does not, yet two of her three grandchildren have stiff little fingers. How can this inheritance pattern be explained?

The gene for stiff little fingers exhibits incomplete penetrance—it is expressed in some individuals with the gene, but not at all in others. Her child must be heterozygous for the dominant allele, but the allele was not expressed. The child passed the allele to at least two of the grandchildren, and it was completely expressed in them.

Answers to Objective Questions

16.1 *c*
16.2 *b*
16.3 *a*
16.4 *d*
16.5 *a*
16.6 gene pair; allele
16.7 epistatic; expression
16.8 collaboration
16.9 separate; complementarity
16.11 *a*
16.12 *a*

16.13 *a* [A very light-skinned child would require all three recessives in duplicate. The probability for each recessive occurring in the homozygous state is $\frac{1}{4}$; the probability of all three being present in the homozygous state is $(\frac{1}{4})^3$.]
16.14 F_2; F_1
16.15 discontinuous; continuous
16.16 gene pairs; continuous

16.18 *d*
16.19 *a*
16.20 allele; pleiotropic
16.21 common; rare
16.23 *b*
16.24 *c*
16.25 *d*
16.26 expressivity
16.27 penetrance; expressivity
16.28 other genes; the environment
16.29 high; low

CHAPTER 17
Chromosomal Inheritance

DEVELOPMENT OF THE CHROMOSOMAL THEORY*

17.1   Mitosis and meiosis were first described during the

(*a*) 4th century B.C.   (*b*) 4th century A.D.   (*c*) early 17th century.   (*d*) late 19th century.

17.2   Mendel's work was rediscovered, in 1901, by

(*a*) Charles Darwin.   (*b*) T. H. Morgan.   (*c*) K. Correns, E. Tschermak, and H. de Vries.   (*d*) W. Bateson and R. C. Punnett.

17.3   The relation between the behavior of chromosomes and the behavior of Mendel's factors was first recognized by W. S. Sutton and T. Boveri in

(*a*) 1869.   (*b*) 1890.   (*c*) 1902.   (*d*) 1938.

17.4   Each pair of Mendel's factors, such as *T* and *t*, is located in

(*a*) a pair of nonhomologous chromosomes.   (*b*) a pair of homologous chromosomes.   (*c*) the two sex chromosomes.
(*d*) two pairs of homologous chromosomes—one factor for each pair of homologous chromosomes.

17.5   In Mendel's dihybrid crosses, the two pairs of factors (e.g., *T/t* and *R/r*) are located in

(*a*) a pair of nonhomologous chromosomes.   (*b*) a pair of homologous chromosomes.   (*c*) the two sex chromosomes.
(*d*) two pairs of homologous chromosomes—one pair of factors for each pair of homologous chromosomes.

17.6   Thomas Hunt Morgan, in 1910, was the first person to

(*a*) rediscover Mendel's work.   (*b*) observe meiosis.   (*c*) associate a specific gene with a specific chromosome.
(*d*) carry out controlled breeding experiments.

17.7   W. Bateson and R. C. Punnett found that dihybrid crosses involving pollen color and pollen shape in sweet peas did not give a Mendelian ratio of 9:3:3:1. Instead, they found that most of the phenotypes were of just two kinds, in an approximately 3:1 ratio. This pattern occurred because the alleles for pollen color and the alleles for pollen shape are

(*a*) alleles of each other.   (*b*) in nonhomologous chromosomes.   (*c*) in the same chromosome.   (*d*) incompletely penetrant.

17.8   Each pair of Mendel's factors, such as *Y* and *y*, becomes segregated during the _____ division of meiosis, when each _____ of a homologous pair moves to a different pole of the cell.

17.9   In Mendel's experiments, the two pairs of factors assort independently during the _____ division of _____, when the way in which one pair of _____ chromosomes segregates in no way influences segregation in another pair. Thus, _____ chromosomes assort independently of one another.

17.10   The first mutant that T. H. Morgan worked with was _____, which he observed to occur much more frequently in the _____ sex. Morgan deduced from this observation that the mutant gene was _____ to the normal wild allele and located in the _____ chromosome.

17.11   In fruit flies, the male sex chromosomes are _____, and the female sex chromosomes are _____.

* Answers to Chapter 17 objective questions appear on page 128

17.12 When Morgan crossed a mutant, white-eyed male with a normal, red-eyed female fruit fly, all F_1 flies had red eyes. When he then crossbred these F_1 flies, he did not get the expected ratio of three red-eyed flies for every white-eyed fly. Instead, approximately _____% of the females had red eyes, _____% of the females had white eyes, _____% of the males had red eyes, and _____% of the males had white eyes.

17.13 After the experiment described in Question 17.12, Morgan crossed the original white-eyed male with one of the F_1 females. The offspring of this cross were approximately _____% red-eyed females, _____% white-eyed females, _____% red-eyed males, and _____% white-eyed males.

17.14 Genes located in the same chromosome are said to be _____ in inheritance.

17.15 What is the advantage of using fruit flies in genetic experiments?

🐌 A geneticist wants to perform many experiments with large sample sizes in as short a time as possible. For studies of relatively complex animals, the fruit fly (genus *Drosophila*) is ideal.

Fruit flies reproduce rapidly—about 100 eggs are laid at a time, and these eggs become reproducing adults within just 12 days. They have eukaryotic cells, and each cell has only four pairs of chromosomes, making it relatively easy to establish gene linkages. Additionally, the salivary gland cells are *polytene*: they consist of many identical DNA molecules positioned side by side. These giant chromosomes facilitate gene mapping, since their banding patterns and the positions of chromosomal puffs (where DNA is unwound for transcription) are easy to observe under a light microscope.

Fruit flies are simple to breed in a laboratory. They are tiny (3 mm long), feed on rotting fruit, and can be kept in half-pint bottles.

There are many species of *Drosophila*, and since each species is genetically quite variable, there are many loci with multiple alleles for study. The complex behaviors of fruit flies, especially their mating dances, provide geneticists with a good system for unraveling the relation between genes and behavior.

CHROMOSOMAL BASIS OF SEX

17.16 The sex-determination system in which males are X/Y and females are X/X is found in all

(*a*) multicellular organisms. (*b*) animals. (*c*) vertebrates. (*d*) mammals.

17.17 A dioecious plant has

(*a*) both an X and a Y chromosome. (*b*) two X chromosomes. (*c*) both sexes in the same individual.
(*d*) the two sexes in separate individuals.

17.18 A monoecious plant is

(*a*) haploid. (*b*) polyploid. (*c*) either male or female. (*d*) both male and female.

17.19 The males of ants, bees, and wasps are

(*a*) haploid. (*b*) polyploid. (*c*) X/X. (*d*) X/O.

17.20 The syndrome in humans in which an individual's somatic cells contain the three sex chromosomes XXX is called

(*a*) Klinefelter's. (*b*) Turner's. (*c*) Down's. (*d*) superfemale.

17.21 The syndrome in humans in which an individual's somatic cells contain the three sex chromosomes XXY is called

(*a*) Klinefelter's. (*b*) Turner's. (*c*) Down's. (*d*) superfemale.

17.22 The syndrome in humans in which an individual's somatic cells contain only the one sex chromosome X/O is called

(*a*) Klinefelter's. (*b*) Turner's. (*c*) Down's. (*d*) superfemale.

17.23 The sex chromosomes are segregated during the _____ division of _____. Where X/Y is male and X/X is female, the X chromosome is found in _____% of the sperm and _____% of the eggs. Random fertilization leads to a sex ratio of _____. The sex of the offspring, determined at fertilization, is a consequence of the sex chromosome carried in the _____ gamete.

17.24 Too many or too few sex chromosomes are the consequence of chromosomal _____ during _____.

17.25 What role does the Y chromosome play in determining the human phenotype?

⚛ The Y chromosome determines maleness in humans. People with XY, XXY, and XYY karyotypes are males; people with XO, XX, and XXX karyotypes are females. Very few functional genes are carried in the Y chromosome. The only gene known for certain to be Y-linked produces the H-Y antigen, which causes development of the testes; it is found in all male cells and no female cells. The testes, in turn, control development of the other male traits. Other genes suspected of being carried only in the Y chromosome code for hair on the ears and overall height. The Y chromosome varies more in length than other chromosomes of the human karyotype, probably because much of its information is not used in the development of the phenotype.

KARYOTYPES

17.26 To make a karyotype, chromosomes are photographed during

(*a*) fertilization. (*b*) meiosis. (*c*) mitosis. (*d*) interphase.

17.27 How many pairs of homologous chromosomes are there in the normal human karyotype?

(*a*) 11; (*b*) 21; (*c*) 23; (*d*) 46

17.28 Patterns of horizontal bands on chromosomes, revealed by stains, reflect the positions of

(*a*) RNA molecules. (*b*) histones as compared with nonhistones. (*c*) guanine and cytosine bases as compared with adenine and thymine bases. (*d*) breaks in the DNA molecules.

17.29 The normal human karyotype has _____ sex chromosomes and _____ autosomes.

17.30 The number of chromosomes per cell is the same for all the _____ cells of an individual and for all individuals of a _____.

17.31 Chromosomes are identified by their length, which reflects the length of the DNA molecule as well as the amount of _____, and by their shape, which depends on the position of the _____.

SEX-LINKED INHERITANCE

17.32 A woman receives her X chromosomes from

(*a*) her mother only. (*b*) her father only. (*c*) both her mother and her father. (*d*) extranuclear DNA in her mother's egg.

17.33 A man receives his X chromosome from

(*a*) his mother only. (*b*) his father only. (*c*) both his mother and his father (part from each). (*d*) either his mother or his father.

17.34 Mary's father has hemophilia, an X-linked recessive trait, but her husband does not. What is the chance her son will have the disease?

(*a*) 0%; (*b*) 25%; (*c*) 50%; (*d*) 100%

17.35 If Mary (from Question 17.34) has a daughter, what is the chance she will have the disease?

(*a*) 0%; (*b*) 25%; (*c*) 50%; (*d*) 100%

17.36 Matthew is color-blind. What is the chance his son will inherit color blindness from him?

(*a*) 0%; (*b*) 25%; (*c*) 50%; (*d*) 100%

17.37   Joseph has hairy ears, a trait carried by a gene in his Y chromosome. What is the chance that his grandson (the son of his son) will inherit the trait from him?

(**a**) 0%;   (**b**) 25%;   (**c**) 50%;   (**d**) 100%

17.38   A Barr body is a

(**a**) supernumerary Y chromosome.   (**b**) coiled, inert X chromosome.   (**c**) extranuclear molecule of DNA. (**d**) connection between two X chromosomes.

17.39   When the male is the heterogametic sex, he is _____ with regard to all genes on the X chromosome.

17.40   An X-linked, recessive allele is much more likely to be expressed in _____ than in _____.

17.41   Only one X chromosome is active in each _____ of a woman; the other is inactive and called a _____. One of the chromosomes becomes inactive during early development (by the 16th day after fertilization); which one remains active is determined by _____.

17.42   The development of sweat glands is controlled by genes in the X chromosome. A defective allele at this locus in a man causes _____% of his skin to have no sweat glands, whereas in a woman a defective allele in one X chromosome causes approximately _____% of her skin to be without sweat glands.

17.43   Traits that are coded for in autosomes but expressed in only one of the sexes are known as _____ traits. They develop in response to relative amounts of male and female sex hormones in the body.

17.44   Traits that are coded for in autosomes but appear more frequently (although not exclusively) in one of the sexes are known as _____ traits.

17.45   Calico cats, with hair patches of three colors, are almost always females. Yet, occasionally one sees a male calico cat. What accounts for this type of inheritance pattern?

    The hair of a calico cat occurs in patches of three colors: black, orange, and white. The code for hair pigment, either black or orange, is located within the X chromosome of a cat. Thus, a calico cat is almost always a female, for the two X chromosomes carry the codes for two colors, with the white color developing where neither of the two alleles is expressed. A normal male cat, with just one X chromosome, can be black and white, or orange and white, but not black, orange, and white.

    The colors of a calico occur in patches. Each patch consists of cells with the same X chromosome active (the other is inactive and coiled into a Barr body). All of the cells within a patch developed by mitosis from the same ancestral cell in the young embryo. In that ancestral cell, one of the X chromosomes formed a Barr body, and all the descendants of that cell have the same X chromosome inactive as a Barr body. The patches represent the distribution of cells in the very young embryo.

    A male calico is occasionally seen. He has inherited, by an error (*nondisjunction*) during meiosis, three sex chromosomes—two X chromosomes and one Y chromosome. One of its X chromosomes is formed into a Barr body in each cell, just as in the female calico cat. A calico tomcat is almost always sterile. The XXY condition also occurs in human; it is called Klinefelter's syndrome and produces a sterile male.

EXTRANUCLEAR INHERITANCE

17.46   Genes not located within the nucleus are almost always found in the

(**a**) cytosol.   (**b**) organelles.   (**c**) cell membrane.   (**d**) cytoskeleton.

17.47   Variegated coloration of leaves, first studied by K. Correns in 1909, is inherited only from the female parent. The genes coding for this trait are located in the

(**a**) plastids.   (**b**) endoplasmic reticulum.   (**c**) nucleus.   (**d**) plasma membrane.

17.48   In higher eukaryotes, traits coded for in extranuclear DNA are inherited solely from the _____ parent. They are transmitted from one generation to the next in the cytoplasm of the _____.

17.49   Mitochondrial DNA, RNA, and ribosomes are more similar to the DNA, RNA, and ribosomes found in _____ than in eukaryotic cells of plants, animals, and fungi.

17.50 Of what significance is extranuclear DNA to the hypotheses about the origin of eukaryotic cells?

☞ There are two main hypotheses about how eukaryotic cells evolved from prokaryotic cells. The *autogenous hypothesis* states that complex structures within eukaryotic cells, such as the mitochondria and plastids, evolved gradually as indentations and modifications of the plasma membrane. Through successive generations of cells, the organelles became more specialized in structure and function. The main strength of this hypothesis is that it does not depart from the prevailing view that the evolutionary process has been a series of small changes. According to the *endosymbiotic hypothesis*, by contrast, organelles within the eukaryotic cell are believed to have originated as free-living prokaryotic cells. (*Symbiosis* occurs when two different types of organisms live together and both benefit from the association.) Endosymbiosis between two kinds of prokaryotic cells is viewed as having developed when a predatory cell ingested but did not digest a smaller cell. The two types of cells survived together and over time became increasingly dependent on each other as they became more specialized in structure and function. When the smaller cell living inside the larger cell was capable of using oxygen in the catabolism of glucose, it developed into a mitochondrion. When the smaller cell was a photosynthetic prokaryote, it developed into a plastid.

It has been found that both mitochondria and chloroplasts contain circular DNA molecules and RNA molecules, as well as ribosomes that are more typical of prokaryotic cells than of the kinds found outside the organelles of eukaryotic cells. This discovery provides strong evidence in support of the endosymbiotic hypothesis. Free-living prokaryotic cells must have had such DNA, RNA, and ribosomes prior to their postulated incorporation into other cells, and there is no apparent reason for such materials in organelles within cells that have other elaborate machinery for protein synthesis.

Answers to Objective Questions

17.1 *d*	**17.18** *d*	**17.36** *a* (Color blindness is a sex-linked trait carried in the X chromosome. A male inherits his X chromosome from his mother.)
17.2 *c*	**17.19** *a*	
17.3 *c*	**17.20** *d*	
17.4 *b*	**17.21** *a*	
17.5 *d*	**17.22** *b*	
17.6 *c*	**17.23** first; meiosis; 50; 100; 1:1; male	**17.37** *d*
17.7 *b*		**17.38** *b*
17.8 first; chromosome	**17.24** nondisjunction; meiosis	**17.39** haploid
17.9 first; meiosis; homologous; nonhomologous	**17.26** *c*	**17.40** males; females
	17.27 *c*	**17.41** cell; Barr body; chance
17.10 white eyes; male; recessive; X	**17.28** *c*	**17.42** 100; 50
	17.29 2; 44	**17.43** sex-limited
17.11 X/Y; X/X	**17.30** somatic; species	**17.44** sex-influenced
17.12 100; 0; 50; 50	**17.31** coiling; centromere	**17.46** *b*
17.13 50; 50; 50; 50	**17.32** *c*	**17.47** *a*
17.14 linked	**17.33** *a*	**17.48** females; eggs
17.16 *d*	**17.34** *c*	**17.49** bacteria
17.17 *d*	**17.35** *a*	

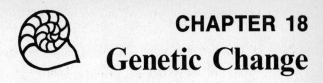

GENE MUTATIONS*

18.1 When a mutation is limited to the substitution of one nucleotide pair for another, it is called a

(*a*) translocation. (*b*) point mutation. (*c*) sugar-phosphate deletion. (*d*) base inversion.

18.2 Not all base-pair substitutions in DNA alter the activity of the product enzyme's activity. Those that do must alter the enzyme's

(*a*) total size. (*b*) secondary structure. (*c*) tertiary structure. (*d*) ratio of sulfur to nitrogen.

18.3 The insertion or deletion of a base pair into the genetic code will cause a frameshift mutation unless the number of base pairs inserted or deleted is

(*a*) just one. (*b*) two. (*c*) three. (*d*) ten.

18.4 A temperature-sensitive mutation makes the product protein nonfunctional at one temperature, but normal in activity at another temperature. This kind of mutation is an example of a

(*a*) nonsensitive mutation. (*b*) frameshift mutation. (*c*) missense mutation. (*d*) conditional mutation.

18.5 The creation of mutations is called

(*a*) mutagenesis. (*b*) evolution. (*c*) saltatory changes. (*d*) radiation.

18.6 Errors during DNA replication, repair, or recombination can lead to base-pair substitutions. Such changes are called

(*a*) conditional mutations. (*b*) mutagens. (*c*) spontaneous mutations. (*d*) saltatory changes.

18.7 Which of the following alterations of the codons ATTGCC is most serious?

(*a*) ATCGCC; (*b*) ATTGCA; (*c*) ATTCCCGCC; (*d*) ATTTGCC

18.8 A normal spontaneous mutation rate for a single gene is one mutation in every

(*a*) 10 replications. (*b*) 100 replications. (*c*) 10^6 to 10^9 replications. (*d*) 10^{50} to 10^{100} replications.

18.9 A mutation that changes a codon from the code for one amino acid to the code for another amino acid is a _____ mutation, whereas a mutation that changes a codon from a code for an amino acid to a code for a start or stop signal is a _____ mutation. Of the two kinds of mutation, the _____ kind is more likely to be deleterious.

18.10 When a base pair has been inserted into or deleted from the code, the triplet groupings may be altered. Such a mutation is called a _____ mutation.

18.11 Physical and chemical agents that interact with DNA to cause mutations are called _____.

18.12 The factor that causes most mutations in nature is _____.

18.13 The ultimate source of all genetic variation is _____, as they yield new alleles.

18.14 Mobile segments of DNA that can disrupt the function of the gene that they insert into, and so cause a mutation, are known as _____, or "jumping genes."

18.15 Ultraviolet light causes abnormal bonding of thymine, producing _____, which, if not repaired, can inactivate the DNA strand by preventing _____ and _____.

* Answers to Chapter 18 objective questions appear on page 135.

18.16   The ability to increase the rate of mutation was an important step in experimental genetics. It was discovered in 1927 by H. J. Müller, who used _____ as the mutagen.

RECOMBINATIONS

18.17   Independent assortment during meiosis produces gametes with all possible combinations of maternal and paternal chromosomes. With regard to chromosomes, then, a diploid cell with four chromosomes produces how many different kinds of haploid gametes?

   (*a*) Two;   (*b*) Four;   (*c*) Eight;   (*d*) Sixteen

18.18   In general, independent assortment of chromosomes in a cell with *n* pairs of chromosomes yields how many different kinds of gametes?

   (*a*) n;   (*b*) n^2;   (*c*) 2^n;   (*d*) $\frac{1}{2}n$

18.19   How many different kinds of fertilized eggs, with regard to kinds of chromosomes, can a particular man and woman produce?

   (*a*) 2^{22};   (*b*) 2^{23};   (*c*) $(2^{23})(2^{23})$;   (*d*) $(23^2)(23^2)$

18.20   Crossing-over takes place during which phase of meiosis?

   (*a*) Prophase of meiosis I;   (*b*) Prophase of meiosis II;   (*c*) Anaphase of meiosis I;   (*d*) Anaphase of meiosis II

18.21   Crossing-over occurs when genetic information is exchanged between two

   (*a*) chromatids of a chromosome.   (*b*) long arms of a chromosome.   (*c*) chromatids of two homologous chromosomes.   (*d*) nonhomologous chromosomes.

18.22   The probability of a crossover occurring between two gene loci is proportional to

   (*a*) the activity of the two loci.   (*b*) how far the loci are from the centromere.   (*c*) the distance between the two loci.   (*d*) how tightly the chromosomes are packed in the nucleus.

18.23   The maximum frequency of a recombination of genes (i.e., the percent recombinant forms in zygotes) at two loci is

   (*a*) 25%.   (*b*) 50%.   (*c*) 75%.   (*d*) 100%.

18.24   Crossovers between two loci very far apart on a chromosome produce results in breeding experiments that are the same as

   (*a*) independent assortment of nonalleles.   (*b*) a very close linkage of nonalleles.   (*c*) mitotic, rather than meiotic, division of chromosomes.   (*d*) segregation of alleles at the same locus.

18.25   The recombination frequency between gene *A* and gene *B* is 9 percent; between *A* and *C* is 17 percent; and between *B* and *C* is 26 percent. What is the sequence of genes in the chromosome?

   (*a*) Cannot be determined from the information provided;   (*b*) *ABC*;   (*c*) *ACB*;   (*d*) *BAC*

18.26   Two events that take place during meiosis contribute to genetic variability: _____ and _____. The general term for production of new gene combinations is genetic _____.

18.27   The more chromosomes an organism has, the more genetic variability it gets from _____.

18.28   The longer the chromosomes of an organism, the more genetic variability it gets from _____.

18.29   Assume that the genes for hair color and eye color are closely linked, with the alleles for brown hair and brown eyes on one chromosome of a homologous pair, and the alleles for blond hair and blue eyes on the other chromosome of the pair. A crossover between these two loci would produce a child with _____ hair and _____ eyes, or _____ hair and _____ eyes.

18.30   After a single crossover has occurred, there are _____ different kinds of gametes with regard to this kind of chromosome: _____ recombinant chromosome(s) and _____ nonrecombinant chromosome(s).

18.31 Independent assortment recombines genes from _____ chromosomes, and crossing-over recombines genes from _____ chromosomes.

18.32 A. H. Sturtevant, one of T. H. Morgan's students, defined one map unit on a chromosome as the equivalent of a _____ percent recombination frequency.

18.33 It turns out that seed color and flower color—two traits studied by Mendel—are on the same chromosome, yet Mendel found evidence of independent assortment of these traits. The two loci must be _____ on the chromosome.

18.34 How was crossing-over discovered?

Crossing-over takes place during meiosis I when nonsister chromatids from homologous chromosomes exchange segments of genetic material. It increases the number of genetic combinations a mating can produce and so contributes greatly to the overall genetic variability within a species.

Crossing-over was discovered in 1911 by T. H. Morgan. Working with fruit flies, he developed a mutant strain with a black body (allele b) and vestigial wings (allele vg). Both traits are caused by recessive alleles and differ from the normal gray body (b^+) and long wings (vg^+). In an experiment designed to reveal whether the loci for body color and wing shape are in the same chromosome, Morgan crossed flies heterozygous for the two genes with flies homozygous for both mutant alleles: b^+/b; vg^+/vg was crossed with b/b; vg/vg. He predicted that this cross would result in equal numbers of the two parental phenotypes if the genes were linked (Table 18.1) and equal numbers of four phenotypes if the genes assorted independently of each other (Table 18.2).

TABLE 18.1 Predicted Results If the Genes Are Linked

	gametes from the heterozygous parent	
	b^+; vg^+	b; vg
gamete from the homozygous parent b/vg	b^+/b; vg^+/vg gray with long wings	b/b; vg/vg black with vestigial wings

TABLE 18.2 Predicted Results If the Genes Are Not Linked

	gametes from the heterozygous parent			
	b^+/vg^+	b^+; vg	b; vg^+	b/vg
gamete from the homozygous parent b/vg	b^+/b; vg^+/vg gray with long wings	b^+/b; vg/vg gray with vestigial wings	b/b; vg^+/vg black with long wings	b/b; vg/vg black with vestigial wings

Results from the cross were puzzling. Most of the offspring resembled the two parental types, suggesting that the two loci are indeed linked. Yet 17 percent of the offspring were recombinant forms: some gray with vestigial wings and others black with long wings. The genes appeared to be linked most, but not all, of the time.

Morgan hypothesized from the results of this and other experiments that incomplete linkage occurs when there is a physical change in the chromosomes. The physical change had actually been described earlier, in 1909, by F. Janssens. While studying meiosis in salamanders, Janssens noticed cross-shaped structures, which he named *chiasmata*, within the chromatids of homologous chromosomes during prophase I of meiosis. He suggested that the chiasmata represent areas of exchange between maternal and paternal homologues. After reviewing Janssens' work, Morgan predicted that gene linkages are disrupted whenever a chiasma forms within the chromatids of a homologous pair of chromosomes. He named such disruptions *crossovers*.

18.35   How are crossovers used to map chromosomes?

⚓   The probability of a crossover between two loci in a chromosome is proportional to the distance between the two loci. Since a crossover can occur at any place in the chromosome, the more crossover sites there are (i.e., the longer the chromosome segment) between two loci, the greater the chance that one will take place.

The relationship between crossover frequency and distance between loci was discovered, in 1913, by A. H. Sturtevant, an undergraduate student working at the time in T. H. Morgan's laboratory. Sturtevant wanted to know why the frequency of recombination is always the same between two particular loci, but different for other pairs of loci. It occurred to him that the frequency of recombination must be related to the position of the genes in the chromosome. He developed the hypothesis that: (1) genes have fixed positions in a linear array within a chromosome; (2) crossovers occur less often between genes that are close together than between genes that are far apart in the linear array; and (3) by knowing recombination frequencies, the sequence of genes within the array can be known.

As a hypothetical example, let us say we have observed the percentages of recombinant forms (of all zygotes from a particular mating) among genes *A*, *B*, *C*, and *D* shown in Table 18.3.

TABLE 18.3

gene loci	% recombinants
A and B	5
B and C	17
C and D	18
A and C	12
B and D	1
A and D	6

From these data, we know that genes *C* and *D* are farthest apart; *B* and *D* are closest together; *A* is closer to *B* than to *C*. Their positions with regard to one another must be something like this.

$$C \qquad\qquad\qquad A \qquad B\cdot\ \ D$$

Sturtevant suggested that, since real distance cannot be known, a 1 percent recombination frequency be equivalent to one map unit in the chromosome. We can now state more precisely the positions of our four genes.

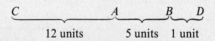

Genes very far apart in a chromosome cannot be mapped in this way, since after a certain distance, the number of crossovers between them becomes so great that the chance of an odd number of crossovers (seen as a recombination of genes) or an even number of crossovers (seen as no recombination of genes) is equal. Thus, the maximum distance would be 50 units (50% recombination), and it would be the same for all pairs of loci located at varying distances—all far apart—in the chromosome. Two distant loci can be mapped only by looking at recombination frequencies of other loci between them.

CHROMOSOMAL CHANGES

18.36   The condition in which there is one too many or one too few chromosomes is called

(*a*) aneuploidy.   (*b*) polytene.   (*c*) polyploidy.   (*d*) monoploidy.

18.37   The condition in which there are more than two complete sets of chromosomes is called

(*a*) aneuploidy.   (*b*) polytene.   (*c*) polyploidy.   (*d*) monoploidy.

18.38   Down's syndrome is an example of

(*a*) aneuploidy.   (*b*) polytene.   (*c*) polyploidy.   (*d*) monoploidy.

18.39   Deletions occur most often in chromosomal fragments

(*a*) of polytene chromosomes.   (*b*) with inversions.   (*c*) without centromeres.   (*d*) with centromeres.

18.40 Which of the following chromosomal changes is usually the most damaging when in the homozygous condition?

(a) Deletion;   (b) Duplication;   (c) Translocation;   (d) Inversion

18.41 Down's syndrome is found most often when the mother is

(a) less than 17 years old.   (b) more than 35 years old.   (c) already a mother of at least four children.
(d) having her first child.

18.42 An inversion, when present in just one of the chromosomes, suppresses

(a) mutations.   (b) crossovers.   (c) duplications.   (d) translocations.

18.43 Unusual numbers of chromosomes arise from _____ during _____ or _____.

18.44 A tetraploid cell has _____ copies of each chromosomes, or _____ copies of each pair of homologous chromosomes.

18.45 Polyploidy is most common in the _____ kingdom.

18.46 When a chromosomal fragment joins with its homologous chromosome, it becomes a _____; when it joins with a nonhomologous chromosome, it is a _____; when it reattaches to the original chromosome, but in the reverse orientation, it is an _____.

18.47 Translocations and duplications usually have little effect on a cell's function, since they do not result in a loss of genes. They do, however, cause problems during _____.

18.48 A normal gene sequence in a chromosomal sequence is *ABCDEFGH*. If it is changed to *ABCGH*, a _____ has occurred; if changed to *ABCABCDEFGH*, a _____ has occurred; and if changed to *ABCFEDGH*, an _____ has occurred.

18.49 How does an XYY zygote form?

🐚   An extra chromosome in a zygote is the consequence of nondisjunction during gamete formation, in which two homologous chromosomes fail to separate during meiosis I or two chromatids of a chromosome fail to separate during meiosis II.

   The extra chromosome in an XYY zygote is a Y rather than the X, since YY is not a normal genotype. The Y chromosome is carried only in sperm, which means that an egg carrying an X chromosome must have been fertilized by a sperm carrying two Y chromosomes to get the XYY zygote. Nondisjunction of sex chromosomes during meiosis in the male parent produced the abnormal sperm, but did it happen during meiosis I or II?

   Nondisjunction during meiosis I could not lead to a YY sperm, since only sperm with no sex chromosomes or sperm with both X and Y chromosomes could be produced at this point (Fig. 18.1). If these sperm are allowed to fertilize eggs (all eggs carry a single X), then the resulting zygotes have genotypes XO and XXY.

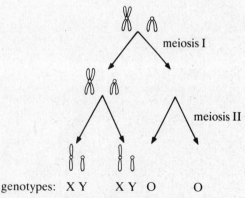

genotypes: X Y   X Y O   O

Fig. 18.1. Nondisjunction of mammalian male sex chromosomes during meiosis I.

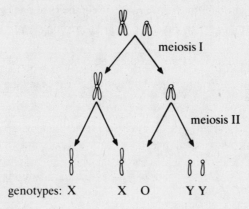

Fig. 18.2. Nondisjunction of mammalian male sex chromosomes during meiosis II.

genotypes: X X O Y Y

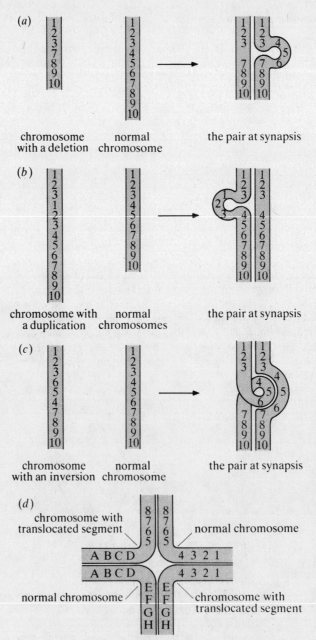

Fig. 18.3. Diagram of structural alterations of chromosomes visible during synapsis. In (a), one member of a homologous pair has been altered by a deletion. In (b), one pair member has incurred a duplication. In (c), one of the homologues has been altered by an inversion. Part (d) shows a reciprocal translocation, which involves *two* pairs of homologous chromosomes.

A YY sperm can be formed from nondisjunction during meiosis II, if both copies of the Y chromosome (the two chromatids) go to the same gamete (Fig. 18.2). An XYY zygote would then form when the YY sperm fertilized an egg.

18.50 How can a structural alteration of a chromosome be detected by looking at the chromosomes through a microscope?

🐚 Four kinds of structural alterations are possible in a chromosome: deletion, duplication, inversion, and translocation. Each kind can be detected by eye (through a microscope) during prophase of meiosis I, when homologous chromosomes come close together to form an association known as *synapsis*, if a homologous pair consists of one normal and one altered chromosome.

Deletions and duplications appear as bulges in one of the chromosomes of the homologous pair during synapsis. When a segment has been deleted, a bulge appears in the normal homologue, because the segment has no matching segment with which to pair (Fig. 18.3a). A duplicated segment appears as a bulge in the altered chromosome rather than in the normal one (Fig. 18.3b).

An inversion is seen as a loop in the altered chromosome and a bulge in the unaltered chromosome, as similar regions in the two chromosomes come to lie near each other (Fig. 18.3c).

A translocation, when reciprocal, appears as a cross-shaped synapsis involving four chromosomes—two pairs of homologous chromosomes. In Fig. 18.3d, the segment 5678 of one chromosome has been exchanged with the segment EFGH of a nonhomologous chromosome (Fig. 18.3d).

Answers to Objective Questions

18.1 *b*

18.2 *c*

18.3 *c*

18.4 *d*

18.5 *a*

18.6 *c*

18.7 *d* [For (a) and (b), one base has been substituted for another, which means that at worst one amino acid will be substituted for another. In (c), three bases (a triplet) have been inserted, so an amino acid will be inserted into the polypeptide. In (d) a single base has been inserted, which changes all subsequent triplets and therefore all subsequent amino acids in the polypeptide.]

18.8 *c*

18.9 missense; nonsense; nonsense

18.10 frameshift

18.11 mutagens

18.12 radiation

18.13 mutations

18.14 transposons

18.15 thymine dimers; transcription; replication

18.16 x-rays

18.17 *b*

18.18 *c*

18.19 *c*

18.20 *a*

18.21 *c*

18.22 *c*

18.23 *b*

18.24 *a*

18.25 *d* (Frequency of recombination depends on the distance between two genes: the greater the distance, the more likely that crossing-over will occur. Hence *B* and *C* must be farther apart than *A–C* and *A–B*. This means *A* must be in the middle:

```
 |—— 9 ——|—— 17 ——|
 B       A         C
 |———————— 26 ————————|
```

18.26 independent assortment; crossing-over; recombination

18.27 independent assortment

18.28 crossing-over

18.29 brown; blue; blond; brown

18.30 four; two; two

18.31 nonhomologous; homologous

18.32 one

18.33 far apart

18.36 *a*

18.37 *c*

18.38 *a*

18.39 *c*

18.40 *a*

18.41 *b*

18.42 *b*

18.43 nondisjunction; meiosis I; meiosis II

18.44 four; two

18.45 plant

18.46 duplication; translocation; inversion

18.47 meiosis

18.48 deletion; duplication; inversion

CHAPTER 19
Evolutionary Theory

PRE-DARWINIAN IDEAS*

19.1 Charles Darwin's book, *On the origin of Species by Means of Natural Selection*, was first published in

(*a*) 1779. (*b*) 1831. (*c*) 1859. (*d*) 1901.

19.2 Aristotle believed that all living things can be arranged in order of increasing complexity, with no vacancies and no possibility of position change within the fixed order. This view of life is known as the

(*a*) inheritance of acquired characteristics. (*b*) preevolutionary ladder. (*c*) philosophy of essentialism.
(*d*) *Scala Naturae*.

19.3 Natural theologians believed that adaptations of organisms are

(*a*) evidence that organisms are designed by a Creator. (*b*) evidence that organisms are not designed by a Creator.
(*c*) incomplete and of no consequence. (*d*) an illusion, based on belief rather than on proof.

19.4 George Cuvier realized that the history of life is recorded in fossils and believed that the replacement of one species by another is caused by

(*a*) massive numbers of mutations. (*b*) the wrath of God. (*c*) extinctions due to catastrophes, such as floods.
(*d*) genetic inbreeding.

19.5 Most fossils are found in

(*a*) granite. (*b*) sedimentary rocks. (*c*) lava flows. (*d*) black soil.

19.6 Lyell reasoned that if most geologic events occur slowly, rather than catastrophically, then the earth must be

(*a*) very old. (*b*) younger than 10,000 years. (*c*) replicated elsewhere in the universe.
(*d*) formed from part of another planet.

19.7 Lamarck believed certain parts of the body get larger and more complex through the generations because they

(*a*) are used more extensively than other parts. (*b*) contribute to greater reproductive success.
(*c*) are predetermined to do so. (*d*) are most similar to God's perfection.

19.8 According to Lamarck, a giraffe has a long neck because

(*a*) a Creator designed it that way. (*b*) catastrophes eliminated short-necked forms. (*c*) its ancestors stretched their necks to get food. (*d*) ancestral giraffes with slightly longer necks than others got more food and left more surviving offspring.

19.9 The binomial system of classification names every kind of organism according to _____ and _____. The branch of biology devoted to naming and classifying organisms is _____.

19.10 The study of fossils, a branch of biology and geology called _____, was founded by Georges Cuvier.

19.11 Match the idea associated with the person by placing the letter of the person in the blank next to the idea.

(*a*) Aristotle (384–322 B.C.)   (*d*) Jean-Baptiste de Lamarck (1744–1829)
(*b*) Georges Cuvier (1769–1832)   (*e*) James Hutton (1726–1797)
(*c*) Carolus Linnaeus (1707–1778)

_____ uniformitarianism

_____ inheritance of acquired characteristics

* Answers to Chapter 19 objective questions appear on page 142.

_____ *Scala Naturae*

_____ catastrophism

_____ binomial classification

19.12 According to Cuvier, an area where extinctions have occurred is repopulated by _____ species, thereby explaining the turnover of species through time.

19.13 Lyell believed that profound geologic changes result from _____ and _____ events.

19.14 The one predecessor of Darwin and Wallace to develop a comprehensive theory of evolution, including its mechanism, was _____.

19.15 Why do almost all modern biologists reject Lamarck's theory of evolution?

🐚 Jean-Baptiste de Lamarck, a well-known French naturalist, proposed in 1809 a theory of evolution by inheritance of acquired characteristics, rather than by natural selection. The theory states: (1) organisms change, or evolve, through time in ways that adapt them to their local environments and (2) such changes occur when the environment alters the organism's phenotype, and information about this phenotypic change is passed from the somatic cells to the reproductive cells of the body, and from there via gametes to the offspring. Lamarck used as an example the giraffe's neck. He believed that giraffes' necks became longer through the generations because giraffes stretched their necks to reach leaves on tall trees. His explanation was that information about neck-stretching was transmitted in some way to the gametes, and thus long necks became a permanent trait, acquired within a giraffe's lifetime and passed thereafter from generation to generation by hereditary factors.

The theory of evolution by inheritance of acquired characteristics has not been disproved, but so little evidence has appeared in its support that most biologists reject it completely. (The theory of evolution by natural selection has a huge amount of evidence in its support.) Everything we now know about genes indicates there is no way that changes in somatic cells can cause directed changes in the genes of reproductive cell. Modifications of an individual's phenotype during its lifetime are not passed on to offspring. All changes in the DNA of a reproductive cell are random changes (mutations) rather than directed changes that improve an organism's adaptation to its environment. Natural selection, acting on these random changes, removes from the population those mutations that reduce an individual's fitness (i.e., its *reproductive* success relative to the rest of the population's), so that the mutations, or new alleles, that persist either have no effect on or improve an organism's adaptation to its environment. Beginning with a population of giraffes with somewhat variable neck lengths, giraffes that could not reach the leaves on tall trees did not get enough food to survive and/or reproduce; their genes were not passed on to future generations. Giraffes with longer necks got more food, left more offspring, and contributed more genes to future generations.

DARWIN AND HIS THEORY

19.16 The primary mission of the voyage of *H. M. S. Beagle* (1831–1836) was to

(*a*) carry arms to the New World. (*b*) chart the South American coastline. (*c*) find out how many species there were in the world. (*d*) disprove Lamarck's theory.

19.17 On the voyage of the *Beagle*, Charles Darwin (1809–1882) found that the plants and animals of temperate South America are most similar to plants and animals of

(*a*) tropical South America. (*b*) Australia. (*c*) Asia. (*d*) Europe.

19.18 Darwin also found that South American fossils are most similar to

(*a*) Australian fossils. (*b*) Asian fossils. (*c*) living species of South America. (*d*) living species of North America.

19.19 Darwin believed that certain parts of the body get larger and more complex through the generations because they

(*a*) are used more extensively than other parts. (*b*) contribute to greater reproductive success. (*c*) are predetermined to do so. (*d*) are most similar to God's perfection.

19.20 Darwin believed that a giraffe has a long neck because

(*a*) a Creator designed it that way. (*b*) catastrophes eliminated short-necked forms. (*c*) its ancestors stretched their necks to get food. (*d*) ancestral giraffes with slightly longer necks than others got more food and left more surviving offspring.

19.21   According to Darwin, two different areas within a continent have different species because they have different

(*a*) evolutionary mechanisms.   (*b*) ancestors.   (*c*) environments.   (*d*) evolutionary times.

19.22   On the average, each female of species X leaves 10 female offspring in her lifetime. If all offspring survive to reproduce, then how many female descendants will a single female leave after 10 generations?

(*a*) 100;   (*b*) 100,000;   (*c*) 10,000,000;   (*d*) 10,000,000,000

19.23   The struggle for existence is a consequence of

(*a*) each organism leaving more offspring than needed to replace itself.   (*b*) innate competitive tendencies. (*c*) the inevitable difficulty of coping with climatic conditions.   (*d*) territories and dominance hierarchies.

19.24   Of all the species that ever lived, approximately how many have gone extinct?

(*a*) Less than 1%;   (*b*) 20%;   (*c*) 60%;   (*d*) More than 99%

19.25   Both C. Darwin and A. R. Wallace developed, independently of each other, the theory of evolution by natural selection. Yet Darwin is given credit for the theory because he

(*a*) published it first.   (*b*) had traveled outside Europe for his evidence.   (*c*) was older and more respected. (*d*) presented more evidence.

19.26   Darwin read Lyell's *Principles of Geology* while on the *Beagle*. From this, he made an important step in his progress toward an evolutionary theory, in accepting that the earth is _____ and _____.

19.27   Darwin did not use the word "evolution" in the first edition of the *Origin of Species by Means of Natural Selection*. Instead he referred to descent with _____, which expressed his belief in the _____ of life.

19.28   Darwin was influenced by Thomas Malthus, who, in 1798, wrote that much of human misery is caused by the fact that human populations increase _____, whereas their resources increases _____.

19.29   Plants and animals of the Galapagos Islands resemble most closely the plants and animals of

(*a*) North America.   (*b*) South America.   (*c*) Asia.   (*d*) Australia.

19.30   Each island in the Galapagos Archipelago has its own form of giant tortoise. These reptiles vary from island to island because they have evolved _____ since reaching the islands.

19.31   Darwin used as evidence of evolution the breeding of domestic animals, a process know as *artificial selection*. In artificial selection, _____ are the selective agent, whereas in natural selection the selective agent is _____.

19.32   Natural selection operates only on _____ traits.

19.33   For evolution to take place, a population must have both _____ and _____.

19.34   How did the Galapagos finches contribute to the development of Darwin's ideas?

🐚   The Galapagos finches, or Darwin's finches, are a group of 14 species that form their own subfamily— Geospizinae—in the finch family (Fringillidae). Thirteen of the species are found only in the Galapagos Archipelago, and one is found only on Cocos Island, about 1000 km northeast of the Galapagos Islands.

When Darwin visited these islands, he was impressed by the differences in body size, beak shape, and feeding habits among these closely related birds. Some of the species were apparently restricted to just a single island (they are not good fliers), and others were seen on several islands. By and large, these finches, as well as other plants and animals of the Galapagos Islands, resembled the plants and animals of South America, located approximately 1000 km to the east. Darwin wondered why, if these organisms were created specifically for the Galapagos, they resembled the organisms of South America rather than the organisms of, say, Africa or Asia. Knowing the islands are volcanic, and therefore considerably younger than South America, Darwin speculated that a few individuals of an ancestral finch species in South America flew to these islands shortly after the islands rose from the ocean floor. As the local population grew and spread to all the islands, it became fragmented into separate populations on separate islands. Each isolated population experienced a unique set of environmental conditions with a unique set of selective pressures, and each gradually evolved a unique set of adaptations.

19.35 Describe Darwin's theory in the context of the scientific process.

🐚 Darwin was unusually talented in both inductive and deductive logic. He amassed enormous quantities of information from his own observations and experiments and from correspondence with other naturalists. From the factual information he collected, which pertained to only a small percentage of all living organisms, Darwin made generalizations (inductive logic) about the characteristics of all forms of life. These hypotheses were educated guesses about general patterns of nature.

Darwin then evaluated what he could predict if his hypotheses were true and determined, by deductive logic, what the mechanisms of natural selection were. Darwin's theory of evolution by natural selection is based on only four hypotheses and two deductions (predictions) derived from the hypotheses.

Hypothesis I: All organisms tend to leave more offspring than are needed to replace themselves when they die.

Hypothesis II: The number of individuals within each species remains approximately constant over time.

First Deduction: If hypotheses I and II are correct, then not all individuals survive and/or not all individuals who survive leave offspring. There is a struggle for existence.

Hypothesis III: Not all individuals of a species are alike.

Hypothesis IV: Some of the characteristics of individuals are passed from parent to offspring.

Second Deduction: If individuals within a species are different (hypothesis III), then certain kinds of individuals are more successful in the struggle for existence and leave a greater number of offspring. If the characteristics that contribute to superior survival and reproduction are passed from parent to offspring (hypothesis IV), then these same characteristics will increase in frequency from generation to generation. Whether a particular characteristic is superior or inferior depends on local environmental conditions.

Is the theory of evolution correct? A theory is a human interpretation of reality that must be repeatedly tested before it is accepted by the scientific community. A theory is tested by examining its logical consequences; predictions arising from the theory must hold true if the theory is correct. The predictions from Darwin's theory have been repeatedly tested and thus far have been found to be correct.

EVIDENCE OF EVOLUTION

19.36 The idea of common descent was first suggested to Darwin by his observations on

(*a*) geographic distributions of species. (*b*) human pedigrees. (*c*) comparative embryology. (*d*) blood groups of birds.

19.37 The wings of a bird and the forelegs of a horse are

(*a*) analogous structures. (*b*) homologous structures. (*c*) vestigial structures. (*d*) phylogenetic structures.

19.38 The wings of a bird and the wings of an insect are

(*a*) analogous structures. (*b*) homologous structures. (*c*) vestigial structures. (*d*) phylogenetic structures.

19.39 The pelvis and the leg bones of a snake are

(*a*) analogous structures. (*b*) homologous structures. (*c*) vestigial structures. (*d*) phylogenetic structures.

19.40 In humans, the two sets of muscles that move the ears are

(*a*) analogous structures. (*b*) homologous structures. (*c*) vestigial structures. (*d*) phylogenetic structures.

19.41 The best test of the relatedness of two species is in the similarity of their

(*a*) anatomy. (*b*) DNA and proteins. (*c*) development. (*d*) courtship behaviors.

19.42 Populations of peppered moths (*Biston betularia*) of England changed from 1 percent dark and 99 percent light individuals to 99 percent dark and 1 percent light individuals between 1848 and 1898. The selective agent causing the change was

(*a*) humans. (*b*) toxins from smoke. (*c*) birds. (*d*) tree bark.

19.43 After pollution destroyed lichens (which are light in color) on the trees, the survival of the dark-colored peppered moths increased, because they were

(*a*) protected from carcinogens.   (*b*) protected from lichen poisons.   (*c*) more robust.   (*d*) protected from predation.

19.44 Many bacteria are now resistant to penicillin, because

(*a*) penicillin causes gene mutations, some of which are beneficial.   (*b*) previously resistant forms survived and reproduced better than nonresistant forms.   (*c*) the hospital environment inhibits competition among bacteria. (*d*) penicillin triggers the synthesis of resistant proteins.

19.45 Much of the evidence in support of evolution is in the form of _____, studied by paleontologists.

19.46 Gill pouches are found not only in fishes, but at some stage of life in all _____.

19.47 The fossil record clearly shows that the major groups of organisms appeared on earth in a _____ pattern. An explanation for this pattern is that _____ groups gave rise to _____ groups.

19.48 Evolved features that make organisms better suited to live and reproduce in their environments are called _____.

19.49 Evidence that species are not created for life in a specific place is that oceanic islands often have _____, but no other kinds of mammals (except those introduced by humans).

19.50 Is Darwin's theory of evolution supported by our relatively recent knowledge of molecular biology?

❀   If all organisms evolved from a common ancestral stock, then (1) many of the basic biologic processes should be similar in all organisms and (2) the molecules of closely related organisms (as classified by some other criteria) should be more similar than the molecules of organisms that are distantly related.

Molecular biologists have found support for the first prediction: many basic processes are similar in all organisms, from bacteria to humans. In cellular respiration, for example, all cells use cytochromes for electron transport and ATP for capturing the released energy. Likewise, all cells store information in DNA and transcribe it into RNA prior to the synthesis of proteins, and many of the enzymes (e.g., RNA polymerase) involved in protein synthesis are similar among the diverse types of organisms. Furthermore, except for some DNA in mitochondria and chloroplasts, all organisms use the same genetic code of three nucleotides to signify a particular amino acid in a protein.

Information from molecular biology also supports the second prediction: closely related organisms, as classified, prior to knowledge about molecular biology, have more similar nucleotide sequences in their DNA and more similar amino acid sequences in their proteins than distantly related organisms. Some of the data on taxonomic relationships and hemoglobin similarities are given in Table 19.1.

TABLE 19.1 Comparisons of Similarities in Taxonomy and in the Beta Chain of Hemoglobin

species	number of amino acid differences compared to human hemoglobin
Human	0
Gorilla	1
Gibbon	2
Rhesus monkey	8
Dog	15
Horse, cow	25
Mouse	27
Gray kangaroo	38
Chicken	45
Frog	67
Lamprey	125

NEO-DARWINISM: THE SYNTHETIC THEORY

19.51 The most important evidence since Darwin that bears on his theory has been in the area of

(*a*) paleontology.   (*b*) genetics.   (*c*) comparative anatomy.   (*d*) comparative embryology.

19.52 The unit of evolution is now known to be the

(*a*) individual.   (*b*) family.   (*c*) population.   (*d*) species.

19.53 The unit of natural selection is the

(*a*) individual.   (*b*) family.   (*c*) population.   (*d*) species.

19.54 The Darwinian fitness of an organism is a measure of

(*a*) its ability, relative to others in the population, to pass its genes to the next generation.   (*b*) the number of offspring it produces.   (*c*) its lifespan.   (*d*) its physical vigor.

19.55 An important addition to Darwin's work was the discovery that _____ occur, providing a source for the observed inherited variations.

19.56 Darwin could not explain completely the mechanisms of evolution, because he was ignorant of the mechanisms of _____ .

19.57 The branch of biology that emerged from the synthesis of Darwinian evolution and Mendelian genetics is _____ .

19.58 Evolution is a change, over time, in the frequency of _____ within a _____ , caused by differential reproduction in response to local environmental conditions.

19.59 How does the neo-Darwinian synthesis differ from the Darwinian theory of evolution?

🐚   The basic theory developed by Darwin and all information acquired from repeatedly testing the theory have been incorporated into a comprehensive, or neo-Darwinian, theory of evolution by natural selection. Information acquired since 1859 has refined, but not substantially altered, the basic structure of Darwin's theory. Important changes include a redefined unit of evolution, a knowledge of genetics, and the appreciation that not all kinds of mortality or differential reproduction produce evolutionary change.

The unit of evolution is now recognized to be the *population* (see Question 19.60). Although Darwin's theory deals with changes in species, we now know that most species are subdivided into local populations with varying degrees of reproductive isolation. Evolution is defined as a change in the frequency of an allele within a population in response to local environmental conditions.

An important addition to Darwin's theory is knowledge about the physical basis of heredity, i.e., about genes and how they are transmitted from parent to offspring. (The neo-Darwinian synthesis refers to the synthesis, or merging, of evolution and genetics.) We now know that differences among individuals result from an accumulation of mutations (alleles) in the population and from the recombination of genes (independent assortment, crossovers, and fertilization) during sexual reproduction. Each offspring of a mated pair inherits a unique array of genes, and interactions between genotypes and environmental factors determine the phenotypes. These expressed traits, in turn, influence which individuals reproduce more successfully and, therefore, which genes increase in frequency within the local population.

Darwin predicted that individuals with certain traits will be more successful in the struggle for existence and leave more offspring than other individuals in the species. We are now aware that this is not always true. Many mortalities in populations are nonselective; particular genotypes do not make individuals more or less vulnerable to certain causes of mortality. Catastrophes, such as floods and fires, can remove the majority of individuals in a population, regardless of their genotypes; chance factors, such as the genotypes of the few individuals that colonize an island, play a greater role in evolution than Darwin realized.

19.60 Why has the focus of evolutionary theory changed, since Darwin, from the species to the population?

🐚   Darwin recognized that evolution proceeds within a group of individuals who reproduce with one another but are reproductively isolated from other groups of individuals. For this reason he chose the species as the unit of evolution, since a species is a group of similar organisms that can mate and reproduce with one another. We now know, however, that a species is not a homogenous group of individuals, but rather a mosaic of populations. Each population consists of individuals that live in close proximity and have a high probability of actually mating and producing offspring. Individuals of the same species are in different populations when they are so separated from one another that it is highly unlikely they will meet and reproduce; mating could occur but does not.

The individuals of a population form a unique set of genotypes, or gene pool, and local environmental factors act as selective agents to alter the gene pool in ways that adapt the organisms to the local conditions. Thus, each population of a species follows its own course of evolution. Interbreeding among the populations of a species may occur often enough to prevent total reproductive isolation of the populations, so that all individuals within a species remain sufficiently similar for interpopulation matings to continue. Alternatively, interbreeding may be so rare that each population, following its own course of evolution, may become so different in morphology or habits that there can be no interbreeding among the populations. When this happens, the isolated populations become separate species, as occurred among the giant tortoises and the finches of the Galapagos Islands.

Answers to Objective Questions

19.1 *c*

19.2 *d*

19.3 *a*

19.4 *c*

19.5 *b*

19.6 *a*

19.7 *a*

19.8 *c*

19.9 genus; species; taxonomy

19.10 paleontology

19.11 (*a*) *Scala Naturae*;
(*b*) catastrophism;
(*c*) binomial classification;
(*d*) inheritance of acquired characteristics;
(*e*) uniformitarianism

19.12 immigrant, or neighboring

19.13 slow; continuous

19.14 Lamarck

19.16 *b*

19.17 *a*

19.18 *c*

19.19 *b*

19.20 *d*

19.21 *c*

19.22 *d*

19.23 *a*

19.24 *d*

19.25 *d*

19.26 very old; continuously changing

19.27 modification; continuity

19.28 exponentially (or geometrically); arithmetically

19.29 *b*

19.30 separately (in isolation)

19.31 humans; the environment

19.32 inherited

19.33 genetic variability; differential reproduction

19.36 *a*

19.37 *b*

19.38 *a*

19.39 *c*

19.40 *c*

19.41 *b*

19.42 *c*

19.43 *d*

19.44 *b*

19.45 fossils

19.46 vertebrate animals (or chordates)

19.47 sequential; primitive; advanced

19.48 adaptations

19.49 bats

19.51 *b*

19.52 *c*

19.53 *a*

19.54 *a*

19.55 mutations

19.56 inheritance

19.57 population genetics

19.58 an allele; population

CHAPTER 20

POPULATION GENETICS*

20.1   The unit of evolution is the

       (**a**) individual. (**b**) social group. (**c**) population. (**d**) species.

20.2   The total collection of genes, at any one time, in a unit of evolution is called the

       (**a**) genotype. (**b**) demotype. (**c**) multiple-allelic group. (**d**) gene pool.

20.3   A change in the relative abundance of an allele (the allelic frequency) within a population, over a succession of generations, is called

       (**a**) microevolution, or adaptive evolution. (**b**) macroevolution, or speciation. (**c**) coevolution. (**d**) phylogenetic evolution.

20.4   Imagine a population of 100 snails in which shell color is controlled by two alleles: B (black) and b (yellow). What is the total number of loci for the gene for shell color in this population?

       (**a**) 3; (**b**) 60; (**c**) 100; (**d**) 200

20.5   In the snail population described above, 20 of the snails are yellow (b/b) and 80 are black (B/B or B/b). Of the 80 black snails, 30 are homozygous and 50 are heterozygous. How many of the loci for this gene are occupied by the B allele?

       (**a**) 80; (**b**) 90; (**c**) 100; (**d**) 110

20.6   In the snail population described above, what is the allelic frequency of B?

       (**a**) 0.45; (**b**) 0.55; (**c**) 0.75; (**d**) 0.80

20.7   Assuming sexual reproduction with random mating, no gene flow, and no selection, what will be the frequency of yellow snails in the next generation of the population described above?

       (**a**) 0.20; (**b**) 0.30; (**c**) 0.45; (**d**) 0.55

20.8   What will be the frequency of the b allele in the next generation of the snail population described above?

       (**a**) 0.20; (**b**) 0.30; (**c**) 0.45; (**d**) 0.55

20.9   In natural selection, _____ are selected for or against, and _____ evolve.

20.10   A group of individuals with the potential to interbreed is a _____, whereas a group of individuals with a high probability of interbreeding is a _____.

20.11   A gene pool consists of all _____ at all gene loci in all _____ of the population.

20.12   When all members of a population are homozygous for the same allele, that allele is said to be _____ in the gene pool.

20.13   Mendel described the frequency of _____ for the offspring of a single _____; Hardy and Weinberg described the frequency of _____ for an entire _____.

---

* Answers to Chapter 20 objective questions appear on page 149.

20.14 Assume that allele C occurs at 60 percent of the loci and allele c at 40 percent of the loci for a particular gene in a population. Assuming Hardy-Weinberg equilibrium, the frequency of genotype C/C in the next generation will be _____; the frequency of genotype C/c will be _____; and the frequency of genotype c/c will be _____.

20.15 If the frequency of one allele is p, then the frequency of the alternative allele in the population is _____.

20.16 One out of every 10,000 newborns in the United States has phenylketonuria (PKU), a debilitating disease (when untreated) caused by a recessive allele. The frequency of carriers of this disease is _____.

20.17 The Hardy-Weinberg equation describes conditions that are not found in natural populations. What then is its value?

🐉 The Hardy-Weinberg equation, developed independently by G. H. Hardy, an English mathematician, and G. Weinberg, a German physician, in 1908, describes the relationship between allelic frequencies and genotypic frequencies in successive generations of a population that is at equilibrium—is not evolving. The Hardy-Weinberg equation is

$$p^2 + 2pq + q^2 = 1$$

where p = frequency of one allele (e.g., A) at a locus
   q = frequency of the alternative allele (e.g., a) at the same locus
   p^2 = frequency of the genotype homozygous for the allele present in frequency p (e.g., A/A)
   $2pq$ = frequency of the heterozygous genotype (e.g., A/a)
   q^2 = frequency of the genotype homozygous for the allele present in frequency q (e.g., a/a)

If the frequency of one of the alleles (e.g., p) is known, then the frequency of the other allele ($q = 1 - p$) is known, and the frequencies of the homozygous genotypes (p^2 and q^2) as well as those of the heterozygous genotype ($2pq$) can be calculated. Or, if the frequency of homozygous recessive individuals in the population (a/a, or q^2) is known, then the frequencies of the a allele (q) and the A allele (p or $1 - q$) can be calculated. It is then possible to predict genotypic frequencies in the present and future generations.

The Hardy-Weinberg principle states that the frequencies of alleles and genotypes remain the same from generation to generation—are not altered by genetic recombinations—provided that the following conditions hold.

1. No mutations
2. An infinitely large population (no genetic drift)
3. No emigration out of or immigration into the population (no gene flow)
4. Random matings between individuals (no assortative matings)
5. Equal reproductive success among the genotypes (no natural selection)

No natural population experiences such conditions. The function of the Hardy-Weinberg principle, and its equation, is as an experimental control—a prediction of what the allelic and genotypic frequencies should be if nothing acts to alter the gene pool. Thus, if q is known to be 0.40, then q^2 in the next generation should be 0.16. If, instead, it is 0.02, then we know that a change has occurred in the gene pool, the magnitude of that change, and that it was caused by: mutations, genetic drift, gene flow, assortative mating, or natural selection. We can then design experiments to test which of the five agents of change contributed most to the change in allelic and genotypic frequencies.

FACTORS THAT CAUSE CHANGES IN THE GENE POOL

20.18 Genetic drift, or changes in allelic frequency due to chance factors, occurs in populations that are very

(a) isolated. (b) small in number. (c) mobile. (d) closely adapted to local environments.

20.19 An isolated population of humans, with approximately equal numbers of blue-eyed and brown-eyed individuals, was decimated by an earthquake. Only a few brown-eyed people remained to form the next generation. This kind of change in the gene pool is called a

(a) Hardy-Weinberg equilibrium. (b) blocked gene flow. (c) bottleneck effect. (d) founder effect.

20.20 A potential danger to a population that has been greatly reduced in number is the

(a) loss of genetic variability. (b) tendency toward assortative mating. (c) reduced gene flow. (d) Hardy-Weinberg disequilibrium.

20.21 Genetic drift occurs when a few individuals of a species colonize an island. This particular phenomenon is known as

(*a*) the bottleneck effect. (*b*) the founder effect. (*c*) assortative mating. (*d*) random mating.

20.22 A new mutation spreads from one population to another by means of

(*a*) removed bottlenecks. (*b*) emigrants and immigrants. (*c*) mutation pressures. (*d*) crossovers.

20.23 If a new allele suddenly becomes very abundant in a population, most likely it is

(*a*) mutating rapidly. (*b*) flowing with emigrants. (*c*) strongly selected for. (*d*) a product of assortative mating.

20.24 A plant population that reproduces by self-pollination is an extreme example of

(*a*) the bottleneck effect. (*b*) the founder effect. (*c*) rapid gene flow. (*d*) assortative mating.

20.25 Natural selection is best defined as occurring when the environment causes

(*a*) differential success in reproduction. (*b*) differential mortality. (*c*) assortative mating. (*d*) a reduced gene pool.

20.26 Microevolution can be measured by comparing observed allelic frequencies with those predicted by

(*a*) chance. (*b*) the Hardy-Weinberg equation. (*c*) Mendelian ratios. (*d*) all known environmental factors.

20.27 Of all the causes of gene-pool changes, only _____ adapts a population to its environment.

20.28 A change in the gene pool of a small population due to chance is called _____. Effects of this general phenomenon are of two types: _____ effects and _____ effects.

20.29 The northern population of elephant seals was reduced by hunting to only 20 animals; it then returned to a large population of over 30,000. In the 24 gene loci examined by researchers, only a single allele was found at each of the loci. This is an example of allelic _____ caused by a population _____.

20.30 Genetic drift in a new colony is known as the _____ effect.

20.31 The loss or gain of alleles in a population due to emigration or immigration is known as _____; it decreases genetic differences among populations.

20.32 Nonrandom mating of individuals within a population is called _____ and can cause deviations from the Hardy-Weinberg prediction.

20.33 When the environment causes a change in the gene pool by coontrolling reproductive success according to genotype, it is called _____.

20.34 What is the relation between agents of evolution and conditions of the Hardy-Weinberg equilibrium?

🐚 There are two forms of evolution: *microevolution*, which involves changes in allelic frequencies within a gene pool, and *macroevolution*, which involves large-scale changes among groups of species. The potential agents of microevolution, those that can cause changes in the gene pool, are: mutations, genetic drift, gene flow, assortative mating, and natural selection. Each of the five agents violates one of the five conditions of the Hardy-Weinberg equation: no mutations, an infinitely large population, no emigration or immigration, random matings, and equal reproductive success among the genotypes. Of the five agents of change, only natural selection can adapt a population to its local environment; the other four are nonadaptive changes. Thus, when evolution is defined as a change in allelic frequency within a population, then the term "evolution" includes both nonadaptive and adaptive changes. When evolution is defined as a change in allelic frequency within a population in response to local conditions, then the term includes only adaptive changes.

20.35 What are some examples of assortative mating, and how do they affect the Hardy-Weinberg equilibrium?

🐚 Nonassortative mating occurs when the mate of each individual is selected at random from the population without regard to genotype. Such random mating probably never happens, simply because of the nonrandom spatial distribution, with regard to ancestry, of individuals in the environment and the tendency of neighbors to mate with one another.

Positive assortative mating occurs when similar organisms mate more often with each other than would be expected if mating were random. It is caused by inbreeding (mating with close relatives) and by attractions between phenotypically similar individuals. Inbreeding is most extreme when an individual self-fertilizes, as in self-pollinating plants, but is common in a less extreme form whenever relatives remain nearer one another than nonrelatives and so tend to mate with one another. Inbreeding always occurs to some extent unless there are very effective mechanisms for dispersal from the natal site. Attractions between phenotypically similar individuals are seen in animal populations where both males and females acquire status in dominance hierarchies on the basis of the same phenotypic traits, and males tend to mate with females of similar status. Positive assortative mating leads to a higher frequency of homozygotes and a lower frequency of heterozygotes than predicted by the Hardy-Weinberg equation. With inbreeding, the increased homozygosity develops at all gene loci, whereas in phenotypic attractions it is restricted to the loci that influence the particular traits involved.

Negative assortative mating occurs when dissimilar individuals mate more often than expected if mating were random. An example is found in populations of plants that are dimorphic for length of the style (the tube through which the sperm nucleus moves to the egg). Pollination in these plants is restricted to crosses between long-styled and short-styled flowers. Negative assortative mating is seen also in fruit flies who, after several generations of inbreeding, show little interest in courtship and mating, but are stimulated to normal levels of reproductive behavior when a new strain of flies is added to the inbred population. This type of mating between dissimilar individuals causes an increase in heterozygosity and a decrease in homozygosity, as compared with the frequencies predicted by the Hardy-Weinberg equation. Where it involves matings between genetically distant individuals, the increase in heterozygosity is found at all loci; where it involves matings between individuals who are dissimilar in one or a few phenotypic traits, then the increased heterozygosity appears only at the loci influencing those particular traits.

GENETIC VARIATION

20.36   Yarrow plants (*Achillea lanulosa*) in California become shorter with increases in elevation of the land (e.g., slopes of the Sierra), a change attributed in part to genetic differences. Such a change in gene pool with an environmental gradient is called a

(*a*) gradualism.   (*b*) cline.   (*c*) gradient of diploidy.   (*d*) balanced polymorphism.

20.37   House sparrows (*Passer domesticus*) are larger the farther north they live, a difference due in part to their genes. This difference is an example of a

(*a*) gradualism.   (*b*) cline.   (*c*) gradient of diploidy.   (*d*) polymorphism.

20.38   Human blood groups—A, B, AB, and O—are an example of a

(*a*) gradualism.   (*b*) cline.   (*c*) gradient of diploidy.   (*d*) polymorphism.

20.39   All alleles originate from

(*a*) mutations.   (*b*) crossovers.   (*c*) gene flow.   (*d*) nondisjunctions.

20.40   In diploid organisms, a great deal of genetic variation is concealed—i.e., is not subject to natural selection—because it is present in the form of

(*a*) somatic mutations.   (*b*) asexual differences.   (*c*) recessive alleles.   (*d*) gametic alleles.

20.41   People who carry an allele for normal hemoglobin and an allele for sickle cell are resistant to malaria. They are examples of

(*a*) heterozygote advantage.   (*b*) extreme diploidy.   (*c*) outbreeding.   (*d*) recessive superiority.

20.42   Hybrid vigor is often seen in the offspring of two purebred lines of crop plants (e.g., corn). Such vigor is an example of

(*a*) heterozygote advantage.   (*b*) extreme diploidy.   (*c*) hermaphroditism.   (*d*) recessive superiority.

20.43   Diversity of genotypes at a single location is called _____ variation, whereas diversity of genotypes over a broad region is called _____ variation.

20.44 Genetic variation that parallels a gradient in the environment (e.g., a rainfall gradient) is called a
_____.

20.45 When two or more distinct forms of individuals, such as brown grasshoppers and green grasshoppers, are found
in the same population, such a population is known as a _____ population. When the frequency of
each form does not change through the generations, this is called a _____.

20.46 When and where a mutation occurs depends on _____.

20.47 Heterozygosity protects _____ from natural selection.

20.48 The diversity of human fingerprints is an example of _____ variation, since it seems to confer no
selective advantages.

20.49 In British land snails (*Cepaea nemoralis*), there are several forms of shell color and banding pattern. Each form
is well-camouflaged from predatory birds within a particular microenvironment. This is an example of
_____ polymorphism; it is preserved by _____.

20.50 What are the advantages of diploidy as compared with haploidy?

🐚 A population of diploid organisms carries a great deal of genetic variability, in the form of recessive alleles,
that is not subject to natural selection and so is preserved through the generations. Although such recessive
alleles may be deleterious under existing conditions and removed by natural selection when homozygous, they
may turn out to be advantageous to future generations existing under different conditions. A population of
haploid organisms, by contrast, has all its alleles tested by natural selection in each generation, with most of the
alleles being eliminated. Because a diploid population carries so much more genetic variability than a haploid
population and because genetic variability is the raw material of evolution, a diploid population evolves more
rapidly in response to changes in its environment.

An individual organism itself benefits from diploidy if it is heterozygous and one of the alleles does not code
for a functional product. Thus, having two copies of each gene ensures that each type of protein can be made
and normal cell functions can be carried out. A diploid individual has another advantage in that having two
functional forms of the same gene sometimes is better than having only one form in duplicate. Such a *heterozygote advantage* may develop when each of the two proteins coded for by the two alleles functions better
under different environmental conditions. For example, slightly different forms of an enzyme often function
optimally at different temperatures, so that a particular chemical reaction could be facilitated by one of the enzymes
when the cell is cooler and by the other enzyme when it is warmer. An organism that is heterozygous for the
enzyme can rapidly perform this chemical reaction over a broader range of temperatures than an organism that
is homozygous and has only one form of the enzyme.

Although diploidy confers clear advantages, to both the population and the heterozygous individual, many
organisms are haploid throughout their adult lives. Their continued existence demonstrates that the diploid
condition is not always superior to the haploid condition.

ADAPTIVE EVOLUTION

20.51 Another term for adaptive evolution is

(*a*) clinal change.   (*b*) speciation.   (*c*) microevolution.   (*d*) macroevolution.

20.52 In a population of land snails, some have dark shells and others have light shells. Each morph produces 100
offspring per year, but the dark-shelled morphs live long enough to reproduce for five seasons, whereas the light-
shelled morphs, which are easily seen by bird predators, live to reproduce for only one season. The Darwinian
fitness of the light-shelled morphs is

(*a*) 0.   (*b*) 0.20.   (*c*) 5.   (*d*) 100.

20.53 In a population of large- and small-flowered daisies, those with large flowers leave an average of 1000 surviving
offspring, whereas those with small flowers leave an average of only 250 offspring. The Darwinian fitness of the
large-flowered daisies is

(*a*) 1000.   (*b*) 4.   (*c*) 1.00.   (*d*) 0.25.

20.54 The selection coefficient of the two types of daisies described above is

(*a*) 0.25. (*b*) 0.75. (*c*) 1.00. (*d*) 4.00.

20.55 A lethal gene has a selection coefficient of

(*a*) 0. (*b*) 0.50. (*c*) 1.00. (*d*) 100.

20.56 A deleterious allele decreases more rapidly in frequency if it is

(*a*) recently mutated. (*b*) rare. (*c*) dominant. (*d*) recessive.

20.57 A beneficial allele increases more rapidly in frequency if it is

(*a*) recently mutated. (*b*) rare. (*c*) dominant. (*d*) recessive.

20.58 Natural selection acts on an organism's

(*a*) dominant alleles. (*b*) recessive, homozygous alleles. (*c*) phenotype. (*d*) combined genotype.

20.59 Interdependent genes, with related functions, form

(*a*) a coadapted gene complex. (*b*) an inversion. (*c*) a fitness set. (*d*) a super mutation.

20.60 A single genotype can give rise to a range of phenotypes, called the genotype's

(*a*) norm of reaction. (*b*) fitness set. (*c*) adaptive complex. (*d*) supergene.

20.61 Stabilizing selection favors

(*a*) both extreme forms of a trait. (*b*) intermediate forms of a trait. (*c*) environmental differences.
(*d*) one extreme form over the other extreme form and over intermediate forms of a trait.

20.62 Directional selection favors

(*a*) both extreme forms of a trait. (*b*) intermediate forms of a trait. (*c*) environmental differences.
(*d*) one extreme form over the other extreme form and over intermediate forms of a trait.

20.63 Disruptive selection favors

(*a*) both extreme forms of a trait. (*b*) intermediate forms of a trait. (*c*) environmental differences.
(*d*) one extreme form over the other extreme form and over intermediate forms of a trait.

20.64 In some birds, such as the peacock and pheasant, the males are more colorful than the females. The selective agent producing the evolution of such conspicuous features is

(*a*) females. (*b*) predators. (*c*) humans. (*d*) climate.

20.65 Selection acts on all traits that influence _____ and _____.

20.66 Darwinian fitness is the _____ contribution of an individual to the gene pool of the next generation. Its values range from _____ to _____.

20.67 An individual who survives to old age but leaves no offspring has a fitness of _____.

20.68 The difference between two fitness values, usually between an inferior genotype and the most fit genotype, is known as the _____ coefficient. If a genotype is lethal, this difference is _____.

20.69 The rate at which an allele changes frequency over the generations depends on the strength of _____, measured as the magnitude of the _____.

20.70 When coadapted genes are located close together on the same chromosome, they form a _____.

20.71 Unusually large and unusually small newborns have higher mortality rates than newborns of average weight. This is an example of _____ selection.

20.72 When one population evolves in response to another, and vice versa, this is called _____. An example is the evolution of flowers and their _____.

20.73 Peppered moths changed from predominantly light gray to predominantly dark grey as industrial pollution became more prevalent in Britain. This is an example of _____ selection.

20.74 Stabilizing selection tends to _____ variation.

20.75 A population of mice, with coat colors that range from white to black, including all intermediate shades, placed in an environment of white sand and black lava and exposed to an aerial predator would experience _____ selection.

20.76 The steady increase in body size that occurred during evolution of the horse is an example of _____ selection.

20.77 Conspicuous differences between males and females (other than in reproductive organs) are special cases of polymorphism known as _____.

20.78 In many populations of deer, the male is larger than the female and has large antlers. These traits evolved because the largest males with the largest weapons had the greatest _____.

20.79 Why is it so difficult to predict rates of evolution?

◈ Several genetic factors obscure the results of natural selection. One gene may affect many characteristics, or many genes may determine one characteristic. Therefore, it is difficult to predict the exact effects of selection on the population. A particular gene is combined with thousands of other genes in an individual, so a beneficial and a detrimental gene may occur in the same individual or a gene that is beneficial at one stage of life may be detrimental at a later stage of life. Natural selection affects the whole individual; it either lives or dies, reproduces or fails to achieve its reproductive potential. Whether a particular allele increases in frequency depends on its effects and on the effects of all other alleles in the organism. It is therefore not usually possible to predict the precise rate at which a particular allele will increase or decrease within the population.

20.80 Considering the amount of time that natural selection has been operating, why hasn't it produced organisms that are perfectly adapted to their environments?

◈ Because environmental factors continually remove maladapted genotypes from the population, it seems that a perfect fit between genotypes and their environments should be achieved at some point. This is not true, however, mainly because environments are always changing. Not only is the physical environment altered as a result of climatic changes, but other species in the environment also change, either as a result of their own evolution or the extinction and replacement of other species. A predator population, for example, causes evolutionary changes in its prey population by selectively removing the genotypes that are easiest to capture. If only certain individuals in the predator population can capture food, then changes in the prey population will, in turn, cause evolutionary changes in the predator population. Similarly, when resources are scarce and individuals compete for a limited food supply, the best competitors will leave the most offspring. Successive generations of a population are always composed of individuals whose parents performed best in the past, making the competition more and more keen. This condition of continuous environmental change and continuous evolution is known as the *Red Queen effect*, after the character in Lewis Carroll's story, *Through the Looking Glass*, who said, "You always have to run faster to stay in place."

Answers to Objective Questions

20.1 c

20.2 d

20.3 a

20.4 d

20.5 d [$(30 \times 2) + 50 = 110$]

20.6 b (110 loci occupied by $B \div 200$ total loci = 0.55)

20.7 a (Under the conditions specified, the frequency of yellow snails would remain the same from generation to generation. See discussion of Hardy-Weinberg principle in Question 20.17.)

20.8 c (We know from Question 20.7 that $q^2 = 0.20$. Thus, $q = 0.45$.)

20.9 individuals (or phenotypes); populations (or gene pools)

20.10 species; population

20.11 alleles; individuals

20.12 fixed

20.13 genotypes; mated pair; alleles; population

20.14 0.36; 0.48; 0.16 (For explanation, see answer to Question 20.17.)

20.15 $1 - p$

20.16 0.02, or 2% (We need to find $2pq$ of the Hardy-Weinberg equation. Since $q^2 = 0.0001$, then $q = 0.01$ and $p = 1 - 0.01$. Therefore, $2pq = 0.0198 \cong 0.02$.)

20.18 *b*

20.19 *c*

20.20 *a*

20.21 *b*

20.22 *b*

20.23 *c*

20.24 *d*

20.25 *a*

20.26 *b*

20.27 natural selection

20.28 genetic drift; bottleneck; founder

20.29 fixation; bottleneck

20.30 founder

20.31 gene flow

20.32 assortative mating

20.33 natural selection

20.36 *b*

20.37 *b*

20.38 *d*

20.39 *a* (By definition, alleles are multiple forms of a gene and hence stem from the mutation of a gene.)

20.40 *c*

20.41 *a*

20.42 *a*

20.43 individual; geographic

20.44 cline

20.45 polymorphic; balanced polymorphism

20.46 chance

20.47 recessive alleles

20.48 neutral

20.49 balanced; natural selection

20.51 *c*

20.52 *b* (5 seasons = 100%; light-shelled snails live only $\frac{1}{5}$ as long, so $\frac{1}{5}(100\%) = 20\%$, or 0.20.)

20.53 *c*

20.54 *b* (Selection coefficient is the difference in fitness values: $1 - 0.25 = 0.75$.)

20.55 *c* (the fitness value of a lethal gene is 0. The selection coefficient is: $1 - 0 = 1$.)

20.56 *c*

20.57 *c*

20.58 *c*

20.59 *a*

20.60 *a*

20.61 *b*

20.62 *d*

20.63 *a*

20.64 *a*

20.65 survival; reproduction

20.66 relative; zero; one

20.67 zero

20.68 selection; one

20.69 selection; selection coefficient

20.70 supergene

20.71 stabilizing

20.72 coevolution; pollinators

20.73 directional

20.74 reduce

20.75 disruptive

20.76 directional

20.77 sexual dimorphisms

20.78 number of offspring

REPRODUCTIVE ISOLATION*

21.1   The formation of a new species through change in a single lineage is known as

(*a*) anagenesis, or phyletic evolution.   (*b*) cladogenesis, or divergent evolution.   (*c*) convergent evolution.
(*d*) allopatry.

21.2   The formation of two species from one ancestral species is known as

(*a*) anagenesis, or phyletic evolution.   (*b*) cladogenesis, or divergent evolution.   (*c*) convergent evolution.
(*d*) allopatry.

21.3   Members of a biologic species are potentially able to

(*a*) compete.   (*b*) express all the same genes.   (*c*) introgress.   (*d*) interbreed.

21.4   A prezygotic isolating mechanism prevents successful

(*a*) gamete production.   (*b*) fertilization.   (*c*) zygote development.   (*d*) reproduction of hybrids.

21.5   Two species of garter snakes occur in the same geographic areas, but one lives mainly in water and the other
mainly on land. Consequently, they do not encounter one another and so do not interbreed. This is an example
of prezygotic isolation caused by

(*a*) ecological isolation.   (*b*) temporal isolation.   (*c*) behavioral isolation.   (*d*) mechanical isolation.

21.6   Male fireflies attract mates by blinking their "lights"; each species does so in a characteristic pattern recognized
only by females of the species. This is an example of prezygotic isolation by

(*a*) ecological isolation.   (*b*) temporal isolation.   (*c*) behavioral isolation.   (*d*) mechanical isolation.

21.7   Different species of dragonflies do not mate with each other because the males of each species have appendages
that can clasp and hold, for copulation, only females of their own species. This is an example of

(*a*) ecological isolation.   (*b*) temporal isolation.   (*c*) behavioral isolation.   (*d*) mechanical isolation.

21.8   Eastern and western meadowlarks look almost the same and inhabit the same areas of prairie. They recognize
mates of their own species by distinctive courtship songs, an example of prezygotic isolation by

(*a*) ecological isolation.   (*b*) behavioral isolation.   (*c*) mechanical isolation.   (*d*) gametic isolation.

21.9   Very similar species of fish release their eggs and sperm into the same water, but the sperm of one species
cannot penetrate the eggs of another species. This is an example of prezygotic isolation by

(*a*) ecological isolation.   (*b*) behavioral isolation.   (*c*) mechanical isolation.   (*d*) gametic isolation.

21.10   Two species of pines, *Pinus radiata* and *Pinus muricata*, occur sympatrically in California and are capable of
forming hybrids. They do not interbreed, however, because one releases pollen in February and the other in
April. They are an example of prezygotic isolation by

(*a*) ecological isolation.   (*b*) temporal isolation.   (*c*) gametic isolation.   (*d*) geographic isolation.

21.11   The genus *Rhagoletis* is a group of small, brightly colored flies. Each species in the genus feeds, during its larval
stage, on the fruit of just one plant family, and when the larvae hatch into adults, they court and mate on the
same fruit. The species that feed on fruits from different plant families are reproductively isolated by

(*a*) ecological isolation.   (*b*) temporal isolation.   (*c*) behavioral isolation.   (*d*) mechanical isolation.

* Answers to Chapter 21 objective questions appear on page 155.

21.12 A postzygotic isolating mechanism prevents successful

(*a*) courtship. (*b*) copulation. (*c*) fertilization. (*d*) development, survival, or reproduction of the hybrid.

21.13 A horse has a karyotype of 64 chromosomes, and a donkey has a karyotype of 62 chromosomes. The hybrid offspring of a horse-donkey cross is a mule, which has 63 chromosomes. A mule is sterile because it cannot successfully

(*a*) court other mules. (*b*) copulate with mules, donkeys, or horses. (*c*) form gametes. (*d*) complete development of the zygote.

21.14 Most often the factor that initiates the speciation of two populations is

(*a*) geographic separation. (*b*) inability of gametes to fuse. (*c*) different courtship behaviors. (*d*) different copulatory organs.

21.15 A morphospecies is defined by its _____ features, whereas a biologic species is defined by its _____ features.

21.16 Isolated populations of the same species are likely to become different because they begin with different _____ and then experience different _____ and _____.

21.17 Reproductive isolation based on characteristics of the organisms themselves is said to be _____ isolation, whereas reproductive isolation based on environmental conditions is _____ isolation. Usually the _____ isolation occurs first.

21.18 Reproductive isolating mechanisms prevent populations of different _____ from _____. They isolate gene pools from _____.

21.19 A reproductive isolating mechanism that prevents mating or fertilization is known as a _____ barrier; one that decreases the success of hybrids is a _____ barrier. Usually the _____ barrier develops first and then strongly selects for the _____ barrier.

21.20 When reproductive isolating mechanisms fail to prevent gene flow between species, the phenomenon is called _____.

21.21 Of the intrinsic isolating mechanisms, the _____ forms are more costly, in terms of time, energy, and fitness, than the _____ forms.

21.22 What are some limitations of the biologic species concept?

⊛ The biologic species concept was first proposed in 1942 by Ernst Mayr, a systematist and biogeographer from Harvard University. It defines a *biologic species* as a group of individuals with the potential to interbreed and produce fertile offspring. Prior to this concept, a species was a morphospecies, defined as a group of individuals with similar anatomies and separated from other groups by discontinuities in the frequency distributions of of compatibility are not only expensive, in terms of time and money, but often give false results. Many animals

One obvious limitation of the biologic species concept is that it does not apply to asexual organisms, which form recognizable groups even though there is little or no gene exchange among their members. (Presumably, gene exchange once occurred or the individuals of an asexual species would not be so similar.)

Another major limitation of the biologic species concept is that the reproductive compatability of individuals has to be tested to determine whether they belong to the same species. Such a test is impossible with dead specimens and fossils. Even among living individuals it is not easy to determine compatability. Laboratory tests of compatibility are not only expensive, in terms of time and money, but often give false results. Many animals that would not mate in the wild will do so under the artificial conditions of a laboratory, and many that do mate in the wild will not do so in the laboratory.

There is no completely satisfactory way to define a species. The biologic species concept is an evolutionary way of viewing a species, but is impractical because it cannot be accurately tested in many situations. The morphospecies concept, while practical, does not take into account the process by which species form. Both concepts are used and are, of course, interrelated since reproductive isolation leads to morphological dissimilarities.

MODES OF SPECIATION

21.23 In allopatric speciation, the initial barrier to gene flow is

(*a*) behavioral. (*b*) postzygotic. (*c*) geographic. (*d*) ecological.

21.24   Populations of Kaibab squirrels on the north rim of the Grand Canyon do not mate with populations on the south rim. They are isolated by a

     (*a*) sympatric barrier.   (*b*) autopatric barrier.   (*c*) geographic barrier.   (*d*) genetic barrier.

21.25   The Kaibab squirrels described above are examples of

     (*a*) allopatric populations.   (*b*) parapatric populations.   (*c*) sympatric populations.   (*d*) autopatric populations.

21.26   Since the Pleistocene Ice Age, deserts have gradually formed in the southwestern United States. As the lakes and rivers of these areas shrunk into isolated springs, the fishes developed strong potential for

     (*a*) introgression.   (*b*) speciation.   (*c*) autopolyploidy.   (*d*) allopolyploidy.

21.27   Isolated populations with the potential for rapid speciation are

     (*a*) small in number.   (*b*) large in number.   (*c*) dimorphic.   (*d*) inbred.

21.28   When two related populations that have been geographically isolated come back into contact, retain their reproductive isolation, and compete for resources, there may be a divergence in traits known as

     (*a*) character convergence.   (*b*) sibling speciation.   (*c*) phyletic evolution.   (*d*) character displacement.

21.29   Adaptive radiation has occurred often on islands, because the island populations are

     (*a*) dimorphic.   (*b*) small in number and isolated.   (*c*) asexual and flightless.   (*d*) without predators.

21.30   When populations of a plant species are located adjacent to one another because of abrupt changes in soil conditions, they are called

     (*a*) allopolyploid.   (*b*) autopolyploid.   (*c*) sympatric.   (*d*) parapatric.

21.31   Reproductive isolation in sympatric speciation develops without a

     (*a*) geographic barrier.   (*b*) barrier to gene flow.   (*c*) change in chromosome number.   (*d*) barrier to mating.

21.32   Sympatric speciation occurs most commonly in

     (*a*) mammals.   (*b*) fishes.   (*c*) plants.   (*d*) birds.

21.33   An autopolyploid has four or more sets of chromosomes, which come from

     (*a*) a single parental species.   (*b*) two parental species.   (*c*) four parental species.   (*d*) multiple introgressions.

21.34   An allopolyploid has four or more sets of chromosomes, which come from

     (*a*) a single parental species.   (*b*) two parental species.   (*c*) four parental species.   (*d*) multiple introgressions.

21.35   An allopolyploid is a diploid hybrid in which there has been

     (*a*) chromosomal replication without cell division.   (*b*) chromosomal breakages.   (*c*) multiple translocations. (*d*) multiple crossovers.

21.36   An allopolyploid can reproduce with individuals from

     (*a*) its paternal population.   (*b*) its maternal population.   (*c*) both maternal and paternal populations. (*d*) neither maternal nor paternal populations.

21.37   Populations segregated by a geographic barrier are known as _____ populations.

21.38   Populations with overlapping geographic ranges are known as _____ populations in the areas of overlap.

21.39   Populations with adjacent geographic ranges are known as _____ populations.

21.40   An isolated population that is small in number is more likely than a large population to form a new species, because of _____ .

21.41 A population found in only one restricted area is said to be _____ to the area.

21.42 The formation of many species from a single common ancestor, as happened during the evolution of Darwin's finches, is called _____.

21.43 The tendency of closely related sympatric species to diverge rapidly in response to competition is known as _____.

21.44 When a hybrid is formed from the mating of two different species and the hybrid doubles its number of chromosomes (by chromosome replication without cell division), the resulting individual is said to be _____.

21.45 A tetraploid individual forms _____ offspring when it crosses with a normal diploid from its parental species. Organisms with this number of chromosomes are _____. A new species forms when a tetraploid mates with _____ or _____.

21.46 A hybrid individual, formed from diploid parents of two different species, is usually sterile because of problems during _____. It can overcome these problems by _____ its chromosome number. Hybrids that do this instantly form a new species, since they cannot reproduce with either parental species. This type of sympatric speciation is known as _____.

21.47 N. Eldredge and S. J. Gould suggested, in 1972, that there are periods of rapid speciation and periods of very little speciation. This idea is known as the _____ hypothesis. The alternative hypothesis, that speciation occurs as a steady accumulation of small changes, is known as the _____ hypothesis.

21.48 Why is sympatric speciation common in plants but rare in animals?

⚉ Sympatric speciation occurs when a new species arises within the geographic range of its parent population, without geographic isolation of the two. It is rare in animals, because almost always there is some gene flow between populations living in the same area, regardless of any ecological or behavioral differences that might exist between the two. Even a small amount of gene flow can prevent speciation. Only in plants can there be development of complete reproductive isolation between sympatric populations, and they do so by changing levels of *ploidy* (the number of sets of chromosomes in each cell), thereby eliminating any gene flow between plants of one ploidy level and plants of another. Polyploidy is rare in animals; their systems of sex determination rely so heavily on a diploid condition (e.g., XX or XY chromosomes) that polyploid individuals are almost always sterile.

Polyploidy is common among plants—about half the 235,000 existing species of flowering plants originated by polyploidy. Sympatric speciation almost always occurs by allopolyploidy, in which the new species has four sets of chromosomes—a diploid set from each of its two parental species. An allopolyploid individual originates when gametes of two species unite to form a hybrid offspring, which is sterile if it remains diploid because its two sets of "homologous" chromosomes are so different that they do not pair well during meiosis I. The hybrid becomes fertile if, by some accident, it doubles its chromosomes so that there are two copies of each chromosome, and they pair with each other (rather than with the "homologue") during meiosis. The tetraploid yields viable gametes. A cell goes from diploid to tetraploid when the chromosomes are replicated but there is no subsequent cell division. Once a tetraploid has formed, it can mate with a diploid from its parents' populations, but the triploid offspring from such matings are sterile, since three homologous chromosomes cannot form pairs during meiosis I. Tetraploids can, however, mate with themselves (self-fertilization) or with one another, and when they do so they instantly form a new species; there is no gene flow between the tetraploids and the original diploid populations.

Autopolyploidy is similar to allopolyploidy except it begins with chromosome doubling in an individual formed of gametes from a single parental species rather than from two parental species. It is rare in nature, because with four copies of each chromosome, chaos usually results as the chromosomes attempt to pair during meiosis I.

21.49 Describe the most common sequence of events during animal speciation.

⚉ Animal speciation is usually allopatric speciation, in which populations of a species initially become segregated by a geographic barrier. The populations may be somewhat different to begin with, if they are very small samples of the original population or if they are different parts of a cline and adapted to slightly different parts of an environmental gradient. Whether or not two populations have different gene pools to begin with, the geographic barrier to gene flow (e.g., a mountain, glacier, or river for terrestrial populations; emerging land among shrinking lakes for aquatic populations) causes each population to experience unique mutations and selection, and so evolve in unique ways. The isolation enables populations to become differentiated; they undergo divergent evolution.

After a period of geographic separation and independent evolution, the populations may develop, quite by accident, traits that prevent interbreeding or that make hybrids less successful than offspring from intrapopulation matings. In time the two populations will become reproductively incompatible and are then separate species. If at some point during this process the two populations come to occupy the same area, their potential for interbreeding is tested. They may: (1) fail to interbreed at all; (2) interbreed to form normal offspring, so that the hybrids are no different, with regard to fitness, than the offspring from intrapopulation matings; or (3) interbreed, but with the hybrids being less fit than the offspring from intrapopulation matings. In the first alternative the populations are separate species, in the second they form a single species, and in the third the process of speciation is taking place.

If the third alternative develops, then the inferior fitness of hybrids becomes a postzygotic reproductive isolating mechanism. The populations are largely isolated from gene flow because of selection against the hybrid zygotes: matings occur and zygotes form, but they fail to develop, or they may develop but fail to yield offspring, or those offspring are reproductively inferior to offspring of intrapopulation matings. Thus, the tendency of individuals from different populations to mate with each other is selected against, since those that do are less fit (because fitness is defined by relative number of offspring) than those that do not. This selection then leads to prezygotic reproductive isolating mechanisms. Any traits that inhibit cross-matings are selected for, including population-specific mate recognition (e.g., courtship songs and dances), mating time and place, and copulatory structures.

In summary, speciation in most animal populations begins with geographic separation of the populations, followed by a gradual differentiation of the populations in response to initial differences in gene pools and to different kinds of mutations and selection pressures. As the populations become different, some traits cause hybrids to be less fit, and these then become postzygotic reproductive isolating mechanisms, which in turn select for prezygotic reproductive isolating mechanisms.

21.50 Why do some animals have very elaborate courtship behaviors whereas others do not?

🐚 Animals with elaborate courtship behaviors evolve in areas where there is strong selection for choosing a mate with care. Such an area is one where many similar species coexist—where it would be easy to choose a mate from the wrong species and consequently leave few or no surviving offspring. Many closely related species of ducks, for example, usually coexist in the same lake or river, and they typically have highly species-specific coloration and elaborate courtship rituals. By contrast, a species living with no other closely related species is unlikely to make the mistake of mating outside its own species, and so selection for behavior that enhances species recognition is weak and elaborate courtship behaviors do not evolve.

Answers to Objective Questions

21.1 *a*	**21.18** species; interbreeding; gene flow	**21.34** *b*
21.2 *b*		**21.35** *a*
21.3 *d*	**21.19** prezygotic; postzygotic; postzygotic; prezygotic	**21.36** *d*
21.4 *b*		**21.37** allopatric
21.5 *a*	**21.20** introgression	**21.38** sympatric
21.6 *c*	**21.21** postzygotic; prezygotic	**21.39** parapatric
21.7 *d*	**21.23** *c*	**21.40** genetic drift
21.8 *b*	**21.24** *c*	**21.41** endemic
21.9 *d*	**21.25** *a*	**21.42** adaptive radiation
21.10 *b*	**21.26** *b*	**21.43** character displacement
21.11 *a*	**21.27** *a*	**21.44** allopolyploid
21.12 *d*	**21.28** *d*	**21.45** triploid; sterile; itself; another tetraploid
21.13 *c*	**21.29** *b*	
21.14 *a*	**21.30** *d*	**21.46** meiosis I; doubling; allopolyploidy
21.15 anatomic; reproductive	**21.31** *a*	
21.16 gene pools; mutations; selection	**21.32** *c*	**21.47** punctuated equilibrium; gradualism
21.17 intrinsic; extrinsic; extrinsic	**21.33** *a*	

CHAPTER 22
Phylogeny: Classification and Evolution

PHYLOGENY*

22.1 Phylogeny describes a species'

(*a*) morphological similarities with other species.   (*b*) reproductive compatabilities with other species.   (*c*) evolutionary history.   (*d*) geographic distribution.

22.2 In the binomial system of taxonomy, developed during the 18th century by C. Linnaeus, the first word of an organism's name (e.g., of *Homo sapiens*) is its

(*a*) species.   (*b*) genus.   (*c*) race.   (*d*) family.

22.3 Of all the taxa, the only one that exists in nature as a biologically cohesive unit is the

(*a*) species.   (*b*) genus.   (*c*) phylum or division.   (*d*) kingdom.

22.4 A taxonomic system based on all phenotypic similarities, equally weighted and without regard to evolutionary relationships, is called

(*a*) phylogeny.   (*b*) cladistics.   (*c*) classical evolutionary taxonomy.   (*d*) phenetics.

22.5 A taxonomic system based only on the traits that reflect the order in time in which branches arose in a phylogenetic tree is called

(*a*) phylogeny.   (*b*) cladistics.   (*c*) classical evolutionary taxonomy.   (*d*) phenetics.

22.6 A taxonomic system that uses phenotypic similarities as well as judgments about homologies along a branching sequence is called

(*a*) phylogeny.   (*b*) cladistics.   (*c*) classical evolutionary taxonomy.   (*d*) phenetics.

22.7 In the five-kingdom system of classification developed by Robert Whittaker, members of the kingdom Plantae are: autotrophic, eukaryotic, and

(*a*) multicellular.   (*b*) motile.   (*c*) either unicellular or multicellular.   (*d*) have sexual reproduction.

22.8 The evolutionary history of a species or group of related species is its _____. The identification and classification of species is an area of biology known as _____.

22.9 Arrange the following in order of increasing group size, beginning with the smallest: family, kingdom, species, phylum (or division), genus, order, and class.

(*a*) _____   (*e*) _____

(*b*) _____   (*f*) _____

(*c*) _____   (*g*) _____

(*d*) _____

22.10 Arrange the following in order of increasing group size, beginning with the smallest: Carnivora, *lynx*, Animalia, Felidae, *Felix*, Mammalia, Chordata.

(*a*) _____   (*e*) _____

(*b*) _____   (*f*) _____

(*c*) _____   (*g*) _____

(*d*) _____

* Answers to Chapter 22 objective questions appear on page 160.

22.11 Classification reflects phylogeny when the hierarchy of groups reflects their _____.

22.12 C. Linnaeus divided all known forms of life into two kingdoms: _____ and _____. Bacteria were placed in the kingdom _____ because they have cell walls, and protozoa were placed in the kingdom _____ because they move from place to place and ingest food.

22.13 The most common system of classification used today, developed in 1969 by Robert Whittaker of Cornell University, uses five kingdoms: _____, _____, _____, _____, and _____.

22.14 Whittaker's five-kingdom system of classification recognizes two basic types of cells: _____ and _____.

22.15 What logic is used to divide all organisms into five kingdoms?

🐚   First, the two basic types of cells are separated, with all prokaryotic organisms placed in the kingdom Monera. Then all eukaryotic organisms that are unicellular during most of their lives are placed in a second kingdom—Protista. The remaining eukaryotic, multicellular organisms are divided according to how they acquire energy and nutrients. The kingdom Plantae includes all photosynthetic autotrophs, the kingdom Fungi includes all absorptive heterotrophs, and the kingdom Animalia includes all ingestive heterotrophs.

A recent trend is to redefine the Protista as all eukaryotic organisms that are unicellular or relatively simple multicellular, with little or no specializations of cell functions. This new group, which includes the algae, is called the kingdom Protoctista.

Another recent suggestion, by Lynn Margulis of Boston University, is to avoid any attempt at classifying multicellular organisms on the basis of nutrition, since there are autotrophic animals and heterotrophic plants. She suggests, instead, that a five-kingdom system be constructed by first separating out the Monera, based on their prokaryotic cells, and then defining the kingdom Plantae as all organisms that begin life as diploid embryos supported by maternal tissue, the kingdom Fungi as all organisms that begin life as haploid spores, and the kingdom Animalia as all organisms that begin life when a haploid sperm and haploid egg unite to form a zygote which, after several cell divisions, becomes a blastula. All organisms not belonging to these four kingdoms are to be placed in the kingdom Protoctista.

PHYLOGENETIC EVIDENCE

22.16 Biologists who study the sequences of organisms in the fossil record are

(a) taxonomists. (b) paleobiologists. (c) museologists. (d) systematists.

22.17 The richest source of fossils is

(a) basalt. (b) granite. (c) lava. (d) sedimentary rock.

22.18 The earliest era in the geologic record is the

(a) Cenozoic. (b) Precambrian. (c) Paleozoic. (d) Mesozoic.

22.19 The Carboniferous period, during which amphibians flourished, occurred approximately

(a) 25 million years ago. (b) 135 million years ago. (c) 345 million years ago. (d) 500 million years ago.

22.20 The Ordovician period, during which the first vertebrates appeared, occurred approximately

(a) 25 million years ago. (b) 135 million years ago. (c) 345 million years ago. (d) 500 million years ago.

22.21 The Permian period, during which most modern orders of insects appeared, occurred approximately

(a) 80 million years ago. (b) 150 million years ago. (c) 280 million years ago. (d) 550 million years ago.

22.22 The Cretaceous period, during which flowering plants appeared, occurred approximately

(a) 80 million years ago. (b) 135 million years ago. (c) 280 million years ago. (d) 345 million years ago.

22.23 Rocks and fossils are dated by measuring relative amounts of isotopes, a method known as _____ dating.

22.24 We can date rocks and fossils by measuring the amount of carbon that has been converted as a result of radioactive decay from an atomic weight of _____ to _____.

22.25 We can determine how long an organism has been dead by measuring the amount of its _____ amino acids that have been converted to _____ amino acids.

22.26 A widespread fossil that is used to establish the relative dates of different rock strata is called an _____ fossil.

22.27 The Tertiary period is composed of five epochs: Eocene, Miocene, Oligocene, Paleocene, and Pliocene. Place them in the correct order, from oldest to most recent.

(**a**) _____   (**d**) _____

(**b**) _____   (**e**) _____

(**c**) _____

22.28 Humans (genus *Homo*) first appear in the fossil record during the _____ epoch of the _____ period of the _____ era.

22.29 Dinosaurs were dominant during the _____ period of the _____ era.

22.30 An argument against evolution is the presence of gaps in the fossil record. How do paleobiologists explain these gaps?

🐚   The fossil record is a very small and biased sample of the species that once existed. Only a minute portion of the species formed fossils, few of these fossils persisted, and of those that persisted, few have been found.

A fossil is a remnant or imprint of an organism. To form a remnant, an organism must remain intact after death—i.e., not be eaten by a predator or scavenger and not be decomposed or dissolved. Most fossil remnants are organisms that were rapidly buried in deep, anaerobic sediments beneath lakes and oceans. The fossil record is biased in favor of aquatic organisms that existed during warmer periods, when more of the earth's surface was covered with water (rather than with ice).

To form an imprint in rock, an organism must have hard or resistant parts and be buried in sand, silt, or chalk that later forms sedimentary rock. The fossil record is biased in favor of hard-bodied organisms that lived where sedimentary rocks formed.

Once a fossil forms, there is a very small chance it will be preserved. Distortions of sediment and rocks, caused by upwellings, weathering, or pressure, destroy most fossils. Even if a fossil is preserved, it is highly unlikely that it will ever be exposed to air and seen by a human.

MECHANISMS OF MACROEVOLUTION

22.31 Macroevolution is the evolution of

(**a**) macromolecules.   (**b**) phylogenetic gaps.   (**c**) major events occurring over geologic time.   (**d**) large organisms.

22.32 A structure, such as a feather, that evolved in one context and was then used for a completely new function, is a

(**a**) mystery to macroevolutionists.   (**b**) preadaptation.   (**c**) macrostructure.   (**d**) paedomorph.

22.33 Retention in an adult organism of the juvenile features of its ancestors is known as

(**a**) allometry.   (**b**) preadaptation.   (**c**) macrodevelopment.   (**d**) paedomorphosis.

22.34 Marsupial mammals moved from South America to Australia via

(**a**) Antarctica.   (**b**) Africa.   (**c**) the Galapagos Archipelago.   (**d**) Madagascar.

22.35 Australia has unusual organisms because their evolution for the past 38 million years has been

(**a**) rapid.   (**b**) slow.   (**c**) isolated from other organisms.   (**d**) punctuated.

22.36 North American organisms are different from South American organisms, because the two continents

(**a**) have very different climates.   (**b**) have never been connected.   (**c**) were physically separated for about 35 million years, until about 2 million years ago.   (**d**) have very different geographies.

22.37 The theory, developed in the early 1960s, to explain the mechanism of continental drift is known as _____.

22.38 About 250 million years ago, all the land masses formed a supercontinent known as _____. When it formed, there were massive extinctions among marine organisms because the formation of a supercontinent from many separate land masses reduced in area the _____ habitats. The interior of the supercontinent developed an unusually _____ climate, which favored colonization by _____ vertebrates and _____ plants.

22.39 The supercontinent began to split into northern and southern land masses (Laurasia and Gondwanaland) about 180 million years ago, an event that explains the present distribution of _____ mammals and _____ mammals.

22.40 Walter and Luis Alvarez, of the University of California, Berkeley, have suggested that the massive extinctions of dinosaurs during the Cretaceous was caused by climatic changes and darkness resulting from _____.

MAJOR PATTERNS OF MACROEVOLUTION

22.41 Closely related organisms with very different traits have experienced

(*a*) coevolution. (*b*) convergent evolution. (*c*) divergent evolution. (*d*) parallel evolution.

22.42 Distantly related organisms with similar traits have experienced

(*a*) coevolution. (*b*) convergent evolution. (*c*) divergent evolution. (*d*) parallel evolution.

22.43 Similar traits resulting from similar selection pressures acting on similar gene pools is

(*a*) coevolution. (*b*) convergent evolution. (*c*) divergent evolution. (*d*) parallel evolution.

22.44 The evolution of one population in response to the evolution of another population, and vice versa, is called

(*a*) coevolution. (*b*) convergent evolution. (*c*) divergent evolution. (*d*) parallel evolution.

22.45 Two similar structures with the same ancestry are _____ structures; two similar structures with dissimilar ancestries are _____ structures.

22.46 The evolution of aquatic ichthyosaurs and of fishes is an example of _____ evolution; the limbs of ichthyosaurs and the arms of octopuses are _____ structures, whereas the limbs of ichthyosaurs and the limbs of pterosaurs are _____ structures.

22.47 The evolution of speed in elk and speed in gray wolves is an example of ongoing _____.

22.48 The Tasmanian wolf (a marsupial) and the American timber wolf (a placental) may have evolved along similar lines because of similar selection pressures acting on similar gene pools. If so, they are an example of _____ evolution.

22.49 A pronounced trend within some animal lines has been the evolution of larger bodies. What produced this trend?

🐚 The tendency within several animal lines to evolve larger bodies, known as Cope's rule, is the product of regular selection for larger animals in the populations. Larger animals usually have advantages with regard to predator-prey interactions, acquiring mates, and performing many physiological functions.

Increased body size was selected for early in the evolution of animals, when the larger heterotrophs (made of many rather than few cells) captured and ingested a greater range of prey organisms because of their superior control over locomotion and their larger feeding structures. Larger predators then selected for the evolution of larger prey, since greater size increased the prey's ability to evade predation. Coevolution of predator and prey continued to select for larger bodies in some animal lines. All early mammals, for example, were very small. As they evolved, larger and larger predators caught more prey and left more offspring, and larger and larger prey survived predation to leave offspring. For both populations, larger bodies conferred greater speed and physical strength.

Many animals became larger in response to sexual selection. The females of these populations chose larger males or larger males attained social dominance because of their superior strength in combat. Thus, the larger males of each generation fathered the most offspring.

A larger endotherm (bird or mammal) is better able to retain body heat because it has a smaller ratio of body surface (site of heat loss) to body volume (site of heat production) than has a smaller endotherm. Selection during cool periods, such as the Pleistocene epoch, favored larger mammals. Some of the largest animals appeared during this epoch, including the wooly mammoth and saber-toothed tiger.

Finally, larger bodies evolved in some lines because of selection for increased size of some particular structure, such as the brain or antlers. In order to increase the size of one body structure, the entire body of the animal had to get larger. Thus, selection for greater intelligence may have selected for larger heads, which, in turn, selected for larger bodies.

22.50 Is evolution progressive? Does a lineage progress in a given direction?

The idea that evolution is oriented in a particular direction, by some internal force of the organisms, is known as the *theory of orthogenesis*. There is no evidence of such an internal force, whether it be an inner need, an *élan vital*, or the appearance of mutations as they are needed to achieve some goal. Instead, all evidence indicates that evolution produces a variety of forms, through random mutations and recombinations, and only some of these forms persist.

Take, for example, evolution of the horse. It appears to be a straight-line progression from a fox-sized five-toed small-brained omnivore to a larger, one-toed large-brained grazer. Yet all along this evolutionary "pathway," a variety of different horselike animals existed. All but three forms—the horse, the donkey, and the zebra—have become extinct; their "progressive" lines led nowhere. Furthermore, no single trend occurred at all times throughout evolution of the horse. There was no continuous overall increase in body size, for example, but rather long periods of no change and some periods, in some lines, of a reverse trend toward smaller body size.

Evolution does not adjust organisms to future environments. Instead, each generation is exposed to natural selection and the animals best suited to their present environment survive and leave the most offspring. A trend in evolution appears when the environment continuously selects for the same traits—continuously selects, for example, for the largest animals in the population.

Answers to Objective Questions

22.1 *c*

22.2 *b*

22.3 *a*

22.4 *d*

22.5 *b*

22.6 *c*

22.7 *a*

22.8 phylogeny; taxonomy

22.9 (*a*) species; (*b*) genus; (*c*) family; (*d*) order; (*e*) class; (*f*) phylum (or division); (*g*) kingdom

22.10 (*a*) *lynx*; (*b*) *Felix*; (*c*) Felidae; (*d*) Carnivora; (*e*) Mammalia; (*f*) Chordata; (*g*) Animalia

22.11 evolution

22.12 Plantae; Animalia; Plantae; Animalia

22.13 Monera; Protista; Plantae; Fungi; Animalia

22.14 prokaryotic; eukaryotic

22.16 *b*

22.17 *d*

22.18 *b*

22.19 *c*

22.20 *d*

22.21 *c*

22.22 *b*

22.23 radioactive

22.24 14; 12

22.25 left-handed (L); right-handed (D)

22.26 index

22.27 (*a*) Paleocene; (*b*) Eocene; (*c*) Oligocene; (*d*) Miocene; (*e*) Pliocene

22.28 Pleistocene; Quaternary; Cenozoic

22.29 Jurassic; Mesozoic

22.31 *c*

22.32 *b*

22.33 *d*

22.34 *a*

22.35 *c*

22.36 *c*

22.37 plate tectonics

22.38 Pangaea; coastal; dry; reptilian; gymnosperm

22.39 placental; marsupial

22.40 dust from a fallen asteriod

22.41 *c*

22.42 *b*

22.43 *d*

22.44 *a*

22.45 homologous; analogous

22.46 convergent; analogous; homologous

22.47 coevolution

22.48 parallel

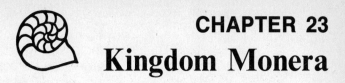

PROKARYOTIC FORM AND FUNCTION*

23.1 Which of the following is *not* true of organisms in the kingdom Monera?

(*a*) They reproduce by mitosis. (*b*) They have prokaryotic cellular organization. (*c*) They originated at least 3.5 billion years ago. (*d*) Most have cell walls.

23.2 When bacteria are rod-shaped, they are called

(*a*) cocci. (*b*) spirilla. (*c*) vibrios. (*d*) bacilli.

23.3 Surface appendages used by bacteria to attach to one another, and to host organisms, are called

(*a*) spirilla. (*b*) pili. (*c*) mesosomes. (*d*) thylakoids.

23.4 Compared to gram-negative bacteria, gram-positive bacteria

(*a*) have more complex cell walls. (*b*) are more resistant to antibiotics. (*c*) retain the violet dye rather than the red. (*d*) have less peptidoglycan.

23.5 Bacteria that must have organic molecules both for energy and as a source of carbon are called

(*a*) photoautotrophs. (*b*) photoheterotrophs. (*c*) chemoheterotrophs. (*d*) chemoautotrophs.

23.6 Bacteria that get their energy by fermentation and for whom oxygen is lethal are called

(*a*) obligate anaerobes. (*b*) obligate aerobes. (*c*) facultative aerobes. (*d*) facultative anaerobes.

23.7 Spherical bacteria called _____ are found in pairs called _____, or long chainlike clusters called _____, or grapelike aggregates called _____.

23.8 Bacteria with helically coiled shapes are called _____.

23.9 Unlike plant cell walls, which are made of _____, most bacterial cell walls contain _____.

23.10 The rotating, whiplike attachments to bacterial cells are called _____. Other external structures on bacterial surfaces are enclosing jellylike layers called _____ and straight, filamentlike structures called _____.

23.11 The thick-walled, dehydrated cells produced by some bacteria when there is a scarcity of nutrients are called _____.

23.12 In *Escherichia coli* bacteria, when the _____ spin in a _____ direction the resulting movement of the cell is called running. When the _____ rotate in a _____ direction the cell's movement is called tumbling.

23.13 Whereas in anaerobic photosynthetic bacteria the light-trapping pigments are located in _____, in most aerobic photosynthetic bacteria the pigments are located in _____.

23.14 How do eukaryotic flagella differ from bacterial flagella?

In eukaryotes, flagella are thin, cylindrical stalks that are outward extensions of the cell's interior. Each flagellum contains a 9 + 2 array of microtubules: nine pairs of microtubules arranged in a ring around the

---

* Answers to Chapter 23 objective questions appear on page 165.

periphery of the cylinder, with two individual microtubules in the center. This assembly is derived from and attached to a basal body within the cell and enclosed within a cytoplasm-filled continuation of the cell's plasma membrane. Such flagella are identical in internal construction to eukaryotic cilia, but by convention they are called flagella when they are few and relatively long and cilia when they are dense on the surface and relatively short. Both cilia and flagella beat back and forth in a whiplike motion produced by an ATP-powered sliding of microtubule pairs past one another.

A few types of bacteria, certain of the spirochetes, are also propelled by beating, microtubule-containing flagella, but the great majority of bacteria achieve motility by one of two other mechanisms: gliding and propulsion by bacterial flagella. So-called gliding bacteria, e.g., the myxobacteria, produce a slimy substance and then glide along this pathway. Other motile bacteria are propelled by bacterial flagella, which are remarkably complex mechanisms unique to prokaryotes.

Bacterial flagella are very different from eukaryotic flagella in both construction and mode of action. They are much thinner, approximately the diameter of one microtubule in a eukaryotic flagellum, and instead of being projections from the cell's interior, they are independent structures attached to the cell's surface. They do not contain microtubules, but instead are constructed from a single, solid crystal of the protein flagellin. The final and perhaps major difference is that eukaryotic flagella beat back and forth like oars while bacterial flagella rotate around their bases like propellers.

The model shown in Fig. 23.1 depicts the flagellum of a gram-negative bacterium (gram-positive bacteria have only two basal rings). There is an outward extending filament of flagellin attached to a curved hook that extends inward to a base structure (rod and rings) embedded in the cell wall and plasma membrane. The flagellum rotates when the inner rings turn, and this rotation is powered by diffusion of hydrogen ions into the cell down an electrochemical gradient through ports in the inner rings. Such rotating flagella may be distributed, depending on the species, all over the bacterium or concentrated at one or both ends.

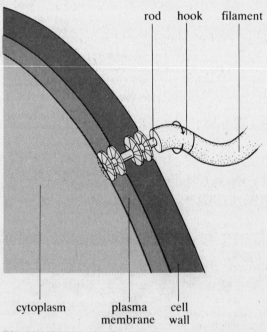

Fig. 23.1. Model of a flagellum in a gram-negative bacterium.

23.15 What are the differences between chemotactic, phototactic, and magnetotactic bacteria?

☞ A *taxis* is a movement oriented toward (positive taxis) or away (negative taxis) from some specific stimulus. For example, *Escherichia coli*, the common bacteria of the human colon, and other flagellated bacteria have been shown to be chemotactic, moving toward food such as sugars and away from noxious, repellent molecules. This movement is controlled by some unknown form of coordination between protein receptor molecules on the cell's surface and the rotary motors of the flagella. When the motors turn counterclockwise the flagella work together and the cell moves in a sustained forward movement called running. When the motors reverse and turn clockwise the flagella rotate independently and the cell tumbles randomly. It has been estimated that *E. coli* have at least 12 attractant-detector molecules and eight repellent-detector molecules.

Phototactic bacteria move toward (positive) or away (negative) from light. Motile bacteria that are photosynthetic generally show positive phototaxis, moving always to stay within the light. Little is known of the receptor molecules for phototaxis, but one positively phototactic form, a halophilic ("salt-loving") type, has been shown to have the pigment rhodopsin in its cell membrane; rhodopsin is the light-absorbing substance in the retinas of vertebrate eyes.

Magnetotactic bacteria are able to orient along the lines of the earth's magnetic field. A few species of aquatic bacteria have this capacity because they form an internal magnet. Such bacteria synthesize a chain of about 20 crystals of iron-containing magnetite (Fe_3O_4), and this chain, running parallel to the long axis of the cell, is then a magnet with north-seeking and south-seeking poles. It has been found that in the southern hemisphere the magnetotactic bacteria are south-seeking, following the earth's magnetic lines as they point both to the south and downward to the earth's surface. This keeps the bacteria down in the nutrient-rich sediments at the bottom of the ponds where they live. In the northern hemisphere, the magnetotactic forms are north-seeking, as the magnetic lines now slope downward as they go north. At the earth's magnetic equator, the magnetotactic bacteria are equally divided between north-seeking and south-seeking forms.

CLASSIFICATION OF PROKARYOTES

23.16   Which of the following are archaebacteria?

(*a*) Green sulfur;   (*b*) Methanogens;   (*c*) Pseudomonads;   (*d*) Chlamydias

23.17   The bacteria (*Clostridium botulinum*) that cause botulism are

(*a*) obligate aerobes.   (*b*) facultative anaerobes.   (*c*) obligate anaerobes.   (*d*) facultative aerobes.

23.18   Cyanobacteria are

(*a*) photoheterotrophs.   (*b*) photoautotrophs.   (*c*) chemoautotrophs.   (*d*) chemoheterotrophs.

23.19   Cells in some filamentous cyanobacteria that are specialized for nitrogen fixation are called

(*a*) phycobilisomes.   (*b*) chromatophores.   (*c*) grana.   (*d*) heterocysts.

23.20   The bacteria (*Treponema pallidum*) that cause the venereal disease syphilis are

(*a*) pseudomonads.   (*b*) purple nonsulfur.   (*c*) rickettsias.   (*d*) spirochetes.

23.21   The gliding bacteria that aggregate to form spore-releasing fruiting bodies under harsh conditions are

(*a*) myxobacteria.   (*b*) actinomycetes.   (*c*) mycoplasmas.   (*d*) chlamydias.

23.22   The organisms in the kingdom Monera are so diverse that classification is difficult and controversial. In the five-kingdom system of Robert Whittaker, used in this book, the kingdom is divided into three divisions: Schizonta, Cyanochloronta, and Archaebacteria. The common names for these divisions are: _____, _____, and _____.

23.23   Three groups of archaebacteria are the: _____ that produce marsh gas; the _____ that live in very concentrated salt water like the Dead Sea; and the _____ that live in very hot and acidic environments.

23.24   Methanogens have a unique form of energy metabolism in which _____ is used to reduce _____ to _____.

23.25   Photosynthetic bacteria, originally called blue-green _____, that utilize the same kind of chlorophyll found in higher plants, namely, _____, are the _____.

23.26   Photosynthetic sulfur bacteria differ from higher plants in that they do not have the pigment _____, and they do not use _____ as the electron donor in photosynthesis.

23.27 It is now thought that the smallest of all cells are the _____, which are also, along with the spiro-plasmas, the only prokaryotes without _____.

23.28 Bacteria that cause both tuberculosis and leprosy are the _____.

23.29 Why is it said that bacteria are alive and viruses are not?

🐌 In Chapter 1 (Question 1.19), many properties were listed that distinguish life from nonlife. It is generally accepted that bacteria are alive because they display all the required properties, and most biologists agree that viruses are not alive because they lack several of the most fundamental properties.

Bacteria, no matter how small, are always prokaryotic cells, with all the genetic and protein-synthesizing systems needed for self-maintenance and reproduction: DNA and RNA; integrated multienzyme systems; ribosomes; and at least one system for generating ATP. They have greater metabolic diversity than all eukaryotic forms combined, showing all forms of nutrition found in eukaryotes plus some unique forms. They reproduce by binary fission, a process in which the original cell divides into two daughter cells, each receiving an exact copy of the original genetic material. While most bacteria are unicellular, some live as aggregates of cells, and others (certain filamentous cyanobacteria) show the most basic form of multicellularity (division of labor between specialized cells).

While some of the viruses are larger than the smallest bacteria (the mycoplasmas that are roughly 0.1–1.0 μm in diameter), no virus is a cell. Instead, they are inert particles consisting in their simplest forms of a single nucleic acid molecule enclosed in a protein shell called a *capsid*. The nucleic acid can be either DNA or RNA but never both; the capsid can be constructed from the repetitions of a few or many kinds of proteins. In addition, many viruses develop an envelope around the capsid that is composed of proteins, lipids, and glycoproteins. On their own, viruses do not conduct protein synthesis or energy metabolism and do not contain the cellular machinery required for these functions.

Viruses are, essentially, a set of genetic instructions for making copies of themselves. This copying is done by invading a host cell (animal, plant, or bacterial) and using the cell's genetic machinery to produce new viruses. Under the direction of the viral genes, sometimes with the aid of enzymes brought by the virus, the host replicates the viral genome and synthesizes viral proteins. These components form into new viruses, which then leave the cell. The dependence of viruses on a host cell for their own reproduction, and the complete absence of metabolic machinery, are the main reasons that most biologists do not consider viruses to be alive.

It was once thought that viruses were either relics from a precellular stage of evolution or degenerate cells. Instead it is now believed that they came from the bacterial, animal or plant groups that they infect; that they are escaped fragments of genomes that subsequently acquired protein sheaths and envelopes, and the ability to use the hosts from which they came for protein synthesis and gene replication.

23.30 Why were cyanobacteria once classified as plants but are now placed in the kingdom Monera?

🐌 Cyanobacteria, formerly known as blue-green algae, are the largest and most diverse group of photosynthetic bacteria. Their great variety of sizes, shapes, and metabolic activities allows them to thrive in many environments: in thermal hot springs where temperatures can be over 80°C; in the snows of high mountains; in marine and fresh waters; in soils; even on otherwise lifeless volcanic rock. In the two-kingdom classification system, the cyanobacteria were called algae, and placed with the plants because they share many characteristics: the use of chlorophyll *a* as the main photosynthetic pigment; the use of water as a source of electrons and hydrogen for fixing CO_2; the oxidation of water with two photosystems; the release of oxygen as a waste product of photosynthesis; the presence of cell walls; and the green or blue-green coloration of some cyanobacteria.

It is now clear, however, that while cyanobacteria and plants have many common features, they are really very different. While plants are eukaryotes, cyanobacteria have the principal defining characteristic of the kingdom Monera: They are prokaryotes. The cyanobacteria evolved at least 2.5 billion years ago, which is roughly 1 billion years before the first eukaryotes. While both plants and cyanobacteria have cell walls, the plant wall is constructed from cellulose, while the bacterial wall is built from peptidoglycan. While some of the cyanobacteria are indeed green or blue-green, many forms are other colors (yellow, red, brown, black). And finally, a major difference, many forms of cyanobacteria can fix atmospheric nitrogen.

The ability to fix nitrogen—to reduce atmospheric N_2 to ammonia (NH_3), a form of nitrogen that can be incorporated into proteins and nucleic acids—is restricted to certain strictly anaerobic prokaryotes and to the cyanobacteria. This ability is dependent on the enzyme nitrogenase, which can only function under anaerobic conditions. While cyanobacteria do generate oxygen as a product of photosynthesis, certain filamentous types produce specialized cells called *heterocysts* that both contain nitrogenase and are impervious to oxygen. The cyanobacteria that can carry out both nitrogen fixation and oxygen-releasing photosynthesis are considered the most nutritionally independent organisms on earth. All they need for survival are CO_2, N_2, sunlight, water, and a few minerals.

Answers to Objective Questions

23.1 *a*

23.2 *d*

23.3 *b*

23.4 *c*

23.5 *c*

23.6 *a*

23.7 cocci; diplococci; streptococci; staphylococci

23.8 spirilla

23.9 cellulose; peptidoglycan

23.10 bacterial flagella; capsules; pili

23.11 endospores

23.12 flagella; counterclockwise; flagella; clockwise

23.13 chromatophores; thylakoids

23.16 *b*

23.17 *c*

23.18 *b*

23.19 *d*

23.20 *d*

23.21 *a*

23.22 eubacteria; cyanobacteria; archaebacteria

23.23 methanogens; extreme halophiles; thermoacidophiles

23.24 H_2; CO_2; methane

23.25 algae; chlorophyll *a*; cyanobacteria

23.26 chlorophyll *a*; water

23.27 mycoplasmas; cell walls

23.28 actinomycetes

CHAPTER 24
Kingdom Protista

CLASSIFICATION OF PROTISTS*

24.1   The first eukaryotes appeared

(*a*) 1 billion years ago.   (*b*) 1.5 billion years ago.   (*c*) 2.5 billion years ago.   (*d*) 3.5 billion years ago.

24.2   In the Whittaker five-kingdom system, organisms in the kingdom Protista are _____ or _____ eukaryotes.

24.3   Why is it so difficult for biologists to agree on a classification of protists?

Protists are difficult to classify because unicellular organisms do not form a natural group. In fact, the protistan group is often referred to as the "garbage can" of classification, because it contains all organisms not placed in other groups.

The only easy part of protistan classification is separating eukaryotic organisms from prokaryotic organisms, for the differences between their cells are unambiguous. Once this is done, the eukaryotic organisms have to be subdivided in some manner. One way to group the protists is to separate all unicellular eukaryotes from multicellular eukaryotes. But what about such unicellular organisms as *Volvox*, which form colonies, and what about slime molds, which are sometimes unicellular and sometimes multicellular? Robert H. Whittaker solved this problem, in 1969, by placing in the kingdom Protista all organisms that are unicellular during most of their life cycle and all organisms that are unicellular and colonial.

A criticism of Whittaker's system is that primitive multicellular organisms belong with the unicellular organisms rather than with plants, fungi, or animals. Such organisms have little or no differentiation among their many body cells and so are not much different from unicellular colonial organisms. Problems arise especially with the algae, including the giant kelp and other seaweeds, and with the water molds. Both groups are sometimes added to the protists, and the kingdom is then referred to as Protoctista rather than Protista.

Once a kingdom has been formed, whether it be Protista, Protoctista, or some other group, the organisms in it have to be subdivided. Whittaker sorted the organisms in Protista on the basis of how they acquire energy and nutrients, which produced three subkingdoms: the plantlike Protophyta (photosynthetic autotrophs), the funguslike Gynomycota (absorb externally digested nutrients), and the animal-like Protozoa (ingest nutrients but digest them internally). Again, problems arise from this system. Most dinoflagellates, for example, are photosynthetic autotrophs, but some are ingestive heterotrophs. The slime molds are remarkably similar to fungi during some stages of their lives but resemble animals during other stages.

A pitfall in Whittaker's system is that it implies that unicellular eukaryotes are primarily precursors of the plants, fungi, and animals. Some of the ancestors of protists did give rise to the multicellular groups, but the protists we see today did not. Instead, comtemporary forms have been evolving, adapting, and diversifying as unicellular eukaryotes for about 1.5 billion years. Slime molds, for example, probably resemble fungi because of convergent evolution rather than descent from a common ancestor. Three current views of protistan evolution are diagramed in Fig. 24.1.

Protistan classification remains a subject of debate among biologists. We can only hope that further work on biochemical affinities, together with the discovery of more fossils, will help sort out these many and diverse organisms.

ANIMAL-LIKE PROTISTS

24.4   Which of the following statements is true of amoebas?

(*a*) They form pseudopodia;   (*b*) None has an outer shell;   (*c*) They have a flagellated phase in their life cycle;   (*d*) They do not have food vacuoles

24.5   Which of the following statements is *not* true of *Paramecium*?

(*a*) They are predatory ciliates;   (*b*) They use pseudopodia for capturing prey;   (*c*) They are preyed upon by *Didinium*;   (*d*) They use contractile vacuoles for removing excess water

---

* Answers to Chapter 24 objective questions appear on page 171.

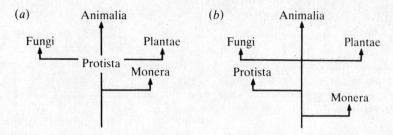

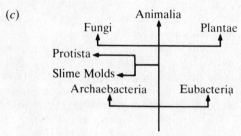

Fig. 24.1. Three views of protistan evolution. (*a*) The protistans as precursors of multicellular organisms. (*b*) The protistans as a separate evolutionary line. (*c*) The protistans as a separate evolutionary line, with slime molds forming their own group, branching off from the protistans early in eukaryotic evolution. Biologists who place slime molds separately also replace the kingdom Monera with Archaebacteria and Eubacteria.

24.6 Which of the following protozoans lives in the guts of termites and helps them digest cellulose?

(*a*) *Plasmodium*;   (*b*) *Amoeba proteus*;   (*c*) *Trichonympha*;   (*d*) *Trypanosoma*

24.7 The protozoans that cause malaria in humans are

(*a*) radiolarians.   (*b*) trichosomes.   (*c*) dinoflagellates.   (*d*) sporozoans.

24.8 The protozoan *Trypanosoma gambiense* causes which disease?

(*a*) Malaria;   (*b*) African sleeping sickness;   (*c*) Elephantiasis;   (*d*) Dysentery

24.9 Ciliates differ from all other protozoans in

(*a*) having two types of nuclei.   (*b*) capturing prey with pseudopodia.   (*c*) having contractile vacuoles. (*d*) not using flagella for locomotion.

24.10 The protists given the name that means "first animals" are the _____.

24.11 The insect host (or vector) required for the transmission of malaria to humans is the _____, and the one required for the transmission of African sleeping sickness is the _____.

24.12 The two types of nuclei in *Paramecium* are the _____, which controls normal cellular metabolism, and the _____, which is involved in reproduction.

24.13 The four groups of amoeboid protozoans are: _____, _____, _____, and _____.

24.14 Chalky deposits that form the White Cliffs of Dover are accumulations of _____ shells.

24.15 An exchange of genetic information occurs in ciliates when cells _____ and exchange haploid _____.

24.16 A protozoan locomotes by one of three structures: _____; _____; or _____.

24.17 The Sporozoa are all internal _____ that typically have an infective _____ stage in their life cycle. An example of Sporozoa are the organisms in the genus _____, which cause malaria.

24.18   Why is malaria controlled by eradicating the *Anopheles* mosquito?

⚫   Four different species of *Plasmodium* (phylum Sporozoa) cause malaria in birds and mammals. These unicellular, eukaryotic organisms are nonmotile, possessing neither cilia nor flagella, and are obligate parasites of other organisms. All have complex life cycles, with sexual phases in mosquitoes of the genus *Anopheles* and asexual phases in birds or mammals.

The malaria-causing organisms are injected into a human by the bite of a female *Anopheles* mosquito. The parasite at this stage of its life cycle is a spindle-shaped *sporozoite* that thrives in liver cells. The sporozoites pass rapidly from the saliva of the mosquito, via human blood, to the liver, where they grow for 5–15 days and then reproduce asexually. Sporozoites transform themselves into *merozoites*, a form that moves into red blood cells and multiplies again by mitosis. At regular intervals, the merozoites break out of the red blood cells (by bursting them) and invade new red blood cells. The entire population within a host acts in synchrony, invading red blood cells at the same time and breaking out of the cells at the same time. Whenever the red blood cells rupture, the afflicted person suffers chills and high fever caused by toxic by-products released from the ruptured cells.

Some of the merozoites in the blood develop into immature male and female gametes. If red blood cells containing these forms are ingested by a female mosquito during her blood meal, the gametes migrate to the mosquito's midgut where they unite to form zygotes. The newly formed diploid cells invade the lining of the gut and develop into thick-walled cysts. Meiosis within the cysts yields infective, haploid sporozoites, which move out of the cysts to the mosquito's salivary glands. There they are in position to enter another human host.

There is neither a cure nor a vaccine for malaria. The disease has been treated with some success in the past by quinine, a molecule found naturally in the bark of the cinchona tree, and by chemically related drugs synthesized by chemists. The disease has been controlled also by applying contact insecticides to the mosquitoes. However, drug-resistant populations of *Plasmodium* and insecticide-resistant populations of *Anopheles* have evolved in the past few decades, and so these methods are no longer effective. At present the only remaining avenue of attack is to destroy the habitats where the *Anopheles* mosquito breeds. In the future, alternative methods may be developed from current research. For example, scientists are exploring the possibility of using biologic controls and genetic engineering as a means of eradicating the vector (*Anopheles*); also, research into rodent malaria shows that active immunization against the disease may one day prove possible.

24.19   Why are some protozoans said to be acellular?

⚫   Some protozoans are so complex, with regard to internal structure and function, that they are not equivalent to other eukaryotic cells. The organelles of these unicellular organisms resemble organs more than they resemble other subcellular structures. Such protozoans are said to be acellular to emphasize their elaborate intracellular morphology.

Most often it is the ciliates (phylum Cilia) that are labeled acellular. Each of these eukaryotic cells has: an oral groove covered with cilia for the capture of food and, in some, for the release of poisonous darts; a cytopharynx for food intake; an anal pore for removal of undigested food; contractile fibrils for locomotion; stiffened plates (like a skeleton) for support; a stalk (in some) composed of contractile fibrils that is attached to the substrate and used to thrust the cell body toward food or away from danger. Additionally, each ciliate has two types of nuclei—a large polyploid macronucleus for control of protein synthesis and one or more small micronuclei for reproduction.

Acellular protozoans have attained a degree of specialization, through development of subcellular structures, that equals the degree of specialization attained by multicellular organisms. The cell of one of these protozoans is much more complex than is the single cell of a plant, fungus, or animal.

FUNGUSLIKE PROTISTS

24.20   Spores of true slime molds are produced in structures called

(*a*) sporocytes.   (*b*) plasmodia.   (*c*) sporangia.   (*d*) pseudoplasmodia.

24.21   Which of the following groups is considered to contain true funguslike protists?

(*a*) Hyphochytrids;   (*b*) True slime molds;   (*c*) *Euglena*;   (*d*) *Plasmodium*

24.22   Slime molds in the division Myxomycota (true slime molds) have

(*a*) feeding stages consisting of solitary, individual cells.   (*b*) spores that develop into flagellated gametes.
(*c*) pseudoplasmodia.   (*d*) spores that develop into free-living amoeboid cells.

24.23   The sluglike phase of the cellular slime mold life cycle is called a

(*a*) plasmodium.   (*b*) pseudoplasmodium.   (*c*) macrocyst.   (*d*) sporangia.

24.24   The mass of streaming protoplasm in plasmodial slime molds is called the _____.

24.25   In chytrids, which are _____ funguslike protists, the haploid body can be a simple saclike container called a _____ that lives entirely within the host cell. When flagellated _____ develop within this container, they are released via a tube through the membrane of the host cell.

24.26   Cellular slime molds are _____ with regard to chromosome number, while most phases of the life cycles of plasmodial slime molds are _____.

24.27   How do plasmodial slime molds differ from cellular slime molds?

    The two kinds of slime molds differ in their morphologies and life cycles. Plasmodial slime molds have *coenocytic* plasmodia (multinucleate mass lacking internal cell boundaries) and diploid nuclei, undergo sexual reproduction regularly, and have flagellated gametes. Cellular slime molds have multicellular plasmodia and haploid nuclei, undergo sexual reproduction rarely, and have gametes that lack flagella.

    The life cycle of a plasmodial slime mold (division Myxomycota) begins with a diploid, amoeboid (i.e., moves by pseudopodia) cell, which feeds, grows, and undergoes mitosis without cytokinesis to form a feeding plasmodium—a multinucleated streaming mass of protoplasm. This so-called *coenocyte*, which may cover a circular area as large as 1 m in diameter, moves like an amoeba as it engulfs bacteria and other organic materials. As it grows, its nuclei continue to divide by mitosis. When food becomes scarce or the substrate too dry, the feeding plasmodium breaks up into several spore-forming plasmodia. Each of these sedentary plasmodia produces a stalked fruiting body, and the nuclei within this structure divide by meiosis to form haploid spores, which break out of the plasmodium and develop into flagellated gametes. Zygotes form when the gametes fuse, and each newly formed diploid cell then develops into another feeding plasmodium. The life cycle of a plasmodial slime mold is diagramed in Fig. 24.2a.

    Cellular slime molds (division Acrasiomycota) have a more complex life cycle. Spores do not become flagellated gametes and zygotes do not develop into coenocytic masses, as happens with the plasmodial slime molds. Instead, spores develop into solitary, haploid, amoeboid cells that feed on bacteria and other organic materials. When they reach a certain size, they divide by mitosis and cytokinesis to produce independent daughter cells. This form of life continues as long as food is abundant. When the food supply dwindles, they enter either an asexual phase or a sexual phase of their life cycle (Fig. 24.2b), depending on whether the soil is dry or wet.

    In dry soil, the haploid cells of a cellular slime mold aggregate to form a multicellular plasmodium, known as a *pseudoplasmodium*, which moves about as a coordinated unit. In time the pseudoplasmodium becomes sedentary and forms a fruiting body, within which haploid spores are developed and released. Each spore becomes a solitary, haploid, amoeboid cell. This ends the asexual phase of the life cycle.

    In wet soil, spores do not disperse well; cellular slime molds that experience insufficient food supplies in wet soil enter the sexual phase of their life cycle. Solitary, haploid, amoeboid cells come together, and if the first two are of opposite sexes, they fuse to form a diploid zygote. Other cells that join the aggregate are consumed by the zygote, which grows to be quite large. Eventually, the large diploid cell forms four haploid cells by meiosis, and these cells multiply by mitosis and cytokinesis to form spores within a structure known as a *macrocyst*. When conditions favor a solitary phase of the life cycle, the macrocyst ruptures to release spores that develop into solitary, haploid, amoeboid cells. This ends the sexual phase of the life cycle.

PLANTLIKE PROTISTS

24.28   Which of the following groups does *not* contain unicellular algal protists?

    (*a*) Heliozoans;   (*b*) Euglenoids;   (*c*) Diatoms;   (*d*) Dinoflagellates

24.29   Which species of protists are known as the "whirling whips" because of the spin produced by two flagella beating in opposing grooves along their hard-surfaced bodies?

    (*a*) Diatoms;   (*b*) Chrysophytes;   (*c*) Dinoflagellates;   (*d*) Golden-brown algae

24.30   Which of the following statements is true of *Euglena*?

    (*a*) They are negatively phototactic;   (*b*) They locomote by means of a flagellum;   (*c*) They have a rigid cell wall; (*d*) They do not have chloroplasts

24.31   Euglenoid species that have chlorophyll are

    (*a*) obligate autotrophs.   (*b*) facultative autotrophs.   (*c*) facultative heterotrophs.   (*d*) obligate heterotrophs.

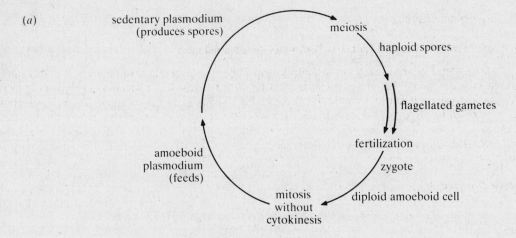

(a)

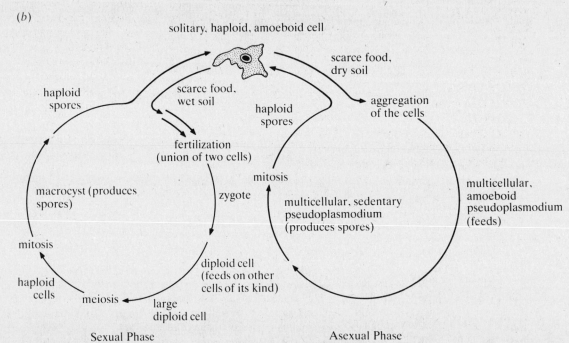

(b)

Fig. 24.2. Slime mold life cycles. (a) The life cycle of a plasmodial slime mold. (b) The life cycle of a cellular slime mold.

24.32 Diatoms are

(a) euglenoids. (b) chrysophytes. (c) dinoflagellates. (d) pyrrophytes.

24.33 The "fire" algae responsible for red tides are the _____.

24.34 All unicellular algae have one photosynthetic pigment in common; it is _____.

24.35 Most green euglenoids have an organelle called a _____ that produces a unique storage product called _____.

24.36 Diatoms are unusual in that their vegetative cells are typically _____ with regard to chromosome number.

24.37 Plankton are typically divided into two groups: plantlike organisms called _____; and animal-like organisms called _____.

24.38 The chromosomes of dinoflagellates differ from all other organisms in that they lack _____ and are permanently _____.

24.39 Chrysophytes store energy as _____ rather than as starch.

24.40 Why is it dangerous to eat shellfish taken from water during a red tide?

🐚 Red tides develop when red-colored dinoflagellates experience favorable conditions and multiply rapidly in warm coastal waters. They become so abundant that the waters turn red. A population explosion of this type of planktonic organism is known as a bloom. Some of the dinoflagellates that contribute to a red tide synthesize a neurotoxin that paralyzes vertebrate animals. Fish in a red tide die as they acquire the toxin through their food chains, but clams, oysters, mussels, and other shellfish accumulate it with no adverse effects. When shellfish from these waters are eaten by humans, however, the neurotoxin in the shellfish bodies causes paralysis and often death in the human consumers.

Answers to Objective Questions

24.1 *b*
24.2 unicellular; colonial
24.4 *a*
24.5 *b*
24.6 *c*
24.7 *d*
24.8 *b*
24.9 *a*
24.10 protozoans
24.11 *Anopheles* mosquito; tsetse fly
24.12 macronucleus; micronucleus
24.13 amoebas; foraminiferans; radiolarians; heliozoans

24.14 Foraminifera
24.15 conjugate; micronuclei
24.16 flagella; cilia; pseudopodia
24.17 parasites; cyst; *Plasmodium*
24.20 *c*
24.21 *a*
24.22 *b*
24.23 *b*
24.24 plasmodium
24.25 true; thallus; zoospores
24.26 haploid; diploid
24.28 *a*
24.29 *c*
24.30 *b*

24.31 *c*
24.32 *b*
24.33 red dinoflagellates
24.34 chlorophyll *a*
24.35 pyrenoid; paramylum
24.36 diploid
24.37 phytoplankton; zooplankton
24.38 centromeres; condensed
24.39 oil

CHAPTER 25
Kingdom Fungi

FORM AND FUNCTION*

25.1   Which of the following ways of acquiring nutrients is *not* characteristic of fungi?

(*a*) Heterotrophic;   (*b*) Autotrophic;   (*c*) Saprophytic;   (*d*) Parasitic

25.2   Most fungi develop a multicellular mass of filaments that spreads through the organic matter they are using as food. This mass is called a

(*a*) mycelium.   (*b*) hypha.   (*c*) sporangium.   (*d*) ascoscarp.

25.3   Which of the following is *not* part of asexual reproduction in fungi?

(*a*) Formation of asexual spores;   (*b*) New individuals growing from hyphal fragments;   (*c*) Binary fission;
(*d*) Development of dikaryons

25.4   The tubelike filaments, each with hundreds of haploid nuclei, that are basic to most fungal structures are called

(*a*) hyphae.   (*b*) mycelium.   (*c*) sporangiophores.   (*d*) gametangia.

25.5   During sexual reproduction, two fungal hyphae of complementary mating types fuse and their nuclei remain separate. This fused structure is called a _____, and this stage in reproduction (between haploid and diploid) is called the _____ stage.

25.6   Unlike plant cell walls, which contain _____, the cell walls in most fungi contain _____.

25.7   When fungal hyphae are divided into cells by walls called _____, the fungi are called
_____. When the hyphae are a multinucleated, continuous cytoplasmic mass, the fungi are called
_____.

25.8   Most saprophytic fungi digest food externally, secreting enzymes onto the material and absorbing the products by means of rootlike _____.

25.9   What is external digestion in fungi?

🐚   A fungus is an absorptive heterotroph. It acquires energy and nutrients by releasing digestive enzymes onto other organisms, either living or dead. These enzymes convert large organic molecules into smaller monomers, such as simple sugars and amino acids, by a process known as hydrolysis, or digestion. Each cell of a fungus feeds independently and is able to synthesize a variety of digestive enzymes. The fungus as a whole can make use of many different kinds of foods at the same time. After external digestion is complete, the smaller molecules diffuse through the cell wall and move across the plasma membrane by active or passive transport. Water is essential for diffusion, and most fungi can survive only under conditions of high humidity. Once the smaller molecules are absorbed into the cell, intracellular enzymes either break them down to release the energy they contain or incorporate them into new molecular forms. The waste products of these reactions then leave the cell by diffusion.

25.10   What is the dikaryotic stage of fungal reproduction?

🐚   *Dikaryote* means "two nuclei," and the dikaryotic stage occurs during sexual reproduction in fungi. Two haploid cells of opposite mating types (plus and minus) unite during sexual reproduction. The cells may be gametes, gamete-producing bodies, or hyphae. In most species of fungi, there is then a delay before the two nuclei of the cells fuse to form a single diploid nucleus. The period of time between cytoplasmic fusion and nuclear fusion is the *dikaryotic stage*. It may last a long time, during which the dikaryotic cell may divide repeatedly by mitosis.

* Answers to Chapter 25 objective questions appear on page 175

MAJOR GROUPS OF FUNGI

25.11 Fungi in the division Oomycota are known as

(*a*) egg fungi. (*b*) sac fungi. (*c*) club fungi. (*d*) cup fungi.

25.12 Which division of the fungi is commonly known as club fungi?

(*a*) Oomycota; (*b*) Ascomycota; (*c*) Zygomycota; (*d*) Deuteromycota

25.13 Which of the following groups is *not* comprised of sac fungi?

(*a*) Truffles; (*b*) Morels; (*c*) Mushrooms; (*d*) Yeasts

25.14 The part of a mushroom that is visible above the ground is a

(*a*) basidiocarp. (*b*) zygospore. (*c*) ascoscarp. (*d*) ascogonium.

25.15 Which of the following statements is *not* true of Fungi Imperfecti?

(*a*) They include toadstools, puffballs, and stink horns; (*b*) They do not have a sexual phase; (*c*) They include species that prey on nematodes; (*d*) They include *Aspergillis*, the fungus used to make soy sauce

25.16 The very fine asexual spores characteristic of ascomycetes are called

(*a*) basidiospores. (*b*) conidia. (*c*) zygospores. (*d*) ascospores.

25.17 In the black bread mold (*Rhizopus*), the hyphae that both absorb nutrients and anchor the mycelium are known as

(*a*) sporangiophores. (*b*) stolons. (*c*) rhizoids. (*d*) gametangia.

25.18 The Oomycota, such as water molds, are so different from other fungi that some biologists think they evolved separately. Which of the following is *not* characteristic of Oomycota?

(*a*) Flagellated zoospores; (*b*) Lack of chitin in cell walls; (*c*) Oogamous reproduction; (*d*) Haploid during most of their life cycle

25.19 The devastating famine in Ireland during the 19th century, due to rotting of potatoes, was produced by the egg fungus *Phytophthora infestans*. It causes potato blight, which is also known as _____ blight.

25.20 In the division Zygomycota, sexual reproduction consists of the fusion of two club-shaped _____ to form a diploid zygote. The zygote is then surrounded by a thick wall to form a dormant spore known as a _____.

25.21 In the _____ (division Ascomycota), haploid spores called _____ are produced in saclike structures called _____, which are typically grouped together in a multicelled structure called an _____.

25.22 The antibiotic penicillin is derived from fungal species in the genus _____, which is a _____ in the division Deuteromycota.

25.23 In the division Basidiomycota, haploid spores that are formed externally on club-shaped _____ are called _____.

25.24 The commercially cultivated common field mushroom, *Agaricus campestris*, and the most highly poisonous of mushrooms in the genus *Amanita* are both _____ fungi in the division _____.

25.25 What is the role of the aboveground structure in the life cycle of a mushroom?

🐚 The aboveground part, or *basidiocarp*, of a mushroom is its reproductive body. Formed of nonfeeding hyphae, it is connected to, and nourished by, an elaborate underground network of feeding hyphae, known collectively as the *mycelium*. Materials flow freely from cell to cell within the hyphae and from mycelium to basidiocarp. This extensive support system enables a mycelium to rapidly form a basidiocarp whenever environmental conditions are favorable for reproduction. Reproduction in the division Basidiomycota (the mushrooms, shelf fungi, puffballs, and stinkhorns) is always sexual. The life cycle of a mushroom is diagramed in Fig. 25.1.

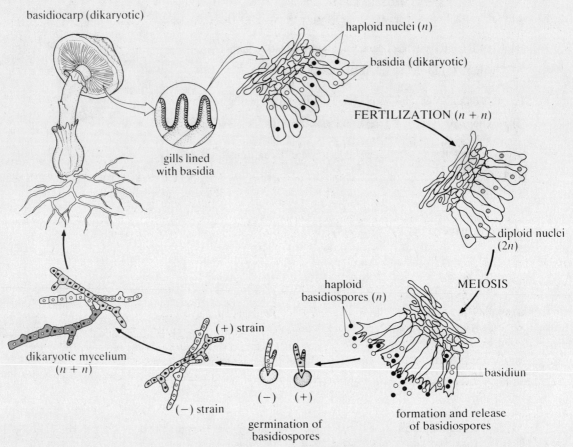

Fig. 25.1. The life cycle of a mushroom. All cells within a basidiocarp are dikaryotic. Within cells of the basidia (a structure in the basidiocarp), the two haploid nuclei fuse and subsequent meiosis produces haploid spores. Each basidiospore disperses and, if it germinates, reproduces by mitosis to form a mycelium. When two mycelia of opposite mating types (plus or minus, as determined by their nuclei) lie adjacent to each other, nuclei move from one to the other so that some cells become dikaryotic, with one nucleus of each mating type. These dikaryotic cells then multiply by mitosis to form another basidiocarp, and the life cycle is completed.

Reproductive propagules are wind-dispersed, haploid spores called *basidiospores*. They form within club-shaped structures known as *basidia*, which line the gills on the underside of the basidiocarp cap. All cells of the basidiocarp are dikaryotic, with nuclei of both mating types. In cells of the basidia, the two haploid nuclei fuse to form a zygote, which divides by meiosis to produce four haploid cells. A capsule develops around each haploid cell, and it is then a spore, ready to be ejected from the basidiocarp and capable of forming a new mycelium.

A basidiocarp forms when mycelia of opposite types, as determined by their haploid nuclei, come together and live side by side. Cytoplasmic bridges develop between the two mycelia, and nuclei migrate from one to the other. Dikaryotic cells, with nuclei of both mating types, form and then divide repeatedly by mitosis to form a basidiocarp. This completes the life cycle of a mushroom.

25.26 Why are yeasts, which are unicellular, classified as fungi rather than as protists?

⊛ Evidence suggests that yeasts were once multicellular and then secondarily evolved a unicellular way of life. Thus, they belong with their closer relatives, the multicellular fungi, rather than with the unicellular protists.

A striking similarity between yeasts and other fungi in the division Ascomycota is that the products of meiosis (four haploid spores, or eight if a mitotic division follows meiosis) remain for a while in a sac known as an *ascus*. In yeasts, this sac forms from the wall of the zygote, whereas in other members of the Ascomycota the sac is constructed specifically for this function.

SYMBIOTIC RELATIONSHIPS OF THE FUNGI

25.27 A _____ is a symbiotic relationship between a fungus and the roots of a vascular plant. If the fungal hyphae penetrate the roots, the relationship is called an _____ and the fungus is usually a _____. If the fungal hyphae form only a sheath around the roots, the relationship is called an _____ and the fungus is usually a _____.

25.28 A lichen is a symbiotic relationship between a _____ or a _____ fungus and photosynthetic organisms, which are almost always either _____ or _____.

25.29 How does a lichen reproduce?

🐚 Reproduction by a lichen is complex, since the organism is really two different kinds of organisms in one. Lichens reproduce only asexually, either by fragmenting or by forming reproductive bodies made of algae embedded within fungal hyphae. These "starters" are dispersed by wind or rain.

Sexual reproduction is accomplished indirectly, when each organism of the lichen reproduces sexually on its own. Then, if the offspring of the fungus and the offspring of the algae by chance come together, a new lichen, with new combinations of genes, is formed from the products of sexual reproduction.

25.30 Why is it necessary to incorporate forest soil along with a forest tree when it is transplanted to a treeless area?

🐚 Forest trees do not survive well without special fungi that form associations, known as *mycorrhizae*, with the tree roots. These associations are called *endo*mycorrhizae when the fungal hyphae extend into the root cells, and *ecto*mycorrhizae when the hyphae surround but do not penetrate the roots. In either case, the fungus greatly increases the surface area of the root for absorption of minerals (especially phosphorus). In return for supplying the tree with minerals, the fungus receives organic molecules synthesized by the tree.

Approximately 90 percent of all tree species form mycorrhizae and do not grow well without them. When planting a tree where other trees may never have grown, a small amount of forest soil is added to the soil in order to inoculate it with the fungus, which ensures that mycorrhizae develop.

Answers to Objective Questions

25.1 *b*
25.2 *a*
25.3 *d*
25.4 *a*
25.5 dikaryon; dikaryotic
25.6 cellulose; chitin
25.7 septa; septate; aseptate
25.8 haustoria
25.11 *a*
25.12 *b*
25.13 *c*

25.14 *a*
25.15 *a*
25.16 *b*
25.17 *c*
25.18 *d*
25.19 late
25.20 gametangia; zygospore
25.21 sac fungi; ascospores; asci; ascoscarp
25.22 *Penicillium*; Fungi Imperfecti

25.23 basidium; basidiospores
25.24 gill; Basidiomycota
25.27 mycorrhizae; endomycorrhizae; zygomycete; ectomycorrhizae; basidiomycete
25.28 sac; club; cyanobacteria; green algae

CHAPTER 26
Kingdom Plantae

THALLOPHYTA (THE ALGAE)*

26.1 In the plant kingdom, all divisions (or phyla) in the group called Thallophyta are similar in that they

(*a*) have chlorophyll *d*.   (*b*) have flagella at some stage.   (*c*) have relatively little tissue differentiation.
(*d*) are smaller than most land plants.

26.2 A thallus is a plant body with

(*a*) no distinguishable roots, stems, or leaves.   (*b*) a vascular system.   (*c*) a stem and roots.
(*d*) attached reproductive structures (gametangia).

26.3 Zygotes of species in the group Thallophyta

(*a*) do not retain progeny as embryos within the maternal parent.   (*b*) are flagellated.
(*c*) have triploid nuclei.   (*d*) form from the union of diploid cells.

26.4 Green algae are in the division

(*a*) Charophyta.   (*b*) Phaeophyta.   (*c*) Chlorophyta.   (*d*) Rhodophyta.

26.5 Most green algae live in

(*a*) hot springs.   (*b*) deep seas.   (*c*) rocky coasts.   (*d*) fresh water.

26.6 *Chlamydomonas* is a genus of

(*a*) multicellular haploid organisms.   (*b*) multicellular diploid organisms.   (*c*) unicellular haploid organisms.
(*d*) unicellular diploid organisms.

26.7 *Chlamydomonas* differs from others genera of green algae in having

(*a*) cell walls of glycoprotein rather than of cellulose.   (*b*) neither chlorophyll *a* nor chlorophyll *b*.
(*c*) only chlorophyll *b* or chlorophyll *d* as accessory pigments.   (*d*) no cell walls.

26.8 The genus *Gonium*, in the division Chlorophyta, is an example of multicellularity at the level of a

(*a*) mating pair of haploid cells (syngamy).   (*b*) temporary feeding group.   (*c*) simple colony.
(*d*) differentiated body.

26.9 *Pandorina*, in the division Chlorophyta, is considered a more advanced genus than *Gonium*, because it has a more differentiated

(*a*) zygote structure.   (*b*) temporary feeding group.   (*c*) colony.   (*d*) root system.

26.10 Which of the following genera exhibits an alternation of generations, with haploid and diploid multicellular phases?

(*a*) *Chlamydomonas*;   (*b*) *Ulva*;   (*c*) *Ulothrix*;   (*d*) *Volvox*

26.11 Most brown algae (division Phaeophyta) live in

(*a*) freshwater streams.   (*b*) freshwater lakes.   (*c*) cool coastal waters of oceans.   (*d*) warm coastal waters of oceans.

26.12 Red algae differ from the green algae and brown algae in having

(*a*) no chlorophyll *a*.   (*b*) no differentiated cells.   (*c*) hemoglobin within their cells.
(*d*) no flagellated stages in their life cycles.

* Answers to Chapter 26 objective questions appear on page 185.

26.13 Most red algae (division Rhodophyta) live in

(*a*) freshwater streams. (*b*) freshwater lakes. (*c*) cool coastal waters of oceans. (*d*) warm coastal waters of oceans.

26.14 All divisions, or phyla, in the plant kingdom can be assembled into two groups—Thallophyta and Embryophyta. The _____ group is the more primitive of the two groups. It contains three kinds of plants: the _____, _____, and _____ algae.

26.15 The only algal division that has not been a phylogenetic dead end is _____, which most biologists believe led to the evolution of land plants.

26.16 A *Chlamydomonas* moves by means of two _____.

26.17 With regard to ploidy level, the dominant stages of the *Chlamydomonas* life cycle are _____, a characteristic of primitive plants and, presumably, of the ancestral plant condition.

26.18 Match the terms on the left with the definitions on the right, by writing the letter of the term in the space before its definition.

(*a*) isogamy   (1) _____ Two kinds of gametes, one mobile and the other nonmobile
(*b*) syngamy   (2) _____ Two kinds of morphologically distinct gametes
(*c*) heterogamy   (3) _____ The union of two gametes
(*d*) anisogamy   (4) _____ Both gametes morphologically indistinguishable
(*e*) oogamy   (5) _____ Two kinds of gametes, one larger than the other

26.19 The multicellular stage of many green algae is a _____ thallus—a small thread of undifferentiated cells attached to the substrate by a specialized cell, the _____. Any cell in the structure except the attached one can reproduce asexually to form a motile _____, which disperses by means of four _____. The asexually produced cell eventually settles onto the substrate and forms a new thallus.

26.20 Where there is alternation of generations, the haploid multicellular plant is called a _____ and the diploid multicellular plant is called a _____. Multicellularity in plants first appeared in the _____ generation. Many green algae have no _____ generation.

26.21 The common name of algae in the genus *Ulva* is _____, because of its three-dimensional, leaflike thallus. The two generations in *Ulva* are *isomorphic*, meaning they are _____ in _____.

26.22 The difference between a spore and a gamete is that a spore develops into a _____, whereas a gamete develops into a _____.

26.23 The common name for most brown and red algae is _____.

26.24 Phaeophyta are unusual in that their chloroplasts contain chlorophyll _____ as well as the carotenoid pigment _____, which gives them their brown color.

26.25 Sexual reproduction in some brown algae involves gametangia, which are structures made of _____ cell(s). They produce _____.

26.26 Rhodophyta are unique among plants in having the accessory pigments chlorophyll _____ and _____; the latter pigment gives them a reddish color.

26.27 Where the ranges of algae from divisions Phaeophyta and Rhodophyta overlap, the _____ are found in deeper water than the _____, because their accessory pigments adapt them to _____ and _____ light.

26.28 What do the algae tell us about the origin of sperm and egg?

🐚 Gametes are any haploid cells that unite to form a diploid cell. They come in many forms, from the unspecialized cells of protists to the highly dimorphic sperm and egg of animals and some plants. Morphology of the gametes seems unrelated to morphology of the body, since all forms of gametes occur among the algae, and form is not related to whether the alga is unicellular, colonial, filamentous, or truly multicellular.

The unicellular algae (genus *Chlamydomonas*; division Chlorophyta) exhibit all three major patterns: isogamy, anisogamy, and oogamy. In isogamous species, the two gametes are morphologically identical. Gametes of some species of *Chlamydomonas* are not only identical to each other but also to nonreproductive cells. They swim by means of two flagella, and sexual reproduction takes place when two cells of opposite strain (plus and minus) become chemically attracted to each other and fuse to form a diploid cell. Other unicellular green algae have anisogamous gametes, with a difference in size as well as chemistry between the two types of gametes. In anisogamy, the smaller gamete is always called the male gamete. Still other species of *Chlamydomonas* have oogamy, in which the smaller gamete retains its two flagella and hence its mobility, whereas the larger gamete loses its flagella and thus becomes immobile. These dimorphic gametes resemble the sperm and egg of higher organisms.

Multicellular algae differ from the unicellular algae in that the gametes of multicellular algae are special cells of the mature organism, and they are produced by single somatic cells, specialized organs (*gametangia*), or specialized individuals in the life cycle (*gametophytes*). Multicellular green algae (division Chlorophyta) have a variety of gametes. In *Spirogyra*, for example, two algae of a mating pair become joined, and amoeboid gametes creep from one to the other. Both gametes are morphologically identical. *Ulva*, another form of green alga, also has isogamous gametes, but they move by two flagella rather than by creeping. Such flagellated gametes resemble nonreproductive, unicellular algae. Yet another genus of Chlorophyta—*Oedogonium*—has oogamy with a multiflagellated, mobile sperm and a larger, nonmobile egg.

The other divisions of algae have less gametic diversity than the Chlorophyta. Brown algae (Phaeophyta) and stoneworts (Charophyta) generally have oogamy, with the smaller sperm moving by means of two flagella. Oogamy is also the main form in red algae (Rhodophyta), but here the smaller—the male—gamete moves by water currents and amoeboid creeping; it has no flagella.

The lack of correlation between gamete form and taxonomic group among the algae suggests that anisogamy and oogamy originated many times during the evolution of multicellular organisms. The environment presumably exerts strong selective pressure on gamete morphology, evolving the size and shape that best facilitate zygote formation.

26.29 How did the algae evolve multicellularity?

⊛ A group of genera in the division Chlorophyta, called the volvoccine series, may represent how multicellularity evolved in the algae. Organisms in this series become increasingly more complex through formation of colonies of flagellated cells (Fig. 26.1). Algae in the series do not represent the evolutionary sequence itself, since these are algae that exist today, but probably resemble the sequence through which many organisms passed on their way toward multicellularity.

The first algae in the series are *Chlamydomonas*—unicellular organisms, each with a cup-shaped chloroplast and two flagella. The next algae in the series have bodies that are primitively multicellular, resembling colonies of just a few *Chlamydomonas* cells. These algae are in the genus *Gonium*. Each cell in a *Gonium* individual retains most of its individuality and is only loosely associated with the others. The entire organism moves from place to place by movements, albeit uncoordinated, of its many flagella. Next in complexity are species in the genus *Pandorina*, again with cells that resemble *Chlamydomonas*, but now they form larger colonies and individual cells are less independent than those of *Gonium* individuals.

The volvoccine series culminates with the spectacular *Volvox* (sometimes classified as protists). Individuals in this genus are large, hollow spheres of between 500 and 60,000 flagellated cells that tumble through the water, propelled by synchronous movements of the flagella. There is considerable division of labor among the cells of a *Volvox* individual—only some cells, for example, have reproductive functions. As with all other colonies in the

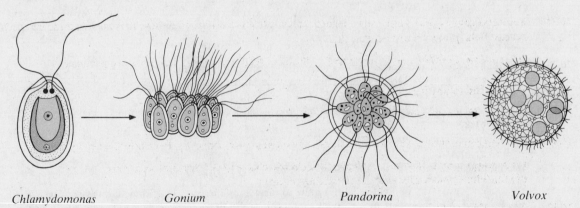

Chlamydomonas   *Gonium*   *Pandorina*   *Volvox*

Fig. 26.1. The volvoccine series. The increasing complexity of these four genera of green algae may resemble the evolution of multicellularity in many primitive plants and animals.

series, an individual forms when a zygote germinates into an independent cell, which is very similar to *Chlamydomonas*, and this cell divides repeatedly by mitosis. All the daughter cells remain together, embedded within a gelatinous matrix.

26.30 What effects do different algal pigments have on where the algae live?

🐚 The three divisions of multicellular algae are distinguished by their green, brown, and red colors. Each color is the result of pigments contained within their plastids. All plants have chlorophyll *a* as their main photosynthetic pigment, as well as various other pigments used as accessories (to pass light energy to chlorophyll *a*) and as protection against photochemical damage. Because only certain portions of the light spectrum penetrate very far through water, the pigments used by algae in photosynthesis control how deep they can live in the water.

The green algae (division Chlorophyta) are biochemically similar to terrestrial plants. Their plastids contain chlorophyll *a*, chlorophyll *b*, and beta-carotene. The chlorophylls of green algae absorb mostly blue and red light, so that, like terrestrial plants, they thrive in full sunlight. The beta-carotene functions mostly to prevent cell damage from bright light. Green algae live in shallow water, where they can absorb the blue and red light that reaches the earth's surface.

The brown algae (division Phaeophyta) resemble the green algae in photosynthetic pigments, in spite of their pronounced difference in color. Brown algae have chlorophyll *a* and chlorophyll *c*, which absorb red and blue light, as well as large amounts of the brown pigment fucoxanthin, which protects these algae from photochemical damage. Since their chlorophyll absorbs most of the light, brown algae thrive in shallow water, where they take maximum advantage of blue and red light. The brown pigment enables them to do this without damage from the bright light.

The red algae (division Rhodophyta) have chlorophyll *a*, chlorophyll *d* (usually), and both phycocyanin and phycoerythrin—two phycobilin pigments similar to those found in cyanobacteria. Phycoerythrin absorbs mostly green light, and phycocyanin absorbs mostly yellow light. Red algae are especially adapted for living in deep water, where only blue and green light penetrate. In such an environment, the chlorophylls of red algae absorb blue light and the phycoerythrin absorbs green light, thus enabling photosynthesis to continue in the near darkness of deep water. Red algae are not always red; their color varies with water depth. In the full sunlight of shallow water, phycoerythrin is broken down by light and the algae lose their red color, becoming dark green or brown as light is reflected from chlorophyll and carotene. The algae become redder as the water becomes deeper and more phycoerythrin is present.

EMBRYOPHYTA: THE BRYOPHYTES

26.31 Bryophytes acquire most of their water through

(*a*) aboveground structures. (*b*) true roots. (*c*) underground cuplike structures called gemmae. (*d*) mycorrhyzae.

26.32 Most bryophytes live in the

(*a*) tropical zone. (*b*) northern temperate zone. (*c*) southern temperate zone. (*d*) arctic zones.

26.33 A moss sperm moves by means of

(*a*) pseudopodia. (*b*) cilia. (*c*) a flagellum. (*d*) two flagella.

26.34 Some mosses have elongated cells through which water is transported. These structures and the tracheids of vascular plants are the results of

(*a*) convergent evolution. (*b*) divergent evolution. (*c*) coevolution. (*d*) regressive phylogeny.

26.35 Bryophytes occupy habitats that are

(*a*) dry. (*b*) moist. (*c*) salty. (*d*) in full sun.

26.36 The bryophyte sperm, just like the sperm of green algae and ferns, is attracted to the egg by

(*a*) moving currents of water. (*b*) opposite electric charges. (*c*) chemical secretions. (*d*) threadlike guides produced by the archegonium.

26.37 The rootlike and leaflike structures of a moss and the roots and leaves of a vascular plant are

(*a*) analogous structures. (*b*) homologous structures. (*c*) embryonic structures. (*d*) vestigial structures.

26.38 Embryonic development of the bryophyte zygote takes place in the

(*a*) protonema.   (*b*) sporangium.   (*c*) antheridium.   (*d*) archegonium. '

26.39 The oldest bryophyte fossils are about

(*a*) 57 million years old.   (*b*) 350 million years old.   (*c*) 600 million years old.   (*d*) 1 billion years old.

26.40 The division Bryophyta consists of three classes: _____, _____, and _____.

26.41 Bryophytes are nonvascular plants, i.e., they have no _____ or _____.

26.42 Bryophytes have a life cycle with alternation of a haploid, sexual generation with a diploid, asexual generation. Unlike vascular plants, in bryophytes the _____ is usually larger than the _____.

26.43 A moss is attached to its substrate by elongated cells called _____.

26.44 Bryophytes are adapted to land by having a _____ on aboveground parts.

26.45 The sperm of a moss are produced by the gametophyte within special organs called _____. Mature sperm move from this structure to the _____, usually on another plant, where fusion with the immobile egg takes place. Movement of sperm to the egg requires the presence of _____.

26.46 Bryophytes are usually short (seldom taller than 20 cm), because they lack a _____ of _____.

26.47 Bryophyte gametophytes develop from _____, produced in a structure known as a _____ on the sporophyte. The sporophyte depends on the _____ for water and nutrients. Bryophytes are distinct from all other land plants in having an independent _____ and a dependent _____.

26.48 One stage in the life cycle of a moss closely resembles the thallus of a filamentous green alga. This stage is called the _____, and it develops from a _____.

26.49 Asexual reproduction in liverworts sometimes occurs by production of special cells called _____, which are held in cuplike structures on the surface of the _____. Each of these structures can grow into a _____.

26.50 How does the life cycle of a moss (class Musci; division Bryophyta) differ from the life cycle of a sea lettuce (genus *Ulva*; division Chlorophyta)?

⚛   Both mosses and sea lettuce (a green alga) have alternation of generations, with a diploid sporophyte and a haploid gametophyte. The moss life cycle differs from the sea lettuce life cycle in having: (1) heteromorphic gametophyte and sporophyte; (2) an algalike protonema stage prior to development of the gametophyte; (3) development of gametes within multicellular sex organs; (4) oogamy rather than isogamy; (5) development of embryos within the female sex organ; and (6) persistence of the sporophyte as a "parasite" on the gametophyte.

The sea lettuce life cycle (Fig. 26.2*a*) has a free-living sporophyte with special cells, called *sporangia*, that undergo meiosis to produce flagellated spores, or zoospores. (Presence of a sporophyte is unusual among the Chlorophyta; most green algae have only a gametophyte stage.) Each zoospore develops into a free-living gametophyte, which forms and releases isogamous gametes, each with two flagella. Gametes of opposite mating types swim to meet each other, unite, and form a diploid zygote. Mitosis of the zygote forms another sporophyte. The sporophyte and gametophyte of a sea lettuce are almost identical in appearance (are isomorphic) and have about equal lifespans.

The moss life cycle (Fig. 26.2*b*) has a sporophyte that lives on the gametophyte. Meiosis occurs within a special tissue, the *sporangium*, to form nonmotile spores. Each spore grows into a green, threadlike body, called a *protonema*, which resembles a filamentous green alga. The protonema gives rise to a gametophyte. Gametes are produced by multicellular sex organs (the *gametangia*) on the gametophyte: an *antheridium* produces small, flagellated sperm, and an *archegonium* produces large, nonmotile eggs. The outer layers of the gametangia are made of jacket cells, which protect the gametes from desiccation. Sperm swim from the antheridium to the archegonium (usually of another plant), where they find and fertilize an egg. The developing embryo remains within the archegonium, where it is protected from desiccation. An adult sporophyte forms, and it, too, remains

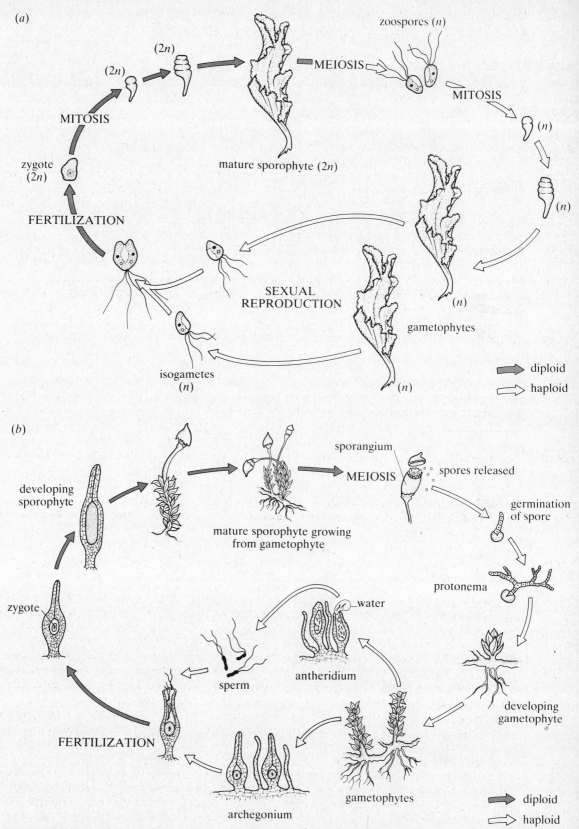

Fig. 26.2. Life cycles of a chlorophyte and a bryophyte. (a) Of the two, the sea lettuce (genus *Ulva*; division Chlorophyta) has the simpler life cycle, with a free-living sporophyte and a free-living gametophyte. (b) A moss (class Musci; division Bryophyta) has a more complex life cycle, with a protonema stage and a sporophyte that is parasitic on the gametophyte.

on the gametophyte, from which it acquires its water and nutrients. The "parasitic" sporophyte consists of three structures: a foot that anchors it to the gametophyte; a stalk that gives it height; and a distal capsule, or sporangium, that produces spores.

EMBRYOPHYTA: THE TRACHEOPHYTES

26.51 A plant in the division Tracheophyta has a sporophyte with

(*a*) isogametes. (*b*) roots, stem, and leaves. (*c*) vessels that transport fluids. (*d*) no independent life.

26.52 A plant in the subdivision Psilopsida has no true

(*a*) gametes. (*b*) leaves and roots. (*c*) gametophyte. (*d*) sporophyte.

26.53 The earth's first forests were formed of plants in the subdivision

(*a*) Psilopsida. (*b*) Lycopsida. (*c*) Sphenopsida. (*d*) Pteropsida.

26.54 A plant in the subdivision Lycopsida differs from one in the subdivision Psilopsida in having

(*a*) oogamy. (*b*) true stems. (*c*) true roots and leaves. (*d*) a gametophyte stage.

26.55 Plants in the subdivision Sphenopsida have true

(*a*) roots, but not leaves. (*b*) leaves, but not roots. (*c*) stems, but not roots and leaves. (*d*) roots, stems, and leaves.

26.56 In the Lycopsida, the leaves are emergence leaves called microphylls. Each leaf has a single, unbranched vein. They evolved as

(*a*) modified gametophytes. (*b*) miniaturized sporangia. (*c*) scalelike outgrowths of the stem. (*d*) enlarged gametangia.

26.57 Unlike emergent leaves seen in the Lycopsida, the leaves of ferns (subdivision Pteropsida) are macrophylls, with branched systems of veins. An advantage of these leaves in comparison with emergence leaves is that they provide

(*a*) more surface area for photosynthesis. (*b*) less water loss from transpiration. (*c*) more surface area for gametangia. (*d*) more structural support.

26.58 Which of the following plants is in the class Pteridospermae (subdivision Spermopsida)?

(*a*) Maidenhair tree; (*b*) Horsetail; (*c*) Seed fern; (*d*) Palm tree

26.59 Which of the following plants is in the class Ginkgoae (subdivision Spermopsida)?

(*a*) Maidenhair tree; (*b*) Horsetail; (*c*) Seed fern; (*d*) Palm tree

26.60 Which of the following plants is in the subdivision Sphenopsida?

(*a*) Maidenhair tree; (*b*) Horsetail; (*c*) Seed fern; (*d*) Palm tree

26.61 The sporangia of a conifer are located on the

(*a*) scales of the cones. (*b*) tips of the needles. (*c*) bases of the needles. (*d*) axils of the branches.

26.62 The macrospore of a conifer, which is never released from the sporangium, divides by mitosis to produce a

(*a*) multicellular embryo. (*b*) needle. (*c*) female gametophyte. (*d*) pollen grain.

26.63 The microspore of a conifer, which is released from the sporangium, divides by mitosis to produce a

(*a*) multicellular embryo. (*b*) needle. (*c*) female gametophyte. (*d*) pollen grain.

26.64 The endosperm of an angiosperm differs from that of a gymnosperm in that it

(*a*) contains less fat. (*b*) contains glycogen rather than starch. (*c*) does not form until fertilization takes place. (*d*) only lasts a few days.

26.65 Plants in the subdivisions Psilopsida and Lycopsida have alternation of generations, in which the _____ is prominent and the tiny _____ is usually subterranean and nourished by symbiotic fungi. The two plants of the life cycle are said to be _____ morphic.

26.66 The sporangia of plants in the subdivision Psilopsida are on the _____ of the sporophyte. The sporangia of plants in the subdivision Lycopsida are on special _____, called sporophylls, of the sporophyte. Sporophylls sometimes cluster to form club-shaped structures that give these plants their common name of _____.

26.67 Some genera (e.g., *Selaginella*) in the subdivision Lycopsida have two types of sporangia that produce two types of spores: megaspores, which develop into _____ gametophytes with gametangia called _____, and microspores, which develop into _____ gametophytes with gametangia called _____. Such plants, with two types of spores, are said to be _____.

26.68 Other genera (e.g., *Lycopodium*) in the subdivision Lycopsida have just one type of spore; it forms a gametophyte with both _____ and _____. Such plants, with just one type of spore, are said to be _____.

26.69 In the life cycle of a fern, the large and conspicuous plant is a _____, and the tiny and obscure plant is a _____. Sporangia are on the _____ of the _____.

26.70 All plants in the subdivision Spermopsida have _____. They are better suited to _____ climates than other forms of tracheophytes. The free-living plants of this subdivision are the _____ stage of the life cycle.

26.71 The reproductive structures of a conifer are its _____, of which there are two kinds: _____, which produce megaspores, and _____, which produce microspores.

26.72 A megasporangium enclosed within an integument is the _____ of a seed plant. It produces the female gametophyte and remains on the sporophyte.

26.73 Each microspore produced in a sporangium of a seed plant becomes a _____, which is a multi-cellular structure that is _____ with regard to ploidy level. It becomes the _____ gametophyte and is shed from the sporangium.

26.74 In a conifer, two sperm nuclei enter an egg cell. One unites with the egg nucleus, and the other _____.

26.75 In an angiosperm, two sperm nuclei enter the female gametophyte. One joins with the _____ to form a _____, and the other joins with two _____ to form a triploid nucleus, which becomes the _____.

26.76 The endosperm of a gymnosperm develops _____ fertilization, whereas the endosperm of an angiosperm develops _____ fertilization.

26.77 Like the gymnosperm seed, the angiosperm seed consists of _____, _____, and _____. Unlike a gymnosperm seed, which is naked, an angiosperm seed is enclosed within a _____, which develops from the _____.

26.78 Identify the reproductive structures of the angiosperm shown in Fig. 26.3.

26.79 The tracheophytes we see in nature are sporophytes. What are the gametophytes of these plants like?

⚜ Before we describe the gametophytes of vascular plants, we will briefly review the life cycles of nonvascular plants. The first plants were gametophytes—gamete-forming, multicellular, haploid organisms. Union of their gametes resulted in diploid zygotes, which immediately divided by meiosis to form haploid cells rather than dividing by mitosis to form sporophytes. These haploid cells then developed into more gametophytes. There was no multicellular diploid plant in the life cycle of a primitive plant. This type of cycle persists in some contemporary algae, but most plants have an alternation of generations, with both a sporophyte and a gametophyte.

A few plants, such as *Ulva* (a green alga) and brown algae, have equally prominent gametophytes and sporophytes. Most plants, however, have one form that is larger and with a longer lifespan than the other. The gametophyte is dominant in bryophytes, whereas the sporophyte is dominant in most algae and all vascular plants.

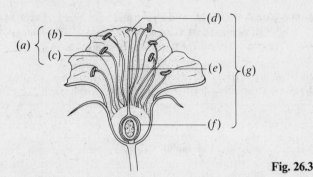

Fig. 26.3

The gametophytes of seedless vascular plants (subdivisions Psilopsida, Pteropsida, Lycopsida, and Sphenopsida) are tiny, free-living plants (Fig. 26.4a). Some have no chlorophyll and live beneath the soil, where they acquire nutrients from detritus or from food stores supplied by their parental sporophyte. Other gametophytes have chlorophyll and live aboveground, building their own sugars by photosynthesis and absorbing water and ions through rhizoids that penetrate the soil. Some groups of seedless plants have a single type of gametophyte, with both antheridia and archegonia; other groups have both a male gametophyte, with antheridia, and a female gametophyte, with archegonia.

Gametophytes of seed plants (subdivision Spermopsida) are tiny structures within the cones or flowers of the sporophytes; they are entirely dependent on the larger sporophytes for energy and nutrients. In gymnosperms, the smaller, male cones contain microsporangia that form haploid microspores. A pollen grain—the male gametophyte—develops from a microspore (Fig. 26.4b). As the gametophyte matures, it forms a pollen tube and two sperm cells, which develop directly rather than from antheridia. Macrosporangia in the larger, female cones produce haploid microspores that develop into female gametophytes (Fig. 26.4c). The macrosporangium and gametophyte are enclosed within a protective integument; together the three structures form an ovule. The female gametophyte is a mass of cells that differentiates into two or more archegonia, each of which produces a single egg cell. Development of gametophytes in gymnosperms takes many months.

Sporangia in the anthers of a flower form angiosperm microspores. A microspore develops into a pollen grain, which, when mature, has a pollen tube and two sperm nuclei (just as in gymnosperms). Female gametophytes

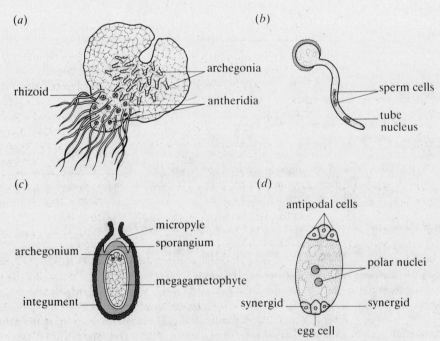

Fig. 26.4. Gametophytes of vascular plants. (a) A fern gametophyte, approximately 6 mm wide, with both antheridium and archegonium. (b) The male gametophyte of a gymnosperm or angiosperm. (c) The female gametophyte of a gymnosperm. (d) The female gametophyte of an angiosperm.

develop within ovules inside the ovary of a flower (Fig. 26.4d). The female gametophyte of an angiosperm forms an egg cell directly rather than by way of an archegonium. Angiosperm gametophytes develop rapidly; the entire flower is short-lived compared with the cones of a gymnosperm.

26.80 Some vascular plants have swimming sperm and others do not. How do male and female gametes meet in (a) plants that have swimming sperm and (b) those that do not?

🐚 (a) The small gametophytes of vascular plants produce male and female gametes. In a fern, these are tiny, flagellated sperm and large, unmotile eggs. A sperm swims through water from an antheridium, where it is formed, to an archegonium, where it finds and fertilizes an egg. Each zygote then develops into a sporophyte, often nourished by materials from the gametophyte. Sexual reproduction in a fern requires a moist environment around the gametophyte for the swimming sperm.

(b) There are no swimming sperm in gymnosperms. The male gametophyte begins as a pollen grain that is carried by the wind to a female cone. A sticky fluid within the cone traps the pollen and, as it dries, draws the pollen to the ovules. Once in contact with an ovule, a pollen grain develops a pollen tube and two unflagellated sperm cells. The pollen tube grows through the ovule to the archegonium, and one of the sperm cells moves to the egg cell, fertilizes it, and forms a zygote. The other sperm cell degenerates. Each zygote develops into an embryo within the ovule, where it is nourished by organic molecules (endosperm) deposited there prior to fertilization.

An angiosperm, like a gymnosperm, has no swimming sperm. The male gametophyte, or pollen grain, is formed within an anther of a flower and carried by either wind or animal to the female parts of a flower. There the pollen grain adheres to the sticky end of a stigma and grows a pollen tube through the stigma to an ovule. Two sperm nuclei move through the pollen tube and into the ovule, where one joins with the egg nucleus to form a zygote and the other joins with two polar nuclei of the female gametophyte to form a triploid endosperm, which surrounds and nourishes the developing embryo.

Answers to Objective Questions

26.1 c

26.2 a

26.3 a

26.4 c

26.5 d

26.6 c

26.7 a

26.8 c

26.9 c

26.10 b

26.11 c

26.12 d

26.13 d

26.14 Thallophyta; green; brown; red

26.15 Chlorophyta

26.16 flagella

26.17 haploid

26.18 (1) e; (2) c; (3) b; (4) a; (5) d

26.19 filamentous; holdfast; zoospore; flagella

26.20 gametophyte; sporophyte; gametophyte; sporophyte

26.21 sea lettuce; identical; morphology

26.22 gametophyte; sporophyte (or zygote)

26.23 seaweed

26.24 c; fucoxanthin

26.25 many; gametes

26.26 d; phycoerythrin

26.27 Rhodophyta; Phaeophyta; blue; green

26.31 a

26.32 a

26.33 d

26.34 a

26.35 b

26.36 c

26.37 a

26.38 d

26.39 b

26.40 Hepatica (liverworts); Anthocerotae (hornworts); Musci (mosses)

26.41 xylem; phloem

26.42 gametophyte (or haploid plant); sporophyte (or diploid plant)

26.43 rhizoids

26.44 waxy cuticle

26.45 antheridia; archegonia; free water

26.46 skeleton; lignin-embedded cell walls (vascular tissue)

26.47 spores; sporangium; gametophyte; gametophyte; sporophyte

26.48 protonemia; spore

26.49 gemmae; gametophyte; gametophyte

26.51 c

26.52 b

26.53 b

26.54 c

26.55 d

26.56 c

26.57 a

26.58 c

26.59 a

26.60 b

26.61 a

26.62 c

26.63 d

26.64 c

26.65 sporophyte; gametophyte; hetero

26.66 stem; leaves; club mosses

26.67 female; archegonia; male; antheridia; heterosporous

26.68 archegonia; antheridia; homosporous

26.69 sporophyte; gametophyte; leaves; sporophyte

26.70 seeds; dry; sporophyte

26.71 cones; female; male

26.72 ovule

26.73 pollen grain; haploid; male

26.74 degenerates

26.75 egg cell; zygote; polar nuclei; endosperm

26.76 before; after

26.77 embryo; endosperm; seed coat; fruit; ovary

26.78 (a) stamen; (b) anther; (c) filament; (d) stigma; (e) style; (f) ovary; (g) pistil (or carpel)

CHAPTER 27
Kingdom Animalia

ANIMAL CHARACTERISTICS*

27.1   Approximately what percentage of existing animal species are invertebrates?

(*a*) 20;   (*b*) 50;   (*c*) 70;   (*d*) 95

27.2   Which of the following is *not* a characteristic of organisms in the kingdom Animalia?

(*a*) Storage of carbohydrates as starch;   (*b*) Multicellularity;   (*c*) Obtaining nutrients by ingestion;
(*d*) Having eukaryotic cells without walls

27.3   Most animal phyla occur in _____ habitats.

27.4   The only haploid stage in an animal life cycle is the _____.

27.5   The three diagrams in Fig. 27.1 are schematic cross sections through bilaterally symmetrical animals. Identify the primary germ layers and structures indicated.

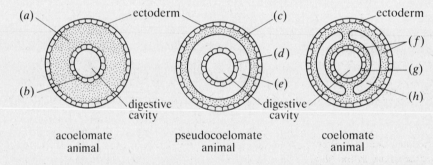

acoelomate   pseudocoelomate   coelomate
animal   animal   animal   **Fig. 27.1**

27.6   What characteristics are used in classifying animals?

Animals are multicellular heterotrophs that acquire energy and monomers by ingesting the organic molecules of other organisms. There are 26 animal phyla, according to the classification system of R. H. Whittaker. Each phylum is composed of animals with a similar overall body plan and, presumably, a common ancestor. The characteristics that differentiate the 11 major phyla are diagrammed in Fig. 27.2 and are discussed below.

The sponges (phylum Porifera) are distinct from all other animals in having little cellular differentiation. A sponge is more advanced than a colony of protozoa but has less division of labor and interdependence among its cells than other kinds of animals.

Animals that are not sponges are divided into two groups, depending on whether their bodies have radial or bilateral symmetry. In radial symmetry, a cut through the axis of the body at any point gives two equal sections that are mirror images of each other. Radial symmetry is characteristic of the phyla Cnidaria (jellyfish and sea anemones) and Ctenophora (comb jellies). All other animals have (at least at some stage) bilateral symmetry, in which there is a left and right side and only one particular cut yields two mirror-image sections. Bilateral symmetry adapts an animal for directed movement; an animal with a left and a right side also has an anterior end and a posterior end, and the anterior end (which first encounters new environments) can become *cephalized*—specialized in sensory perception and integration of information.

All phyla except Porifera, Cnidaria, and Ctenophora are grouped on the basis of whether they have a *coelom*, which is a fluid-filled cavity between the gut and outer body wall. (In humans, the coelom is the cavity of the chest and abdomen within which our organs are suspended.) A true coelom, in a coelomate animal, is lined with mesoderm (the middle germ layer). A *pseudocoelom*, in a pseudocoelomate animal, arises from the *blastocoel* (the interior of the blastula) and is lined on one side by endoderm and the other by mesoderm. An *acoelomate* animal

* Answers to Chapter 27 objective questions appear on page 197.

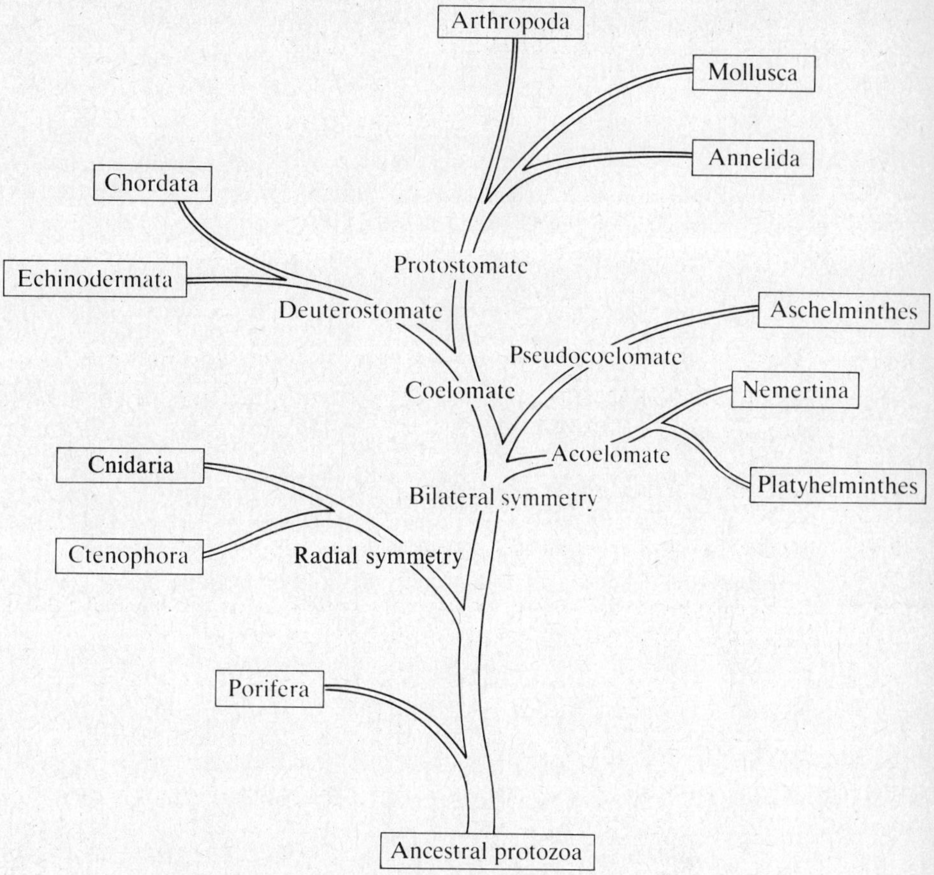

Fig. 27.2. Characteristics used to classify animals, and the classification of 11 major phyla.

has no coelom at all. Pseudocoelomates are in the phylum Aschelminthes (rotifers and roundworms), and acoelomates are in the phyla Platyhelminthes (flatworms) and Nemertina (proboscis worms).

Animals with both bilateral symmetry and true coeloms are divided into two groups according to whether the *blastopore* (the opening into the blastula) develops into a mouth or an anus. In *protostomes* (= first mouth), the blastopore becomes the mouth and the anus develops from a new opening. In *deuterostomes* (= second mouth), the blastopore becomes the anus and the mouth develops from a new opening. Protostomes are also *schizocoelous* (the coelom develops from splits in the mesoderm) with embryonic cleavage that is *spiral* (cleavage planes are oblique to the polar axis) and *determinate* (fate of cells is fixed very early in development). Deuterostomes are *enterocoelous* (the coelom forms from the primitive gut) with embryonic cleavage that is *radial* (cleavage planes are either parallel or perpendicular to the polar axis) and *indeterminate* (fate of cells is not fixed early). Major protostome phyla are the Mollusca (snails, squids, bivalves), Annelida (earthworms, leeches), and Arthropoda (insects, lobsters). Major deuterostome phyla are the Chordata (tunicates and vertebrates) and Echinodermata (sea stars, sea urchins).

Many of the characteristics used in classifying animals, as described above, are developmental traits. The way in which an organism develops from a zygote is usually more indicative of its ancestral lineage than are its adult morphological traits. This is because the evolution of development is more conservative (i.e., ancestral characteristics tend to be retained) than that of adult morphological traits, which evolve in response to natural selection pressures for survival in local environments and so are subject to divergent and convergent patterns of evolution.

SPONGES

27.7   Most sponges are

    (*a*) bilaterally symmetrical.   (*b*) radially symmetrical.   (*c*) vertically symmetrical.   (*d*) asymmetrical.

27.8   Water exits from a sponge through the

    (*a*) osculum.   (*b*) spicule.   (*c*) choanocyte.   (*d*) amoebocyte.

27.9 Which of the following is *not* a function of the amoebocytes in a sponge?

(*a*) Secretion of skeletal materials;   (*b*) Control of pores by contraction;   (*c*) Transport of food to the epidermal cells;   (*d*) Participation in reproduction

27.10 Which of the following is *not* true of reproduction in sponges?

(*a*) Asexual reproduction by gemmules;   (*b*) External fertilization;   (*c*) Internal fertilization;
(*d*) Gamete production by epidermal cells

27.11 Sponges acquire food by filtering water. The food-containing water enters a sponge through _____ and is then moved through the internal cavity to the _____ by the flagella of _____. As the water moves, food is removed by the _____.

27.12 The cells of a sponge that regulate the entry of water by closing pores in response to irritating stimuli are the _____ cells.

27.13 Match the following structures of a sponge with their respective functions.

structure	function
(*a*) amoebocyte	1. _____ Control of water entry
(*b*) osculum	2. _____ Exit for water
(*c*) epidermal cells	3. _____ Movement of water and filtering of food
(*d*) collar cells	4. _____ Skeletal support element
(*e*) spicules	5. _____ Transport of food to nonfeeding cells

27.14 Sponges are in the phylum _____.

27.15 During internal fertilization in sponges, _____ cells are carried by water currents from one sponge to the _____ of another. There they are captured by _____ and transported to _____, which then move them to ripe eggs.

27.16 Why are all sponges, regardless of size, limited to feeding on microscopic food particles?

☘   Adult sponges are sessile (fixed in place) and range in diameter from a few millimeters to 2 m. The tube-shaped, asymmetrical body wall of a sponge is made of two kinds of cells—an inner layer of mostly choanocytes (flagellated collar cells) and an outer layer of epidermal cells. Between these layers is a gel-like substance through which amoebocytes wander. The choanocytes remove food and sperm cells from the water, the epidermal cells regulate the size of pores through which water enters, and the amoebocytes transport food to epidermal cells and have roles in both asexual reproduction (form gemmules) and sexual reproduction (form gametes and transport sperm cells to the ripe eggs).

A sponge is a filter feeder; it acquires food by filtering suspended microorganisms and detritus from the water of its environment. Water enters through many small pores, moves through an internal cavity (the *spongocoel*), and leaves by way of a larger channel (the *osculum*). The water is moved through a sponge by flagella on the choanocytes that line the internal cavity. Food suspended in the water is trapped on the sticky surfaces of the choanocytes and then is either ingested by them or passed to amoebocytes for digestion or distribution to epidermal cells. Unlike other animals, in a sponge digestion is entirely intracellular; digestive enzymes within food vacuoles of the cells break down the ingested food. Materials that a sponge can use as food are limited to microscopic particles that can enter a sponge cell by endocytosis.

RADIALLY SYMMETRICAL ANIMALS

27.17 Which of the following is a radially symmetrical animal?

(*a*) Planarian;   (*b*) Rotifer;   (*c*) Fluke;   (*d*) Sea anemone

27.18 A distinguishing feature of cnidarians is the specialized cells that contain nematocytes. They are located on the surfaces of tentacles and body walls and are used for capturing prey. These cells are called

(*a*) cnidocytes.   (*b*) flame cells.   (*c*) nephridiopores.   (*d*) statocysts.

27.19   The ciliated, free-swimming larval stage of the cnidarian *Aurelia* (jellyfish) is called a

(*a*) blastula.   (*b*) planula.   (*c*) polyp.   (*d*) medusa.

27.20   A *Hydra* has the simplest form of nervous system for integrating the functions of the body. It is called a

(*a*) ladder system.   (*b*) nerve net system.   (*c*) ganglionic system.   (*d*) ventral solid cord system.

27.21   Scyphozoan medusae are more commonly known as

(*a*) sea anemones.   (*b*) hydras.   (*c*) jellyfish.   (*d*) corals.

27.22   The three major classes of cnidarians are: _____, which includes *Hydra*; _____, which includes jellyfish; and _____, which includes corals. The cnidarians are also known as _____.

27.23   The two phyla of radially symmetrical animals that have a digestive cavity with a single opening, called a _____, are _____ and _____.

27.24   Cnidarians are said to be _____, because they have two tissue layers: _____ and _____. There is a noncellular, gel-like layer of secretions between the two tissue layers called the _____.

27.25   In the life cycle of the colonial hydrozoan *Obelia*, there is: asexual reproduction by the tube-shaped _____; sexual reproduction by the bowl-shaped _____; and habitat selection by the ciliated, free-swimming _____.

27.26   The _____ in the phylum Ctenophora get their name from their eight longitudinal bands of comblike plates formed of fused _____.

27.27   How is food processed within a digestive cavity that has just a single opening?

❀   Cnidarians and ctenophores have saclike digestive cavities with a single opening, which serves as both mouth and anus. This type of digestive cavity is considered primitive and is certainly inefficient. Food enters through the opening. Tentacles around the opening paralyze and hold the prey, which range from unicellular organisms to fish. Once immobilized, the prey is moved into the digestive, or gastrovascular, cavity, where digestive enzymes are secreted and the food polymers hydrolyzed into their component monomers. Portions of the food that cannot be digested are moved out of the body, in the form of feces, through the same opening. Because there is just a single opening, food entering the cavity cannot be separated from feces leaving the cavity. To prevent food and feces from mixing, food is not taken in at the same time that feces leave—a restriction that limits the rate of food intake in these animals.

27.28   What are the two body forms of a cnidarian, and how do they influence the life of the animal?

❀   The body of a cnidarian is either a polyp or a medusa. Both forms have similar structures: a mouth surrounded by tentacles and a gastrovascular cavity with a single opening. The *polyp* is shaped like a tube, with the mouth and tentacles on the dorsal surface, directed upward. It is a sessile animal, attached by its ventral surface to the bottom substrate. The *medusa* is a free-swimming animal. It is shaped like an umbrella, with the mouth and tentacles on the ventral surface, directed downward. A medusa is really a floating, upside-down polyp.

An individual cnidarian may spend its entire life as either a polyp or a medusa, or it may assume both forms at different times of its life. Sea anemones always occur in the polyp form, whereas jellyfish always occur in the medusa form. Some cnidarians have both forms at different times of their life; in these, the medusa produces the sperm and eggs. A fertilized egg develops into a larva, which settles to the bottom and becomes a polyp. Fragments of the polyp eventually break off (asexual reproduction), and each fragment develops into a medusa. It is not known whether the larva, the polyp, or the medusa appeared first in the course of evolution.

PROTOSTOMES: NONARTHROPODS

27.29   Flatworms (phylum Platyhelminthes) have three tissue layers and only one body cavity—the digestive cavity. They are called

(*a*) acoelomates.   (*b*) pseudo-acoelomates.   (*c*) pseudocoelomates.   (*d*) coelomates.

27.30 Round worms (phylum Aschelminthes, class Nematoda) have three tissue layers, a digestive cavity, and an additional cavity between the endoderm and mesoderm. They are called

(*a*) acoelomates. (*b*) pseudo-acoelomates. (*c*) pseudocoelomates. (*d*) coelomates.

27.31 Squid and octopuses (phylum Mollusca, class Cephalopoda) have three tissue layers, a digestive cavity, and a fluid-filled cavity within the mesoderm. They are called

(*a*) acoelomates. (*b*) pseudo-acoelomates. (*c*) pseudocoelomates. (*d*) coelomates.

27.32 Which of the following are pseudocoelomates?

(*a*) Trematodes; (*b*) Nematodes; (*c*) Gnathostomulids; (*d*) Cestodes

27.33 Which of the following is *not* true of protostome coelomates?

(*a*) The early cell division of the zygote exhibits radial cleavage. (*b*) The mouth develops at or near the blastopore. (*c*) The animals included in this category are mollusks, annelids, and arthropods. (*d*) The coelom forms by a schizocoelus process in which the mesoderm is split.

27.34 In a mollusk, nitrogenous wastes are removed from the body by tubular structures that connect the coelom with the mantle cavity. These structures are the

(*a*) radula. (*b*) opercula. (*c*) nephridia. (*d*) manticula.

27.35 In all mollusks except bivalves, there is a tonguelike, toothed structure that is used to scrape off food from the surface of rocks and to convey it toward the digestive cavity. This structure is called a

(*a*) metanephridium. (*b*) radula. (*c*) ctenidium. (*d*) palp.

27.36 Which of the following animals is in the class Gastropoda (phylum Mollusca)?

(*a*) Clam; (*b*) Cuttlefish; (*c*) Slug; (*d*) Mussel

27.37 Which of the following characteristics is *not* found in gastropods?

(*a*) They have two shells. (*b*) They are asymmetrical because of torsion. (*c*) Some can digest cellulose. (*d*) Many are hermaphrodites.

27.38 Earthworms are in the phylum

(*a*) Platyhelminthes. (*b*) Arthropoda. (*c*) Annelida. (*d*) Pogonophora.

27.39 Which of the following animals does not have a body composed of many segments?

(*a*) Flatworm; (*b*) Earthworm; (*c*) Grasshopper; (*d*) Lobster

27.40 In a protostome, the coelom forms by a _____ process in which the mesoderm is split. In a deuterostome, the coelom forms by a _____ process, which is an outpouching of the embryonic gut.

27.41 All animals not in the phyla Porifera, Cnidaria, or Ctenophora are _____ in at least a stage of their life cycle. They are also triploblastic, with three primary germ layers: _____; _____; and _____.

27.42 The three classes of flatworms in the phylum Platyhelminthes are: class _____, which includes planaria; class _____, which includes flukes; and class _____, which includes tapeworms.

27.43 Match the following structures of a planarian with their respective functions.

structure	function
(*a*) cerebral ganglia	1. _____ Moves wastes out of excretory openings
(*b*) flame cell	2. _____ Anterior aggregation of nerve cells for reception and integration of sensory stimuli

(*c*) ocelli	3. _____ Excretory opening
(*d*) copulatory sac	4. _____ Repository for sperm
(*e*) pharynx	5. _____ Light-sensitive organ
(*f*) nephridiopore	6. _____ Extendable feeding tube

27.44 Flukes and tapeworms are both parasitic flatworms that attach to their victims for feeding. However, while the fluke feeds through its _____, the tapeworm feeds through its _____.

27.45 The head region of a tapeworm, called the _____, is a structure composed of hooks and suckers. Behind the head region is a series of sexually complete, hermaphroditic segments called _____.

27.46 The three major classes within the phylum Mollusca are: _____, which includes clams; _____, which includes snails; and _____, which includes squids.

27.47 In Fig. 27.3, the drawing of a snail shows the typical body plan of a gastropod. Identify the indicated structures.

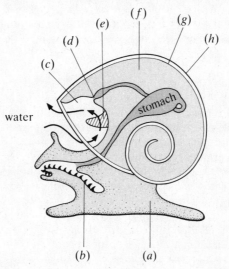

water

stomach

Fig. 27.3

27.48 All mollusks except cephalopods have an _____ circulatory system in which the blood moves from the gills to the heart and then is released directly into a space called a _____.

27.49 Gas exchange in a mollusk occurs across the moist membranes of the _____ and _____. Gas exchange in a spider is accomplished by _____. In insects, oxygen is supplied directly to the tissues by _____.

27.50 Class _____ of the phylum Mollusca gets its name from its two-part shell. The shell is closed against dangers by large _____.

27.51 Gastropods are asymmetrical because of _____, which is a 180° twist of the body relative to the foot.

27.52 Most annelids and marine mollusks go through a larval stage known as a _____ larva, while echinoderms and some invertebrate chordates go through a larval stage known as a _____ larva.

27.53 The three classes in the phylum Annelida are: _____, which includes sandworms; _____, which includes earthworms; and _____, which includes leeches.

27.54 An earthworm has a digestive tract with a muscular _____ that sucks in food-containing soil through the mouth. Behind this is a narrow _____ that leads to a storage area called the _____. Behind this storage area is the _____, where food is ground with soil particles. Next, the ground food is digested in the _____. An earthworm has a _____ circulatory system, driven by _____ pairs of hearts. Wastes are removed from the blood and coelomic fluids by _____.

27.55 Polychaetes, such as sandworms, are segmented worms; each segment has two fleshy extensions called _____. These extensions, which function in both locomotion and gas exchange, are covered with bristles called _____.

27.56 Phoronid worms, bryozoans, and brachiopods are called _____ because of their characteristic filter-feeding apparatus, the _____.

27.57 Contrast the excretory systems of a paramecium, a planarian, and a freshwater mollusk.

🐚 An excretory system eliminates metabolic wastes, expecially excess nitrogen, and regulates the concentration of salt and water in the body. All heterotrophs need to excrete materials, since what they acquire in the diet does not exactly match what they need for cellular function.

A paramecium is small enough to get rid of excess nitrogen by diffusion alone. Nitrogen, in the form of ammonia, moves by diffusion from where it is formed in the cytoplasm to the plasma membrane and then through the membrane into the external environment. Because a paramecium lives in fresh water, its internal environment is hypertonic to (i.e., contains more salts than) its external environment. Consequently, water continuously moves by osmosis into a paramecium, and it must be continuously removed to prevent the cell from swelling and bursting. _Contractile vacuoles_ are the excretory structures of a paramecium. These organelles grow as they fill with water and then contract to pump water out of the cell. Exactly how a contractile vacuole works is not known, but a current hypothesis is that smaller vesicles fill with isotonic fluid, and then they actively transport solutes out to form membrane-enclosed spaces filled with hypotonic fluid. Many of these small vesicles then fuse to form a growing contractile vacuole, which eventually contracts to move water through small openings in the plasma membrane.

A planarian has the same excretory problems, and similar solutions to them, as does a paramecium. Because a planarian is so flat, every cell of its body is near the external environment; hence a planarian can get rid of nitrogenous wastes by diffusion of ammonia from the internal cells to the outer surface of the body. A planarian lives in fresh water and has the problem of continuously getting rid of excess water. A special excretory structure, the _protonephridium_, performs this function. The structure consists of many branching tubes that connect the interior of the body to the external environment. The interior end of each tube is closed and contains a cup-shaped, ciliated cell—called a _flame cell_, because the waving movements of its long cilia resemble the flame of a candle. Excess water in the body enters one of these tubes through the flame cell and is moved by the cilia. The water exits through a _nephridiopore_ at the other, external end of the tube. Less is known about how a protonephridium of a planarian works with regard to osmoregulation than about how the contractile vacuole of a paramecium works.

The excretory system of most mollusks consists of a pair of _metanephridia_—excretory tubes that are open at both ends and found only in coelomates. The inner end connects with the coelom, and the outer end connects with the external environment. Fluid from the coelom (the pericardial cavity) enters a metanephridium, by way of a _nephrostome_ (a funnel-shaped opening of the tube), and is converted into urine. Nitrogenous wastes (ammonia) are retained within the fluid, and nutrients are reabsorbed into the coelomic fluid. The urine is moved through the metanephridium by wavelike motions of cilia and eliminated through a nephridiopore into the mantle cavity. Some bivalves have parts of their metanephridia enlarged as bladders for urine storage when their shells are tightly closed. The metanephridia of freshwater mollusks transport large amounts of water, from which most of the salts are reabsorbed, so urine that is formed is hypotonic to the coelomic fluid.

27.58 How does a clam feed?

🐚 A clam is a filter feeder. Water, moved by cilia on the gills, enters the mantle cavity posterioventrally, makes a U-turn at the gills, and leaves posteriodorsally. Thus, a clam can feed while burrowed with only its posterior end above the substrate. As water flows over the gills, suspended food particles are trapped in mucus and conveyed by cilia to a pair of _labial palps_—slender appendages on either side of the mouth that sort the food particles, rejecting those that are too large or inorganic and sending the rest on to the mouth. Food moves from the mouth to the stomach, where digestive enzymes break it down into component monomers and most of the monomers are absorbed into the body fluid. Some absorption also takes place in the intestine, but this structure is mostly for transport of undigested materials (feces) out of the body through the anus.

27.59 Why is hermaphroditism common among snails?

🐚 A _hermaphrodite_ has both male and female reproductive organs. A _simultaneous_ hermaphrodite, which most snails are, has both types of organs and can function as both male and female at the same time. A hermaphrodite usually mates with another hermaphrodite rather than with itself.

Snails have internal fertilization, with movement of sperm from a sperm tube through a female opening, so that if they were not hermaphroditic, a male and female would have to meet in order for fertilization to take place. Snails move so slowly that they seldom encounter another member of their species. It is therefore a great advantage for them to be hermaphrodites, since any encounter between two snails can lead to fertilization. Hermaphroditism doubles a snail's chance of reproducing compared with its chance if it could only mate with a member of the opposite sex. Mating between snails is one of mutual insemination, in which each animal both gives and receives sperm. Another advantage of hermaphroditism is that each animal produces the larger gametes— the eggs—so that almost twice as many offspring are formed than would be the case if one snail produced sperm and the other eggs. Because of these advantages, hermaphroditism has evolved many times during the evolution of snails.

27.60 Why are cephalopods considered the most advanced of invertebrates?

✿ Cephalopods include such animals as squid and octopuses. They are the most complex invertebrates, in terms of structure and function, and are perhaps the most intelligent. Each member of this class has a *closed* circulatory system and a well-developed head surrounded by arms formed from the anterior part of the foot. The posterior part of the foot is modified into a funnel that expels water and propels the animal from place to place. Cephalopods are carnivores, with both a radula and beak for tearing food. They have *chromatophores* for rapid color changes, as well as ink glands for releasing clouds of dark fluid that conceal them from their enemies.

The most important cephalopod traits, with regard to evolutionary position, are their eyes and brain. Their two large eyes, one on each side of the head, are strikingly similar to vertebrate eyes. Each has a transparent cornea, an iris for regulation of incoming light, a lens for focusing, and a retina for transducing light energy into electrochemical impulses. The eyes are capable of forming images. The cephalopod brain, a true brain, is formed by the fusion of several ganglia that are independent in other mollusks. It integrates all incoming information and coordinates all body actiyities.

PROTOSTOMES: ARTHROPODS

27.61 Which of the following is *not* an arthropod characteristic?

(*a*) Jointed appendages;   (*b*) Nonsegmented body;   (*c*) Periodic molting;   (*d*) Articulated exoskeleton

27.62 Which of the following arthropods are *not* mandibulates?

(*a*) Insects;   (*b*) Crabs;   (*c*) Shrimp;   (*d*) Spiders

27.63 Lobsters, crayfish, and crabs are

(*a*) isopods.   (*b*) copepods.   (*c*) decapods.   (*d*) diplopods.

27.64 Which of the following arthropods is a chelicerate?

(*a*) Horseshoe crab;   (*b*) Lobster;   (*c*) Millipede;   (*d*) Grasshopper

27.65 Which of the following is *not* a characteristic of insects?

(*a*) Three main body segments: head, thorax, abdomen;   (*b*) Three pairs of legs;   (*c*) Two pairs of antennae; (*d*) Excretion by Malpighian tubules

27.66 Which of the following animals does *not* have a hydrostatic support system?

(*a*) Insect;   (*b*) Earthworm;   (*c*) Snail;   (*d*) Jellyfish

27.67 The stages between larval molts in an insect are called

(*a*) pupae.   (*b*) instars.   (*c*) grubs.   (*d*) caterpillars.

27.68 There are three types of arthropods: chelicerates; _____ mandibulates; and _____ mandibulates. Chelicerates do not have the _____ and _____ found in mandibulates, but they do have distinctive first appendages called _____, and some have unique respiratory structures called _____ lungs.

27.69 Excretory organs in terrestrial arthropods are the _____.

27.70 In a lobster, crayfish, or other crustacean, the head and thorax are fused into a _____ that is covered by a _____.

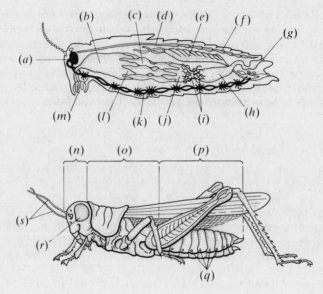

Fig. 27.4

27.71 Refer to Fig. 27.4, and identify the indicated internal and external parts of a grasshopper.

27.72 The only arthropods with two pairs of antennae are the _____.

27.73 The only invertebrates capable of flight are those in the class _____.

27.74 The four largest orders of insects are: _____, which includes flies and mosquitoes; _____, which includes moths and butterflies; _____, which includes ants and bees; and _____, which are the beetles.

27.75 Most insects go through a change in body form called a complete _____. It typically occurs in three stages: _____, _____, and _____. In the butterfly, these three stages are called the _____, _____, and _____.

27.76 Insects in the order Diptera are characterized by having _____ pair(s) of wings, whereas other winged insects have _____ pair(s).

27.77 What characteristics distinguish arthropods from annelids and mollusks?

🐚   Coelomate protostomes form three major phyla: Annelida, Mollusca, and Arthropoda. These phyla are indirectly linked in that both mollusks and annelida have trochophore larvae, and both annelids and arthropods have similar body segmentation.

The phylum Arthropoda includes the crustaceans (barnacles, lobsters, crabs), the arachnids (spiders, mites, ticks), and the insects. Characteristics that distinguish these animals from annelids and mollusks are:

1. Absence of a trochophore larva
2. An external skeleton made of *chitin* (a polysaccharide) and protein rather than a shell made chiefly of mineral salts
3. Subdivision of the legs into movable segments
4. Distinct groups of muscles, derived from many body segments, that move the separate parts of the exoskeleton
5. Distinct mandibles or chelicerae

27.78 What are the advantages and disadvantages of the arthropod exoskeleton?

🐚   An arthropod has an *articulated* (jointed) exoskeleton made chiefly of chitin and proteins secreted by underlying epidermal cells. In some aquatic forms, such as crabs and lobsters, the exoskeleton is impregnated with calcium salts for added strength.

An exoskeleton has many advantages. Its original function in marine ancestors was to protect the animal from predators. In terrestrial arthropods, the waterproof outer covering has been of tremendous importance in preventing evaporation of internal water into the surrounding dry air. A third function has to do with locomotion.

The exoskeleton provides rigid plates for muscle attachment and for support, so the body can be raised above the substrate and locomotion accomplished entirely by leg movements, rather than by undulating movements of a body dragged over the substrate. Arthropod locomotion is more rapid and efficient than the wormlike movements of other invertebrates. It also enables the coelom to be greatly reduced in arthropods, since these animals do not need it for hydrostatic support.

There is just a single disadvantage, but it is a serious one. An exoskeleton does not grow along with the rest of the animal, so it has to be periodically shed, a process known as *molting*. During the time the animal is forming its new exoskeleton, it is vulnerable to both predation and evaporative water loss. Moreover, periodic synthesis of a new exoskeleton is costly to the animal in terms of energy and materials.

DEUTEROSTOMES

27.79   Which of the following animals is a deuterostome?

(*a*) Starfish;   (*b*) Sea anemone;   (*c*) Ant;   (*d*) Octopus

27.80   Which of the following statements is *not* true of deuterostomes?

(*a*) The cleavage pattern is radial.   (*b*) The mouth develops at or near the blastopore.   (*c*) The coelom is produced by enterocoelous formation.   (*d*) They include sea lilies, starfish, arrow worms, and birds.

27.81   Which of the following traits is *not* characteristic of echinoderms?

(*a*) Water-vascular system;   (*b*) Trochophore larva;   (*c*) Tube feet;   (*d*) Interior skeleton with projecting spines

27.82   Which of the following statements is *not* true of jawless fishes in the class Agnatha?

(*a*) They include hagfish and lampreys.   (*b*) They have notochords throughout their lives.   (*c*) They are known as cyclostomes.   (*d*) They have bony skeletons.

27.83   Which of the following animals is a reptile?

(*a*) Salamander;   (*b*) Turtle;   (*c*) Newt;   (*d*) Toad

27.84   Which of the following traits is *not* characteristic of amphibians?

(*a*) Thin, scaleless skin;   (*b*) Usually requires water for reproduction;   (*c*) Amniote egg;   (*d*) Skin used as supplementary respiratory organ

27.85   Which of the following traits is *not* characteristic of birds?

(*a*) Air sacs attached to the lungs;   (*b*) Hollow bones;   (*c*) Ectothermic;   (*d*) Amniote egg

27.86   There are four phyla of deuterostomes: _____, which includes the starfish; _____, which includes the arrow worms; _____, which includes the acorn worms; and _____, which includes humans.

27.87   In most echinoderms the larvae are _____ symmetrical and the adults are _____ symmetrical.

27.88   A starfish walks by using a _____ system, in which rows of fluid-filled _____ in each arm are interconnected by _____ and a _____.

27.89   A characteristic of cephalochordates and vertebrates that is not seen in tunicates is _____.

27.90   Two important characteristics that hemichordates share with chordates are a _____ nerve cord and a _____ with _____.

27.91   The phylum Chordata has three subphyla: _____ (the tunicates); _____ (the lancelets); and _____ (the vertebrates).

27.92   Refer to Fig. 27.5, and identify the three defining characteristics of chordates on this diagram of *Amphioxus* (genus *Branchiostoma*; a lancelet).

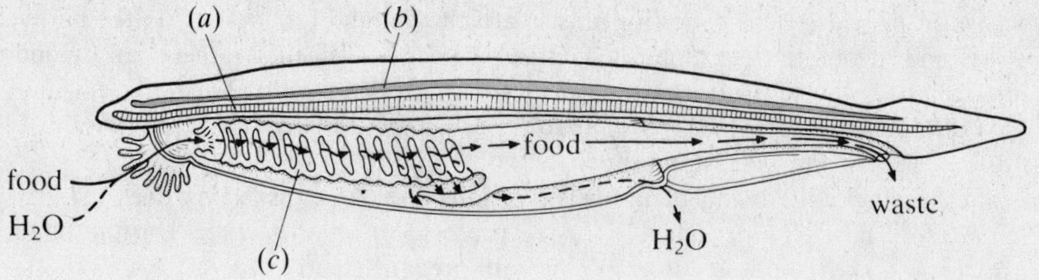

Fig. 27.5

27.93 Vertebrates differ from other chordates in having the _____ replaced, in adults, by a _____.

27.94 The seven living classes of vertebrates are: _____, the jawless fishes such as lampreys; _____, the cartilagenous fishes such as sharks; _____, the bony fishes such as salmon; _____, the semiaquatic vertebrates such as frogs; _____, the scale-covered vertebrates such as snakes, turtles, and crocodiles; _____, the feathered vertebrates such as eagles; and _____, the haired vertebrates such as monkeys.

27.95 Unlike amphibians, reptiles do not require free water for reproduction, because they have _____ eggs.

27.96 Mammals are distinguished from other vertebrates by having _____ and by providing milk from _____.

27.97 Most mammals are _____, which have young that develop for a long period within the mother and are connected to her circulatory system during embryogenesis by a _____. Some mammals, the _____ (e.g., kangaroos), bear immature young that move into a protective pouch on their mother for development. Still other mammals, the _____ (e.g., the duckbilled platypus), lay shelled eggs but then provide milk for the young after hatching.

27.98 Five important orders of living placental mammals are: _____, including the apes; _____, including the rats; _____, including the dogs; _____, including the horses; and _____, including the pigs.

27.99 What major differences separate the echinoderms and chordates from the mollusks, annelids, and arthropods?

🐚   There are two major groups of advanced animals. One group includes the Echinodermata and Chordata, and the other group includes the Mollusca, Annelida, and Arthropoda. The two groups are strikingly different in aspects of their development.

One difference between the groups is in the consequences of cleavage, when the zygote first undergoes cell division to form a multicellular animal. After the zygote divides into four cells in the echinoderms and the chordates, four complete individuals develop if these cells are separated. When the first cells are separated in the mollusks, annelids, and arthropods, none of the cells develops normally. The first pattern is *indeterminate* and the second pattern is *determinate* cleavage.

The two groups of advanced animals differ also in the way in which the first few cell divisions of the zygote occur. The early cells of an echinoderm or chordate develop in a *radial* pattern, in which the daughter cells lie directly above or adjacent to one another. In the mollusks, annelids, and arthropods, a *spiral* pattern develops, in which the daughter cells lie at an oblique angle to one another, so that the cells are arranged in a spiraling pattern.

Lastly, there are striking differences in the larvae of these animals. Mollusca and Annelida have a *trochophore* larva, which has a band of cilia surrounding the midregion and resembles a wheel (*trochophore* = wheel-bearing). Echinodermata have a *dipleurula* larva, which has long, winding bands of cilia rather than a single band around the midregion. Arthropoda have larvae unique to their phylum, as do Chordata.

27.100 What characteristics distinguish the phylum Chordata?

🐚   Most of the chordates are vertebrates—fishes, amphibians, reptiles, birds, and mammals. In addition to the subphylum Vertebrata, the phylum Chordata contains the subphyla Urochordata and Cephalochordata. At some time in their lives, all chordates exhibit the following three characteristics.

1. A flexible internal skeleton, or notochord, which is a support structure in the form of a rod that extends through the length of the body. (In humans and other vertebrates, the notochord exists only in the embryonic stage of life.)

2. A dorsal hollow nerve cord, or spinal cord, that lies dorsal to the notochord.

3. A pharynx with gill slits. The pharynx is the first part of the digestive tract, and gill slits are openings in the pharynx to the outside of the body. In most higher vertebrates, gill slits appear briefly and develop only partially in very young embryos.

Answers to Objective Questions

27.1 *d*

27.2 *a*

27.3 marine

27.4 gametes

27.5 (*a*) mesoderm; (*b*) endoderm; (*c*) mesoderm; (*d*) endoderm; (*e*) pseudocoelom; (*f*) mesoderm; (*g*) endoderm; (*h*) coelom

27.7 *d*

27.8 *a*

27.9 *b*

27.10 *d*

27.11 pores; osculum; choanocytes (or collar cells); choanocytes

27.12 epidermal

27.13 *c; b; d; e; a*

27.14 Porifera

27.15 sperm; internal cavity; choanocytes; amoebocytes

27.17 *d*

27.18 *a*

27.19 *b*

27.20 *b*

27.21 *c*

27.22 Hydrozoa; Scyphozoa; Anthozoa; coelenterates

27.23 gastrovascular cavity; Cnidaria; Ctenophora

27.24 diploblastic; epidermis; gastrodermis; mesoglea

27.25 polyp; medusa; planula

27.26 comb jellies; cilia

27.29 *a*

27.30 *c*

27.31 *d*

27.32 *b*

27.33 *a*

27.34 *c*

27.35 *b*

27.36 *c*

27.37 *a*

27.38 *c*

27.39 *a*

27.40 schizocoelous; enterocoelous

27.41 bilaterally symmetrical; ectoderm; mesoderm; endoderm

27.42 Turbellaria; Trematoda; Cestoda

27.43 (1) *b*; (2) *a*; (3) *f*; (4) *d*; (5) *c*; (6) *e*

27.44 mouth; body surface

27.45 scolex; proglottids

27.46 Bilvalva; Gastropoda; Cephalopoda

27.47 (*a*) foot; (*b*) radula; (*c*) mantle cavity; (*d*) anus; (*e*) gill; (*f*) visceral mass; (*g*) mantle; (*h*) shell

27.48 open; hemocoel

27.49 mantle cavity; gills; book lungs; tracheae

27.50 Bivalva; adductor muscles

27.51 torsion

27.52 trochophore; dipleurula

27.53 Polychaeta; Oligochaeta; Hirudinea

27.54 pharynx; esophagus; crop; gizzard; intestine; closed; five; nephridia

27.55 parapodia; setae

27.56 lophophorates; lophophore

27.61 *b*

27.62 *d*

27.63 *c*

27.64 *a*

27.65 *c*

27.66 *a*

27.67 *b*

27.68 aquatic; terrestrial; antennae; mandibles; chelicerae; book

27.69 Malpighian tubules

27.70 cephalothorax; carapace

27.71 (*a*) brain; (*b*) crop; (*c*) gastric pouch; (*d*) aorta; (*e*) ovary; (*f*) heart; (*g*) anus; (*h*) hindgut; (*i*) Malpighian tubules; (*j*) stomach; (*k*) nerve cord; (*l*) foregut;

(*m*) mandible; (*n*) head; (*o*) thorax; (*p*) abdomen; (*q*) spiracles; (*r*) compound eye; (*s*) antennae

27.72 crustaceans

27.73 Insecta

27.74 Diptera; Lepidoptera; Hymenoptera; Coleoptera

27.75 metamorphosis; larva; pupa (or chrysalis); adult (or imago); caterpillar; cocoon; butterfly

27.76 one; two

27.79 *a*

27.80 *b*

27.81 *b*

27.82 *d*

27.83 *b*

27.84 *c*

27.85 *c*

27.86 Echinodermata; Chaetognatha; Hemichordata; Chordata

27.87 bilaterally; radially

27.88 water-vascular; tube feet; radial canals; central ring

27.89 segmentation

27.90 dorsal; pharynx; gill slits

27.91 Urochordata; Cephalochordata; Vertebrata

27.92 (*a*) notochord; (*b*) dorsal hollow nerve cord; (*c*) pharynx with gill slits

27.93 notochord; vertebral column

27.94 Agnatha; Chondrichthyes; Osteichthyes; Amphibia; Reptilia; Aves; Mammalia

27.95 amniote

27.96 hair; mammary glands

27.97 placentals; placenta; marsupials; monotremes

27.98 Primata; Rodentia; Carnivora; Perissodactyla; Artiodactyla

CHAPTER 28
Origin of Cells

HISTORY OF IDEAS*

28.1 The idea of spontaneous generation—that living things can originate spontaneously from nonliving things—was

(*a*) disproved by Aristotle. (*b*) widely believed prior to the seventeenth century. (*c*) never accepted by European scientists. (*d*) demonstrated, in 1873, to be true for bacteria and viruses.

28.2 Spontaneous generation of flies from rotting meat was disproved in 1668 by

(*a*) Francesco Redi. (*b*) Charles Darwin. (*c*) Louis Pasteur. (*d*) Marie Curie.

28.3 Spontaneous generation of bacteria from decomposing broth was disproved in 1860 by

(*a*) Francesco Redi. (*b*) Charles Darwin. (*c*) Louis Pasteur. (*d*) Marie Curie.

28.4 The cell theory, presented in 1858 by Rudolf Virchow, states that cells arise from _____.

28.5 Spontaneous generation must have taken place, and thus the cell theory violated, when _____.

28.6 One of the first experiments in biology was performed in 1668 by the Italian scientist Francesco Redi. What was this experiment supposed to test, and how was it designed?

It was commonly accepted during Redi's time that life could form spontaneously from nonliving materials, for example, mice could form from decaying grain and maggots from rotting meat. Francesco Redi questioned the idea of spontaneous generation of life and proposed instead that all life comes from prior life. He observed that flies hover around rotting meat and guessed that the appearance of maggots in the meat is somehow caused by the flies. To test this idea, Redi performed one of the first experiments in biology.

Redi's experiment consisted of placing rotting meat in three groups of jars: one with tight lids, another covered with fine gauze, and a third group with no covers. Redi reasoned that if the maggots were spontaneously generated from rotting meat, then they would appear in all three types of jars, but if the flies caused the maggots, then they would appear only in the uncovered jars, to which the flies had access.

The results of his experiment were that maggots appeared only in the meat within the uncovered jars, and where the flies could see and smell, but not contact, the meat (the gauze-covered jars), fly eggs appeared on the covers. Redi's results supported his hypothesis that all life arises from previous life and refuted the prevailing belief in the spontaneous generation of life.

FORMATION OF THE EARTH

28.7 The sun, like other stars, formed from

(*a*) aggregates of uranium. (*b*) clouds of gas and dust. (*c*) divisions of preexisting stars. (*d*) collisions of meteors.

28.8 Energy emitted from the sun comes from

(*a*) decaying uranium. (*b*) smoldering uranium. (*c*) nuclear fusion reactions. (*d*) nuclear fission reactions.

28.9 The earth, like other planets, formed from

(*a*) aggregates of uranium. (*b*) clouds of gas and dust. (*c*) divisions of preexisting planets. (*d*) collisions of meteors.

28.10 About how long ago was the earth formed?

(*a*) 20 billion years ago; (*b*) 10 billion years ago; (*c*) 5 billion years ago; (*d*) 3 billion years ago

28.11 The first atmosphere of the earth was composed mostly of _____, which escaped into space because it was not held by _____.

* Answers to Chapter 28 objective questions appear on page 203.

28.12 The second atmosphere of the earth, formed mainly from gases released from volcanoes, consisted chiefly of
_____ , _____ , _____ , _____ , _____ , and
_____ .

28.13 The first seas formed from water that came from the _____ .

ABIOTIC SYNTHESIS OF ORGANIC MONOMERS

28.14 Most biologists agree that the first cells on earth developed

(a) on other planets, probably Mars.   (b) in the soil.   (c) in the oceans.   (d) in rocks warmed by radioactive decay.

28.15 Life could not originate from inorganic materials now because

(a) the atmosphere contains too much oxygen gas.   (b) temperatures are too cool.   (c) temperatures are too warm.   (d) the raw materials are no longer present.

28.16 The hypothesis that the early atmosphere, combined with an energy source, produced organic monomers was developed in the 1920s by

(a) A. I. Oparin and J. B. S. Haldane.   (b) S. Miller and H. Urey.   (c) M. Curie and L. Pasteur.   (d) S. Fox and L. Pauling.

28.17 The hypothesis that the early atmosphere, combined with an energy source, produced organic monomers was tested in 1953 by

(a) A. I. Oparin and J. B. S. Haldane.   (b) S. Miller and H. Urey.   (c) M. Curie and L. Pasteur.   (d) S. Fox and L. Pauling.

28.18 An important feature of the early atmosphere was the virtual absence of

(a) nitrogen gas.   (b) carbon dioxide.   (c) hydrogen cyanide.   (d) oxygen gas.

28.19 It has now been demonstrated repeatedly that organic monomers could

(a) not have existed in the primitive oceans.   (b) not have formed from gases.   (c) not have formed from the particular gases of the early atmosphere.   (d) have formed from the particular gases of the early atmosphere.

28.20 The appearance of cells must have been preceded by a long period of _____ evolution, in which natural selection favored the more _____ .

28.21 The early atmosphere of the earth was a chemically _____ environment, whereas the present atmosphere is a chemically _____ environment. The event that changed the earth's atmosphere from the first to the second type was the evolution of _____ .

28.22 Two intense sources of energy for precellular chemical reactions were electric energy, furnished by _____ , and _____ , which was more intense then than now because the earth originally lacked an ozone layer.

28.23 The gases used in the Miller-Urey experiment were _____ , _____ , _____ , and _____ .

28.24 The energy used in the Miller-Urey experiment was an _____ .

28.25 Two controls were used in the Miller-Urey experiment: one in which the experiment was run without a source of energy and the other in which the experiment was run under sterile conditions. These controls were used to rule out the possibility that the molecules were formed by _____ .

28.26 The category of molecules produced by the Miller-Urey experiment was _____ .

28.27 Recent tests of the Oparin hypothesis differ from the Miller-Urey test in that they use gases typical of _____ . The results of these experiments, however, are fundamentally the same as the results of the one done by Miller and Urey.

28.28 Organic monomers formed abiotically today would be broken down by _____ or by their chemical interactions with _____ .

28.29   What is the Oparin hypothesis, and why did it take so long for someone to test it?

🐚   Alexander I. Oparin was a Russian biochemist who, in the 1920s, hypothesized that conditions favoring the abiotic formation of organic monomers existed in the primitive atmosphere. This atmosphere, he proposed, was a reducing one, rich in hydrogen gas and deficient in oxygen gas. It consisted chiefly of methane, ammonia, water vapor, hydrogen gas, nitrogen gas, and some carbon monoxide and carbon dioxide. An energy source, such as solar radiation, lightning, or hot volcanic ash, would have interacted with these gases to form organic monomers. Carried to the earth's surface by rainwater, the monomers then would have accumulated in the oceans as a warm, dilute "soup." In this way, Oparin suggested, the stage was set for the origin of cells.

Oparin first published his hypothesis in Russian in 1924. A similar hypothesis, developed independently, was published in 1929 by the British biologist J. B. S. Haldane. Neither publication was taken seriously, largely because the scientific community rejected any notions of spontaneous generation. It was not until Oparin greatly expanded his ideas and presented them as a book, in 1936, and the book was translated into other languages, that the Oparin hypothesis was considered seriously. Even then, it was not tested until after the turmoil of the Second World War. In 1953, Stanley Miller, a graduate student working with Harold Urey at the University of Chicago, performed the first experimental test of Oparin's hypothesis.

28.30   How was Oparin's hypothesis first tested?

🐚   Oparin's hypothesis about the origin of life has been tested, indirectly, in many experiments. All of them attempted to simulate conditions of the primitive earth. In the first of these experiments, by Stanley Miller in 1953, the simulation was as follows: (1) creating an atmosphere of methane, ammonia, hydrogen gas, and water vapor—the four gases believed abundant in the primitive atmosphere—in a closed environment; (2) placing this

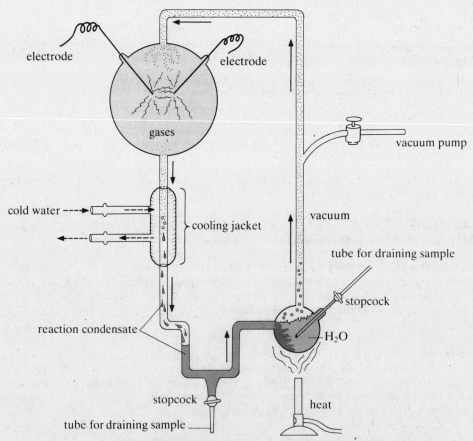

Fig. 28.1. The apparatus used in the Miller-Urey experiments. Two connected flasks held simulations of the primitive ocean and the primitive atmosphere. Water evaporated from the hot liquid, joined the other gases, and then returned to the liquid as a condenser cooled the flask of gases. When electric sparks were added, monomers formed from the gases and moved with the water from the flask of gases to the flask of water; there they accumulated to form a "soup" of diverse organic molecules.

atmosphere over hot water, as probably existed on the cooling earth; and (3) subjecting the atmosphere to an electric discharge, as from lightning. The apparatus used is diagrammed in Fig. 28.1. Under these remarkably simple conditions, many of the organic monomers found in all living organisms were formed. This particular experiment is known as the Miller-Urey experiment, in honor of both the graduate student, Stanley Miller, and his professor, Harold Urey, of the University of Chicago.

Miller also performed two control experiments to rule out the possibility that organic molecules were synthesized by microorganisms in the apparatus. In one control he omitted the electric discharge, and in the other he maintained absolutely sterile conditions. Both control experiments failed to yield organic monomers.

Since this first experiment, many similar tests using somewhat different materials and conditions have yielded a variety of biologically important molecules. All the results support Oparin's hypothesis that the molecular components of primitive organisms were formed from simple gases present in the atmosphere at that time. The formation of organic monomers turns out to be remarkably simple: a few gases, treated appropriately, interact to form all the unique and basic components of life.

ABIOTIC SYNTHESIS OF POLYMERS

28.31 A polymer is

(*a*) a large molecule made of repeating units of a monomer. (*b*) an organic droplet. (*c*) a long sequence of carbon atoms. (*d*) an aggregate of ribosomes.

28.32 A polymer is formed by

(*a*) hydrolysis. (*b*) hydration. (*c*) dehydration synthesis. (*d*) methylation.

28.33 In the aquatic environment of a cell, rapid polymer formation is possible because of

(*a*) higher temperatures than under abiotic conditions. (*b*) higher salt concentrations than under abiotic conditions. (*c*) enzymes and ATP. (*d*) coacervates.

28.34 Which of the following substances is the best for concentrating monomers?

(*a*) Sand; (*b*) Glass; (*c*) Clay; (*d*) Granite

28.35 If and when protobionts first formed, competition among them could not have led to evolution, because the most successful would not have been able to

(*a*) break down into monomers. (*b*) vary in composition. (*c*) accumulate organic monomers from the environment. (*d*) reproduce themselves.

28.36 Sidney Fox, of the University of Miami, has made what he calls proteinoids, which are _____ produced by dropping dilute solutions of _____ onto a hot surface.

28.37 When mixed with cool water, proteinoids self-assemble into droplets called _____. Lipids self-assemble into droplets called _____. Solutions of polypeptides, nucleic acids, and polysaccharides self-assemble into droplets called _____, as first demonstrated by A. I. Oparin. All these aggregates of abiotically produced molecules are known collectively as _____; they may have been precellular biochemical units.

28.38 A recent hypothesis suggests that the first genes were not DNA, but rather short polymers of _____, which could have replicated themselves and directed protein synthesis prior to the appearance of cells. These polymers are easy to produce abiotically in a test tube, and populations of them do evolve, since they are able to reproduce themselves.

28.39 An organic polymer that is not a protein, yet can fold spontaneously to form tertiary structures that act as catalysts, is _____.

28.40 How could polymers have formed from monomers prior to the existence of cells?

🐚 It is difficult to imagine how monomers were joined to form polymers prior to the existence of cells. There had to have been some way of bringing the monomers together and then of removing a water molecule wherever two monomers joined. Such *dehydration synthesis* would not have taken place spontaneously in the primitive oceans, since water would have tended *not* to move away from monomers, up a concentration gradient, into the aqueous surroundings. Both monomer concentration and dehydration synthesis occur within the aqueous environments of cells, but only with the help of membranes, enzymes, and ATP.

There are several ways in which monomers could have become concentrated in the primitive oceans. The evaporation of water from tidepools, for example, or the aggregation of monomers on such surfaces as clay, could have produced local areas of highly concentrated monomers. An energy source, such as lightning or ultraviolet radiation, could then have driven the removal of water molecules from the monomers.

Once some polymers formed, they may have self-assembled into spherical structures called *protobionts*. Such structures form readily in the laboratory. Protobionts made of polypeptides are called *microspheres*, those of lipids are called *liposomes*, and those of combinations of polypeptides, nucleic acids, and polysaccharides are called *coacervates*. The isolated environments within these structures would have promoted a diversity of chemical reactions, and their relatively dry interiors would have facilitated dehydration synthesis of polymers. Perhaps gradual changes in such protobionts led to the formation of cells.

THE FIRST CELLS

28.41 Selection for cells with longer biochemical pathways occurred as the early cells

(*a*) used up the organic molecules they could use directly. (*b*) became behaviorally more complex. (*c*) settled on clay substrates. (*d*) began to eat one another.

28.42 The fact that all living things use ATP as their main energy currency implies that ATP

(*a*) is the best possible molecule for the task. (*b*) was an early evolutionary development. (*c*) moved readily from one cell to another, via viruses. (*d*) appeared prior to any other polymer.

28.43 The oldest fossil cells resemble

(*a*) amoeba. (*b*) red algae. (*c*) heterotrophic bacteria. (*d*) autotrophic bacteria.

28.44 The oldest known fossils are from rock that is

(*a*) 2.3 billion years old. (*b*) 2.7 billion years old. (*c*) 3.5 billion years old. (*d*) 4.5 billion years old.

28.45 Evidence of earlier forms of cells may never be seen, since

(*a*) rocks were too fluid at that time to form fossils. (*b*) they had no cell walls. (*c*) they had no calcium deposits in their membranes. (*d*) rocks containing them would be too deep to excavate.

28.46 The first cells were almost certainly _____, obtaining energy and nutrients from organic molecules in their environment.

28.47 The earliest form of cellular respiration must have been _____.

28.48 Two monomers that form part of RNA, ATP, NAD, FAD, and acetyl coenzyme A are _____ and _____. Both monomers form readily under simulated precellular conditions.

28.49 The oldest known fossils appear in stromatolites—banded domes of _____, which adhere to the sticky surfaces of prokaryotes and thus are glued together to form deposits.

28.50 What structures must have been present in the first cells?

⊛ A characteristic of living systems is the persistence of high concentrations of both energy and materials despite the natural tendency of energy to dissipate (entropy) and materials to move away from areas where their concentration is high (diffusion). Living systems maintain this unusual state because the chemical reactions of life occur within cells, where the environment is enclosed and controlled, and where energy is continuously used to counteract the natural tendencies of entropy and diffusion.

It is reasonable to assume that the first cells on earth were simple in structure and function and that more complex cells evolved from them. It is also reasonable to assume that each primitive cell was a complete organism. From what we now know about living systems, the basic structure of the first cell must have included:

1. An outer membrane to control movement of materials into and out of the cell and to promote high concentrations of energy and molecule
2. ATP to store and transport energy

3. Enzymes to regulate chemical reactions
4. Ribosomes to assemble proteins from amino acids
5. Nucleic acids to provide both instructions for building proteins from amino acids and a system of self-replication

Answers to Objective Questions

28.1 b
28.2 a
28.3 c
28.4 preexisting cells
28.5 the first cells arose
28.7 b
28.8 c
28.9 b
28.10 c
28.11 hydrogen; gravity
28.12 water vapor; carbon monoxide; carbon dioxide; nitrogen gas; hydrogen sulfide; hydrogen gas
28.13 atmosphere
28.14 c
28.15 a
28.16 a

28.17 b
28.18 d
28.19 d
28.20 chemical; stable molecules
28.21 reducing; oxidizing; photosynthesis
28.22 lightning; ultraviolet radiation
28.23 water vapor; methane; ammonia; hydrogen gas
28.24 electric spark
28.25 microorganisms
28.26 organic monomers
28.27 volcanic eruptions
28.28 decomposing action of organisms; oxygen gas
28.31 a
28.32 c

28.33 c
28.34 c
28.35 d
28.36 polypeptides; amino acids
28.37 microspheres; liposomes; coacervates; protobionts
28.38 ribonucleotides
28.39 ribonucleic acid
28.41 a
28.42 b
28.43 c
28.44 c
28.45 a
28.46 heterotrophs
28.47 fermentation
28.48 adenine; ribose
28.49 sediments

CHAPTER 29
Unicellular Evolution

EVOLUTION OF PROKARYOTES*

29.1 The oldest known fossil cells are about the same size as

(*a*) ribosomes. (*b*) modern prokaryotes. (*c*) human skin cells. (*d*) amoebas.

29.2 Some of the oldest known fossil cells appear as parts of stromatolites, which are formed today from sediments and

(*a*) marine invertebrates. (*b*) heterotrophic prokaryotes. (*c*) photosynthetic prokaryotes. (*d*) amoebas.

29.3 The earliest prokaryotes must have been

(*a*) photoautotrophs. (*b*) chemoautotrophs. (*c*) chemoheterotrophs. (*d*) lipotrophs.

29.4 The earliest prokaryotes must have acquired energy from

(*a*) sulfur. (*b*) lipids in their membranes. (*c*) fermentation of organic molecules. (*d*) aerobic cellular respiration of organic molecules.

29.5 The earliest autotrophs must have been

(*a*) anaerobic chemoautotrophs. (*b*) aerobic chemoautotrophs. (*c*) anaerobic photoautotrophs. (*d*) anaerobic photoautotrophs.

29.6 Oxygen-releasing prokaryotes first appeared at least

(*a*) 600 million years ago. (*b*) 1.5 billion years ago. (*c*) 2.5 billion years ago. (*d*) 3.4 billion years ago.

29.7 The first organisms to give off oxygen gas were probably the

(*a*) methanogens. (*b*) cyanobacteria. (*c*) anaerobic chemoautotrophs. (*d*) *Euglena*.

29.8 The last aspect of photosynthesis to evolve was the ability to

(*a*) acquire carbon dioxide by active transport. (*b*) reduce carbon dioxide. (*c*) synthesize ATP. (*d*) use water as a source of hydrogen atoms.

29.9 When a primitive bacterium is exposed to oxygen gas, it

(*a*) becomes activated. (*b*) makes and stores ATP. (*c*) synthesizes glycogen. (*d*) dies.

29.10 Heterotrophic prokaryotes benefited from the evolution of cyanobacteria, mostly because these new forms provided materials for

(*a*) endosymbiosis. (*b*) aerobic cellular respiration. (*c*) complex predator-prey interactions. (*d*) heterotrophic parasitisms.

29.11 The cell walls of bacteria and the cell walls of plants are

(*a*) homologous. (*b*) analogous. (*c*) nonevolutionary. (*d*) the same with regard to molecular composition.

29.12 The greatest diversity of metabolism is found among the

(*a*) prokaryotes. (*b*) fungi. (*c*) plants. (*d*) animals.

29.13 The oldest known fossil cells are _____ years old, from the _____ period of the geologic record.

* Answers to Chapter 29 objective questions appear on page 208.

29.14 One organic molecule that was probably abundant in the oceans when prokaryotes first appeared, and used by them as a perfect source of energy, was _____. As the supply of this food molecule diminished, selection favored any prokaryote that had the enzymes to synthesize the molecule from _____ and _____ in their environment, a step that led to the evolution of the biochemical pathway known as _____, present in all cells and presumably an ancient pathway.

29.15 The first major toxic pollutant produced by life was probably _____.

29.16 A photosynthetic cell requires a source of _____ to reduce _____. Photosynthetic prokaryotes other than cyanobacteria do not use water as a source of _____. Consequently, they do not give off _____. The green and purple sulfur bacteria, for example, obtain their _____ from hydrogen sulfide and give off _____.

29.17 Contemporary prokaryotes most similar to the earliest photosynthesizing bacteria are the _____ and the _____ bacteria.

29.18 Organisms that can grow with or without oxygen gas are called _____. Organisms that are poisoned by oxygen gas are _____. Organisms that cannot grow without oxygen gas are _____.

29.19 The first photosynthetic bacteria had only one of the two photosystems; it was _____ and used only the _____ pathway of photophosphorylation. Two photosystems evolved with the cyanobacteria, since it is more difficult to oxidize _____ than _____.

29.20 Aerobic cellular respiration probably appeared first in photosynthetic prokaryotes, since they already had _____ for photosynthesis.

29.21 Prokaryotic evolution was relatively slow; prokaryotes were limited in genetic variability because they reproduced by _____. The major source of genetic variability in prokaryotes is _____.

29.22 Prokaryotic evolution prior to the appearance of eukaryotes continued for approximately _____ years.

29.23 How do contemporary cells compare with the first cells on earth?

    The oldest known fossil cells were prokaryotic cells—without nuclei, complex chromosomes, or organelles. Structurally, they resembled contemporary heterotrophic bacteria. But even if the first cells were not morphologically similar to any contemporary cells, it would be reasonable to assume that primitive cells took advantage of the abundant supply of abiotically formed organic molecules, such as ATP, in their environment. Like contemporary detritivores, which live on partially decomposed organisms, the first cells were probably chemoheterotrophs capable of moving organic molecules from their surroundings into their interiors and breaking the molecules down into smaller units to release the energy and building materials needed to maintain cellular life.

    Were the earliest cells, however, similar in structure to the oldest known fossil cells, and therefore to the modern forms of heterotrophic bacteria? Recent evidence suggests the oldest known fossils were not the earliest cells, but instead a later stage in cellular evolution. Comparisons between biochemical pathways and nucleic acid structures of contemporary heterotrophic bacteria—which acquire energy from degrading organic molecules—and contemporary methanogens—which acquire energy from splitting H_2—demonstrate that these two forms of modern prokaryotes are quite different. The implication is that heterotrophs and methanogens had a common ancestor that existed prior to the appearance of either of these simple cells. We do not know what the first cells were like, and so cannot compare them with contemporary cells.

29.24 What conditions led to the evolution of photoautotrophs?

    The first heterotrophs found abundant food in their surroundings. As the best foods—ATP for energy and organic molecules most similar to the ones needed for biosynthesis—became scarce, natural selection would have favored the early heterotrophs with enzymes capable of converting inferior foods into the materials they needed. Longer and longer biochemical pathways evolved. One pathway that must have appeared early in life was glycolysis, since it breaks down organic molecules anaerobically to generate ATP and is seen in the same form in all cells. The final step in fermentation, however, in which pyruvic acid is converted to a waste product, varies greatly among prokaryotes.

The next phase of cellular evolution occurred as even the simplest organic molecules became scarce in the oceanic environment. The only potential nutrients available then would have been inorganic molecules, and any organism capable of acquiring energy and structural materials from inorganic sources would have had a tremendous advantage. The first cells with this capability were chemoautotrophs; they acquired energy from the covalent bonds of such inorganic molecules as molecular hydrogen (H_2) and used it to build organic molecules from carbon dioxide and hydrogen.

Photoautotrophs appeared approximately three billion years ago, somewhat later than the chemoautotrophs. They used sunlight rather than inorganic molecules as a source of energy for converting carbon dioxide into organic molecules. Their source of hydrogen atoms for reducing carbon dioxide was not water, as it is for plants and cyanobacteria, but rather H_2S. These first photoautotrophs resembled the green sulfur and purple sulfur bacteria that exist today; they use H_2S as a source of hydrogen atoms and, consequently, do not give off molecular oxygen as a waste product. The earliest photoautotrophs, like the sulfur bacteria, had only photosystem I and could only carry out cyclic photophosphorylation.

Cyanobacteria appeared approximately 2.5 billion years ago. These more advanced photoautotrophs used water as a source of hydrogen atoms and had both photosystems I and II, which operate in series (noncyclic photophosphorylation), since it takes more energy to oxidize water than to oxidize hydrogen sulfide. Cyanobacteria release molecular oxygen (O_2), a molecule at first toxic to life but later used to great advantage in aerobic cellular respiration.

ORIGIN OF THE EUKARYOTIC CELL

29.25 A eukaryotic cell differs from a prokaryotic cell in having

(a) aerobic rather than anaerobic cellular respiration. (b) three photosystems. (c) true cell membranes. (d) organelles.

29.26 The oldest eukaryotic fossil is

(a) 600 million years old. (b) 1.5 billion years old. (c) 2.5 billion years old. (d) 3.5 billion years old.

29.27 The first eukaryotic cell probably acquired energy from

(a) ATP in its environment. (b) ATP captured from prokaryotes. (c) aerobic cellular respiration. (d) anaerobic cellular respiration.

29.28 Ribosomes in the cytoplasm of eukaryotic cells are

(a) the same size and composition as in bacteria. (b) larger than in bacteria, but of similar composition. (c) smaller than in bacteria, and different in composition. (d) the same size but completely different in composition from the ribosomes in bacteria.

29.29 Ribosomes in the chloroplasts of eukaryotic cells are

(a) the same size and composition as in bacteria. (b) larger than in bacteria, but of similar composition. (c) smaller than in bacteria, and different in composition. (d) the same size but completely different in composition from the ribosomes in bacteria.

29.30 The greatest differences among cells are between _____ and _____ cells.

29.31 According to the autogenous hypothesis, eukaryotic cells evolved by specializations of internal membranes derived from the _____ of prokaryotes. According to the endosymbiotic hypothesis, eukaryotic cells evolved from the symbiosis of several _____. In this view, chloroplasts are descendants of _____ and mitochondria of _____.

29.32 The flagellum of a eukaryote is made of _____ protein fibrils, arranged in a _____ pattern. The flagellum of a bacterium is made of _____ coiled protein strand(s).

29.33 Mitochondria and chloroplasts reproduce in a manner similar to _____ in _____. Mitochondria come only from preexisting _____ and chloroplasts from preexisting _____. A sexually reproducing organism inherits its mitochondria and chloroplasts from its _____.

29.34 DNA in mitochondria and chloroplasts is in the form of a _____ molecule, as seen also in _____.

29.35 The inner membrane and its attached enzymes within a mitochondrion resemble the _____ of a _____.

29.36 Compare the two major hypotheses explaining the origin of eukaryotic cells.

🐚 Fossils of cells of an intermediate structure between prokaryotes and eukaryotes have yet to be discovered. Biologists therefore know nothing about how the cellular organelles characteristic of eukaryotic cells originated. Many hypotheses have been developed to explain the transition from prokaryotic to eukaryotic cells. Two of the more widely accepted hypotheses are the autogenous hypothesis and the endosymbiotic hypothesis.

The *autogenous hypothesis* is that eukaryotic cells evolved as prokaryotic cells gradually increased in complexity. Complex structures, such as the mitochondria and plastids, evolved as indentations and modifications of the plasma membrane. Through successive generations of cells, the organelles became more specialized in structure and function. The main strength of this more traditional hypothesis is that it does not depart from the prevailing scientific view that the evolutionary process has been a series of small, gradual changes.

The *endosymbiotic hypothesis* is that structures within the eukaryotic cell arose suddenly from the union of different kinds of prokaryotic cells. According to this view, larger prokaryotic cells engulfed but did not digest smaller prokaryotic cells and an endosymbiotic relationship developed, in which the smaller cells became specialized in some functions and the larger cells in others. Such a relationship, in which members of two species form an intimate association, is what the term symbiosis means (*endo* refers to the fact that one of the organisms exists within the other). In time, the smaller cells became organelles, incapable of existing any longer on their own. What we call mitochondria were once smaller, free-living prokaryotic heterotrophs capable of aerobic cellular respiration. What we now call chloroplasts were once smaller, free-living, photosynthesizing prokaryotes. These and other organelles in eukaryotic cells have undergone millions of years of evolution within the larger cells.

There is considerable evidence in support of the endosymbiotic hypothesis: both mitochondria and chloroplasts contain circular DNA molecules, like those found in prokaryotes; the ribosomes and RNA molecules of the organelles are more typical of prokaryotes than of eukaryotes; both organelles synthesize some of their own proteins; both organelles are similar in size to prokaryotic cells. Organelles within eukaryotic cells appear to be remnants of prokaryotic cells that once existed as independent organisms.

Until cells or fossils of cells representing the intermediate stages of evolution between prokaryotes and eukaryotes are found, both the autogenous hypothesis and the endosymbiotic hypothesis provide valid explanations of the origin of eukaryotic cells.

29.37 How does the endosymbiotic hypothesis explain differences among the chloroplasts?

🐚 Proponents of the endosymbiotic hypothesis explain differences among chloroplasts as the result of different endosymbiotic events. They search for lineages that have produced both the chloroplast and a modern prokaryotic cell.

Three kinds of chloroplasts differentiate the red algae, green algae, and brown algae. Chloroplasts of red algae are similar to the cyanobacteria in terms of thylakoid arrangement and pigment composition; both the chloroplast and the cyanobacteria are presumed to have had a common ancestor prior to the evolution of eukaryotic cells. Similarly, chloroplasts of green algae (and higher plants) are distinct in having chlorophyll *b*. This accessory pigment is also found in prokaryotes, but only in the genus *Prochloron*, a grass-green eubacteria (*eu* = true). Thus, *Prochloron* and the chloroplasts of green algae are thought to have had a common ancestor prior to the evolution of eukaryotic cells. A third type of chloroplast occurs in brown algae. It has thylakoid membranes in stacks of three, and chlorophyll *c* and fucoxanthin as accessory pigments. No prokaryote with these attributes has been found. Proponents of the endosymbiotic hypothesis believe such a cell exists but has not yet been discovered, or it once existed and is now extinct.

EVOLUTION OF UNICELLULAR EUKARYOTES

29.38 Modern unicellular eukaryotes represent

(*a*) precursors to the plants and animals. (*b*) many quite different phylogenetic lineages. (*c*) an evolutionary dead end. (*d*) degenerate evolution.

29.39 Primitive eukaryotes led to the evolution of

(*a*) fungi and plants. (*b*) animals and plants. (*c*) unicellular eukaryotes only. (*d*) fungi, plants, animals, and protists.

29.40 The group of organisms most difficult to classify is the

(*a*) prokaryotes. (*b*) unicellular eukaryotes. (*c*) plants. (*d*) animals.

29.41 The most complex cellular structures are found in

(*a*) bacteria. (*b*) protozoa. (*c*) algae. (*d*) fungi.

29.42 Prokaryotes are more diverse than eukaryotes in terms of _____, whereas eukaryotes are more diverse than prokaryotes in terms of _____.

29.43 Unicellular eukaryotes include: algae, which typically acquire energy and nutrients in a manner similar to _____; slime molds, which typically acquire energy and nutrients in a manner similar to _____; and protozoa, which typically acquire energy and nutrients in a manner similar to _____.

29.44 Unicellular eukaryotes divide by _____ and _____. Sexual reproduction is by _____ of two _____ cells.

29.45 Eukaryotic cells have separate chromosomes. When diploid, they acquire genetic variation by _____ and _____ of the chromosomes, as well as by mutations.

29.46 Multicellular aggregates, in which each cell preserves a high degree of independent function, are known as _____. The many cells of an aggregate are usually integrated by _____.

29.47 A eukaryotic cell that has undergone repeated nuclear divisions without subsequent cytoplasmic divisions has many nuclei and is known as a _____.

29.48 Some of the green algae, such as *Ulva*, obtain multicellularity by cell divisions and adherence of the daughter cells to each other by their _____.

29.49 Multicellular algae, plants, and fungi probably had their origins as _____, whereas most animals probably had their origins as _____.

29.50 How did multicellular organisms arise from unicellular eukaryotes?

☘ True multicellularity occurs only in eukaryotes and is defined as a group of genetically identical (or similar) cells that remain in contact and coordinate their activities with regard to one another. The advantage of multicellularity is the division of labor among cells; each cell can become more efficient, through specialization of structure and function, in performing just a single task.

Multicellularity evolved many times, but exactly how it evolved we will never know. Precursors of contemporary plants, animals, and fungi are likely to have been unicellular eukaryotes that either lived in colonies or formed coenocytes.

A colony of cells could become a multicellular organism if the cells remained together long enough to become dependent on one another. Once the ability for independent life was lost, the many cells of a colony would become a multicellular organism. Most biologists believe the sponges, cnidarians (jellyfish, sea anemones, etc.), and fungi evolved from colonies. Some biologists believe plants also evolved from colonies of independent cells.

A coenocyte is a large multinucleated cell which develops when there is repeated nuclear division without subsequent cytoplasmic division. It could become a multicellular organism simply by forming membranes between its nuclei and thus producing a single body composed of many smaller cells. Most biologists believe that all animals except the sponges and cnidarians evolved from multinucleated protozoans. Some biologists believe that plants also evolved in this way; they point out that the formation of a cell plate during mitosis resembles formation of partitions among the many nuclei of a coenocyte.

Answers to Objective Questions

29.1 *b*	**29.7** *b*	**29.13** 3.5 billion; Precambrian
29.2 *c*	**29.8** *d*	**29.14** ATP; ADP; phosphate; glycolysis
29.3 *c*	**29.9** *d*	
29.4 *c*	**29.10** *b*	**29.15** molecular oxygen (O_2)
29.5 *a*	**29.11** *b*	**29.16** hydrogen atoms (or electrons); CO_2; hydrogen
29.6 *c*	**29.12** *a*	

atoms; O_2; hydrogen atoms; sulfur

29.17 green sulfur; purple sulfur

29.18 facultative anaerobes; obligate anaerobes; obligate aerobes

29.19 photosystem I; cyclic; H_2O; H_2S

29.20 electron transport chains

29.21 binary fission; mutations

29.22 2 billion

29.25 *d*

29.26 *b*

29.27 *c*

29.28 *b*

29.29 *a*

29.30 prokaryotic; eukaryotic

29.31 plasma membrane; prokaryotes; photoautotrophic bacteria; aerobic, heterotrophic bacteria

29.32 11; 9 + 2; 1

29.33 binary fission; prokaryotes; mitochondria; chloroplasts; mother

29.34 circular; prokaryotes

29.35 plasma membrane; aerobic, heterotrophic bacterium

29.38 *b*

29.39 *d*

29.40 *b*

29.41 *b*

29.42 metabolism; structure

29.43 plants; fungi; animals

29.44 mitosis; meiosis; conjugation; haploid

29.45 independent assortment; crossing-over

29.46 colonies; cytoplasmic strands

29.47 coenocyte

29.48 cell walls

29.49 colonies; coenocytes

CHAPTER 30
Plants and the Colonization of Land

ANCESTORS OF TERRESTRIAL PLANTS*

30.1   Terrestrial plants appear to have evolved from the

(*a*) Chlorophyta.   (*b*) Charophyta.   (*c*) Phaeophyta.   (*d*) Rhodophyta.

30.2   Plants first colonized land about

(*a*) 230 million years ago.   (*b*) 350 million years ago.   (*c*) 500 million years ago.   (*d*) 650 million years ago.

30.3   The first plants to colonize land were probably

(*a*) brown seaweeds (kelp).   (*b*) sea lettuce.   (*c*) *Chlamydomonas*.   (*d*) filamentous green algae.

30.4   Plants that first colonized land were preadapted to their new life by having

(*a*) holdfasts.   (*b*) roots.   (*c*) bladelike leaves.   (*d*) a simple xylem.

30.5   Photosynthesis in the first terrestrial plants took place within cells of the

(*a*) gametangia.   (*b*) holdfast.   (*c*) stem.   (*d*) rhizoids.

30.6   Oceanic coasts are hazardous for algae, since the waters are turbulent and the substrates periodically dry out. Yet algae thrive in these places, because the waters are rich in

(*a*) minerals.   (*b*) shellfish.   (*c*) sand.   (*d*) detritus.

30.7   With regard to phylogeny, the Bryophyta are

(*a*) ancestral to Tracheophyta.   (*b*) evolved from Tracheophyta.   (*c*) a separate line of evolution from Tracheophyta.   (*d*) probably the same as Tracheophyta, and the two divisions should be merged.

30.8   Green algae and vascular plants use chlorophyll _____ and chlorophyll _____, as well as _____, as their main photosynthetic pigments.

30.9   When aquatic algae invaded land during the Silurian period, the continents were _____ and so subject to seasonal changes in water levels. This type of environment selected for algae that could withstand periodic _____.

30.10   The first plants on land must have had _____ to prevent loss of water from aboveground parts. If so, they must also have had _____ for gas exchange.

30.11   The first land plants had no roots, but they did have _____, which penetrated the substrate and absorbed water.

30.12   The first plants to invade land may have acquired minerals through the aid of symbiotic _____.

30.13   The first terrestrial plants gave rise to two plant groups: the _____ and the _____. The main difference between these two groups is that the _____ have no _____.

30.14   What is the evidence that terrestrial plants evolved from green algae?

🐚   There is no direct evidence of the transition from aquatic to terrestrial plants, since the soft bodies of algae tend not to leave fossils. Our evidence is based entirely on logic: If one assumes algae were ancestral to

* Answers to Chapter 30 objective questions appear on page 215.

terrestrial plants, and that biochemical traits are more conservative than structural traits during evolution, then one must conclude that a form of Chlorophyta gave rise to both the Bryophyta and the Tracheophyta.

Some sort of alga is likely to have been the ancestor of land plants, because multicellularity arose in that group and because there are so many similarities between algae and land plants. Most striking, by far, are the similarities between Chlorophyta and contemporary forms of land plants. Green algae and land plants both have: (1) chlorophyll *a*, chlorophyll *b*, and beta-carotene as their main photosynthetic pigments; (2) cellulose and pectates within their cell walls; (3) thylakoid membranes stacked locally as grana within their chloroplasts; (4) starch as their energy-storage molecule; (5) either no flagella or flagella that are anterior and of equal length; (6) cytokinesis by formation of a cell plate rather than by constriction and pinching off of the cell membrane.

Contemporary Chlorophyta are remarkably similar to contemporary Bryophyta and Tracheophyta but are not ancestral to these terrestrial plants. All three contemporary divisions of plants must have shared a common aquatic ancestor about 500 million years ago.

30.15 What conditions led to the colonization of land by plants?

🐚 The first colonizers of barren land were descendants of coastal algae. All aquatic organisms require a regular flow of water over their surfaces in order to exchange gases, minerals, and other materials with their aquatic surroundings. Such a flow can be achieved either by a motile organism traveling through water or by a sedentary organism living in flowing water. Some of the primitive coastal algae adopted the latter method; they attached themselves to the substrate, and the turbulent coastal waters flowed over them. These algae were multicellular, with one cell specialized as a holdfast and other photosynthetic cells attached to it, forming a long filament.

Approximately 500 million years ago, during the early Silurian period, the continents were flat with gradually descending continental shelves. Consequently, the shallow coastlines rose and fell dramatically with seasonal fluctuations in water levels. Coastal organisms within these waters were periodically exposed to the dry air. Algae attached to substrates were unable to move away from the dry, inhospitable environment, and most of them died of desiccation. Each generation, however, a few algae with desiccation-resistant features survived and left offspring with these same features. Gradually, a waxy cuticle evolved and, along with it, small pores (the stomata) for gas exchange through the otherwise impermeable outer covering. These algalike coastal plants became the first terrestrial plants.

ADAPTATIONS TO TERRESTRIAL ENVIRONMENTS

30.16 Terrestrial plants without vascular systems first appear in the fossil record about how many million years ago?

(*a*) 100; (*b*) 230; (*c*) 360; (*d*) 430

30.17 Terrestrial plants with vascular systems first appear in the fossil record about how many million years ago?

(*a*) 100; (*b*) 230; (*c*) 360; (*d*) 430

30.18 Bryophytes and ferns need free water for

(*a*) fertilization. (*b*) mitosis. (*c*) meiosis. (*d*) cytokinesis.

30.19 A seaweed can grow very large because it is supported by water. A vascular plant holds itself upright without support from water. It is able to do this because its cell walls are made rigid by

(*a*) chlorophyll. (*b*) cellulose. (*c*) lignin. (*d*) carotene.

30.20 One subdivision of Tracheophyta has plants known as "living fossils," because they closely resemble early vascular plants. This subdivision is

(*a*) Psilopsida. (*b*) Lycopsida. (*c*) Pteropsida. (*d*) Spheropsida.

30.21 Lycopods, horsetails, and ferns dominated the land during the

(*a*) Silurian period. (*b*) Carboniferous period. (*c*) Permian period. (*d*) Cretaceous period.

30.22 Gymnosperms dominated the land during the

(*a*) Silurian period. (*b*) Carboniferous period. (*c*) Permian period. (*d*) Cretaceous period.

30.23   The first group of terrestrial plants to get rid of the swimming sperm was the

(*a*) club mosses.   (*b*) ferns.   (*c*) gymnosperms.   (*d*) angiosperms.

30.24   The interior of the land became much warmer and drier during the Permian period, a climatic change caused by the

(*a*) formation of Pangaea.   (*b*) breakup of Pangaea.   (*c*) breakup of Gondwanaland.   (*d*) landing of asteroids.

30.25   Which of the following groups did *not* contribute to the enormous coal deposits formed during the Carboniferous period?

(*a*) Lycopod trees;   (*b*) Horsetails;   (*c*) Conifers;   (*d*) Flowering plants

30.26   The gametophytes of conifers are protected from desiccation by living in

(*a*) moist soil.   (*b*) moist tissues of the sporophyte.   (*c*) bogs and marshes.   (*d*) the rainy season only.

30.27   The sperm of conifers are carried to the female gametophyte by

(*a*) flagellar movements.   (*b*) water currents.   (*c*) wind.   (*d*) animals.

30.28   The needlelike shape of a conifer leaf is an adaptation to

(*a*) low amounts of blue light.   (*b*) dry conditions.   (*c*) snow.   (*d*) insect herbivores.

30.29   The most diverse and widespread of all contemporary plants are the

(*a*) mosses.   (*b*) ferns.   (*c*) conifers.   (*d*) angiosperms.

30.30   No contemporary seed plant forms

(*a*) gametophytes.   (*b*) archegonia.   (*c*) antheridia.   (*d*) sporangia.

30.31   The oldest angiosperm fossils are from the

(*a*) Quaternary period.   (*b*) early Cretaceous period.   (*c*) Triassic period.   (*d*) Carboniferous period.

30.32   Two adaptations that prevent desiccation in dry environments and are found in all vascular plants are _____ and jackets of nonreproductive cells around the _____ and _____.

30.33   As soon as plants arrived on land, selection favored cellular differentiation, because the _____ on land are spatially segregated, with _____ and _____ underground and _____ aboveground.

30.34   During their first 100 million years on land, sexual reproduction in terrestrial plants occurred only in moist habitats because these plants had _____.

30.35   Vascular plants were able to become very large by transporting materials from one part of their body to another; they evolved a _____ for transport of water and minerals and a _____ for transport of sugars and other organic molecules.

30.36   Vascular plants of the early Devonian period had no true _____ or _____. The tips of their stems bore _____.

30.37   Seedless plants disperse as _____, whereas seed plants disperse as _____.

30.38   Of the two major classes of extant seed plants, the _____ appear first in the fossil record and then the _____.

30.39   The zygote of a gymnosperm develops into an _____ surrounded by _____ and enclosed within a _____. It is located in the _____ of the sporophyte.

30.40 A seed contains tissues from four different structures of the life cycle: a seed coat formed from the _____; a thick wall (nucellus) inside the seed coat and derived from the _____; an endosperm formed of the _____; and the embryo, which will become a _____ of the next generation.

30.41 Pollen grains reach the ovules of seed plants by a process known as _____.

30.42 In Greek, the term *gymnosperm* means _____ seed; there is no parental tissue around the ovule at the time the pollen grain arrives.

30.43 Double fertilization occurs only in _____; it ensures that _____ develops only in ovules with _____.

30.44 Fill in the missing parts of Table 30.1.

TABLE 30.1

group	dominant stage of the life cycle	homosporous or heterosporous	transport of sperm
Mosses	(a) _____	(b) _____	(c) _____
Ferns	(d) _____	(e) _____	(f) _____
Conifers	(g) _____	(h) _____	(i) _____
Flowering plants	(j) _____	(k) _____	(l) _____

30.45 In what ways are conifers better adapted than ferns to life on land?

🐌 Conifers are gymnosperms, a category of seed plant that evolved from ferns during the late Carboniferous period when the supercontinent Pangaea was forming. Prior to this time, the many separate continents had no vast interiors far from oceanic coasts and their climates were wet. Ferns thrived in these lands, as they had vascular tissues, leaves, and roots, and there was sufficient soil water for their swimming sperm, delicate gametophyte, and young sporophyte, and for evaporative cooling of their very large leaves. (As leaf size increases, the amount of cooling by convection decreases, so more water is required for cooling by evaporation.)

The climate became drier during the Permian period as the enormous interior of Pangaea developed. The moisture-loving ferns, so dominant during the wet Carboniferous period, were outcompeted by the newly evolved gymnosperms in these dry habitats. Some lines of gymnosperms, most notably the conifers, became increasingly less dependent on moist habitats as they evolved a nonswimming sperm, a gametophyte and embryo enclosed within desiccation-resistant tissues, and smaller leaves cooled more by convection than by evaporation.

Contemporary ferns remain tied to moist habitats for sexual reproduction, since their flagellated sperm need a film of water to reach an egg. Moreover, the fragile gametophyte and young sporophyte die of desiccation unless surrounded by humid air. Ferns can and do live in dry habitats, but reproduce only asexually and grow only in shady spots where their leaves require less water for cooling.

Contemporary conifers live in some of the driest habitats on earth. During conifer evolution, the swimming form of sperm was replaced with just a sperm nucleus enclosed within a desiccation-resistant gametophyte, the pollen grain. This nucleus reaches the egg nucleus by traveling first inside the pollen grain and then through a pollen tube—an extension that grows out of the pollen grain. The embryo develops within the female gametophyte, now an endosperm, surrounded by a desiccation-resistant seed coat formed of parental sporophyte tissue. Neither pollination nor early development requires free water. Additionally, the leaves of conifers are needles or scales, which, by being small, conserve water by losing excess heat chiefly through convection rather than through evaporation.

30.46 In what ways is angiosperm reproduction more energetically efficient than conifer reproduction?

🐌 Angiosperm reproduction is similar to conifer reproduction but has two energy-saving innovations: (1) pollination by animals and (2) endosperm development from a triploid nucleus formed of a sperm nucleus and two polar nuclei.

Conifer pollen grains are carried by the wind, and angiosperm pollen grains are carried by animals. Much of the conifer pollen is wasted, since it lands on surfaces other than female gametophytes. Less pollen is wasted in angiosperms, because it is moved by animals along a specific path from anther to ovule. The entire floral structure evolved to increase the probability of a pollen grain moving directly to the stigma in a flower of the same species; once it is in the stigma, the pollen grain grows a pollen tube to the ovule. The color, shape, smell, and nectar reward of a flower attract only certain animals; pollen adheres to these animals and is carried to other flowers of the same type. Flowering plant species and their pollinator species *coevolved* (i.e., evolutionary changes in one species caused evolutionary changes in the other, and vice versa).

The second way in which angiosperms produce less costly zygotes is in endosperm production. In conifers, endosperm exists in every ovule, whether or not fertilization takes place; energy is spent on endosperm that is never used by embryos. In angiosperms, no endosperm develops in an ovule until a sperm nucleus joins with two polar nuclei; no energy is spent on endosperm in ovules without zygotes.

ADAPTATIONS OF ANGIOSPERMS TO ANIMALS

30.47 The first animals to serve as pollinators were

(*a*) ants. (*b*) beetles. (*c*) bees. (*d*) hummingbirds.

30.48 The function of nectar in a flower is to

(*a*) draw pollen grains toward the female gametophyte. (*b*) trap insects in the sticky fluid. (*c*) provide food for the developing embryo. (*d*) provide food for animals.

30.49 The function of colored petals of a flower is to
(*a*) reflect light away from the developing embryo. (*b*) absorb heat and warm the developing embryo. (*c*) enable animals to recognize food sources. (*d*) keep the reproductive structures moist.

30.50 The function of a dry fruit is to

(*a*) nourish the embryo. (*b*) protect the embryo from herbivores. (*c*) disperse the embryo by wind or water, or on animals. (*d*) provide food for animals.

30.51 The function of a fleshy fruit is to

(*a*) nourish the embryo. (*b*) protect the embryo from herbivores. (*c*) disperse the embryo by wind or water, or on animals. (*d*) provide food for animals.

30.52 The seeds of a fleshy fruit reach germination sites by way of

(*a*) flowing water. (*b*) animal feces. (*c*) wind currents. (*d*) gravity (they germinate just below the parent).

30.53 Important defenses of plants against herbivores are

(*a*) fleshy fruits. (*b*) dry fruits. (*c*) secondary metabolic compounds. (*d*) primary metabolic compounds.

30.54 Many flowers and mature fruits are red, because this color is seen most acutely by

(*a*) humans. (*b*) birds. (*c*) insects. (*d*) bats.

30.55 Evolutionary changes in floral morphologies (e.g., length of fused petals) influence evolutionary changes in pollinator morphology (e.g., length of tongue), and vice versa. This type of evolution is known as _____.

30.56 Movement of an offspring away from its parent is called _____. In wild plums and strawberries, the vector is _____. In dandelions and maples the vector is _____. In fruits with hooked spines, such as stick-tights, the vector is _____.

30.57 An advantage of seed dispersal is that it reduces _____ between _____ and _____.

30.58 Flowering plants differ from other seed plants in having their seeds enclosed within special tissues of the sporophyte. These tissues form _____ that mature into _____.

30.59 Molecules synthesized by plants but not used in their metabolism are called _____. They are _____ to herbivores.

30.60 How have flowers changed during their evolution from the primitive types?

⊕   The first flowers evolved from modifications of leaves and branches: stamens and carpels (or pistils) evolved from small, sporangia-bearing branches; sepals evolved from leaves; and the petals of most flowers evolved from flattened stamens that lost their microsporangia. These primitive flowers were radially symmetrical with many spirally arranged sepals, petals, stamens, and carpels. There was little difference between the sepals, which protect the floral buds, and the petals, which attract pollinators; neither structure had much color or specialized form. These first flowers were pollinated by beetles.

Throughout the evolution of flowers, their parts have become increasingly more specialized with regard to form and function, and they have acquired traits that attract only specific pollinators so as to promote more precise pollination. The major trends of flower evolution have been:

1. A change from the spiral arrangement of parts to a series of whorls, with separate whorls of sepals, petals, stamens, and carpels
2. A reduction in the number of floral parts, especially of stamens and carpels
3. A fusion of floral parts that change whorls of carpels or petals into tubes
4. A change from radial symmetry to bilateral symmetry, with the development of landing platforms for such flying pollinators as bees
5. A lowering of the ovary to a position below the petals and sepals (i.e., an inferior ovary), where the ovules are more protected from insect herbivores
6. A loss of either the stamens or carpels in each flower, which prevents self-pollination

Answers to Objective Questions

30.1 *a*
30.2 *c*
30.3 *d*
30.4 *a*
30.5 *c*
30.6 *a*
30.7 *c*
30.8 *a*; *b*; beta-carotene
30.9 flat; drying
30.10 waxy cuticles; pores (or stomata)
30.11 rhizoids
30.12 fungi
30.13 Bryophyta; Tracheophyta; Bryophyta; vascular system
30.16 *c*
30.17 *d*
30.18 *a*
30.19 *c*
30.20 *a*
30.21 *b*
30.22 *c*
30.23 *c*
30.24 *a*
30.25 *d*

30.26 *b*
30.27 *c*
30.28 *b*
30.29 *d*
30.30 *c*
30.31 *b*
30.32 waxy cuticles; gametangia; sporangia
30.33 resources; water; minerals; light
30.34 swimming sperm
30.35 xylem; phloem
30.36 leaves; roots; sporangia
30.37 spores; embryos
30.38 Coniferae; Angiospermae
30.39 embryo; endosperm; seed coat; megacone
30.40 sporophyte; macrosporangium; female gametophyte; sporophyte
30.41 pollination
30.42 naked
30.43 angiosperms; endosperm; zygotes

30.44 (*a*) gametophyte; (*b*) homosporous; (*c*) flagella; (*d*) sporophyte; (*e*) homosporous (mostly); (*f*) flagella; (*g*) sporophyte; (*h*) heterosporous; (*i*) wind; (*j*) sporophyte; (*k*) heterosporous; (*l*) animals
30.47 *b*
30.48 *d*
30.49 *c*
30.50 *c*
30.51 *d*
30.52 *b*
30.53 *c*
30.54 *b*
30.55 coevolution
30.56 dispersal; animals; wind; animals
30.57 competition; parent; offspring
30.58 ovaries; fruits
30.59 secondary metabolic compounds; poisonous

CHAPTER 31
Animals and the Colonization of Land

TERRESTRIAL ARTHROPODS*

31.1 Marine arthropods were preadapted to terrestrial life by having

(*a*) exoskeletons.   (*b*) closed circulatory systems.   (*c*) no coeloms.   (*d*) no body segmentation.

31.2 Most terrestrial arthropods have Malpighian tubules, which drain wastes from the

(*a*) coelom.   (*b*) hemocoel.   (*c*) blood vessels.   (*d*) intestine.

31.3 Nitrogenous wastes in the Malpighian tubules flow into the

(*a*) coelom.   (*b*) hemocoel.   (*c*) blood vessels.   (*d*) intestine.

31.4 Gas exchange in an insect occurs within tracheae, an adaptation for

(*a*) high oxygen consumption.   (*b*) conservation of water.   (*c*) flight.   (*d*) conservation of carbon dioxide.

31.5 In all terrestrial arthropods, fertilization of the eggs takes place

(*a*) in standing water.   (*b*) in moist soil.   (*c*) inside the body of the female.   (*d*) in egg sacs attached to the underside of leaves.

31.6 The oldest terrestrial fossil animal, approximately 400 million years old, is a _____ (phylum Arthropoda; class Diplopoda).

31.7 A great explosion of insect diversity occurred during the Carboniferous and Permian periods, largely in response to the evolution of insect _____. A second large increase in insect diversity occurred during the Cretaceous, in response to the evolution of _____.

31.8 An insect wing is an extension of its _____ rather than a true appendage as it is in birds and bats. Wings formed in this way are an advantage for insects, because flight does not diminish their ability to _____, as it does in birds and bats. All winged insects are metabolous, which means they undergo changes in body form in a process known as _____.

31.9 Insects prevent water loss during gas exchange by having internal respiratory surfaces called _____, which are rigid and formed of _____.

31.10 What were the first terrestrial animals like?

The oldest terrestrial fossils are of millipedes, present on land about 400 million years ago. In the class Diplopoda of the phylum Arthropoda, these animals have a distinct head with mandibles and antennae, a segmented trunk composed of many body segments, and many legs—one or two pairs on most of the body segments. Gas exchange is through tracheae. Nitrogenous wastes are eliminated through Malpighian tubules; they drain fluid from the hemocoel to the intestine, and water and ions are reabsorbed through the walls of the rectum.

While millipedes form the oldest fossils, many biologists believe that animals resembling scorpions were the first invaders of terrestrial habitats, some time prior to 400 million years ago (during the Silurian period). These animals were ancestors of modern arachnids (class Arachnida; phylum Arthropoda): scorpions, spiders, ticks, mites, and daddy longlegs. Arachnids have a cephalothorax (no separate head) with four pairs of legs and an abdomen. Gas exchange is through tracheae and/or book lungs. Nitrogenous wastes are eliminated through *coxal glands* or Malpighian tubules, or both. Coxal glands are remnants of the coelom that drain fluid from the hemocoel, then move it through a renal tubule to an excretory pore located in the coxa (where a leg attaches to the body) of that metamere. Arachnids have *chelicerae*—which are clawlike appendages—rather than mandibles, and lack antennae.

* Answers to Chapter 31 objective questions appear on page 222.

These early terrestrial forms were the first organisms to evolve reproductive methods that did not require free water. The male copulatory organ, or penis, was inserted into the female where the eggs were retained; sperm and fluid were released; and the sperm then swam to meet the eggs. After fertilization, each egg was surrounded with a waterproof material that protected the embryo from drying out. The difficulty of fertilization on dry land was overcome in this remarkable way.

More animal groups invaded land during the Devonian period. Insects evolved from marine arthropods and soon became the dominant class of arthropods on land. An insect has three well-defined regions of its body: a head with antennae and mandibles, a thorax with three pairs of legs, and an abdomen. As with other arthropods, there is a thick, external skeleton that supports the body and prevents desiccation. It also forms an internal system of tubes—the tracheae—through which gases are exchanged. Excretion is by Malpighian tubules, in which the walls of the rectum reabsorb large quantities of water prior to elimination of wastes. Insect mouth parts evolved into many specialized types for sucking, biting, chewing, and rasping, and insects were the first animals to evolve wings for flight. No arthropods have adapted to living on dry land as successfully as the insects have. Insects remain an abundant and diverse group, comprising more than 80 percent of all the animal species on earth today.

AMPHIBIANS

31.11   Amphibians first appear in the fossil record of the

(*a*) Ordovician period.   (*b*) Silurian period.   (*c*) Devonian period.   (*d*) Carboniferous period.

31.12   Amphibians evolved from fish in the class

(*a*) Agnatha.   (*b*) Placodermi.   (*c*) Chondrichthyes.   (*d*) Osteichthyes.

31.13   Lunged fish were the most common bony fish when amphibians evolved. The lungs of these fish were adaptations to

(*a*) stagnant water.   (*b*) fast-flowing rivers.   (*c*) marine coastal waters.   (*d*) deep, cold waters of the ocean.

31.14   Which of the following structures of a fish is homologous with the lung of a frog?

(*a*) Gill pouch;   (*b*) Swim bladder;   (*c*) Stomach;   (*d*) Book lungs

31.15   An extant lobe-finned fish, similar to the first fish that used its fins to crawl on land, is the

(*a*) hagfish.   (*b*) shark.   (*c*) coelacanth.   (*d*) skate.

31.16   The first terrestrial vertebrates acquired energy and nutrients from

(*a*) pollen.   (*b*) fern leaves.   (*c*) terrestrial invertebrates.   (*d*) aquatic invertebrates.

31.17   There are two divergent groups of Osteichthyes: the ray-finned fish, which have rays made of modified scales and gave rise to nearly all the _____ fish seen today; and the lobe-finned fish, which have skeletal elements in the fin and gave rise to the class _____.

31.18   The so-called Age of Amphibians, when these vertebrates flourished, occurred during the _____ period.

31.19   Most amphibians are not truly terrestrial, because most have _____ fertilization that takes place in _____ and their eggs resemble those of _____ rather than the eggs of reptiles or birds. Furthermore, their _____ are aquatic, with adaptations for swimming, breathing, and feeding in fresh water. Exceptions do exist. For example, most salamanders and all _____ fertilize their eggs _____. Some land salamanders deposit their eggs in _____ on land, and most lack _____ forms but hatch instead as small versions of the adults.

31.20   The three major orders of Amphibia are: _____ (with tails, such as salamanders), _____ (without tails, such as frogs), and _____ (without legs, such as caecilians).

31.21   What was the first terrestrial vertebrate like?

🐚   Fish began to invade land successfully during the Devonian period. Many early fish had lungs, but in most groups that were active midwater swimmers, these inflatable structures evolved into swim bladders and gas exchange was restricted to the gills. The swim bladder, when filled with the appropriate amount of gas, allows a fish to maintain a particular depth in the water.

A few types of lobe-finned fish, whose fleshy fins contained bones from the pectoral and pelvic girdles, lived in shallow ponds and retained their lungs. When oxygen concentrations in the stagnant water became low, the fish would occassionally rise above the surface to fill their lungs with air. Although these fish were primarily aquatic, they periodically walked from pond to pond on slightly modified fins. Some of the Devonian "lungfish" evolved true legs and became amphibians. The earliest amphibians had an elongated body with four legs and a tail and were similar to a modern salamander. The class Amphibia now includes the urodeles (salamanders), anurans (frogs and toads), and apodans (caecilians).

Early amphibians thrived on land, and many new forms evolved during the Devonian period, which was exceptionally warm and humid. Amphibians fed mainly on insects, which were already in plentiful supply. Their transition from water to land was facilitated by the presence of large plants and the moist areas provided by their shade.

These early amphibians, like their descendants today, depended on water in many ways. They needed it to reproduce, because both eggs and sperm were released into fresh water and the sperm swam to the egg for fertilization. During the early stages of development, the young lived in fresh water, just as frog tadpoles do today. Primitive amphibians also required water to moisten their skin, which functioned as a second surface for gas exchange, in addition to their simple saclike lungs. Modern amphibians are similar to these early forms and are also restricted to life near water.

Fossils of early amphibians have been found in such unlikely and widely separated places as Greenland and Antarctica. The interpretation of this distribution is that the continents were once connected (Pangaea) and the environments on both land masses were warm and humid.

REPTILES

31.22   The oldest fossils of reptiles are from the

(a) Devonian period.   (b) Carboniferous period.   (c) Permian period.   (d) Triassic period.

31.23   The stem reptiles, or cotylosaurs, fed mainly on

(a) leaves.   (b) seeds.   (c) amphibians.   (d) insects.

31.24   The horny epidermal scales of a reptile are made of

(a) protein.   (b) polysaccharides.   (c) bone.   (d) chitin.

31.25   Sperm of a reptile travels to the eggs by

(a) swimming through a film of groundwater.   (b) moving through a penis and then swimming through the semen.   (c) wind.   (d) ciliated sperm packets.

31.26   A reptile is able to ventilate its lungs more efficiently than an amphibian, because it does so by

(a) moving its rib cage.   (b) swallowing air.   (c) moving its diaphragm.   (d) rotating its forelegs.

31.27   The first major radiation of reptiles occurred during the

(a) Devonian period.   (b) Carboniferous period.   (c) Permian period.   (d) Jurassic period.

31.28   The second major radiation of reptiles, during which dinosaurs evolved, occurred during the

(a) late Triassic.   (b) late Jurassic.   (c) Cretaceous.   (d) early Tertiary.

31.29   Reptilian ancestors of dinosaurs, crocodiles, and birds were the

(a) therapsids.   (b) thecodonts.   (c) pterosaurs.   (d) plesiosaurs.

31.30   Reptilian ancestors of mammals were the

(a) therapsids.   (b) thecodonts.   (c) pterosaurs.   (d) plesiosaurs.

31.31   Most dinosaurs became extinct during the

(a) late Triassic.   (b) late Jurassic.   (c) Cretaceous.   (d) early Tertiary.

31.32 A reptile prevents the loss of water through its skin by having _____, which are made of keratin and are analogous to the _____ of an insect and the _____ of a plant.

31.33 The reptilian kidney, like the one in birds and mammals, must be able to reabsorb into the blood a large amount of _____.

31.34 Reptiles have _____ fertilization and swimming sperm. The embryo develops within a fluid-filled sac, called the _____, which eliminates the need for free water during development. The egg is cleidoic, which means it is enclosed within a _____. The egg of a reptile is analogous to the _____ of a plant.

31.35 As with gymnosperms when they replaced ferns, reptiles replaced amphibians during the _____ period in habitats that were _____. Such habitats became increasingly more prevalent during this period, because of the formation of the supercontinent _____.

31.36 There are three large and diverse orders of extant reptiles: _____ (lizards and snakes), _____ (turtles), and _____ (alligators and crocodiles).

31.37 Why were the early reptiles more successful than amphibians in dry habitats?

🐚 Reptiles appeared during the Carboniferous period and largely replaced amphibians in dry habitats during the Permian period. Reptiles were the first vertebrates to achieve reproduction completely free of water. Like the female arthropod, the female reptile retained her eggs within her body until they were fertilized. As in the male arthropod, a penis evolved in the male reptile and it released swimming sperm and fluid into the female. After fertilization, the embryo developed within a fluid-filled sac, the *amnion*, and was nourished by a supply of stored food—the yolk. Waste materials accumulated in a special container called the *allantois*. Each embryo, with its amnion, yolk, and allantois, was then enclosed within a shell that held the materials and prevented evaporation of water (Fig. 31.1). The eggs were laid after the shells formed, and the young reptiles hatched when they were completely developed. An external aquatic environment was not required for fertilization or development. Amphibians, by contrast, continued to have external fertilization, fishlike eggs, and young forms adapted for swimming, breathing, and finding their own food in aquatic environments.

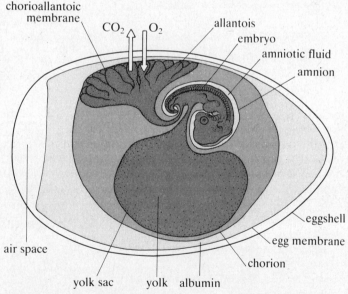

Fig. 31.1. The amniote egg. The embryo produces extraembryonic membranes that surround and protect it. The amniotic membrane cradles the embryo within a fluid, the allantoic membrane holds embryonic wastes and is a place of gas exchange, the yolk sac holds a supply of food, and the chorion encloses the amnion, allantois, and yolk sac. The extraembryonic membranes are surrounded by albumin and covered with a hard outer shell. This type of egg is found in reptiles, birds, and monotremes.

Reptiles, which descended from amphibians and surpassed them in dominance on land, had more efficient lungs than the amphibians and no longer used their skin for gas exchange. A reptilian lung is more subdivided and has more surface area than an amphibian lung. The lung is ventilated by movements of a rib cage rather than by gulping air, which is how an amphibian ventilates its lungs. Freed of its gas-exchange function, the skin of a reptile became dry and covered with scales made of keratin that protected against water loss.

Having escaped the need to live near water, the early reptiles colonized vast land areas in the interior of the supercontinent Pangaea. They became abundant and diverse, forming the ichthyosaurs, plesiosaurs, dinosaurs, and therapsids, as well as the modern orders of Chelonia (turtles and tortoises), Crocodilia (crocodiles and alligators), Squamata (snakes and lizards), and Rhynchocephalia (the tuatara of New Zealand).

31.38   What caused the massive extinction of dinosaurs?

@   The most fascinating of all reptiles—the dinosaurs—evolved into many diverse forms, some of which grew to enormous proportions (as large as 25 m long and 50 tons in weight). Most dinosaurs were land dwellers, but some could fly and others returned to aquatic habitats. Dinosaurs dominated the earth from the end of the Triassic period to the end of the Cretaceous period and then mysteriously became extinct about 65 million years ago. These mass extinctions took place just prior to the extensive evolution of mammals, at a time of cool climates and formation of mountains.

We do not know what caused the extinction of the dinosaurs. A recent hypothesis is that an asteroid (small planet) hit the earth and created a thick dust cloud that darkened the earth's surface, producing extreme cold and suppressing photosynthesis for more than a decade. Under such conditions, plants and the large plant-eating dinosaurs would have died. However, the plants would not have become extinct, because their spores and seeds could have survived in a dormant state during this time. Any animal capable of eating spores or seeds, such as a mammal, could also have survived this dark period.

BIRDS

31.39   The reptilian ancestors of birds were

(a) ichthyosaurs.   (b) dinosaurs.   (c) plesiosaurs.   (d) pterosaurs.

31.40   Modern birds are most closely related to

(a) mammals.   (b) lizards.   (c) crocodiles.   (d) turtles.

31.41   *Archaeopteryx*, a fossil bird with teeth and a long, jointed tail, lived during the

(a) Permian period.   (b) Triassic period.   (c) Jurassic period.   (d) Cretaceous period.

31.42   The wishbone of a bird, which supports the flight muscles, formed from

(a) a fusion of the collar bones.   (b) ventral extensions of the vertebrae.   (c) anterior ribs.   (d) posterior extensions of the larynx.

31.43   Birds are sometimes called glorified reptiles, because they have eggs that are both _____ and _____, and have _____ on their legs. Birds look different from reptiles, however: Their bodies are insulated with _____ (made of _____), and their forelimbs are modified to form _____.

31.44   A bird has no teeth. Instead, it has a _____, made of keratin, for manipulating and tearing its food, and a _____ (the posterior part of the stomach) for grinding its food.

31.45   The sensory organ that has reached its highest level of evolution in birds is the _____.

31.46   Many bones in a bird are hollow and contain _____ that are extensions of the _____. This feature makes the skeleton light in weight, an adaptation for _____.

31.47   What evolutionary changes transformed a group of reptiles into birds?

@   Birds evolved from dinosaurs during the Jurassic period, about 200 million years ago. The evolution of wings, originally used to facilitate running, and of feathers, originally used to retain endogenous heat, set the stage for flight.

Wings and the feathers that cover them are shaped for lifting and propelling the body in air, as well as for soaring. They are moved by strong pectoral muscles attached to a keel, which is a greatly enlarged portion of the sternum, and to a wishbone, which is formed from a fusion of the collar bones. Feathers evolved from scales and, like them, are made of keratin. They are superior to the membranes used by bats and pterosaurs, because they provide more variations in air flow, and therefore more control over flight, and are replaceable after injury. A four-chambered heart, combined with endothermy and superbly efficient lungs, promoted rapid cellular respiration to meet the energetic demands of flight.

Many changes occurred during the evolution of birds to make their bodies lighter in weight. Teeth were lost, one ovary was lost, and the bones became hollow structures filled with air sacs, which are extensions of the lungs.

The nervous system changed as birds evolved from reptiles. Eyesight became more acute, with eyes adapted for distant vision and enlargement of the visual cortex. The cerebellum of the brain also became much larger, to accommodate the many more neurons and synapses required for coordinating the flight muscles.

MAMMALS

31.48 The oldest fossil of a mammal is from the

(a) Permian period. (b) Triassic period. (c) Jurassic period. (d) Cretaceous period.

31.49 The first mammals were probably nocturnal and resembled

(a) sloths. (b) shrews. (c) rats. (d) cats.

31.50 Monotremes—the egg-laying mammals—are found only in

(a) Australia and New Guinea. (b) Asia. (c) South America. (d) the Galapagos Islands.

31.51 A North American marsupial is the

(a) ocelot. (b) skunk. (c) kangaroo rat. (d) opossum.

31.52 Most marsupials live in

(a) Australia. (b) Asia. (c) South America. (d) the Galapagos Islands.

31.53 All mammals

(a) give birth to live young. (b) have a thick coat of hair. (c) nourish their young with milk. (d) have a uterus.

31.54 Mammals have _____ instead of scales or feathers. It is made of _____.

31.55 A mammal has an efficient respiratory system, with large lungs for gas exchange and a _____, as well as a rib cage, for ventilation.

31.56 The fish heart has two chambers. An amphibian heart has _____ chambers, a reptilian heart has _____, a bird heart has _____, and a mammalian heart has _____. Unlike the heart of a reptile, the heart of a mammal allows no mixing of blood from the _____ and the _____.

31.57 A placental mammal does not have an amniotic, cleidoic egg, since the embryo is nourished by the _____.

31.58 The class Mammalia is composed of two subclasses: _____, the egg-laying mammals; and _____, the marsupial and placental mammals. Marsupials and placentals form separate _____ in their subclass.

31.59 Why are the geographic distributions of monotremes and marsupials so restricted, whereas placentals are found almost everywhere?

🐚 Monotremes (subclass Prototheria) are egg-laying mammals found only in Australia and New Guinea. These animals, the spiny anteater and the duck-billed platypus, suckle their young with milk after hatching. Marsupials (subclass Theria) have a uterus for development of the young, but only a rudimentary placenta for connecting the young with their mother's circulatory system. The young are born at a very early stage in their development and move into a pouch on their mother for attachment to a nipple and completion of their development. Marsupials are found primarily in Australia, but many species of marsupial opossums occur in South America and a few extend into North America. Placentals (subclass Theria) are found throughout the world except for Australia and its nearby islands. They have both a uterus and a placenta; development of the young is completed within the mother's body.

The first mammals to evolve were monotremes, which made their appearance sometime during the Triassic period. Marsupials first appear in the fossil record during the early Cretaceous period and apparently eventually replaced monotremes in many areas where both forms coexisted.

When marsupials first appeared, Pangaea was just beginning to break up into separate continents, so that marsupials (as well as monotremes) were distributed throughout the world. Placentals evolved after marsupials during the Cretaceous. They appeared first in North America and had just begun to expand their distributions to South America when Pangaea began to break up. They did not reach Australia before it became isolated from the other continents. Australia and nearby islands contain only monotremes and marsupials because placentals never colonized these lands.

Placentals are better competitors than either marsupials or monotremes and replaced these other forms of mammals wherever they occurred in the same area. They expanded their distributions into South America by way of the Isthmus of Panama and into Eurasia by way of a land bridge between eastern North America and western Europe. From Eurasia, placental mammals moved into Africa and evolved into the unique forms found there today.

31.60   How did the Ice Age affect the mammals of North America?

⚇   During the Pleistocene epoch, or the Ice Age, glaciers covered large parts of North America. The Ice Age began about 3 million years ago and ended only 10,000 years ago. This cold period profoundly affected all life forms. Two effects of the glaciers were: (1) such a great volume of water formed into glaciers that the level of the oceans was lowered, exposing previously submerged lands and providing migratory routes between continents; and (2) the glaciers occupied continents, reducing the amount of land available to terrestrial organisms.

Two areas of exposed land greatly affected the mammals of North America. The land bridge between Siberia and Alaska provided a migratory route for many mammals. Humans, elk, moose, and caribou entered North America over this bridge. Another land bridge permitted mammals to be exchanged between North and South America for the first time since the fragmentation of Pangaea. South America had been isolated from the other continents for so long that its animal populations had not been subjected to competition with other species. North American animals, on the other hand, had evolved under conditions of severe competition, because North America had been connected at many times with Eurasia. When a land bridge formed between North and South America, the North American animals competed successfully with the South American animals, causing most of the latter to become extinct. The only surviving mammals were those with no North American competitor, such as the monkey, anteater, and armadillo. North America acquired a few mammals from South America, including the opossum, armadillo, porcupine, and giant sloth.

Many large North American mammals became extinct during the Ice Age, although massive extinctions did not occur when glaciers advanced on the other continents. Two possible factors may have contributed to the extinction of these mammals: (1) humans may have overhunted them, and (2) habitable areas may have decreased in size to the point that they could not support such large mammals. Forced into smaller and smaller areas, where their populations were extremely reduced in number, the probability of extinction would have been greatly increased by hunting. Some of the large mammals that disappeared from North America at that time were the rhinoceros, mammoth, saber-toothed tiger, horse, and elephant. However, by this time populations of most of these large mammals had migrated to other continents, where their descendants remain today.

Answers to Objective Questions

31.1 *a*	**31.12** *d*	**31.22** *b*
31.2 *b*	**31.13** *a*	**31.23** *d*
31.3 *d*	**31.14** *b*	**31.24** *a*
31.4 *b*	**31.15** *c*	**31.25** *b*
31.5 *c*	**31.16** *c*	**31.26** *a*
31.6 millipede	**31.17** bony; Amphibia	**31.27** *c*
31.7 flight; flowering plants	**31.18** Carboniferous	**31.28** *a*
31.8 exoskeleton; walk; metamorphosis	**31.19** external; water; fish; larvae; caecilians; internally; damp cavities; larval	**31.29** *b*
31.9 tracheae; chitin		**31.30** *a*
31.11 *c*	**31.20** Urodela; Anura; Apoda	**31.31** *c*

31.32 scales; exoskeleton; waxy cuticle

31.33 water

31.34 internal; amnion; shell; seed

31.35 Permian; dry; Pangaea

31.36 Squamata; Chelonia; Crocodilia

31.39 *b*

31.40 *c*

31.41 *c*

31.42 *a*

31.43 amniotic; cleidoic; scales; feathers; keratin; wings

31.44 beak; gizzard

31.45 eye

31.46 air sacs; lungs; flight

31.48 *b*

31.49 *b*

31.50 *a*

31.51 *d*

31.52 *a*

31.53 *c*

31.54 hair; keratin

31.55 diaphragm

31.56 three; three; four; four; left heart; right heart

31.57 mother's circulatory system

31.58 Prototheria; Theria; orders

CHAPTER 32
Human Evolution

EVOLUTION OF PRIMATES*

32.1 Which of the following is considered to be a trend in primate evolution?

(*a*) Development of nonprehensile hands; (*b*) Development of monocular vision; (*c*) Elimination of the clavicle; (*d*) Decreased dependence on smell

32.2 Which primate group (or groups) existed during the first half of the Eocene epoch (53–38 million years ago)?

(*a*) Prosimians; (*b*) Prosimians and monkeys; (*c*) Prosimians, monkeys, and apes; (*d*) Prosimians, monkeys, apes, and hominids

32.3 Which of the following was the second group to appear in primate evolution, with fossil remains dated to the early Oligocene epoch (over 31 million years ago)?

(*a*) Prosimians; (*b*) Anthropoids; (*c*) Great apes; (*d*) Hominids

32.4 Which of these prosimians is now found only on the island of Madagascar?

(*a*) Loris; (*b*) Lemur; (*c*) Galago; (*d*) Bush baby

32.5 Which of the following is *not* an adaptation in prosimians for life in the trees (i.e., an arboreal existence)?

(*a*) Flat, sensitive pads at the ends of fingers and toes; (*b*) Forward-facing eyes; (*c*) Prehensile tails; (*d*) Flat nails on most digits rather than claws

32.6 Which taxonomic group includes both monkeys and humans?

(*a*) Prosimians; (*b*) Anthropoids; (*c*) Hominoids; (*d*) Hominids

32.7 Which of the following is true of New World monkeys?

(*a*) Most have prehensile tails; (*b*) Most have ischial callosities on their buttocks; (*c*) Includes langurs, guenons, and mandrills; (*d*) Forward and downward, rather than lateral, orientation of nostrils

32.8 Which of the following is *not* characteristic of apes?

(*a*) Movement in the trees by brachiation; (*b*) Movement on the ground by knuckle-walking; (*c*) Wrists that bend backward; (*d*) Highly mobile shoulder joints

32.9 Which of the following is a catarrhine primate?

(*a*) Humans; (*b*) Spider monkeys; (*c*) Squirrel monkeys; (*d*) Capuchins

32.10 Evidence from molecular biology, such as comparisons of DNA base-pair sequences in genes, indicates that hominids diverged from the African apes sometime between

(*a*) 500,000 and 1 million years ago. (*b*) 5 million and 10 million years ago. (*c*) 15 million and 20 million years ago. (*d*) 50 million and 60 million years ago.

32.11 The living members of the order Primates (or Primata) are generally placed in one of two suborders: _____, the prosimians; and _____, the monkeys, apes, and humans.

32.12 Primate evolution began roughly 65 million years ago, very early in the _____ era, when small, ground-dwelling, shrewlike _____ began to exploit food resources in the trees.

---

* Answers to Chapter 32 objective questions appear on page 231.

32.13 Fossil remains of the earliest known common ancestors of the African anthropoid primates come from sites dated to the early _____ epoch (roughly 31 million years ago) from the _____ depression of Egypt. Two primate genera from this site that are thought to be possible ancestors to modern anthropoids are _____ and _____.

32.14 One trend in primate evolution is the development of _____ hands and feet that can grasp and hold objects. Another trend is the movement of the eyes from the side of the head to the front, which produces _____ vision and _____ perception.

32.15 While monkeys move along the tops of branches, apes swing from grip to grip along the undersides of branches in a movement called _____. On the ground, African apes use a form of locomotion called _____.

32.16 Refer to Fig. 32.1, and identity the indicated anatomic structures of the monkey skeleton.

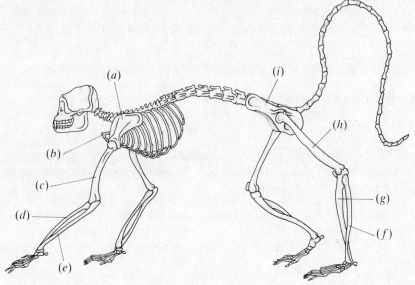

Fig. 32.1

32.17 Many anthropologists place the modern hominoids in three families: _____, the gibbons; _____, the great apes; and _____, the humans.

32.18 The closest living relatives to humans are the African great apes: *Pan troglodytes*, the common _____; *Pan paniscus*, the _____; and *Gorilla gorilla*, the gorilla. Molecular biologic studies indicate that chimpanzees and _____ are genetically more closely related to one another than either is to _____. However, anatomic evidence indicates that chimpanzees and _____ are most closely related.

32.19 Discuss the trends in primate evolution that began as adaptations for life in the trees.

🐚 Modern primates (members of order Primates) are typically placed in one of two suborders: Prosimii (prosimians such as lemurs, pottos, galagos, and others) and Anthropoidea (monkeys, apes, and humans). These diverse and complex mammals are the end products of evolutionary processes that began some 65 million years ago, when ground-dwelling, shrewlike insectivores began to climb toward the abundant stores of food in the trees. From that time to the present, so much of primate evolution has taken place in the trees in response to arboreal selection pressures that it can be said that virtually all major trends in primate evolution began as adaptations for life in the trees. These trends include

1. The development of prehensile (adapted for grasping and holding) hands and feet
2. An increase in the speed, flexibility, and coordination of limb movements
3. A tendency toward upright posture
4. A decreased dependence on smell and a related increased dependence on vision
5. A progressively larger brain, particularly expansion of the outer layer (cortex)
6. A rotation of the head downward relative to the spine

7. A decrease in litter size to typically a single birth per pregnancy

8. An increased life span, coupled with longer periods of childhood dependency

9. The development of a complex social life that involved an increasing proportion of learned behaviors

All these trends began as adaptations for life in the trees, improvements for arboreal life over what the ancestral insectivores had brought with them. Primate ancestors, evolved for life on the forest floor, had claws on their fingers and toes. These, together with relatively inflexible hands and feet, prevented them from grasping small branches and thus restricted them to the wide surfaces of trunks and large branches. Their freedom of movement was also limited by their vision: small eyes on the sides of the head gave them two separate, two-dimensional pictures that lacked depth.

During the Paleocene (65 to 53 million years ago) and early Eocene, a new primate evolved from the ancestral forms—the prosimians. These animals were much better adapted for arboreal life. Having developed long fingers and toes that ended in flat, sensitive pads and having replaced most claws with flat nails, the prosimians were capable of gripping and holding branches. They also had much-improved vision. The eyes had moved from the sides of the head to the front, producing an overlap in the brain of the visual fields from each eye. This overlap provided the three-dimensional depth perception that is essential for rapid and safe movement through the trees. Detail perception had also improved, and some prosimians had color vision.

The first clearly recognizable anthropoids in the primate fossil record were discovered in the Fayum depression of Egypt, and these fossils were radioactively dated to the early Oligocene (38 to 31 million years ago). It is not agreed what happened in anthropoid evolution during the next 10 million years, but it is certain that by 25 to 20 million years ago there were many forms of monkeys and hominoids.

Today, there are two types of monkeys: New World (platyrrhine, or flat-nosed) monkeys found in Central and South America and Old World (catarrhine, or downward-nosed) monkeys from Africa and Asia. Both groups, the products of millions of years of selection for arboreal living, are advanced over prosimians in all major areas of primate evolution. They have fully developed prehensile hands and feet, with the prosimian adaptations plus opposable thumbs and big toes, and delicate movement control of the five digits on each hand and foot. In addition, New World forms (but none of the Old World types) have prehensile tails. The brain, particularly the cortex, has greatly expanded in both forms, with a greater capacity for learning and for the control of rapid and precise movements.

Modern hominoids (members of superfamily Hominoidea) are typically placed in one of three families: Hylobatidae (gibbons); Pongidae (orangutans, gorillas, and chimpanzees); and Hominidae (humans). These families are thought to have originated in an ancestral line of apes (genus *Dryopithecus*) present in the early Miocene (25 to 20 million years ago). These Miocene apes differed from previous tree-dwelling primates in many aspects: new patterns and structures of teeth, major increases in brain size, and a much larger body modified to allow a radically new form of locomotion called *brachiation*. In this locomotion, the ape swings from grip to grip along the undersides of branches. Selection for brachiation changed the ape's arms, shoulders, and upper body to allow suspension in a semierect posture for long periods of time. The apes also developed highly mobile shoulder joints that permitted reaching in all directions.

These semierect Miocene apes produced the ancestral lineage from which the modern hominoids diverged. The estimates of when and how these divergences occurred vary greatly as a function of the techniques used (see Question 32.20), but it is now generally accepted that gibbons branched off first (sometime between 22 to 10 million years ago), then orangutans (sometime between 16 to 8 million years ago), then the African apes (between 10 to 5 million years ago). The final line to humans, the sequence of hominid evolution, is discussed in Questions 32.38 to 32.40.

32.20   Which living ape is the closest primate relative of humans?

⚫   It is generally accepted that the closest living primate relatives of humans are the three species of African great apes: common chimpanzees (*Pan troglodytes*), pygmy chimpanzees (*Pan paniscus*), and gorillas (*Gorilla gorilla*). The other great apes, the orangutans (*Pongo pygmaeus*) of southeastern Asia, are judged to be more distantly related. Although a consensus exists on the human–African ape relationship, considerable disagreement persists on questions of phylogeny. When did these different species diverge from common ancestors? Which of the African apes is most closely related to humans?

Much of the disagreement on phylogeny originates from a fundamental difference in research techniques. On one side are the "molecular" anthropologists, who investigate relationships among living species by examining the components of specific molecules (proteins, DNA) found in each of the species. On the other side are the "nonmolecular," more traditional anthropologists, who also study common features among species (living and extinct), but they concentrate on gross anatomic features, such as the size and shape of the jaw or brain.

Prior to the early 1960s, anthropology was nonmolecular and the phylogenetic picture was relatively simple. All the great apes were considered to be in one family (Pongidae), and the morphological evidence from the living and fossilized forms indicated that the members of this family had diverged from the hominid (human) lineage more than 15 million years ago. The problem remaining was finding the "missing link," the 15- to

10-million-year-old apelike creature that was the first hominid, and it seemed that this problem had been solved when fossils of apes were discovered in India and Pakistan that had lived 14 to 7 million years ago and had teeth that were more human than ape. These supposed first hominids were placed in the genus *Ramapithecus*.

In 1963, this clear picture began to disintegrate when the results of the first molecular study on primates were reported by Morris Goodman. Goodman had taken albumin, a blood plasma protein, from orangutans, gorillas, chimpanzees, and humans and subjected the samples to immunologic tests involving antibody-recognition responses. The results of these tests convinced Goodman that chimpanzees, gorillas, and humans have such similar albumin that they all belong in a single family and that orangutans are a distant relative.

The next major development in molecular anthropology came in 1967, when Vincent Sarich and Allan Wilson developed an interpretation of Goodman's results. Their interpretation, known as the "molecular clock," drastically changed the accepted time scale for hominoid (apes and humans) evolution. Accepting fossil evidence that the hominoid lineage began 30 million years ago when apes split from monkeys and assuming that the immunologic characteristics of hominoid albumins have changed at a constant rate since then, Sarich and Wilson were able, from current differences in albumin between apes and humans, to calculate that humans and African great apes had a common ancestor as recently as 5 million years ago. This surprising date, among other things, eliminated the possibility that *Ramapithecus* (living 14 to 7 million years ago) was the first hominid.

Many other molecular techniques have been used since 1967 to study both phylogenetic relationships and the molecular clock. These techniques include: comparing amino acid sequences in proteins; comparing base-pair sequences in nuclear and mitochondrial DNA; and DNA-DNA hybridization studies in which similarities between single-stranded pieces of DNA are determined from the strands' ability to bond with each other in the form of a hybrid double helix. With regard to the molecular clock, the results of studies vary but consistently show that the divergence between the African great apes and humans took place between 10 to 5 million years ago. On the question of relationships, there is now a body of molecular evidence showing not only that it is chimpanzees that are the closest primate relatives of humans, but further, that chimpanzees and humans are more closely related to each other than either is to gorillas.

While most nonmolecular anthropologists have come to accept that humans and the great apes branched off from one another between 10 to 5 million years ago, many of these same anthropologists have serious doubts about the closeness of the chimpanzee-human relationship. They argue that chimpanzees and gorillas share many anatomic features not found in humans, in particular, modifications of the forelimbs for knuckle-walking and a unique enamel structure on their molar teeth. Because it is very unlikely that chimpanzees and gorillas evolved these complex features independently, or that humans completely lost them in hominid evolution, these nonmolecular anthropologists still want humans placed in a unique family of their own (Hominidae) separate from their African-ape relatives.

EVOLUTION OF HUMANS

32.21   Which of the following is *not* an anatomic change from ape to *Homo sapiens*?

(*a*) From locking to nonlocking knee joints;   (*b*) From a long, thin pelvis to a bowl-like pelvis;   (*c*) From opposable to nonopposable big toes;   (*d*) From flat to arched feet

32.22   Which of the following was *not* an anatomic change in the evolution of the *Homo* line from australopithecine ancestors to *Homo erectus*?

(*a*) Decrease in the ratio of humerus to femur length;   (*b*) Modifications of the limbs for upright walking;   (*c*) Increase in sexual dimorphism;   (*d*) Increase in brain size from roughly 450 cm^3 to roughly 1000 cm^3

32.23   The first true hominids in the fossil record have been placed in the genus

(*a*) *Homo*.   (*b*) *Australopithecus*.   (*c*) *Dryopithecus*.   (*d*) *Aegyptopithecus*.

32.24   For roughly how long did genus *Homo* coexist in Africa with genus *Australopithecus*?

(*a*) 100,000 years;   (*b*) 250,000 years;   (*c*) 500,000 years;   (*d*) 1,000,000 years

32.25   Which hominid left the first clear evidence of human culture (pebbles chipped into tools) in sites roughly two million years old?

(*a*) *Homo sapiens neanderthalensis*;   (*b*) *Homo habilis*;   (*c*) *Homo erectus*;   (*d*) *Homo sapiens sapiens*

32.26   The earliest evidence of the use of fire by hominids is from a site in the Rift valley of Kenya, dated to be 1.4 million years old. The hominids using that fire were from the species

(*a*) *Homo sapiens*.   (*b*) *Homo habilis*.   (*c*) *Homo erectus*.   (*d*) *Australopithecus africanus*.

32.27 The Cro-Magnon people were

(*a*) *Homo sapiens sapiens.*   (*b*) *Homo sapiens neanderthalensis.*   (*c*) *Homo erectus.*   (*d*) *Homo habilis.*

32.28 Which member of the genus *Homo* has (had) the largest brain (a cranial capacity ranging from 1300–1750 cm^3)?

(*a*) *Homo habilis*;   (*b*) *Homo erectus*;   (*c*) *Homo sapiens neanderthalensis*;   (*d*) *Homo sapiens sapiens*

32.29 Roughly how many years ago did the first *Homo sapiens* appear in the fossil record?

(*a*) 1.5 million years ago;   (*b*) 750,000 years ago;   (*c*) 300,000 years ago;   (*d*) 40,000 years ago

32.30 The first australopithecines to appear in the fossil record (roughly _____ million years ago) have been placed in the species _____. One specimen from this species was named _____, after a song by the Beatles. Most anthropologists believe this species was the ancestor to the *Homo* line, but some think it was the later australopithecine, _____. There were also two more robust australopithecines: _____ and _____.

32.31 Indicate the taxonomy of modern humans by filling in the indicated categories in the right column of Table 32.1.

TABLE 32.1 Taxonomy of Modern Humans

taxonomic category	category that includes humans
Kingdom	Animalia
Phylum	Chordata
Subphylum	Vertebrata
Class	Mammalia
Order	(*a*) _____
Suborder	(*b*) _____
Superfamily	(*c*) _____
Family	(*d*) _____
Genus	(*e*) _____
Species	(*f*) _____

32.32 Both hominids and baboons had arboreal ancestors but now live on the ground. While hominids adapted to terrestrial living with a form of locomotion called _____, baboons retained the form of locomotion used by their ancestors that is called _____.

32.33 Refer to Fig. 32.2, and identify the indicated structures in the upper jaws of modern gorillas and modern humans.

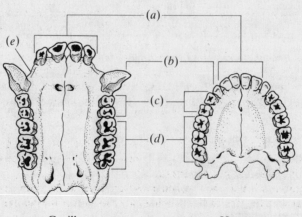

Gorilla   Human   **Fig. 32.2**

32.34 The two extinct species in the genus *Homo* are: _____ and _____. One of these species, _____, now includes the fossils known as Java man and Peking man, which were originally placed in the genus *Pithecanthropus*.

32.35 The total accumulation of human achievements not directly determined by genes, such as language and tool making, is called _____. For the last two million years these achievements were part of a lifestyle in which males hunted big game and females cared for the young and collected seeds, fruits, and small animals. This division of labor is called the _____ lifestyle.

32.36 The anthropologists Louis, Mary, and Richard _____ discovered many important hominid fossils in the _____ Gorge in the _____ Valley of Tanzania.

32.37 While the brain size (cranial capacity) of modern chimpanzees ranges from _____ cm^3 to _____ cm^3, the range for australopithecines was _____ cm^3 to _____ cm^3. In the *Homo* line, brain size for *Homo habilis* was from _____ cm^3 to _____ cm^3, for *Homo erectus* it was from _____ cm^3 to _____ cm^3, and for modern humans (*Homo sapiens sapiens*) the range is _____ cm^3 to _____ cm^3.

32.38 What were the selection pressures that produced bipedal locomotion in hominids?

🐌 Bipedal locomotion (walking upright on two legs) is the most important indicator that a primate is in the family Hominidae (humans). This type of locomotion evolved at some time between the last common ancestor of the African great apes and humans (some 10 to 5 million years ago; see Question 32.20) and the appearance in the fossil record of the first bipedal primate (some 3.75 million years ago). This evolution occurred in Africa at a time when tropical rain forests were rapidly decreasing and semierect apes descended from the trees and migrated onto the plains. The major anatomic changes that occurred when semierect, quadrupedal apes evolved into bipedal hominids can be seen by comparing the skeletons of modern humans and modern gorillas.

The human skeleton is a balanced vertical frame that transmits the weight of the body to flexible, platformlike feet. The skull is round and balanced on top of a vertical column of neck vertebrae. The chest is flattened, and the bones of the spine are interlocked to form a flexible rod that curves backward at the base of the spine, where the spinal column is balanced by a broad, bowl-like pelvis. The gorilla pelvis is long and thin, so the weight is thrown forward onto the knuckles. The gorilla head is elongated with a protruding face, and while the human skull is attached to the spine at its base, the gorilla head is attached at the rear of the skull. While gorilla arms are longer than the legs, human arms are shorter than the legs. Gorilla legs are bent and far apart, whereas human legs are straight and close together, with knee joints that lock into place in the upright position. The gorilla foot is flat with long toes; the big toe can be moved in opposition to the other toes to permit grasping and holding. The human foot is arched and flexible with short toes, and the big toe is not opposable.

The first bipedal primates were more apelike than human, but they clearly had bipedal posture and locomotion and are thus considered to be the first hominids. They were discovered in 1974 in the Hadar region of Ethiopia by Donald C. Johanson, who named one almost complete skeleton Lucy, after the Beatles' song, "Lucy in the Sky with Diamonds." Remains of more of these first hominids, now known as *Australopithecus afarensis*, were subsequently discovered in Laetoli, Tanzania, along with a fossilized set of footprints. These "Laetoli footprints," now considered the earliest evidence of bipedalism, have been dated to 3.75 million years ago. Also clearly showing that *A. afarensis* was bipedal is its bowl-like pelvis, far different from the long, thin ape pelvis and comparable to the modern human pelvis.

It was once generally accepted that the major selection pressure that produced the change from ape to the bipedal *A. afarensis* was a dependence on the use of tools; i.e., because the ability to use tools provided such an advantage in hunting of prey and protection from predators, natural selection favored an upright posture that freed the hands for the manufacture and manipulation of tools. However, current evidence shows that the first use of tools by hominids did not come until almost two million years later. The earliest known tools are the chipped-pebble tools found with the remains of *Homo habilis* and dated to two million years ago.

If it was not tool use that produced bipedalism, then what selection pressures were operating? There are currently three major hypotheses, and each may in part be correct. The first is the scavenger hypothesis, which suggests that bipedalism evolved when these first hominids began to follow migrating herds of ungulates and scavenged by taking the bone marrow and fat from carcasses left by lions and other predators. It is reasoned that the slow, awkward, but energy-efficient bipedal gait would have allowed them to carry their young while following the herds and searching for carcasses.

The second hypothesis is that the first hominids were vegetarians, eating a diet comparable to that of their ape ancestors, and that with the forests disappearing they had to search extensive areas for their widely dispersed food. Again, the bipedal gait would have allowed them to slowly and awkwardly search great distances.

The third hypothesis is that bipedalism allowed social bonding; with the hands freed from the ground, the males could carry food to specific locations where their mates remained with the young.

32.39 Trace the sequence of stages in the evolution of hominids.

    🐚 In the early 1980s, it was generally accepted that the human family tree had two branches (Fig. 32.3a): an australopithecine sequence, from *Australopithecus afarensis* to *A. africanus* to *A. robustus* to *A. boisei*; and a *Homo* sequence from *A. afarensis* to *Homo habilis* to *H. erectus* to *H. sapiens*. However, the 1985 discovery of a hominid fossil very different from previous fossils has convinced many anthropologists that the human tree has three branches (Fig. 32.3b): the *Homo* branch is preserved, but there are now two australopithecine branches (*A. afarensis* to *A. africanus* to *A. robustus*; and *A. afarensis* to *A. boisei*).

    The two-branch tree was proposed in 1979 by the discoverer of *A. afarensis*, Donald C. Johanson, and his colleague Timothy White. They suggested that two bipedal hominid lines branched off from a common ancestor (*A. afarensis*) about three million years ago. One line, the australopithecines, showed a progressive increase in robustness: larger bodies; a shortening of the face but with increasingly massive jaws and facial structures; increasingly larger and flatter cheek teeth (premolars and molars; see Question 32.33), with a corresponding decrease in the size of the front teeth (canines and incisors); and some increase in brain size (from the 350–450 cm^3 of *A. afarensis* to over 500 cm^3). This robust line began in Africa with *A. africanus* (living roughly 2.8 to 2 million years ago), which was about the same size as *A. afarensis* (3–3½ feet tall) but less apelike and more gracile (thin). Next came *A. robustus*, which lived in southern Africa from roughly 2.3 to 1.8 million years ago and showed marked increases in robustness over *A. africanus* in body, face, jaws, and teeth. Finally, the last and most robust form, *A. boisei*, lived in eastern Africa from roughly 1.8 to 1 million years ago.

    The second branch of the Johanson-White model, the *Homo* line, also shows a shortening of the face, but here there is a marked decrease in the size of both the cheek teeth and front teeth. There is also a massive increase in brain size. This line begins with a transition from *A. afarensis* to *H. habilis* ("handy man"), the first hominid to make and use tools, who lived in Africa from roughly 2 to 1.5 million years ago. They had humanlike teeth and a much larger brain than any australopithecine (600–800 cm^3). It had been thought that the size of *H. habilis* was somewhere between *A. afarensis* and *H. erectus*, but the discovery in 1986 of most of an *H. habilis* skeleton (from 1.8 million years ago) has shown anthropologists that *H. habilis* was actually the same size as *A. afarensis* (3–3½ feet tall) and had such apelike features as long arms that dangled below the knees.

    In the 200,000 years from this *H. habilis* skeleton to the first *H. erectus* (1.6 million years ago), there was a remarkable change. *H. erectus* (from 1.6 to 300,000 years ago) was much larger than *H. habilis* in body size (5 to 6 feet tall) and brain size (800–1200 cm^3). They had small human teeth, but a thick and massive skull with a low forehead. They were the first hominids to use fire (at least 1.4 million years ago). They were also the first to leave Africa, and their fossilized remains have been found throughout Europe and Asia.

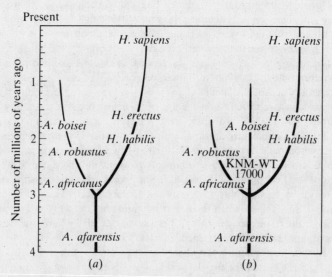

Fig. 32.3. Two-branch (a) versus three-branch (b) model of the human family tree. KNM-WT 17000 is the new boisei fossil discovered in 1985.

Finally, roughly 300,000 years ago, the first of our own species (*H. sapiens*) appeared. They had larger brains than *H. erectus* (1200–1400 cm^3), in a rounder and more vaulted skull that projected outward in the rear. They had reduced humanlike teeth but had so many other primitive jaw and skull features that they are considered to be "archaic" *H. sapiens*. One of these archaic forms, *H. sapiens neanderthalensis*, lived in Europe and the Near East from 100,000 to 35,000 years ago and may have been either an ancestor to modern humans or a side branch to extinction. They were more robust than modern humans, with larger limb bones, larger front teeth, heavy brow ridges, and a low forehead, but they had slightly larger brains than modern humans (1300–1750 cm^3 versus 1200–1600 cm^3).

As a result of molecular biologic surveys of modern populations, many anthropologists currently think that fully modern humans (*H. sapiens sapiens*) first appeared as a single population in Africa some 200,000 years ago and then migrated outward to the rest of the world some 100,000 years ago. By 35,000 years ago, these people, now known to us as Cro-Magnons, had completely replaced Neanderthals and all other archaic *H. sapiens*.

The Johanson-White tree with its australopithecine and *Homo* branches was generally accepted until the discovery in Northern Kenya in 1985 by Alan Walker of a completely new type of hominid skull (known by its museum number: KNW-WT 17000). This skull, dated to about 2.5 million years ago, is the most robust form ever found; it has the massive teeth and jaws of *A. boisei*, combined with a very primitive apelike brain. This indicates that the *A. boisei* form was not the last australopithecine to evolve (as indicated in the two-branch model), but rather one of the first. Walker's discovery has led many anthropologists to conclude that the human family tree requires a third branch, from *A. afarensis* directly to *A. boisei* (see Fig. 32.3*b*).

32.40 What is the relationship, in human evolution, between cultural and biologic evolution?

🐚 Culture is the total accumulation of human achievements, such as language and tool making, not directly determined by genes, that is passed from generation to generation by teaching and observation. The first real evidence of culture in hominid evolution is the chipped-pebble tools found with *H. habilis* remains and dated to two million years ago. However, it is most likely that elements of culture, such as nonpreservable wooden tools or a simple language of sounds and gestures, were present long before that time. We find elements of "culture" today in the behavior of such modern apes as the chimpanzees.

From the first clear appearance of human culture two million years ago to the present, there has been a continual and increasingly rapid cultural evolution brought about by trial-and-error modifications of cultural techniques. Anthropologists have divided cultural evolution into three major stages: the hunter-gatherer stage; the agricultural revolution; and the industrial revolution.

Almost all human biologic evolution occurred under hunter-gatherer conditions. All humans had this lifestyle until about 10,000 years ago, and isolated populations still exist this way today. In this lifestyle, males hunt big game and females stay in a home location where they care for the young and gather nuts, seeds, fruit, and small animals. Under this lifestyle, tool use and cooperative hunting became the strong selection pressures on biologic evolution; there was a continuous feedback between biologic and cultural changes. Thus, for example, the remarkable increase in body and brain size from *H. habilis* (3–3$\frac{1}{2}$ ft in height; 600–800 cm^3 brain) to *H. erectus* (5–6 ft in height; 800–1200 cm^3 brain) is thought to be due to an interaction between (1) the consumption of more and more meat, with selection favoring progressively larger bodies for killing and dragging home the meat, and (2) the need for better tools for butchering and preparing this meat, with selection favoring larger and more intelligent brains.

Rapid feedback between cultural and biologic evolution continued to the second major stage in cultural evolution: the agricultural revolution. This began about 10,000 years ago in the Middle East, when hunter-gatherer nomads learned to plant and raise crops and to domesticate and herd animals. Agriculture led to permanent settlements and supported a great increase in human population size. From the agricultural revolution through the third major stage of cultural evolution—the industrial revolution in late 18th century England, with its first uses of power-driven machinery for mass production—to the present, human populations have been more and more protected from such basic forces of natural selection as starvation, sickness, and temperature extremes. Thus, while biologic evolution has continued during the past 10,000 years, it has been at a much slower pace than cultural evolution.

Answers to Objective Questions

32.1 *d*	**32.7** *a*	**32.13** Oligocene; Fayum; *Aegyptopithecus*; *Propliopithecus*
32.2 *a*	**32.8** *c*	
32.3 *b*	**32.9** *a*	
32.4 *b*	**32.10** *b*	**32.14** prehensile; binocular; depth
32.5 *c*	**32.11** Prosimii; Anthropoidea	**32.15** brachiation; knuckle-walking
32.6 *b*	**32.12** Cenozoic; insectivores	

32.16 (*a*) shoulder blade (scapula);
(*b*) collarbone (clavicle);
(*c*) humerus; (*d*) radius;
(*e*) ulna; (*f*) fibula; (*g*) tibia;
(*h*) femur; (*i*) pelvic bone
32.17 Hylobatidae; Pongidae;
Hominidae
32.18 chimpanzee; pygmy
chimpanzee; humans;
gorillas; gorillas
32.21 *a*
32.22 *c*
32.23 *b*
32.24 *d*

32.25 *b*
32.26 *c*
32.27 *a*
32.28 *c*
32.29 *c*
32.30 3.75; *Australopithecus
afarensis*; Lucy;
Australopithecus africanus;
Australopithecus robustus;
Australopithecus boisei
32.31 (*a*) Primates;
(*b*) Anthropoidea;
(*c*) Hominoidea;
(*d*) Hominidae; (*e*) *Homo*;

(*f*) *sapiens*
32.32 bipedalism;
quadrupedalism
32.33 (*a*) incisors; (*b*) canines;
(*c*) premolars; (*d*) molars;
(*e*) diastema
32.34 *Homo habilis*; *Homo erectus*;
Homo erectus
32.35 culture; hunter-gatherer
32.36 Leakey; Olduvai; Rift
32.37 350, 450; 350, 550; 600, 800;
800, 1200; 1200, 1600

CHAPTER 33

Structure of a Plant

PLANT TISSUES*

33.1   Primary tissues of a plant

(*a*) add to the length of roots and shoots.   (*b*) add to the diameter of existing roots and shoots.
(*c*) are only in the embryo.   (*d*) are only in the seedling.

33.2   Secondary tissues of a plant

(*a*) add to the length of roots and shoots.   (*b*) add to the diameter of existing roots and shoots.
(*c*) are only in the embryo.   (*d*) are only in the seedling.

33.3   The most common type of ground tissue is

(*a*) epidermis.   (*b*) collenchyma.   (*c*) sclerenchyma.   (*d*) parenchyma.

33.4   Mature parenchyma cells take part in regeneration of other plant parts, because they

(*a*) are centrally located in the heartwood.   (*b*) are the only mature cells with nuclei.   (*c*) retain their
ability to divide and differentiate.   (*d*) have no cell walls.

33.5   Most metabolism of a plant is carried out by the

(*a*) epidermis.   (*b*) collenchyma tissues.   (*c*) sclerenchyma tissues.   (*d*) parenchyma tissues.

33.6   Tissues that form long, tough strands, as in the leaf stalks of celery, are

(*a*) epidermis.   (*b*) collenchyma.   (*c*) sclerenchyma.   (*d*) parenchyma.

33.7   Lignin is a component of the secondary cell walls of

(*a*) epidermis.   (*b*) collenchyma.   (*c*) sclerenchyma.   (*d*) parenchyma.

33.8   Which of the following cell types has the thinnest walls?

(*a*) Epidermis;   (*b*) Collenchyma;   (*c*) Sclerenchyma;   (*d*) Parenchyma

33.9   Which of the following cells is often dead when functioning?

(*a*) Epidermis;   (*b*) Collenchyma;   (*c*) Sclerenchyma;   (*d*) Parenchyma

33.10   Which of the following tissues is composed of dead cells?

(*a*) Ground;   (*b*) Xylem;   (*c*) Phloem;   (*d*) Epidermis

33.11   Which of the following tissues is composed of dead cells?

(*a*) Periderm;   (*b*) Collenchyma;   (*c*) Parenchyma;   (*d*) Lateral meristem

33.12   The primary plant body is covered with a layer of cells, the

(*a*) epidermis.   (*b*) periderm.   (*c*) ground tissue.   (*d*) cuticle.

33.13   Root hairs are formed from extensions of the

(*a*) ground tissue.   (*b*) periderm.   (*c*) cuticle.   (*d*) epidermis.

* Answers to Chapter 33 objective questions appear on page 240.

33.14 The function of a root hair is to

(*a*) hold ions by attractions of opposite charges. (*b*) produce air pockets for gas exchange. (*c*) attract symbiotic microorganisms. (*d*) increase the surface area for absorption.

33.15 Dead outer cells of a stem are called

(*a*) epidermis. (*b*) lateral collenchyma. (*c*) cork cells. (*d*) sclerenchyma.

33.16 Dividing cells not yet committed to becoming a particular cell type are

(*a*) ground cells. (*b*) epidermal cells. (*c*) periderm cells. (*d*) meristem cells.

33.17 Primary growth involves activity of the

(*a*) vascular cambium. (*b*) apical meristem. (*c*) cork cambium. (*d*) lateral meristem.

33.18 Secondary growth involves activity of the
(*a*) root tips. (*b*) shoot tips. (*c*) apical meristem. (*d*) lateral meristem.

33.19 Some plant cells have two cell walls: a _____ cell wall that is adjacent to the plasma membrane and a _____ cell wall that forms the outer boundary. The cytoplasms of adjacent cells are connected by _____.

33.20 The three major types of plant tissues are: _____ tissue, which transports fluids; _____ tissue; and _____ tissue, which forms the outer protective covering.

33.21 The three types of ground cells are: _____, which has thin primary walls; _____, which has unevenly thickened primary walls and usually lacks secondary walls; and _____, which has thick secondary walls strengthened with lignin.

33.22 Young stems are supported by a cylinder of _____ cells just beneath their surfaces. Such cells, without lignin or secondary walls, provide support without restricting growth.

33.23 Photosynthesis takes place in the _____ cells of the _____. Other cells of this type, but without chloroplasts, are used mainly in food and water _____.

33.24 Linen and rope are made from long, tapered plant cells—the fiber type of _____ cell. Nutshells and seed coats contain shorter, irregularly shaped cells—the sclereid type of _____ cell.

33.25 The flesh of most fruit is composed of _____ cells.

33.26 Wood is composed mainly of _____ tissue.

33.27 Water and dissolved minerals are transported through a plant by its _____, which has two main types of elongated cells: _____ and _____. Most gymnosperms and primitive angiosperms have only _____, which probably evolved first.

33.28 Sugars are transported through a plant by its _____, of which the main type of cell is a _____ in an angiosperm and a _____ in a fern or gymnosperm.

33.29 In most angiosperms, sugar solutions are transported through the vascular tissues and move from one cell to the next through pores in _____, which are structures formed of _____.

33.30 Fluid moves from tracheid cell to tracheid cell mainly through pits which are formed from thinner regions of the _____, where only the full _____ is present. The end walls of vessel elements are perforated for direct and more efficient flow of water.

33.31 Because the secondary walls of tracheids are hardened with _____, they function in _____ of the plant as well as in fluid transport.

33.32 Mature phloem cells in an angiosperm have active cytoplasm but no functional nucleus. Enzymes that facilitate metabolism in these cells are assembled according to instructions in the DNA of _____, which are a specialized form of _____ cells connected to the phloem cells by _____.

33.33 The surface of a primary plant body is covered with a cellular layer called the _____ and a noncellular layer called the _____. The noncellular layer, formed of a fatty substance called _____, is secreted by the _____. It protects against water loss and invasion by microorganisms.

33.34 _____ replaces _____ as the outer cellular layer of plants in which roots and stems have undergone secondary growth. Composed in part of dead cells known as _____, it forms part of the bark.

33.35 Apical meristem occurs at the tips of _____ and _____. New tissues of the _____ plant body originate in the apical meristems. By contrast, _____ meristem, found in other areas of the plant, is responsible for new tissues of the _____ plant body.

33.36 Apical meristem subdivides into three meristematic areas: the outermost protoderm, which forms the _____; the procambium, which is interior to the protoderm and forms the _____; and the remainder, called ground meristem, which produces parenchymal tissue called the _____ if located at the center of the stem and _____ if located between the epidermis and the vascular tissue.

33.37 Of the lateral meristem, the cork cambium forms _____ and _____, while the vascular cambium forms _____.

33.38 What is the ground tissue of a plant?

⚪   Most of the primary plant body is ground tissue. It is all the permanent (i.e., not meristematic) tissue that is not dermal or vascular. Ground tissue is made of three types of cells: parenchyma, collenchyma, and sclerenchyma.

Parenchyma cells are the most abundant and least specialized of plant cells. They are characterized by very thin primary walls and no secondary walls. Unlike other permanent tissue, parenchyma cells retain their ability to divide and thus play an important role in providing new cells for healing wounds and regenerating lost parts. Parenchyma cells carry out most of the plant's metabolism—photosynthesis, conversion of glucose to other monomers, synthesis of polymers, and storage of starch. Leaves, fruits, and storage areas of roots are mostly parenchyma cells.

Collenchyma cells are characterized by strong, pliable primary walls, unevenly thickened and strengthened with pectin. They provide support for growing stems and for leaves and floral parts. Because of their flexibility, they elongate with growing parts and so provide support without restraining growth. Collenchyma tissue is found in strands or cylinders just beneath the epidermis of young stems and leaf stalks, as well as along the veins of leaves. The strings in celery stalks, for example, are collenchyma cells.

Sclerenchyma cells have thick secondary walls impregnated with lignin. Stronger and more rigid than collenchyma cells, they provide support to tissues that are no longer growing. Most sclerenchyma cells are dead at maturity; only their remaining secondary cell walls function in support. There are two types of sclerenchyma cells: fibers and sclereids. A fiber is an elongated strand with a central cavity; it usually occurs in a bundle with many others. Fibers give support to such tissues as xylem and phloem, and are used to make rope, string, canvas, and linen. Sclereids are irregular in shape, often branched, and of very hard material. They give strength to nutshells and seed coats, as well as a gritty texture to pears.

33.39 What determines the type of dermal tissue in a stem?

⚪   There are two types of dermal tissue—epidermis and periderm. Epidermis covers the primary plant body, and periderm covers the secondary plant body.

The epidermis is sloughed off and replaced by periderm when secondary growth increases the girth of a stem. Periderm, which forms the outer layer of bark (external to the phloem), is composed of an outer layer of cork, a layer of cork cambium, and, sometimes, an inner layer of phelloderm. The cork cambium produces the cork cells—box-shaped, waterproof cells that, when dead, protect the living tissues of the stem against injury.

33.40 Where are the meristematic tissues of a woody angiosperm?

⚪   A woody angiosperm has three kinds of meristematic tissue: apical meristems, vascular cambium, and cork cambium.

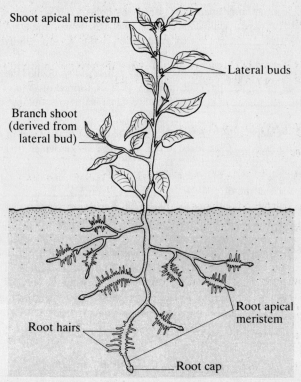

Fig. 33.1. Apical meristematic tissues of an angiosperm. Apical meristem occurs at the tips of shoots and roots. Small pieces of meristem remain in the lateral buds as the shoot, with its meristem, elongates. These bud meristems form lateral branches and flowers.

Apical meristems are dome-shaped regions at the tips of shoots and roots (Fig. 33.1). They give rise to stems, leaves, and new buds (which contain small pieces of meristem that form either branches or flowers). Part of each apical meristem remains undifferentiated, and the rest develops into the three primary meristems: protoderm, which forms epidermis; procambium, which forms primary xylem and phloem; and ground meristem, which forms such ground tissues as the pith and cortex of the stem.

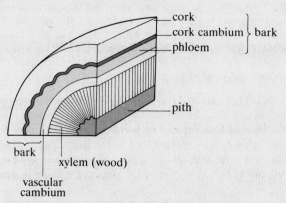

Fig. 33.2. Meristematic tissues of secondary growth. The vascular cambium gives rise to secondary xylem and phloem, and the cork cambium gives rise to cork cells, which form the outer layer of bark.

The vascular cambium forms secondary xylem and phloem. It is an area of actively dividing cells between the xylem and phloem of the stem and root. The cork cambium, a layer of meristem between the phloem and outer bark, adds new cork cells to the bark. A cross section of a stem, showing both vascular and cork cambium, is diagramed in Fig. 33.2.

Lateral roots are formed of parenchymal cells rather than meristem. These cells form a layer, called the *pericycle*, between the endodermis and the vascular tissues of the root.

PRIMARY SHOOT AND ROOT SYSTEMS

33.41   Leaves are attached to the stem at

(*a*) nodes.   (*b*) internodes.   (*c*) auxiliary meristems.   (*d*) apical meristems.

33.42   Buds that develop into lateral branches or flowers form only at

(*a*) nodes.   (*b*) internodes.   (*c*) auxiliary meristems.   (*d*) apical meristems.

33.43   The age of a twig can be determined by counting its

(*a*) nodes.   (*b*) internodes.   (*c*) bud scale scars.   (*d*) lenticels.

33.44   Palisade mesophyll and spongy mesophyll tissues of a leaf are made of

(*a*) dermal cells.   (*b*) collenchymal cells.   (*c*) sclerenchymal cells.   (*d*) parenchymal cells.

33.45   Both the palisade and spongy mesophylls of a leaf function to

(*a*) transport water.   (*b*) transport sugar.   (*c*) synthesize sugar.   (*d*) protect against water loss.

33.46   The function of a root cap is to

(*a*) produce embryonic cells.   (*b*) protect the root apical meristem from damage.   (*c*) absorb water.   (*d*) absorb minerals.

33.47   The tissue in the root that absorbs water and minerals is

(*a*) epidermis.   (*b*) parenchyma.   (*c*) collenchyma.   (*d*) sclerenchyma.

33.48   Movement of water and minerals into the vascular column of a root is controlled by the

(*a*) stomata.   (*b*) spongy mesophyll cells.   (*c*) vascular cambium.   (*d*) endodermis.

33.49   The pericycle, which gives rise to lateral roots, consists of

(*a*) epithelial cells.   (*b*) meristematic cells.   (*c*) parenchymal cells.   (*d*) endodermal cells.

33.50   The pith and cortex of a stem are formed of

(*a*) ground tissue.   (*b*) dermal tissue.   (*c*) vascular tissue.   (*d*) meristematic tissue.

33.51   The cortex of a root functions primarily in

(*a*) water absorption.   (*b*) mineral absorption.   (*c*) food storage.   (*d*) monomer conversions.

33.52   Refer to Fig. 33.3, and identify the indicated structures in the diagrams of a dicot and a monocot stem.

33.53   A dicot leaf typically has two parts: a broad _____ and a stalklike _____ attached to the stem. A simple leaf has only one _____. A monocot leaf typically has just one part: the _____.

33.54   Gases move into and out of a leaf through small pores, usually on the underside of the leaf, called _____. The size of the opening is controlled by specialized epidermal cells known as _____ cells, which swell to open the pores and become flaccid to close the pores.

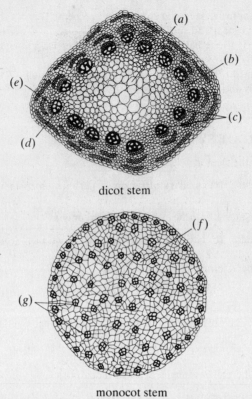

dicot stem

monocot stem   **Fig. 33.3**

33.55   Refer to Fig. 33.4, and identify the indicated parts in the diagram of a leaf.

33.56   Plants that live for less than one year are _____; plants that live two years are _____;
and plants that live many years are _____. Plants that survive all seasons of the year but are without
leaves during one season are called _____. Two conditions that cause such plants to lose all their
leaves are _____ and _____. Plants that always have some leaves are called

_____.

33.57   A primary root and its lateral branches are a _____ root system. The primary root is short-lived in
monocots; in its place, numerous _____ roots form. These roots and their branches form a
_____ root system, with roots of similar diameter. A carrot has a _____ root system;
corn has a _____ root system.

33.58   Endodermal cells of the root control the movement of water and minerals from the cortex to the vascular
column. They do this by having some of their walls impregnated with waxy coats, called _____, that
force fluid to move into the endodermal cells.

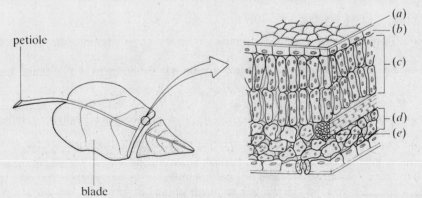

petiole

blade

Fig. 33.4

33.59 What is the function of a guard cell?

🐚 A guard cell is a modified epidermal cell that functions in the exchange of gases between the interior and exterior of a leaf. A pair of guard cells forms a small opening, or *stoma*, through which oxygen and water vapor leave and carbon dioxide enters a leaf. Each guard cell has a thicker cell wall next to the opening. When both cells take up water, turgor pressure causes the thinner walls away from the opening to stretch and the thicker walls next to the opening to bend, thereby enlarging the space between the two guard cells. The opening disappears when the guard cells lose water, become flaccid, and lie close to each other. Guard cells take up or lose water in response to changes in light, humidity, and concentrations of carbon dioxide within the leaf.

33.60 Trace the path taken by water as it moves from the soil to the xylem.

🐚 Water enters a root through an epidermal cell, usually a cellular extension called a root hair. It then moves inside cell walls and between cells of the cortex to the endodermal cells, where it is channeled through the plasma membranes and into the cytoplasm. Waxy deposits, called Casparian strips, line all the walls of endodermal cells except those facing the cortex and the pericycle (Fig. 33.5), thus forcing water into the endodermal cells. Plasma membranes of endodermal cells control which materials in the water enter the xylem. Water then moves out of the endodermal cells, through the thin layer of pericycle, and into the xylem.

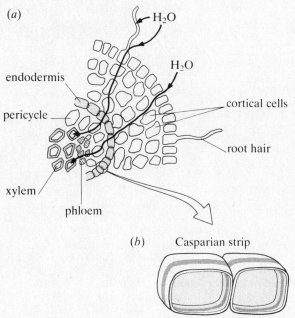

Fig. 33.5. Pathway of water into the root. (*a*) Water moves between cortical cells of the root and along the inner sides of their walls to the endodermis, where it is channeled by Casparian strips into the cytoplasm of these cells. (*b*) Casparian strips are waxy coatings on all walls of endodermal cells except those facing the cortex and the pericycle.

SECONDARY GROWTH

33.61 Plants with little or no secondary growth are

(*a*) dicots. (*b*) herbaceous. (*c*) deciduous. (*d*) evergreen.

33.62 The narrow band of meristematic tissue between the xylem and phloem is the

(*a*) pith meristem. (*b*) cortex meristem. (*c*) cork cambium. (*d*) vascular cambium.

33.63 Meristematic tissue that arises within the cortex is the

(*a*) pith meristem. (*b*) cortex cambium. (*c*) cork cambium. (*d*) vascular cambium.

33.64 One cannot age a tree by its rings if that tree is located in which of the following forests?

(*a*) Tropical deciduous;   (*b*) Tropical evergreen;   (*c*) Temperate deciduous;   (*d*) Temperate evergreen

35.65 Secondary xylem forms on the _____ face, and secondary phloem on the _____ face, of the vascular cambium.

33.66 Tree rings form when early wood alternates with late wood. The xylem cells of early wood, formed during early spring, have _____ diameters and _____ walls than the xylem cells of late wood, formed during summer.

33.67 Refer to Fig. 33.6, and identify the indicated structures in the diagram of a cross section of a tree trunk.

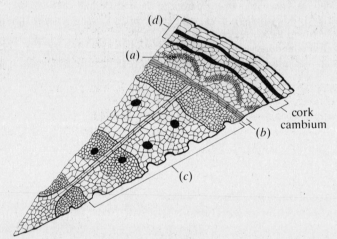

Fig. 33.6

33.68 The older, resin-clogged secondary xylem in the center of a tree trunk is the _____. The younger, outer secondary xylem that still conducts water is the _____.

33.69 Every 50 years, for 200 years, a nail was pounded into a tree, to the same depth and at exactly 1 m above the soil surface. What will be the pattern of the four nails on the tree?

☞   All four nails will be at the same height—1 m—above ground (assuming the ground level has not changed), because a tree grows vertically by adding new cells to the tips of its shoot. The four nails will be embedded at different depths, however, because a tree increases in girth every year. The nails will be embedded to depths proportional to the time they have been in the tree.

33.70 Why is wood made of xylem and not of phloem?

☞   The vascular cambium is a continuous cylinder of meristematic tissue between the xylem and phloem of a tree. It forms secondary xylem on its inner face and secondary phloem on its outer face. The strong, rigid walls of older xylem remain intact, year after year, as new xylem forms around them. The weaker walls of phloem cells, by contrast, collapse under the pressure of an expanding stem. Older, collapsed phloem cells form a thin, compressed layer within the bark that splits and is periodically sloughed off. Only the new phloem cells persist, as a layer of living cells in the inner bark, in the stem of a tree. The barkless stem, or wood, consists of annual xylem, but not phloem, rings.

Answers to Objective Questions

33.1 *a*	**33.9** *c*	**33.17** *b*
33.2 *b*	**33.10** *b*	**33.18** *d*
33.3 *d*	**33.11** *a*	**33.19** secondary; primary;
33.4 *c*	**33.12** *a*	plasmodesmata
33.5 *d*	**33.13** *d*	**33.20** vascular; ground; dermal
33.6 *b*	**33.14** *d*	**33.21** parenchyma; collenchyma;
33.7 *c*	**33.15** *c*	sclerenchyma
33.8 *d*	**33.16** *d*	**33.22** collenchyma

33.23 parenchyma; leaf; storage

33.24 sclerenchyma; sclerenchyma

33.25 parenchyma

33.26 vascular (or xylem)

33.27 xylem; tracheids; vessel elements; tracheids

33.28 phloem; sieve-tube element; sieve cell

33.29 sieve plates; plasmodesmata

33.30 secondary wall; primary wall

33.31 lignin; support

33.32 companion cells; parenchyma; plasmodesmata

33.33 epidermis; cuticle; cutin; epidermis

33.34 periderm; epidermis; cork cells

33.35 shoots; roots; primary; lateral; secondary

33.36 epidermis; primary vascular tissue; pith; cortex

33.37 cork cells; phelloderm; secondary vascular tissues

33.41 *a*

33.42 *a*

33.43 *c*

33.44 *d*

33.45 *c*

33.46 *b*

33.47 *a*

33.48 *d*

33.49 *c*

33.50 *a*

33.51 *c*

33.52 (*a*) pith;   (*b*) cortex; (*c*) vascular bundles; (*d*) xylem;   (*e*) phloem; (*f*) ground tissue;   (*g*) vascular bundles

33.53 blade; petiole; blade; blade

33.54 stomata; guard

33.55 (*a*) cuticle; (*b*) epidermis; (*c*) palisade mesophyll;

(*d*) spongy mesophyll; (*e*) vascular bundle (or vein, or xylem and phloem)

33.56 annuals; biennials; perennials; deciduous; cold; drought; evergreen

33.57 tap-; adventitious; fibrous; tap-; fibrous

33.58 Casparian strips

33.61 *b*

33.62 *d*

33.63 *c*

33.64 *b* (the only forest without pronounced seasons of growth)

33.65 inner; outer

33.66 larger; thinner

33.67 (*a*) secondary phloem; (*b*) vascular cambium; (*c*) secondary xylem; (*d*) periderm

33.68 heartwood; sapwood

CHAPTER 34
Transport within a Plant

ABSORPTION BY ROOTS*

34.1   Which of the following is *not* a process by which water moves through a root?

(*a*) Diffusion;   (*b*) Osmosis;   (*c*) Imbibition;   (*d*) Active transport

34.2   A root concentrates minerals by

(*a*) active transport.   (*b*) facilitated diffusion.   (*c*) osmosis.   (*d*) diffusion.

34.3   As water and minerals move toward the vascular cylinder of a root, they must enter the cytoplasm of

(*a*) xylem cells.   (*b*) cortex cells.   (*c*) endodermal cells.   (*d*) pericycle cells.

34.4   Most vascular plants increase the absorption of minerals by

(*a*) mycorrhizae.   (*b*) convertible phloem.   (*c*) Casparian channels along the phloem.   (*d*) companion cells.

34.5   Uptake of mineral ions into the xylem is controlled by

(*a*) epidermal cells.   (*b*) cortex cells.   (*c*) endodermal cells.   (*d*) xylem cells.

34.6   Which of the following plants is most likely to have endodermal cells in its stem?

(*a*) Water lily;   (*b*) Cactus;   (*c*) Corn;   (*d*) Ivy

34.7   Mineral uptake can be depressed by depriving the roots of oxygen, which indicates that _____ is required; such uptake involves _____ transport.

34.8   A living continuum of cytoplasm connected by plasmodesmata is the _____, whereas a nonliving continuum of cell walls is the _____.

34.9   The nonliving continuum is blocked by waterproof rings of wax, called _____, on the walls of _____ cells. The waxy rings force water and minerals into the living continuum; because the solutes have to cross at least one _____, their uptake is made selective.

34.10   What processes move water from the soil to the xylem?

   Water taken up by root hairs in contact with soil water moves to the xylem by three processes: osmosis, diffusion, and imbibition.

   Water travels by osmosis when soil water enters a root hair, which is part of an epidermal cell, because intracellular concentrations of solutes (ions, sugars, etc.) are higher than extracellular concentrations in the soil water. As water moves into an epidermal cell it dilutes the solutes there, so that intracellular concentrations become lower than in adjacent cells. Water then moves down a concentration gradient from an epidermal cell to a cortex cell, where again it lowers intracellular solute concentrations compared with more internal cells in the root. This self-perpetuating osmotic flow from cell to cell continues until water reaches and is pulled into the xylem. Sodium may be actively transported into some of the more interior root cells so that their solute concentrations become high enough to maintain the osmotic flow.

   Water travels by diffusion when soil water enters a root hair by osmosis, as described above, but then travels from the cytoplasm of one cell to the cytoplasm of another by way of interconnecting plasmodesmata. All movement of water is intracellular, and the driving force is diffusion; water moves down a concentration gradient from an epidermal cell, where dilute water enters, to a xylem cell, where it leaves. This living continuum of cytoplasm is called the *symplast*.

   Imbibition is absorption of water by nonliving materials. Water molecules adhere to the hydrophilic cell walls of root cells and move from epidermal to cortical to endodermal cell walls in the same way they would move through

* Answers to Chapter 34 objective questions appear on page 246.

a paper towel if its edge were placed in water. This nonliving continuum is known as the *apoplast*. At the endodermal cells, water is forced through the cytoplasm by Casparian strips—deposits of waxy suberin on endodermal walls that prevent water from going anywhere except into the cells. The selectively permeable plasma membranes of endodermal cells control the amounts of ions that enter the xylem.

XYLEM FLOW

34.11   Water potential measures the tendency of water to

(*a*) evaporate.   (*b*) move from one place to another.   (*c*) condense.   (*d*) adhere.

34.12   Water potential of a cell is lowered by the

(*a*) addition of solutes.   (*b*) addition of water.   (*c*) addition of heat.   (*d*) removal of heat.

34.13   Root pressure, which plays a small role in xylem flow, is caused by

(*a*) transpiration of water out of the xylem.   (*b*) cohesion of water molecules to one another.   (*c*) adhesion of water molecules to walls of the xylem.   (*d*) osmotic flow of water into the xylem.

34.14   To develop root pressure, energy is used to

(*a*) actively transport minerals into root cells.   (*b*) evaporate water in the leaves.   (*c*) condense water in the xylem.   (*d*) create suction in the xylem.

34.15   Guttation is the release of liquid water from veins at the leaf margins. It is caused by

(*a*) transpiration.   (*b*) high root pressure.   (*c*) high leaf pressure.   (*d*) clogged tracheids or vessel elements.

34.16   According to the transpiration-cohesion theory, water is pulled upward through the xylem. The cause of the pull is

(*a*) guttation.   (*b*) root pressure.   (*c*) transpiration.   (*d*) condensation.

34.17   According to the transpiration-cohesion theory, the upward pull of water is transmitted to other water molecules by cohesion, which is caused by

(*a*) hydrogen bonds.   (*b*) hydrophilic cell walls.   (*c*) turgor pressure.   (*d*) osmosis.

34.18   The energy source that drives the upward flow of water is

(*a*) light.   (*b*) sucrose.   (*c*) solar heat.   (*d*) ATP.

34.19   The lowest water potentials in the xylem are in the

(*a*) root hairs.   (*b*) vascular cylinders of roots.   (*c*) tracheids of the stem.   (*d*) leaves.

34.20   Water flows from where its potential is _____ to where its potential is _____. The water potential of a cell _____ when solutes are added, _____ when water is added, and _____ when pressure is added. Water potential is measured by an _____.

34.21   In a hypotonic environment, the cell initially has a _____ water potential than its surroundings. There is a net _____ of water by the cell. Water potential becomes zero when the difference in solute concentration is offset by _____ from the cell wall.

34.22   From xylem to the air spaces in a leaf, water moves along a gradient of _____ water potential, a gradient maintained by _____ in the leaf.

34.23   Water is pulled upward through the xylem, against gravity, because of _____ between water molecules and _____ of water molecules to the hydrophilic walls of narrow xylem channels.

34.24   Negative pressure (or tension) within the xylem is caused by the upward pull of water. It causes water potential in the root xylem to _____, which in turn favors _____ of water.

34.25 What causes water potential to be lower in the leaves than in the roots?

⚉ Water potential is a physical property, measured by an osmometer, that predicts which way water will move. It is governed by the concentration of solutes and the pressure on the water. Water potential, or the potential for water to leave an area, increases as solute concentration decreases or as pressure increases. Water always moves from areas of higher potential to areas of lower potential.

A hypertonic cell has a lower water potential than its environment; water tends to move into it by osmosis. An isotonic cell under pressure has a higher water potential than its environment; water tends to move out of it, even though it becomes hypertonic to its environment. A hypertonic plant cell takes in water until it becomes turgid, at which point the tendency for water to enter is offset by an equal and opposite tendency for water to leave, caused by pressure from the elastic cell walls.

Water potential is lower in leaves than in roots because of greater solute concentrations in leaf cells than in root cells. Mesophyll cells in the leaves have very high solute concentrations, because pure water evaporates out of them during transpiration. As cells near the stomata lose water by evaporation, they acquire water by osmosis from more interior leaf cells. These more interior cells then become hypertonic to even more interior cells, and so acquire water from them. The flow of water out of mesophyll cells near stomata, and then out of a series of more interior cells, ends at a tracheid of the xylem, where water is pulled from the xylem into a leaf cell.

The xylem fluid itself is a nonliving column of water and minerals; its water potential does not vary much from one end to another. At the root, the xylem receives water and minerals from endodermal cells, and here the gradient of water potential continues. Root cells have higher water potentials than leaf cells, because they do not lose pure water by evaporation. Root cells have lower water potentials, however, than soil water for two reasons: they actively transport dissolved minerals (solutes) into their cytoplasms, and they receive negative pressure from the upward pull of water in the xylem.

34.26 What happens to water transport if an air bubble forms within the xylem?

⚉ As a molecule of water leaves a xylem channel at the leaf, it exerts an attractive force that pulls up the next water molecule in the column, which pulls up the next, and so on, producing a chain of displacements that extends from the upper end of the xylem channel in the leaf to the lower end in the root. As the last molecule in the xylem is pulled up, it pulls another water molecule from the soil into the column. The force of attraction, or cohesion, of water molecules in the column is a result of the hydrogen bonds between them.

An air bubble in the xylem, which may form when the water freezes, interrupts the continuity of water by displacing some of the molecules; they become too far from each other to form hydrogen bonds. Water above the bubble may be pulled up, but it will not be replaced by water from below the bubble because the attractive force has been broken. A xylem channel with an air bubble can no longer transport water upward from the soil.

CONTROL OF TRANSPIRATION

34.27 Which of the following is *not* a function of transpiration?

(*a*) Cooling of leaves;   (*b*) Uptake of minerals;   (*c*) Excretion of minerals;   (*d*) Uptake of water

34.28 Which of the following will *not* cause stomata to open?

(*a*) Internal clock;   (*b*) Light;   (*c*) High carbon dioxide concentrations;   (*d*) Movement of K^+ into guard cells

34.29 A hormone that controls closure of stomata in response to water stress is

(*a*) abscisic acid.   (*b*) gibberellins.   (*c*) auxins.   (*d*) cytokinins.

34.30 Plants that open their stomata at night and close them during the day have

(*a*) C_3 pathways of photosynthesis.   (*b*) C_4 pathways of photosynthesis.   (*c*) Calvin-Benson pathways of photosynthesis.   (*d*) crassulacean acid metabolism (CAM) pathways of photosynthesis.

34.31 Which of the following plants keeps its stomata open during the night and closed during the day?

(*a*) Water lily;   (*b*) Cactus;   (*c*) Corn;   (*d*) Ivy

34.32 A plant needs far more water than an animal does, because the water it takes in does not _____. Instead, more than 90 percent of the water a plant takes in is _____.

34.33 Loss of water through small pores, called _____, in the leaves is a tradeoff for uptake of _____ through the same pores.

34.34 Changes in turgor pressure in guard cells, which open and close pores in the leaves, are mainly the result of movements of _____, which cause an increase in turgor pressure when they move _____ a guard cell and a decrease in turgor pressure when they move _____ a guard cell.

34.35 Keeping the guard cells turgid requires a continuous supply of both _____ ions and _____.

34.36 Transpiration is _____ by higher air temperatures, _____ by higher air humidities, _____ by having stomata on the underside of leaves, _____ by crassulacean acid metabolism, _____ by leaf hairs, _____ by wind, and _____ by having sunken stomata.

34.37 The stomata of most plants _____ in the evening and _____ in the morning. The portion of the solar spectrum that opens stomata, independent of carbon dioxide concentrations, is _____ light. Exposure of onion cells to this light, as well as to potassium ions, causes them to _____.

34.38 Some plants close their stomata at temperatures higher than 35 °C, probably in response to higher concentrations of _____, a result of increased cellular respiration at higher temperatures.

34.39 What factors can trigger the stomata to close?

Plants with open stomata acquire carbon dioxide for photosynthesis but also have the disadvantage of losing water. Plants conserve water by closing their stomata when photosynthesis is not taking place and when there is danger of losing too much water.

The stomata of most plants close at night and open in the morning. This basic pattern is controlled by internal clocks; a plant kept in total darkness continues its daily rhythm of stomatal closing and opening for a while. Other factors reinforce the internal clock and adjust it to seasonal changes in day length. Blue light keeps stomata open during the day by promoting the movement of potassium ions into guard cells. Absence of light at night, therefore, causes potassium ions and water to leave the guard cells, which then become flaccid, and the stomata close. High concentrations of carbon dioxide, an indication that respiration is exceeding photosynthesis, also close the stomata at night.

Stomata close during the day when there is stress from insufficient water or from high air temperatures, which could lead to dehydration. A plant reacts to water deficiency by producing more abscisic acid, a hormone that causes rapid movement of potassium ions (and therefore water) out of the guard cells. When temperatures exceed about 35 °C, stomata close to prevent excessive water loss. They do this in response to higher levels of carbon dioxide resulting from elevated rates of cellular respiration rather than in response to temperature itself.

34.40 What adaptations of leaves help reduce water loss from transpiration?

Most plants in arid environments have small leaves with thick cuticles, which are adaptations that promote heat loss by convection rather than by evaporation of water. The stomata are few and concentrated on the undersides of leaves, out of direct sunshine. Because evaporation is increased by air movements, the stomata of leaves in arid environments are sunken into the leaf and covered with hairs to produce pockets of still air. Extreme modifications of leaves include complete loss of all leaves during the dry season (e.g., tropical deciduous trees) and permanent loss of leaves (e.g., desert cacti) with the stem taking on photosynthetic functions.

Succulent plants in the family Crassulaceae reduce water loss by opening their stomata only at night, when the air is cooler and more humid. Carbon dioxide acquired at night is stored for use in photosynthesis during the following day, when the stomata remain closed to prevent water loss. This chemical adaptation, called crassulacean acid metabolism (CAM), is discussed in Chapter 8.

TRANSPORT IN PHLOEM

34.41 The transport of sugars and other organic molecules within a plant is called

(a) transpirational pull. (b) guttation. (c) translocation. (d) assimilation.

34.42 The most abundant solute in phloem sap is

(a) potassium ions. (b) glucose. (c) sucrose. (d) starch.

34.43   Phloem always flows from a

(*a*) sugar source to a sugar sink.   (*b*) sugar sink to a sugar source.   (*c*) leaf to a root.   (*d*) leaf to the xylem to the phloem.

34.44   Active loading of sugar into a sieve tube is probably driven by

(*a*) gravity.   (*b*) water flow.   (*c*) proton pumps.   (*d*) solar energy.

34.45   Valuable tools in learning about translocation have been

(*a*) aphids.   (*b*) wood-boring beetles.   (*c*) porcupines.   (*d*) leaf miners.

34.46   Sieve tubes carry food from a sugar _____ (an organ that produces sugar) to a sugar _____ (an organ that consumes or stores sugar). A tuber or bulb is a _____ in summer, when it stores starches, and a _____ in early spring, when it breaks down starch and releases transportable sugars.

34.47   The loading of sucrose into sieve tubes is by _____ transport and, consequently, requires _____.

34.48   Sucrose is accumulated by _____ cells, which transport it to sieve tubes via _____.

34.49   High solute concentrations at the source end of a sieve tube _____ the water potential and cause _____ to flow _____ the tube. At the sink end, the removal of sucrose _____ the water potential and causes _____ to flow _____ the tube.

34.50   What is the pressure-flow hypothesis of phloem transport?

☙   The pressure-flow hypothesis states that phloem sap is transported by a massive uptake of water at one end of the phloem, where sugar is produced, and a massive loss of water at the other end, where sugar is used or stored.

Companion cells in the leaves accumulate, by active transport, sugar synthesized in the mesophyll cells. Large amounts of sugar are then moved through plasmodesmata into the phloem, where they produce very low water potentials. Water flows into these cells and causes an increase in their interior pressures, which forces the solution of water and sugar to flow through sieve plates into adjacent sieve tubes. The water pressure in these cells then becomes greater than in each adjacent cell farther along in the phloem column. At the other end of the column, near such sinks as flowers and roots, sugar is actively transported out of the sieve tubes. The high water potentials that develop in these cells cause water to leave the phloem.

Answers to Objective Questions

34.1 *d*	**34.18** *c*	**34.35** potassium; ATP
34.2 *a*	**34.19** *d*	**34.36** increased; decreased;
34.3 *c*	**34.20** higher; lower; decreases;	decreased; decreased;
34.4 *a*	increases; increases;	decreased; increased;
34.5 *c*	osmometer	decreased
34.6 *a*	**34.21** lower; uptake; pressure	**34.37** close; open; blue; swell
34.7 ATP; active	**34.22** decreasing; transpiration	**34.38** carbon dioxide
34.8 symplast; apoplast	**34.23** cohesion; adhesion	**34.41** *c*
34.9 Casparian strips;	**34.24** decrease; uptake	**34.42** *c*
endodermal; plasma	**34.27** *c*	**34.43** *a*
membrane	**34.28** *c*	**34.44** *c*
34.11 *b*	**34.29** *a*	**34.45** *a*
34.12 *a*	**34.30** *d*	**34.46** source; sink; sink; source
34.13 *d*	**34.31** *b*	**34.47** active; ATP
34.14 *a*	**34.32** recirculate; transpired	**34.48** companion; plasmodesmata
34.15 *b*	**34.33** stomata; carbon dioxide	**34.49** lower; water; into; raises;
34.16 *c*	**34.34** potassium ions; into; out of	water; out of
34.17 *a*		

NUTRITIONAL REQUIREMENTS OF PLANTS*

35.1 Most of the organic material in a plant is

(*a*) carbohydrate. (*b*) fat. (*c*) protein. (*d*) nucleic acid.

35.2 Most of the dry weight of a tree comes from atoms acquired from

(*a*) soil. (*b*) water. (*c*) air. (*d*) decomposing leaves.

35.3 Minerals enter a plant mainly by

(*a*) diffusion. (*b*) pressure flow. (*c*) translocation. (*d*) active transport.

35.4 A plant requires nitrogen and sulfur for its

(*a*) cell walls. (*b*) storage vacuoles. (*c*) enzymes. (*d*) energy stores.

35.5 A plant requires phosphorus for its

(*a*) cell walls. (*b*) cell membranes. (*c*) enzymes. (*d*) starch deposits.

35.6 A plant requires magnesium for

(*a*) holding its cells together. (*b*) synthesizing chlorophyll. (*c*) DNA replication. (*d*) opening and closing its stomata.

35.7 A plant requires potassium for

(*a*) holding its cells together. (*b*) synthesizing chlorophyll. (*c*) synthesizing proteins. (*d*) opening and closing its stomata.

35.8 A plant requires calcium for

(*a*) holding its cells together. (*b*) synthesizing chlorophyll. (*c*) DNA replication. (*d*) opening and closing its stomata.

35.9 Mineral uptake by a terrestrial plant is limited by insufficient

(*a*) blue light. (*b*) soil water. (*c*) apoplast. (*d*) phellogen.

35.10 The yellowing of leaves, called chlorosis, is usually caused by insufficient

(*a*) sodium. (*b*) phosphorus. (*c*) calcium. (*d*) magnesium.

35.11 Elements required by plants in relatively large amounts are _____; those required in very small amounts are _____.

35.12 Nine atoms needed by plants in relatively large amounts are: _____, _____, _____, _____, _____, _____, _____, _____, and _____.

35.13 Atoms needed in very small amounts function mainly as _____ of enzymatic reactions.

35.14 Plants absorb minerals in their _____ form, as found in the soil _____.

* Answers to Chapter 35 objective questions appear on page 250.

35.15 In plants, the most common nutrient deficiencies are of _____, _____, and _____.

35.16 Soil minerals bound to soil particles can be released into solution by changing the soil _____.

35.17 How are the nutrient requirements of a plant determined?

☗ A plant's need for minerals can be estimated by examining the minerals it contains. The plant is completely burned, during which carbon, hydrogen, oxygen, nitrogen, and sulfur escape as gases, and the remaining ashes are then analyzed for mineral content. A disadvantage of this method is that the plant may contain materials, such as silicon, that it does not require.

A better way to quantify nutrient requirements is to grow the plant in a *hydroponic* culture. Its roots are suspended in aerated, distilled water (rather than anchored in soil) to which measured amounts of minerals are added. The plant is first grown in the presence of all possible minerals in quantities that promote vigorous growth of the plant. Then it is grown in a solution with one mineral absent or reduced in abundance. The development of abnormal symptoms, such as discoloration of the leaves, or stunted growth indicates that the mineral is an essential nutrient for that plant.

SOILS

35.18 At times of heavy rain, minerals in upper layers of the soil are moved downward by a process known as

(*a*) smearing.　(*b*) leaching.　(*c*) weathering.　(*d*) gravitation.

35.19 The best soils for growing plants are made of

(*a*) pure sand.　(*b*) pure clay.　(*c*) pure silt.　(*d*) sand, clay, and silt combined.

35.20 The wettest soils are made of

(*a*) pure sand.　(*b*) pure clay.　(*c*) pure silt.　(*d*) sand, clay, and silt combined.

35.21 The driest soils are made of

(*a*) pure sand.　(*b*) pure clay.　(*c*) pure silt.　(*d*) sand, clay, and silt combined.

35.22 Most minerals in a soil are in the

(*a*) sand.　(*b*) clay.　(*c*) silt.　(*d*) air pockets.

35.23 Small clay particles hold calcuim, potassium, and magnesium ions because their surfaces are

(*a*) smooth.　(*b*) covered with tiny crevices.　(*c*) negatively charged.　(*d*) waxy.

35.24 The mineral content of most soils depends more on its _____ components than on its parental rock.

35.25 Hydrogen ions released by plants and lichens help _____ rocks and release _____ ions from rock particles.

35.26 Commercial fertilizers usually contain the following three kinds of atoms: _____, _____, and _____.

35.27 How does the size of soil particles influence plant nutrition?

☗ The soil particles of fertile soil provide sufficient air spaces for gas exchange in plant roots and soil animals, as well as large surface areas for holding water and minerals. Sand has the largest soil particles, which gives it the smallest ratio of surface area to volume and the most air spaces. Clay has the smallest soil particles, which gives it the largest ratio of surface area to volume and the fewest air spaces. Silt has intermediate properties. The best soils for plant growth are mixtures of sand, clay, and silt.

NITROGEN ASSIMILATION

35.28 The largest reservoir of nitrogen on earth is

(*a*) the soil.　(*b*) the air.　(*c*) the oceans.　(*d*) granite rocks.

35.29   The bond in molecular nitrogen (N_2) is difficult to break, because it is a

     (*a*) twisted configuration.   (*b*) quadruple hydrogen bond.   (*c*) triple covalent bond.   (*d*) triple ionic bond.

35.30   Which of the following formulas describes nitrogen fixation?

     (*a*) $N_2 + 3H_2 \longrightarrow 2NH_3$;   (*b*) $2NH_4^+ + 2O_2 + 8e^- \longrightarrow N_2 + 4H_2O$;   (*c*) $2NH_3 \longrightarrow N_2 + 3H_2$;   (*d*) $2N_2 + glucose \longrightarrow 2$ amino acids

35.31   Nitrogen fixation by organisms requires conditions that are

     (*a*) highly alkaline.   (*b*) anaerobic.   (*c*) saturated with sunlight.   (*d*) free of water.

35.32   Nitrogen fixation by bacteria requires the enzyme

     (*a*) decarboxylase.   (*b*) nitrogenase.   (*c*) nitrogen deaminase.   (*d*) nitrodioxidase.

35.33   The conversion of ammonia to ammonium occurs

     (*a*) on the ribosomes of cyanobacteria.   (*b*) on the endoplasmic reticulum of green algae. (*c*) spontaneously when ammonia is in water.   (*d*) on the dry surfaces of soil particles.

35.34   Plants that have mutualistic relations with nitrogen-fixing bacteria receive from the bacteria

     (*a*) ammonium.   (*b*) amino acids.   (*c*) nitrate.   (*d*) nitrite.

35.35   Plants that have mutualistic relations with nitrogen-fixing bacteria provide the bacteria with

     (*a*) N_2.   (*b*) enzymes.   (*c*) sugars.   (*d*) nitrite.

35.36   The nodule in a plant root where nitrogen-fixing bacteria live forms from cells of the

     (*a*) epidermis.   (*b*) cortex.   (*c*) endodermis.   (*d*) vascular cylinder.

35.37   Plants, such as clover and beans, that have nitrogen-fixing bacteria in their roots are in which of the following families?

     (*a*) Orchidaceae;   (*b*) Asteraceae;   (*c*) Solanaceae;   (*d*) Leguminosae

35.38   Bacteria that fix nitrogen for such plants as clover and beans are in which of the following genera?

     (*a*) *Denitrovibrio*;   (*b*) *Rhizobium*;   (*c*) *Pseudomonas*;   (*d*) *Nitrobacter*

35.39   Which of the following plants will enrich the soil with nitrogen?

     (*a*) Corn;   (*b*) Alfalfa;   (*c*) Wheatgrass;   (*d*) Beets

35.40   Organisms that fix nitrogen in aquatic habitats are

     (*a*) green algae.   (*b*) cyanobacteria.   (*c*) brown algae.   (*d*) protozoa.

35.41   Plants use nitrogen in the form of _____ or _____. The most abundant form of nitrogen in the biosphere is _____.

35.42   Nitrogen-fixing bacteria convert _____ to _____. Nitrifying bacteria convert _____ to _____.

35.43   How does a root nodule develop?

     Nitrogen-fixing bacteria in the genus *Rhizobium* live within nodules in the roots of leguminous plants. In their mutualism, the bacteria provide the plant with ammonium in exchange for sugars.

     The mutualism begins when bacteria in the soil convert tryptophan, released by a root hair, into indoleacetic acid (auxin), which causes the root hair to curl up and open a site for bacterial entry. The bacteria enter only after mutual recognition is established, by means of a molecular template involving surface proteins on the root hair and polysaccharides on the bacterial cell walls. Bacteria enter the root hair and travel to the cortex of the root through a branching canal, called the *infection thread*, constructed of cellulose and pectin by the root cells. The bacteria move into vesicles within cortex cells and release a hormone—cytokinin—that causes cortex cells to proliferate and to make direct connections with the xylem and phloem. This tumorlike mass of cells, containing colonies of bacteria, becomes the root nodule. The bacteria become swollen and specialized in synthesizing massive quantities of nitrogenase, the enzyme that converts molecular nitrogen (N_2) and hydrogen (H_2) into ammonia (NH_3).

35.44 How can a cyanobacterium carry out both nitrogen fixation, which requires anaerobic conditions, and photosynthesis, which produces oxygen gas?

🐚 No single prokaryotic cell can carry out both photosynthesis and nitrogen fixation, because oxygen released during photosynthesis irreversibly damages the nitrogen-fixing enzyme nitrogenase; a prokaryotic cell does not have organelles for separating the two processes. Only *filamentous* cyanobacteria have both processes, which are isolated in different cells of the filament. Some filament cells are specialized for synthesizing sugars by photosynthesis, and others (called heterocysts) are specialized for synthesizing first ammonia, by nitrogen fixation, and then amino acids. The two types of cells in the filament exchange sugars and amino acids by way of plasmodesmata.

NUTRITIONAL ADAPTATIONS

35.45 Carnivorous plants live in soils that are deficient in

(*a*) water. (*b*) worms. (*c*) oxygen. (*d*) nitrogen.

35.46 The traps of carnivorous plants contain

(*a*) polysaccharides. (*b*) digestive enzymes. (*c*) phospholipids. (*d*) herbicides.

35.47 Mycorrhizae are

(*a*) found mainly in ferns. (*b*) found mainly in nonvascular plants. (*c*) common among angiosperms.
(*d*) rare outside tropical forests.

35.48 An epiphyte, such as Spanish moss, gets its nutrients from the _____. A parasite, such as mistletoe, gets its nutrients from the _____.

35.49 A mycorrhizal fungus receives _____ from the host plant and provides _____ and _____ for the plant.

35.50 What environmental conditions favor epiphytes as opposed to parasitic plants?

🐚 Epiphytes, such as Spanish moss and bromeliads, nourish themselves but anchor their roots to stems of other plants. Parasitic plants, such as mistletoe and dodder, are nourished by the vascular tissues of their host plants.

Epiphytes grow on other plants in order to occupy a desirable position within the plant community. They are common in dense tropical forests, where by growing high on trees they gain access to light, and in swamps, where by growing on trees they are elevated above the water. Epiphytes get water and minerals from rainwater and moisture in the air. Many resemble desert plants, with adaptations for conserving water. Others have tanklike structures for accumulating rainwater and, in many species, for trapping insects as well.

Parasites grow on other plants in order to tap their xylem and phloem; they acquire water, minerals, and organic molecules from their host plant. Parasitic plants occur almost everywhere, but are especially common where water and minerals are in short supply.

Answers to Objective Questions

35.1 *a*	35.10 *d*	35.14 ionic; water
35.2 *c*	35.11 macronutrients;	35.15 nitrogen; phosphorus;
35.3 *d*	micronutrients (or trace	potassium
35.4 *c*	elements)	35.16 pH
35.5 *b*	35.12 carbon; hydrogen; oxygen;	35.18 *b*
35.6 *b*	nitrogen; sulfur;	35.19 *d*
35.7 *d*	phosphorus; calcium;	35.20 *b*
35.8 *a*	potassium; magnesium	35.21 *a*
35.9 *b*	35.13 cofactors	35.22 *b*

35.23 *c*

35.24 organic

35.25 dissolve; positive

35.26 nitrogen; phosphorus;
potassium

35.28 *b*

35.29 *c*

35.30 *a*

35.31 *b*

35.32 *b*

35.33 *c*

35.34 *a*

35.35 *c*

35.36 *b*

35.37 *d*

35.38 *b*

35.39 *b*

35.40 *b*

35.41 ammonium; nitrate;
molecular nitrogen (N_2)

35.42 molecular nitrogen;
ammonia; ammonium;
nitrate

35.45 *d*

35.46 *b*

35.47 *c*

35.48 air; host plant

35.49 sugars; water; minerals

CHAPTER 36
Plant Reproduction, Development, and Growth

FORMATION OF ANGIOSPERM GAMETES*

36.1   A flower with stamens, carpels, sepals, and petals is said to be

(*a*) tetraform.   (*b*) complete.   (*c*) perfect.   (*d*) monoecious.

36.2   A flower with both stamens and carpels is said to be

(*a*) sexual.   (*b*) perfect.   (*c*) diform.   (*d*) dioecious.

36.3   A plant species that has, on each individual plant, flowers with stamens and flowers with carpels is

(*a*) perfect.   (*b*) imperfect.   (*c*) monoecious.   (*d*) dioecious.

36.4   An anther produces

(*a*) haploid gametes.   (*b*) diploid gametes.   (*c*) haploid spores.   (*d*) diploid spores.

36.5   Pollination occurs when a pollen grain

(*a*) matures and has three nuclei.   (*b*) lands on a stigma.   (*c*) releases its sperm nuclei.   (*d*) releases its sperm nuclei and they fertilize the egg and polar nuclei.

36.6   Fertilization of the egg takes place inside the

(*a*) anther.   (*b*) stigma.   (*c*) pollen tube.   (*d*) embryo sac.

36.7   The four floral parts, in order from outside to inside the flower, are: _____, _____, _____, and _____.

36.8   A carpel is composed, from top to bottom, of three parts: _____, _____, and _____. A stamen has two parts: the supporting _____ and the pollen-producing _____.

36.9   An imperfect flower is either _____ (without carpels) or _____ (without stamens).

36.10   A species in which some individuals have only stamens and others have only carpels is said to be _____.

36.11   A sporophyte produces a spore by _____ cell division. A spore produces a gametophyte by _____ cell division. The modified leaves that form a flower are parts of the _____ generation. The pollen grains and embryo sacs are the _____ in the life cycle of an angiosperm.

36.12   After pollination, a pollen grain has three haploid nuclei: one _____ nucleus and two _____ nuclei.

36.13   An embryo sac within an ovule has eight nuclei: at one end are the three _____, in the middle are the two _____, and at the other end are the two _____ and the single _____.

36.14   Two sperm nuclei enter the embryo sac through an opening called the _____. One sperm nucleus fertilizes the _____ to form the endosperm, and the other fertilizes the _____ to form the zygote. This process, unique to angiosperms, is known as _____ fertilization.

36.15   How do monoecious plants prevent self-fertilization?

* Answers to Chapter 36 objective questions appear on page 258.

🐚 A monoecious plant has both staminate flowers, with stamens but not carpels, and carpellate flowers, with carpels but not stamens. It can prevent self-fertilization by having the staminate flowers mature at a different time from the carpellate flowers or by being self-incompatible, in which case its own pollen tubes or sperm nuclei are blocked by chemicals in its carpels. Similarly, a plant with perfect flowers (each flower has both stamens and carpels) can prevent self-fertilization by having its stamens mature at a different time from its carpels or by being self-incompatible.

DEVELOPMENT OF THE ANGIOSPERM SEED AND FRUIT

36.16   A dicot proembryo is heart-shaped, because it is developing

(*a*) cork cambium.   (*b*) vascular cambium.   (*c*) heartwood.   (*d*) two cotyledons.

36.17   The shoot apical meristem in a dicot embryo is located

(*a*) between the two cotyledons.   (*b*) within the root apex.   (*c*) around the suspensor.   (*d*) in the endosperm.

36.18   How many copies of each chromosome are in an endosperm nucleus?

(*a*) One;   (*b*) Two;   (*c*) Three;   (*d*) Eight

36.19   Which of the following is a monocot seed?

(*a*) Kidney bean;   (*b*) Peanut;   (*c*) Corn kernel;   (*d*) Pea

36.20   A fruit develops from the walls of the

(*a*) style.   (*b*) ovary.   (*c*) cotyledons.   (*d*) suspensor.

36.21   The function of a fruit is to

(*a*) nourish the embryo.   (*b*) cushion the seed when it dehisces (i.e., splits to discharge seed).   (*c*) aid dispersal of the seed.   (*d*) protect the embryo from extreme temperatures.

36.22   Which of the following is *not* a fruit?

(*a*) Flesh of a strawberry;   (*b*) Flesh of a peach;   (*c*) Pod of a pea;   (*d*) Flesh of a peanut

36.23   A grain of wheat is the

(*a*) embryo.   (*b*) seed.   (*c*) fruit.   (*d*) seed and fruit.

36.24   The part of the embryo between the cotyledons and the embryonic root (the radicle) is called the

(*a*) hypocotyl.   (*b*) epicotyl.   (*c*) suspensor.   (*d*) root apex.

36.25   The part of the embryo above the cotyledons is called the

(*a*) hypocotyl.   (*b*) epicotyl.   (*c*) suspensor.   (*d*) root apex.

36.26   Germination takes place when the

(*a*) previously dormant embryo is activated.   (*b*) cotyledons emerge above ground.   (*c*) hypocotyl or epicotyl emerges above ground.   (*d*) vascular tissues begin to transport fluids.

36.27   A seed coat ruptures because of

(*a*) massive glycolysis in the endosperm and cotyledons.   (*b*) massive entry of water, by imbibition, into the seed.   (*c*) differentiation of the cotyledons.   (*d*) sudden increase in meristem cell division.

36.28   The first part of the dicot embryo to appear above ground is the

(*a*) shoot apical meristem.   (*b*) cotyledons.   (*c*) hypocotyl or epicotyl.   (*d*) coleoptile.

36.29   The first part of the monocot embryo to appear above ground is the

(*a*) shoot apical meristem.   (*b*) cotyledons.   (*c*) hypocotyl or epicotyl.   (*d*) coleoptile.

36.30 After the seedling begins to photosynthesize, the cotyledons become

(*a*) degenerate and fall off.   (*b*) phloem tissue.   (*c*) root tissue.   (*d*) foliage leaves.

36.31 The first cleavage of the zygote splits it into two cells: the _____ cell, which develops into a thread-shaped _____, and the _____ cell, which goes on to form the embryo.

36.32 The three embryonic tissues, or primary meristems, are the _____, which forms epidermis; the _____, which forms vascular tissues; and the _____, which forms the ground tissues of leaves, stems, and roots. The other two structures in the seed—the _____ and the _____—disappear in the seedling.

36.33 In many dicots the food reserves of the endosperm are transferred to the _____ before the seed becomes mature.

36.34 During the last stages of maturation, the seed _____ until its water content is about _____ percent of its weight.

36.35 In a seed, the embryo and its food supply are enclosed within a _____ formed from the outer tissues of the _____.

36.36 A _____ fruit is derived from one carpel or the fused carpels of a single flower. An _____ fruit is derived from several carpels of a single flower. A _____ fruit develops from the many carpels of an inflorescence (group of separate flowers). A pineapple or mulberry is a _____ fruit. A cherry or olive is a _____ fruit. A strawberry or blackberry is an _____ fruit.

36.37 A _____ fruit is dispersed by animals, by way of their digestive tracts. A _____ fruit is dispersed by the wind or the body surfaces (e.g., hair) of animals.

36.38 Most seeds must go through a period of dormancy before they germinate. To break out of dormancy, desert annuals usually require substantial _____, chaparral annuals usually require _____, and many plants of northern climates require _____.

36.39 The first organ to emerge from the germinating seed is the _____.

36.40 How do the embryos of dicots differ from those of monocots?

☃   The two basic forms of angiosperms are dicotyledons and monocotyledons. Their names come from a fundamental difference in their embryos: a dicotyledon has two cotyledons (embryo leaves), whereas a monocotyledon has just one cotyledon. In addition, the embryo of a monocot is enclosed by a sheath that covers the root and a coleoptile that covers the shoot. The two forms also differ in the way the embryo breaks out of the ground. In a dicot, the emerging embryo is bent, so that either the hypocotyl or epicotyl emerges first, thereby protecting the delicate cotyledons and shoot apical meristem. The shoot then straightens so the apical meristem is uppermost. In a monocot, the tough coleoptile, which encloses the shoot, emerges first and the shoot then grows upward through it.

PRIMARY GROWTH

36.41 Root apical meristem cells are distinct from other root cells, because of their

(*a*) smaller size.   (*b*) enlarged water vacuoles.   (*c*) thick cell walls.   (*d*) triploid nuclei.

36.42 A plant cell elongates by

(*a*) producing more cytoplasm.   (*b*) producing more nucleoplasm.   (*c*) taking up water.   (*d*) amoeboid streaming.

36.43 As a plant cell elongates, its cytoplasm becomes

(*a*) more viscous.   (*b*) less viscous.   (*c*) restricted to a thin layer next to the cell wall.   (*d*) spread more evenly throughout the cell.

36.44 New lateral roots arise from the

(*a*) shoot apical meristem.   (*b*) root apical meristem.   (*c*) pericycle.   (*d*) endodermis.

36.45 New leaves arise from the

(*a*) shoot apical meristem.   (*b*) vascular cambium.   (*c*) lateral buds.   (*d*) pericycle.

36.46 Flowers and lateral branches arise from the

(*a*) phellogen.   (*b*) vascular cambium.   (*c*) lateral buds.   (*d*) lenticels.

36.47 Shoot apical meristem excised from a plant and grown in tissue culture produces

(*a*) all the plant tissues.   (*b*) new shoot and root apical meristems.   (*c*) stems only.   (*d*) stems and leaves only.

36.48 Leaf primordium excised from a fern and grown in tissue culture develops into a

(*a*) normal fern leaf.   (*b*) misshapen leaf, not recognizable as a fern leaf.   (*c*) stem with lateral branches.
(*d*) shoot apical meristem.

36.49 All primary growth in a plant originates in the _____ of the shoot and root.

36.50 Growth of the shoot or root of a young plant involves three cellular processes: _____,
_____, and _____.

36.51 Root apical meristem is protected from soil abrasion by a _____. As the cells of this structure wear
away, they are replaced by new cells from the _____.

36.52 Shoot apical meristem that is enclosed within a series of unelongated internodes that in turn are enclosed within
leaf primordia is called a _____.

36.53 The process in which a cell changes from an immature form to a specific type of cell is called _____.

36.54 Leaves develop from meristematic tissue known as leaf _____.

36.55 If a developing seedling is placed horizontally, the shoot grows _____ and the root grows
_____. This phenomenon is known as _____.

36.56 Refer to Fig. 36.1, and identify the structures indicated in the drawing of a seedling.

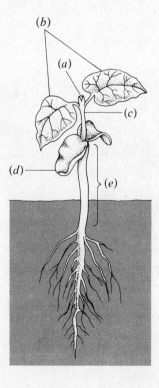

Fig. 36.1

36.57   Refer to Fig. 36.2, and identify the three growth zones in the drawing of a root.

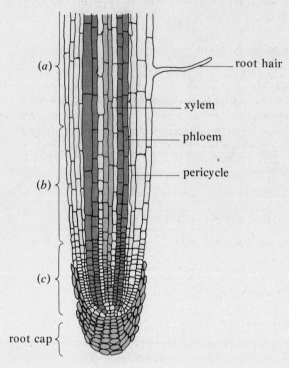

root hair

xylem

phloem

pericycle

root cap {

Fig. 36.2

36.58   Refer to Fig. 36.3, and identify the structures indicated in the drawing of a shoot tip.

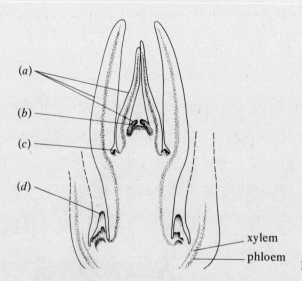

xylem

phloem

Fig. 36.3

36.59   How does a plant cell elongate during plant growth?

⚜   A plant cell elongates when the walls on two opposing sides of the cell become more plastic, allowing water to move into the cell and expand its volume. The walls of growing cells contain cellulose, pectin, hemicellulose, and other polysaccharides. The fundamental structure consists of cylindrical bundles of long cellulose molecules rigidly held to one another and to the other polysaccharides by hydrogen bonds. According to a current hypothesis, known as *the acid-growth hypothesis*, a plant growth hormone named *auxin* stimulates the cell to pump hydrogen ions (protons) into the cell wall, where they activate enzymes that break the hydrogen bonds. The cellulose bundles are then free to slide away from one another and from the other polysaccharides. The more pliable cell wall creates less pressure on the cell, and so more water moves into it by osmosis. So much water enters the cell that there may be as much as a 100-fold increase in cell length. The elongated cell consists mainly of water-filled vacuoles; there has been no increase in cytoplasm.

36.60   What is the structure of a terminal bud?

⎝   A terminal bud consists of shoot apical meristem, internodes that have not yet elongated, and leaf primordia. Each leaf primordium arises from a place on the stem called a node. Regions of the stem between nodes are internodes. A stem grows and the leaves are moved farther apart when the internodes elongate. In a terminal bud, the shoot apical meristem is surrounded by a series of internodes that have not yet elongated. Consequently, the leaf primordia on the nodes are packed together and completely cover the meristem with many layers. The nearer leaf primordia are to the meristem, the younger they are; so when a bud unfolds and the internodes elongate, the youngest leaf primordia form leaves nearest to the apical meristem, i.e., on the most distal parts of the stem.

ASEXUAL REPRODUCTION

36.61   The most common type of vegetative reproduction in plants is

(*a*) advention.   (*b*) fragmentation.   (*c*) self-fertilization.   (*d*) apomixis (or parthenogenesis).

36.62   The asexual production of seeds is called

(*a*) advention.   (*b*) fragmentation.   (*c*) self-fertilization.   (*d*) apomixis (or parthenogenesis).

36.63   Offspring produced by vegetative reproduction are

(*a*) haploid.   (*b*) tetraploid.   (*c*) genetically identical.   (*d*) inferior to offspring produced by sexual reproduction.

36.64   Plants that will develop from fragments readily form _____ roots.

36.65   A population of asexually reproduced, genetically identical individuals is a _____.

36.66   One form of asexual reproduction is from horizontal stems that grow above or below ground; such aboveground stems are called _____, while those growing below ground are called _____. Strawberries have _____, whereas sod-forming grasses have _____.

36.67   Most fruit trees, wine grapes, and roses are propagated by _____ rather than from fragments or seeds.

36.68   In test-tube cloning, a whole plant can be developed by culturing a small piece of _____ or even a single _____ cell. The cultured cells divide to form an undifferentiated _____, which forms shoots and roots. It can then be transplanted to soil for the rest of its growth and development.

36.69   How does a dandelion form seeds by asexual reproduction?

⎝   A dandelion produces seeds without meiosis or fertilization. The adult sporophyte forms diploid, rather than haploid, megaspores that develop into ovules containing diploid, rather than haploid, nuclei. One of the nuclei in each ovule becomes an egg and develops directly, without fertilization, into an embryo that is genetically identical to its parent. This type of asexual reproduction is called *parthenogenesis*, a form of *apomixis*.

36.70   What are the advantages of asexual reproduction as compared with sexual reproduction?

⎝   One advantage of asexual reproduction is that the offspring receive a set of genes identical to an individual (its parent) that has survived to reproduce; the set has already been tested by natural selection and proved successful. If the offspring are exposed to the same environmental conditions as their parent, then they also are likely to survive and reproduce with success.

A second advantage is that an asexual population can grow more rapidly than a sexual population, because all members of an asexual population are capable of producing young.

Last, a plant can rapidly establish its offspring in nearby vacant places by fragmentation, thus filling recently vacated spaces more rapidly than can other plants. Fragments, especially when connected to their parent by runners or rhizomes, not only cover the area more rapidly, but are more robust and likely to survive than seeds.

Answers to Objective Questions

36.1 b
36.2 b
36.3 c
36.4 c
36.5 b
36.6 d
36.7 sepals; petals; stamens; carpels
36.8 stigma; style; ovary; filament; anthers
36.9 staminate; carpellate
36.10 dioecious
36.11 meiotic; mitotic; sporophyte; gametophytes
36.12 tube; sperm
36.13 antipodal cells; polar nuclei; synergids; egg
36.14 micropyle; polar nuclei; egg; double
36.16 d
36.17 a
36.18 c
36.19 c
36.20 b
36.21 c
36.22 d
36.23 d
36.24 a
36.25 b

36.26 a
36.27 b
36.28 c
36.29 d
36.30 a
36.31 basal; suspensor; terminal
36.32 protoderm; procambium; ground meristem; endosperm; cotyledons
36.33 cotyledons
36.34 dehydrates; ten
36.35 seed coat; ovule
36.36 simple; aggregate; multiple; multiple; simple; aggregate
36.37 fleshy; dry
36.38 rainfall; fire; a cold period
36.39 radicle (or root)
36.41 a
36.42 c
36.43 c
36.44 c
36.45 a
36.46 c
36.47 d
36.48 a
36.49 apical meristems
36.50 division; elongation; differentiation

36.51 root cap; root apical meristem
36.52 bud
36.53 differentiation
36.54 primordia
36.55 upward; downward; geotropism (or gravitropism)
36.56 (a) shoot apical meristem; (b) first true leaves; (c) epicotyl; (d) cotyledon; (e) hypocotyl
36.57 (a) zone of differentiation; (b) zone of elongation; (c) zone of cell division
36.58 (a) leaf primordia; (b) shoot apical meristem; (c) lateral bud; (d) lateral bud
36.61 b
36.62 d
36.63 c
36.64 adventitious
36.65 clone
36.66 runners; rhizomes; runners; rhizomes
36.67 grafting
36.68 meristem; parenchyma; callus

CHAPTER 37

Plant Control Systems

PLANT HORMONES*

37.1   A plant hormone is

(*a*) an ion that alters turgor pressure. (*b*) a pigment that responds to environmental changes. (*c*) a chemical messenger that coordinates body cells. (*d*) a secondary metabolic compound.

37.2   A plant responds to its environment primarily by

(*a*) growing. (*b*) synthesizing pigments. (*c*) closing its stomata and curling its leaves. (*d*) promoting abscission of its structures.

37.3   Charles Darwin and his son Frances discovered (around 1880) that a grass seedling bends toward light only if the

(*a*) stem is at least 10 cm long. (*b*) tip of the coleoptile is present and exposed to light. (*c*) cotyledon is present and exposed to light. (*d*) nights are long in comparison with the days.

37.4   In the early part of this century, the Danish botanist Peter Boysen-Jensen and the Hungarian botanist Arpad Paal showed that the bending of a grass seedling toward light is caused by a mobile substance, most likely

(*a*) a diffusible chemical. (*b*) a flow of ions. (*c*) a neural impulse. (*d*) an electrical gradient.

37.5   The natural form of active auxin, produced by plants, is

(*a*) indoleacetic acid. (*b*) coleoptauxin. (*c*) cotyledauxin. (*d*) apical acid.

37.6   The chemical structure of naturally occurring auxin is very similar to the structure of

(*a*) phosphate. (*b*) pectin. (*c*) adenosine monophosphate. (*d*) tryptophan.

37.7   Most of a plant's auxin is produced in its

(*a*) leaves. (*b*) lateral buds. (*c*) shoot apex. (*d*) root apical meristem.

37.8   The main effect of auxin is to stimulate cell

(*a*) division. (*b*) elongation. (*c*) differentiation. (*d*) turgor.

37.9   In the 1940s, Johannes van Overbeek stimulated growth in plant embryos with coconut milk. In the 1950s, Folke Skoog and Carlos O. Miller stimulated cell division in tobacco plants with degraded DNA. The active ingredient in both stimulants, which resembles cytokinins, was modified

(*a*) adenine. (*b*) auxin. (*c*) ribosic acid. (*d*) phosphate.

37.10   Cytokinins stimulate cell

(*a*) division. (*b*) elongation. (*c*) wall thickening. (*d*) turgor.

37.11   When its terminal bud is removed, a plant grows more

(*a*) tall. (*b*) bushy. (*c*) slowly. (*d*) rapidly.

37.12   When a plant is not reproducing, most of its cytokinins are produced in its

(*a*) leaves. (*b*) lateral buds. (*c*) shoot apex. (*d*) roots.

* Answers to Chapter 37 objective questions appear on page 265.

37.13 Gibberellins, produced in the apical portions of both stems and roots, cause

(*a*) stem elongation. (*b*) phototropisms. (*c*) growth of lateral branches. (*d*) abscission of leaves and fruits.

37.14 In the 1920s, the Japanese biologist Ewili Kurosawa and his colleagues discovered that foolish-seedling disease, in which rice plants grow too tall, is caused by

(*a*) a gibberellin secreted by fungi. (*b*) the herbicide 2,4-D. (*c*) degraded nucleic acids. (*d*) too much auxin, due to stagnant water in the fields.

37.15 Primary and secondary growth are inhibited by

(*a*) auxin. (*b*) gibberellins. (*c*) abscisic acid. (*d*) cytokinins.

37.16 An important effect of ethylene is to cause maturation of

(*a*) leaf primordia. (*b*) root meristem from parenchyma cells. (*c*) fruits. (*d*) the vascular cambium.

37.17 Ethylene is an unusual hormone in that it is

(*a*) a gas. (*b*) nonmotile. (*c*) transported by the xylem. (*d*) transported by the phloem.

37.18 In 1926, Fritz Went demonstrated that a _____ produced in the _____ of a grass seedling stimulates growth. The seedling bent toward light because the growth stimulant accumulated on the _____ side of the coleoptile.

37.19 The five known classes of plant hormones are the three growth promoters _____, _____, and _____, and the two growth inhibitors _____ and _____.

37.20 A plant cell's reaction to a hormone depends not on the absolute concentration of the hormone, but on its concentration relative to _____.

37.21 Auxin travels in one direction through a stem by polar transport, in which it moves through the plasma membranes of _____ cells. This type of transport requires an input of _____.

37.22 Auxin stimulates cell elongation by causing the cell to pump _____ into the cell wall, where they stimulate enzymes to loosen the polysaccharides so that elongation can take place (see Question 36.59).

37.23 When parenchyma cells are grown in a tissue culture, the cells _____ but do not _____ or differentiate. Normal development of the tissue requires a specific ratio of two hormones: _____ and _____.

37.24 Apical dominance is the ability of the _____ to suppress development of the _____.

37.25 When there is little root tissue, the greater amount of _____ as compared with _____ present causes growth of more stem. As roots become more extensive, an increased amount of _____ as compared with _____ stimulates growth of more lateral branches.

37.26 Growth of lateral buds apparently involves a balance of three hormones: _____, _____, and _____.

37.27 Dwarf plants produce insufficient amounts of _____ for normal growth.

37.28 Rapid growth of a flower stalk, a phenomenon called _____, is caused by high levels of _____.

37.29 Dormancy in apical buds and seeds is initiated by _____ and broken by _____.

37.30 In most seeds, the ratio of _____ to _____ determines whether the embryo remains dormant or germinates. In many desert plants, for example, germination begins when a heavy rain washes _____ from the seed.

37.31 Abscisic acid, produced in leaves, fruit, and root caps, acts as a stress hormone. When a plant does not have enough water, for example, abscisic acid causes the _____ to close by promoting the movement of _____, and consequently _____, out of the _____ cells.

37.32 Leaf abscission, in which enzymes digest cell walls at the base of the petiole, is prevented by _____ and promoted by _____.

37.33 Match the plant hormones listed below with their major effects.

(a) auxin   (1) _____ Fruit ripening
(b) cytokinins   (2) _____ Phototropism
(c) gibberellins   (3) _____ Formation of winter buds
(d) abscisic acid   (4) _____ Cell division
(e) ethylene   (5) _____ Suppression of cell division
     (6) _____ Stomatal opening and closing
     (7) _____ Growth of lateral buds
     (8) _____ Stem elongation in mature woody plants

37.34 How do gibberellins control plant form?

🐚 Gibberellins promote elongation of a plant's internodes, the regions of a stem between the nodes. Since leaves, lateral branches, and flowers originate at the nodes, gibberellins control the form of a plant by controlling the length of its internodes.

A rosette form of plant, as seen in a cabbage, produces only small amounts of gibberellins during its growing period and so has very short internodes with tightly packed leaves. A sunflower, by contrast, produces large amounts of gibberellins and has long internodes with leaves that are far apart. Application of gibberellins to a developing cabbage converts it into a plant with a form similar to a sunflower. In fact, the domestic cabbage was developed from its tall, spindly ancestor by selectively breeding only plants with shorter internodes, which were plants that produced only small amounts of gibberellins during their growing periods.

Mutant, dwarf varieties of plants produce less gibberellins than their normal-sized counterparts. Such dwarfs grow to normal proportions when treated with gibberellins.

37.35 How does one bad apple spoil the lot?

🐚 A fruit ripens in response to ethylene, a hormone that is produced in all parts of a plant and diffuses out of it as a gas. Ethylene is released in large quantities by fruits that have reached their maximum size and functions to soften the flesh and convert polysaccharides to sugars. One very ripe apple produces so much ethylene that it can hasten the ripening—or overripening—of all other apples in the lot.

In the early part of this century, citrus fruits were picked green and ripened by placing them in sheds heated by kerosene stoves. It was not, however, the heat that caused ripening, but rather the ethylene gas released when kerosene is burned. Our understanding of how ethylene promotes fruit ripening enables us to pick green fruit and control when it ripens.

37.36 How are plant hormones used to suppress weeds?

🐚 Synthetic auxins are used to get rid of dicots, such as dandelions and thistles, in areas reserved for monocots, such as lawns and grain fields. A dicot responds to unnaturally high concentrations of auxins by growing very rapidly and then dying, whereas a monocot, for reasons not yet known, is unaffected by the treatment.

Two widely used herbicides that resemble auxins are 2,4-dichlorophenoxyacetic acid (2,4-D) and 2,4,5-trichlorophenoxyacetic acid (2,4,5-T). The so-called Agent Orange of the Vietnam War was 2,4,5-T, which was sprayed on forests to remove the leaves and reveal enemy hiding places in the understory.

PLANT MOVEMENTS

37.37 A plant detects the direction of light by means of

(a) pigments.   (b) stomatal size.   (c) amyloplasts.   (d) heat receptors.

37.38 A plant distinguishes up from down by means of

(a) auxin flow.   (b) phytochromes.   (c) amyloplasts.   (d) transpirational flow.

37.39 An increase in turgor pressure, which moves leaves and flowers, occurs in response to changes in

(*a*) amyloplast position. (*b*) phytochrome structure. (*c*) the positions of tiny hairs. (*d*) concentrations of potassium ions.

37.40 Three tropisms of plants are: _____, which is growth toward or away from light; _____, which is growth toward or away from gravity; and _____, which is growth in response to touch. The entwining of a pea tendril around a string is an example of a _____.

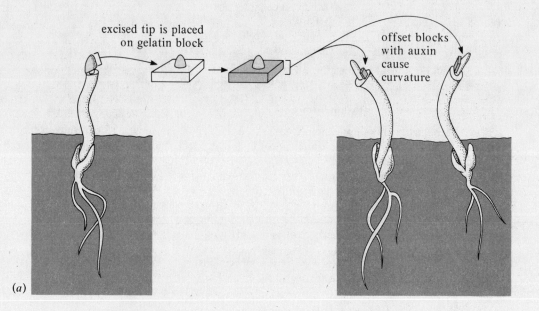

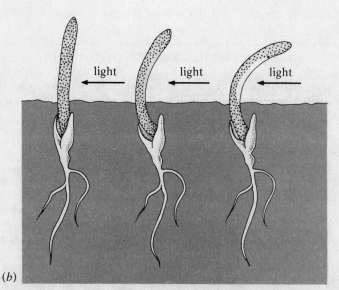

Fig. 37.1. Went's experiment that showed phototropism is caused by movements of a chemical. (*a*) Went removed the tip of a coleoptile (a protective sheath around the new leaf) from a 3-day-old grass seedling and placed it on a block of gelatin for an hour. He then placed the gelatin block on one side of the coleoptile where he had removed the tip. The remaining coleoptile bent away from the side where the block had been placed. A control experiment, in which a clean block of gelatin was similarly placed, produced no bending of the coleoptile. (*b*) Went concluded that a chemical, called auxin and synthesized in the shoot apex, moves toward the shaded side of a plant and causes the cells on that side to elongate; this results in the stem bending toward light.

37.41 A seedling placed on its side will have upward growth of its stem; it grows more rapidly, in response to higher concentrations of the growth hormones _____ and _____, on its lower side. A change in the distribution of hormones is caused by special kinds of chloroplasts, called _____, which are heavy because they contain _____ and _____ and so fall to the lower side of a cell.

37.42 How did Fritz Went demonstrate that phototropism is controlled by a diffusible chemical, rather than by a neural or electrical phenomenon?

✿   In 1926, Fritz Went demonstrated that a chemical produced in the shoot apex causes a plant to bend toward light, a phenomenon called *phototropism* (*photo* = light; *tropism* = orientation in response to a stimulus). In a cleverly designed experiment, illustrated in Fig. 37.1a, Went showed that when a chemical produced in the tip of the coleoptile of a grass seedling is allowed to accumulate on one side of the coleoptile, the chemical causes cells on that side to elongate and the seedling to bend. He did this by removing the tip of the coleoptile and placing it on a block of gelatin, where any chemical it might produce could accumulate. The block of gelatin was then placed on one side of the exposed leaf so that the chemical, if present, could move down one side of the seedling. As Went expected, the side on which the gelatin block was placed elongated and the coleoptile bent away from it. If the stimulus for phototropism had been neural or electrical in nature, it would not have been captured in the gelatin. Only a chemical could produce the results of his experiment. Went concluded that under natural conditions light causes migration of a chemical, which he named *auxin*, from the tip of the coleoptile to the shaded side of the stem, where it produces cell growth (Fig. 37.1b).

DAILY AND SEASONAL RHYTHMS

37.43 A rhythmic phenomenon that occurs about every 24 hours is a

(a) daily phase cycle.   (b) circadian rhythm.   (c) biologic clock.   (d) photoperiodism.

37.44 A physiological response to the duration of light and darkness is a

(a) daily phase cycle.   (b) circadian rhythm.   (c) biologic clock.   (d) photoperiodism.

37.45 If a short-day plant is grown under conditions of long nights and short days and the dark period is interrupted in the middle by a brief exposure to red light, the plant will

(a) wilt.   (b) flower.   (c) fail to flower.   (d) die.

37.46 If a short-day plant is grown under conditions of short nights and long days and the light period is interrupted in the middle by a brief exposure to darkness, the plant will

(a) wilt.   (b) flower.   (c) fail to flower.   (d) die.

37.47 If a long-day plant is grown under conditions of long nights and short days and the dark period is interrupted in the middle by a brief exposure to red light, the plant will

(a) wilt.   (b) flower.   (c) drop its floral buds.   (d) die.

37.48 The receptor in plants that detects photoperiod is a

(a) sensory cell.   (b) sensory organelle.   (c) protein molecule.   (d) gradient of potassium ions.

37.49 A biologic clock measures the length of each night by the

(a) relative amounts of red-absorbing and far-red-absorbing phytochrome present at dawn.   (b) amount of far-red-absorbing phytochrome at dusk.   (c) relative amounts of red-absorbing and far-red-absorbing phytochrome at midday.   (d) rate at which one kind of phytochrome is converted to the other.

37.50 Other than functions related to photoperiod, a major role of phytochrome is to detect the extent of

(a) stem growth.   (b) leaf motions.   (c) leaf shading.   (d) sun tracking.

37.51 A short-day plant, such as a poinsettia, will flower when the days are _____ than a critical level. A long-day plant, such as spinach, will flower when the days are _____ than a critical level (usually about 18 hours). A day-neutral plant, such as a tomato, is unaffected by _____.

37.52 The real control of flowering response is length of the _____, so that short-day plants should be called _____ plants and long-day plants should be called _____ plants.

37.53 Some plants, such as winter wheat, require a cold period before they will respond to photoperiod. This requirement is called _____.

37.54 Photoperiod is detected by the _____ of a plant, and information about it is sent to floral buds, perhaps by an unidentified hormone tentatively named _____.

37.55 A short-day plant subjected to a short exposure of red light during the middle of a long night _____ flower. A short-day plant subjected to a short exposure of red light followed by far-red light in the middle of a long night _____ flower. A short-day plant subjected to a short exposure of far-red light followed by red light in the middle of a long night _____ flower. The photoreceptor responsible for these effects is a protein known as _____, which alternates between two molecular forms to give the different responses.

37.56 Plants synthesize phytochrome in the form of _____, and if a plant is kept in the dark, the phytochrome remains in that form. Light, particularly the red light in sunlight, converts this form of phytochrome to the _____ form. Far-red light (abundant in the shade) or a long period of darkness converts _____ to _____.

37.57 A biologic clock in a plant measures the length of night from the relative amounts of each form of phytochrome at dawn. The more _____ present, the longer the night has been. A flash of red light during the night converts most of the _____ that has formed since dusk to _____, which tells the clock that a short night has passed. A flash of far-red light at night converts most of the _____ to _____, which tells the clock that a long night has passed. A flash of red light followed by a flash of far-red light during the night first converts most of the _____ to _____ and then most of the _____ to _____, which again tells the clock that a long night has passed.

37.58 How do plants receive information about their environment?

⚲ Clearly, plants have mechanisms to receive information from the environment and translate it into stimuli that generate the appropriate responses to environmental conditions. However, plants do not appear to have sensory cells. Instead, specialized molecules and, perhaps, organelles interpret a plant's environmental conditions.

The only known receptor molecule in plants is *phytochrome*—a special pigment that responds to changes in light and then triggers adjustments within the plant. Phytochrome is a protein molecule located within the plasma membranes of leaf cells that is extremely sensitive to certain forms of light. This pigment occurs in two molecular forms—red-absorbing phytochrome (P_r) and far-red-absorbing phytochrome (P_{fr}). When P_r absorbs the red light present in sunlight, it changes to the P_{fr} form (Fig. 37.2). When P_{fr} absorbs the far-red light present in shade, it changes to the P_r form. In complete darkness, P_{fr} reverts, slowly, to the P_r form. The relative amounts of these two molecular forms are determined by light conditions and govern many cellular activities within the plant.

Evidence suggests that plants contain a second receptor pigment, since certain growth phenomena and photo-tropisms occur in response to blue light. However, a receptor molecule that absorbs blue light has not yet been found.

The only known organelle that could receive information about the environment is the *amyloplast*—a specialized chloroplast, heavy with calcium and starch, that may detect gravity. Amyloplasts drop to the lower sides of cells. In ways not yet understood, the accumulation of amyloplasts on one side of cells causes certain hormones

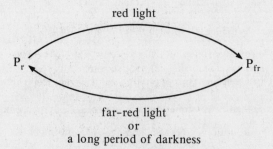

red light

P_r P_{fr}

far-red light
or
a long period of darkness

Fig. 37.2. The molecular conversion of phyto-chrome. The change from red-absorbing phyto-chrome (P_r) to far-red-absorbing phytochrome (P_{fr}), and vice versa, acts as an on-off switch governing a plant's cellular activities in response to photoperiod and shading.

to alter their distributions within the plant structure. Auxin and gibberellins, for example, accumulate on the lower side of a stem, where they cause cell elongation that leads to an upward bending of a horizontal stem.

Plants also respond to electricity, contact with solid objects (*thigmotropism*), and water. Little is known of the receptors that stimulate these reponses.

37.59 How does a plant know when it is the time of year to flower?

❀ Plants reproduce on roughly the same date each year. Certain kinds of flowers appear at specific times—violets and daffodils in the early spring, asters and goldenrod in the autumn. The environmental signal that initiates reproduction in most plants is the photoperiod. The response of each type of plant to a unique photoperiod is programmed into its genes.

The aspect of the photoperiod that initiates reproduction is the length of the night. By keeping plants indoors, where the length of light and dark periods can be manipulated, researchers found that a plant that normally flowers when there are 8 hours of light and 16 hours of dark will not flower if it is briefly exposed to bright light in the middle of the dark period. The disruption of the long dark period is interpreted by the plant's phytochrome system as the end of one *short* night and the beginning of another.

Phytochrome in the leaves stimulates the production of hormones that carry the message from the leaves to the shoot apical meristem and the lateral buds, where flowers are produced. Two hormones are probably involved in flowering. The first, gibberellin, causes the rapid elongation of the stems of some plants, a phenomenon known as *bolting*. The second hormone, tentatively called florigen, has not yet been isolated and may, in fact, be a combination of several already known hormones. This second "hormone" causes meristem tissue to develop into flowers rather than leaves by shifting the emphasis of the maturation process from growth to reproduction.

37.60 What is the evidence that a flowering hormone exists?

❀ Hormonal control of flowering was first suggested by experiments conducted by the Russian biologist M. H. Chailakhian in 1936. Working with chrysanthemums, which are short-day plants that bloom in autumn, he removed the upper leaves and exposed the leafless stem, with its floral buds, to long days while at the same time exposing the lower leaves to short days. The plants flowered. When he reversed the conditions, exposing the leafless area to short days and the leaves to long days, the plants did not flower. Chailakhian concluded the leaves perceive photoperiod and transmit information about it to the floral buds.

Grafting experiments in which two plants were grafted together and exposed to different photoperiods provided more evidence of a chemical messenger. In studies with cockleburs, which are short-day plants, one of the plants was exposed to short days and long nights while the other was exposed to long nights and short days. Both plants flowered, suggesting that a flower-inducing substance moved from the plant exposed to short days to the plant exposed to long days, where it stimulated floral development. The substance will not, however, move through a gelatin block; it seems to require a direct connection between living parts of plants. Other experiments support this evidence of a chemical messenger, although some plants apparently produce a flowering inhibitor when exposed to nonflowering photoperiods.

All attempts to identify a flowering hormone, prematurely named florigen, have failed. There is now considerable doubt that a separate hormone really exists. More likely, flowering is controlled by a combination of two or more other hormones, perhaps gibberellin and auxin, present in a particular ratio that is controlled by photoperiod.

Answers to Objective Questions

37.1 c

37.2 a

37.3 b

37.4 a

37.5 a

37.6 d

37.7 c

37.8 b

37.9 a

37.10 a

37.11 b

37.12 d

37.13 a

37.14 a

37.15 c

37.16 c

37.17 a

37.18 chemical; coleoptile tip; shaded

37.19 auxin; cytokinin; gibberellin; abscisic acid; ethylene

37.20 other hormones

37.21 parenchyma; ATP

37.22 hydrogen ions (or protons)

37.23 enlarge; divide; auxin; cytokinin

37.24 terminal bud; lateral buds

37.25 auxin; cytokinin; cytokinin; auxin

37.26 auxin; cytokinin; ethylene

37.27 gibberellin

37.28 bolting; gibberellin

37.29 abscisic acid; gibberellin

37.30 abscisic acid; gibberellin; abscisic acid

37.31 stomata; potassium ions; water; guard

37.32 auxin; ethylene

37.33 (1) e; (2) a; (3) d; (4) b; (5) e; (6) d; (7) b; (8) c

37.37 a

37.38 c

37.39 d

37.40 phototropism; gravitotropism; thigmotropism; thigmotropism

37.41 auxin; gibberellin; amyloplasts; calcium; starch

37.43 *b*

37.44 *d*

37.45 *c*

37.46 *c*

37.47 *b*

37.48 *c*

37.49 *a*

37.50 *c*

37.51 shorter; longer; day length

37.52 night; long-night; short-night

37.53 vernalization

37.54 leaves; florigen

37.55 will not; will; will not; phytochrome

37.56 red-absorbing phytochrome (P_r); far-red-absorbing phytochrome (P_{fr}); P_{fr}; P_r

37.57 P_r; P_r; P_{fr}; P_{fr}; P_r; P_r; P_{fr}; P_{fr}; P_r

ANIMAL TISSUES*

38.1 A tissue is a

(*a*) group of separate organs that are coordinated in their activities. (*b*) group of similar cells that function together in a specialized activity. (*c*) layer of cells surrounding an organ. (*d*) sheet of cells, one layer thick.

38.2 In order for cells to form a tissue, they must

(*a*) have different membrane proteins. (*b*) have different membrane potentials. (*c*) receive a command from the central nervous system. (*d*) recognize one another.

38.3 An organ system is a

(*a*) group of two or more kinds of tissue, united structurally and coordinated in their activities. (*b*) group of similar cells that function together in a specialized activity. (*c*) multilayered sheet of cells. (*d*) solid structure formed of embryonic mesoderm.

38.4 An organ system is a

(*a*) group of two or more kinds of tissue, united structurally and coordinated in their activities. (*b*) group of tissues forming a negative feedback loop. (*c*) group of organs that function together in an integrated way. (*d*) group of organs that form an individual animal.

38.5 Epithelial tissue always has an exposed outer surface and an inner surface anchored to connective tissue by a thin, noncellular layer called the

(*a*) nonstratified layer. (*b*) stratified layer. (*c*) basement membrane. (*d*) fibroblast.

38.6 Which type of tissue forms the inner lining of a blood vessel?

(*a*) Epithelial; (*b*) Connective; (*c*) Nervous; (*d*) Muscle

38.7 Which type of tissue forms the framework of the external ear?

(*a*) Epithelial; (*b*) Connective; (*c*) Nervous; (*d*) Muscle

38.8 Which type of tissue changes the diameter of a blood vessel?

(*a*) Epithelial; (*b*) Connective; (*c*) Nervous; (*d*) Muscle

38.9 Which type of tissue forms the thin surface for gas exchange in the lungs?

(*a*) Epithelial; (*b*) Connective; (*c*) Nervous; (*d*) Muscle

38.10 Which type of tissue forms glands?

(*a*) Epithelial; (*b*) Connective; (*c*) Nervous; (*d*) Muscle

38.11 Body tissues are composed of _____ cells. Cells in the body that do not form body tissues are _____ cells, which divide to form the _____ or _____.

38.12 The three primordial tissue layers of a vertebrate embryo, which give rise to all other tissues, are: _____, which gives rise to skin and the nervous system; _____, which gives rise to muscles, bones, kidneys, and reproductive organs; and _____, which gives rise to the lining of the digestive tract.

* Answers to Chapter 38 objective questions appear on page 269.

38.13 The four basic types of animal tissue are: _____, which are sheets of cells that cover surfaces; _____, which bind and support; _____, which send messages from one part of the body to another; and _____, which cause movement.

38.14 Everything that goes into and out of the body must pass through _____ tissue.

38.15 How are the more than 200 types of animal cells classified?

⊛ Every animal cell is classified as belonging to one of four basic tissue types—epithelial, connective, nervous, or muscle. Criteria for further subdivisions vary with the type of tissue.

Epithelial tissues are sheets of cells that cover body surfaces. They form the linings of tracts, cavities, and vessels, as well as the outer surfaces of organs, including the skin. Epithelial tissue is always anchored to connective tissue by means of a noncellular layer, known as a *basement membrane*, composed of polysaccharides. Glands are formed of epithelial tissues specialized for synthesizing and secreting particular molecules. Further classification of epithelial tissues is based on cell shape and number of cell layers. There are squamous, cuboidal, and columnar epithelial tissues, as well as simple epithelium (consisting of a single layer of cells) and stratified epithelium (consisting of several layers of cells).

Connective tissues support, protect, and bind together the other tissues. They form, among other structures, the bones, tendons, ligaments, and cartilage of the skeleton. Both blood and lymph are other forms of connective tissues. This type of tissue is different from the other three types in that its cells are far apart, separated from one another by large amounts of intercellular material. Characteristics of the intercellular material are used to further categorize connective tissue.

Muscle tissues contract and relax to provide movement. They are classified by appearance and location. Striated muscle contains bands of darker materials and smooth muscle does not. Skeletal muscle moves bones, cardiac muscle pumps blood, and smooth muscle moves all other organs and tissues.

Nervous tissues carry information from one place to another in the body. They are subdivided according to where they pick up and deliver their messages. *Sensory* neurons receive information from outside the central nervous system (brain and spinal cord) and carry it to the central nervous system. *Motor* neurons receive information from the central nervous system and carry it to effectors (muscles and glands). *Interneurons* carry information within the central nervous system, passing that information from one neuron to another.

HOMEOSTASIS

38.16 Interstitial fluid closely resembles

(*a*) seawater. (*b*) lake water. (*c*) pond water. (*d*) rainwater.

38.17 The idea of homeostasis was first presented, in 1859, by

(*a*) Claude Bernard. (*b*) Julian Huxley. (*c*) Charles Darwin. (*d*) Louis Pasteur.

38.18 Homeostasis occurs in

(*a*) all organisms to some extent. (*b*) multicellular organisms only. (*c*) animals only. (*d*) birds and mammals only.

38.19 The chief regulators of mammalian blood composition are the

(*a*) heart and arteries. (*b*) liver and kidneys. (*c*) lungs and pancreas. (*d*) thyroid and parathyroid glands.

38.20 Which of the following is an example of positive feedback?

(*a*) Allosteric inhibition of enzymes; (*b*) Sexual stimulation; (*c*) Thermostat for a furnace; (*d*) Vessel diameter and blood pressure

38.21 A vertebrate animal has two types of extracellular fluid: the _____, which bathes the cells; and the _____, which is carried in vessels.

38.22 The function of blood is to maintain the composition of the _____, which in turn maintains the composition of _____.

38.23 Homeostasis is maintaining an _____ that is distinctly different from the _____.

38.24 The term *homeostasis* was first used, in 1939, by Harvard physiologist Walter B. Cannon. He also proposed that maintaining internal constancy is possible only through coordinated homeostatic _____.

38.25 Homeostasis is most highly developed in the animal classes _____ and _____ .

38.26 Homeostasis is achieved by _____ , _____ , and _____ adaptations.

38.27 Regardless of conditions outside the body, homeostasis in a human maintains the blood-glucose concentration at _____ ; the blood pH at _____ ; the resting blood pressure at approximately _____ ; and the body temperature at approximately _____ .

38.28 A system in which a change in one direction results in a compensating change in the other direction is a _____ system. A system in which a change in one direction causes further changes in the same direction is a _____ system. Of the two systems, _____ is much more common in organisms and is essential to homeostasis.

38.29 The homeostatic regulation of an animal requires three basic components: _____ to detect changes, _____ to evaluate the changes, and _____ to adjust to the changes.

38.30 How do feedback systems work to bring about homeostasis in an animal?

🐚 Homeostasis is the maintenance of an internal environment that is different, more constant, and more suitable for cellular activities than the external environment. It is accomplished by means of morphological, physiological, and behavioral adaptations. Homeostasis is most highly developed in birds and mammals.

Feedback systems within an animal bring about physiological and behavioral adjustments that minimize deviations in internal conditions. Each system has three basic components: receptors, which detect changes in conditions; integrators, which evaluate these changes; and effectors, which work to bring the body back to its original state. The feedback is usually negative—a change in one direction produces a response in the opposite direction. Thus, an increase in body temperature causes effector activity that decreases body temperature.

Receptors are sensory cells that respond to changes in such internal features as body temperature, carbon dioxide concentration in the blood, blood pressure, and muscle stretch. Receptors convert information about these changes into electrochemical impulses that travel to the brain.

Integrators are special areas of the brain that receive information from receptors, evaluate it, and then send commands to the effectors capable of correcting the deviations from normal. Two major homeostatic centers of the vertebrate brain are the hypothalamus and the medulla oblongata.

Effectors are muscles and glands. They act in ways that return the body to its original, more suitable state after some deviation from normal. Muscles contract and relax to produce movements of the skeleton, circulatory system, and internal organs. Glands synthesize and release special materials, of which some act directly to promote homeostasis and others act indirectly to alter the activities of certain target cells.

Negative feedback operates, for example, to maintain body temperature. Receptors in the skin detect changes in skin temperature and neurons in the hypothalamus detect changes in blood temperature. This information is sent to special areas within the hypothalamus, where it is interpreted and evaluated. The hypothalamus then sends commands to appropriate effectors. When the temperature is above normal, arteries in the skin dilate, which brings warm blood to the surface, and sweat glands release sweat, which evaporates and removes heat from the skin. When the temperature is below normal, arteries in the skin constrict, preventing warm blood from reaching the surface, and skeletal muscles shiver, forming heat from excess cellular respiration. While these adjustments are taking place, the hypothalamus continues to receive information about body temperature and to adjust its commands in response to the information it receives.

Answers to Objective Questions

38.1 *b*

38.2 *d*

38.3 *a*

38.4 *c*

38.5 *c*

38.6 *a*

38.7 *b*

38.8 *d*

38.9 *a*

38.10 *a*

38.11 somatic; germ; sperm; eggs

38.12 ectoderm; mesoderm; endoderm

38.13 epithelial; connective; nervous; muscle

38.14 epithelial

38.16 *a*

38.17 *a*

38.18 *a*

38.19 *b*

38.20 *b*

38.21 interstitial fluid; plasma

38.22 interstitial fluid; cells

38.23 internal environment; external environment

38.24 systems

38.25 Aves; Mammalia

38.26 morphological; physiological; behavioral

38.27 0.1%; 7.4; 120/80; 37 °C

38.28 negative feedback; positive feedback; negative feedback

38.29 receptors; integrators; effectors

CHAPTER 39
Circulation and Gas Exchange

INTERNAL TRANSPORT IN INVERTEBRATES*

39.1   A cnidarian receives nutrients and oxygen, by diffusion, from its

(**a**) blood vessels.   (**b**) lymph vessels.   (**c**) gastrovascular cavity.   (**d**) book lungs and villi.

39.2   A flatworm receives nutrients and oxygen, by diffusion, from its internal cavity and its external environment. This slow transport system suffices, because

(**a**) all cells are near sources of nutrients and oxygen.   (**b**) the blood is replenished rapidly.   (**c**) the environment is especially rich in nutrients and oxygen.   (**d**) the animal moves rapidly away from nutrient-poor environments.

39.3   A circulatory system with blood vessels and at least one heart is required by all animals with

(**a**) aerobic cellular respiration.   (**b**) internal digestion.   (**c**) sedentary lifestyles.   (**d**) many layers of cells.

39.4   In the sinuses of an open circulatory system, blood is not segregated from the

(**a**) cytoplasm.   (**b**) interstitial fluid.   (**c**) digestive cavity.   (**d**) urine.

39.5   In a closed circulatory system, blood is completely enclosed within

(**a**) the skeleton.   (**b**) sinuses.   (**c**) vessels.   (**d**) hearts.

39.6   In an open circulatory system, blood is pumped by _____, which are very muscular forms of _____, and by _____ of the animal.

39.7   In a grasshopper, blood _____ the hearts when the heart muscles relax and _____ the hearts when the heart muscles contract. Blood enters the hearts through pores called _____, which have _____ that ensure a one-way flow of blood into the hearts.

39.8   A hydra receives oxygen and nutrients from its _____. A planarian receives oxygen and nutrients from its _____. An ant's circulatory system is _____, a spider's is _____, an earthworm's is _____, a snail's is _____, a squid's is _____, and a fish's is _____.

39.9   An insect does not transport _____ in its blood, whereas the more sluggish snail does use its blood for transport of this material.

39.10   What are the advantages of a closed, as compared with an open, circulatory system?

Two basic types of transport systems—the open and the closed circulatory systems—occur in the larger invertebrate animals. (Smaller animals do not need transport systems, for all of their body cells are near internal cavities or the external environment.) In an open circulatory system, the blood is not completely enclosed within vessels; the hearts pump blood through arteries into large cavities, or sinuses, where it mixes with interstitial fluid and bathes the cells of the body. The blood is slowly returned to the hearts through small pores, called *ostia*.
In a closed circulatory system, the blood remains within a completely enclosed system of vessels and never comes in direct contact with the body cells. Materials move between the blood and interstitial fluid through the thin walls of capillaries.
   Circulation is slower in an open system, because with some of the blood pooled in sinuses, the hearts cannot build up enough pressure to make the blood flow rapidly. An open system cannot achieve the high rates of oxygen transport that active animals require. Animals with open systems are either quite small and sluggish or use the open system only for transport of food and wastes, and use a different system for transport of gases. Insects, for example, have a separate system of vessels—the *tracheal system*—for gas transport. The insect's circulatory system

* Answers to Chapter 39 objective questions appear on page 277.

is composed of five muscular hearts, which slowly pump the blood, which contains food and wastes (except carbon dioxide), hormones, and other materials, through a system of vessels and open cavities in a forward and downward direction. The blood bathes the cells of the body in open cavities below the vessels, providing the necessary materials (except oxygen) for cellular activities and accumulating waste products (except carbon dioxide) from the cells. The blood then moves slowly from these cavities backward and upward to the hearts. Transport is accelerated during physical activity, when the skeletal muscles contract rhythmically, squeezing the cavities and forcing the blood back toward the hearts.

Invertebrate animals that have open circulatory systems include the arthropods (such as insects, spiders, crabs, and lobsters) and most mollusks (such as snails, oysters, and clams); invertebrates with a closed circulatory system include the annelids (such as earthworms) and some mollusks (such as squids).

CIRCULATION IN VERTEBRATES

39.11   An artery is a vessel that carries blood

(a) with high concentrations of oxygen.   (b) with high concentrations of carbon dioxide.   (c) toward the heart.
(d) away from the heart.

39.12   The exchange of materials between blood and interstitial fluid occurs only at the

(a) veins.   (b) capillaries.   (c) arteries.   (d) arterioles.

39.13   Which of the following animals has the most mixing of oxygenated and unoxygenated blood in its ventricle?

(a) Fish;   (b) Frog;   (c) Snake;   (d) Crocodile

39.14   Which chamber of a bird heart does oxygen-rich blood first enter?

(a) Right atrium;   (b) Left atrium;   (c) Right ventricle;   (d) Left ventricle

39.15   A vertebrate heart consists of one or more _____, which receive blood from the capillaries via _____, and one or more _____, which pump blood to the capillaries via _____.

39.16   A fish has _____ atrium (atria) and _____ ventricle(s). It has a single circuit of blood flow, in which blood pumped from the heart travels through two capillary beds before it returns: one bed is at the _____, where oxygen is acquired, and the other is at the _____, where oxygen is used.

39.17   An amphibian has _____ atrium (atria) and _____ ventricle(s). It has double circulation, in which one artery carries blood from the heart to capillary beds of the _____ and _____ and a second artery carries blood from the heart to capillary beds in the rest of the body.

39.18   A typical reptile has _____ atrium (atria) and _____ ventricle(s). It has double circulation, in which one artery carries blood from the heart to capillary beds of the _____ and a second artery carries blood from the heart to capillary beds in the rest of the body. A crocodile, however, is a reptile with an additional _____, which prevents mixing of _____ and _____ blood.

39.19   A bird or mammal has _____ atrium (atria) and _____ ventricle(s). There is double circulation, as with amphibians and reptiles, but _____ blood from the _____ is completely segregated from _____ blood from the rest of the body.

39.20   How can a frog or a lizard be very active if its oxygen-rich blood mixes with oxygen-poor blood before becoming available to the body cells?

🐚   A frog or lizard has a single ventricle, which receives oxygen-poor blood from the body as well as oxygen-rich blood from the lungs and, in the case of a frog, from the skin. Blood from the ventricles is pumped via one artery to the lungs (and skin, in the case of a frog) and via another artery to the rest of the body. In neither animal, however, is there complete mixing of the two types of blood in the ventricle. A frog has a ridge of heart tissue that partially segregates the ventricle into a left and right side. The ridge diverts unoxygenated blood from the right atrium to the artery leading to the lungs and skin and oxygenated blood from the left atrium to the artery leading to the rest of the body. A lizard has a *septum*, or wall, in its ventricle that performs the same function, but performs it much better than the ridge in a frog's ventricle. The septum almost completely separates the ventricle into a left and right side; there is very little mixing of oxygenated and unoxygenated blood in a lizard heart. The active cells of both a frog and a lizard receive highly oxygenated blood, although not as oxygenated as the blood received by the body cells of a bird or mammal, which have hearts with two completely separate ventricles. A bird or mammal, however, has a greater need for oxygen, because of the high metabolic demands of endothermy.

CIRCULATION IN MAMMALS

39.21 Which chamber of the heart has the thickest muscular walls?

(*a*) Right atrium;   (*b*) Left atrium;   (*c*) Right ventricle;   (*d*) Left ventricle

39.22 Blood enters the heart because muscles of the

(*a*) atria relax.   (*b*) atria contract.   (*c*) ventricles relax.   (*d*) ventricles contract.

39.23 Blood travels from the heart to the lungs by way of the

(*a*) superior (or anterior) vena cava.   (*b*) inferior (or posterior) vena cava.   (*c*) pulmonary artery.
(*d*) pulmonary vein.

39.24 Blood from the head, neck, and arms (or forelimbs) enters the heart by way of the

(*a*) superior (or anterior) vena cava.   (*b*) inferior (or posterior) vena cava.   (*c*) pulmonary artery.
(*d*) pulmonary vein.

39.25 A heart murmur indicates a defective

(*a*) sinoatrial node.   (*b*) atrioventricular node.   (*c*) heart valve.   (*d*) pulmonary artery or aorta.

39.26 In a normal person at rest the cardiac output, or amount of blood pumped per minute by the left ventricle, is approximately

(*a*) $\frac{1}{2}$ liter.   (*b*) 1 liter.   (*c*) 2 liters.   (*d*) 5 liters.

39.27 The sinoatrial node, which generates the electrical impulses that coordinate heart-muscle contractions, is located in the

(*a*) medulla oblongata.   (*b*) inferior (or posterior) vena cava.   (*c*) right atrium.   (*d*) left ventricle.

39.28 Approximately 3 liters of fluid, as well as some blood proteins, leave the capillaries of a healthy person each day. The lost fluid and proteins are returned to the circulatory system by

(*a*) active transport in endothelial cells of the capillary walls.   (*b*) passive diffusion from the interstitial fluid into the capillaries.   (*c*) the lymphatic system.   (*d*) the villi of the small intestine.

39.29 Hypotension, or chronic low blood pressure, may develop from

(*a*) not enough blood proteins due to a low-protein diet.   (*b*) a high-fat, high-cholesterol diet.   (*c*) too much emotional stress.   (*d*) too much caffeine or nicotine.

39.30 Backflow of blood in the heart is prevented by four valves: two atrioventricular valves, which prevent flow from the _____ to the _____, and two semilunar valves, which prevent flow from the _____ and the _____ to the _____.

39.31 The one-way flow of blood through the heart is from the _____, where oxygen-poor blood enters, to the _____, which pumps blood through the _____ artery to the lungs. Oxygen-rich blood returns to the heart by way of the _____ veins, which empty into the _____. Blood then moves to the _____, which pumps the blood through the _____ and then to all the arteries of the body except those carrying blood to the _____.

39.32 The heart cycle consists of two phases: _____, during which the ventricles contract, and _____, during which the ventricles relax. A blood pressure reading for a normal man is about 120/80, in which 120 is the measure of _____ pressure and 80 is the measure of _____ pressure.

39.33   In comparing all mammals, we find an inverse relation between heart rate and _____.

39.34   Cardiac output is determined by the _____ and the _____. Blood pressure is determined by the cardiac output and the size of the _____.

39.35   The wall of an artery or vein consists of three layers: an outer layer of _____ and elastic fibers, a middle layer of _____ and elastic fibers, and an inner lining of _____. The wall of a capillary consists of only _____.

39.36   Blood is transported through veins by contractions of _____ muscles and by _____ movements.

39.37   An accumulation of unusually large quantities of interstitial fluids is called _____. A severe form of this condition is the disease elephantiasis, in which parasitic worms block the _____, thereby preventing return of fluids from the interstitial fluid to the blood.

39.38   Varicose veins develop from damaged _____ in the veins.

39.39   A heart attack occurs when a _____ is blocked. A stroke occurs when a _____ carrying blood to the _____ is blocked or ruptured. Blockage results from either a _____ (clot that develops at the site) or an _____ (clot that develops elsewhere and moves to the site). Most heart attacks and strokes occur in people whose vessels are already partially blocked and made rigid by plaques, a disease known as _____.

39.40   What controls heart rate?

    The rate at which the heart muscles contract is regulated in several ways. The main control is the *sinoatrial node*, or pacemaker, which is a small piece of specialized heart muscle located in the wall of the right atrium. Electrical impulses emitted at regular intervals by this tissue stimulate muscle contractions in the four chambers of the heart. Each impulse travels through both atria, causing them to contract almost simultaneously, and on to another specialized region—the *atrioventricular node*—which transmits the impulse to both ventricles simultaneously. The slight delay in the signal produces a sequence of contractions: first the two atria, then the two ventricles.

    A second regulator of heart rate is an area within the *medulla oblongata* of the brain. The cardio-inhibitory center in this area communicates with the sinoatrial node via the vagus nerves, which contain both afferent and efferent axons. The afferent nerve axons, which originate in the node and terminate in the cardio-inhibitory center, provide information about the heart rate. The efferent nerve axons, which originate in the cardio-inhibitory center and extend to the sinoatrial node, can stimulate the node to decrease the rate of heart-muscle contractions. The cardio-inhibitory center functions to restrain the sinoatrial node, to hold the heart rate in check.

    In addition to feedback from the sinoatrial node, the cardio-inhibitory center receives information from sensory surfaces and from higher brain centers. Sensory cells on the internal and external body surfaces transmit information to the center about such conditions as indigestion, inhalation of irritating fumes, sudden cold temperatures, and blood pressure. When the center receives the information, it stimulates the efferent axons of the vagus nerves, which diminish the heart rate. Certain emotional states also stimulate the cardio-inhibitory center. Many areas of the brain are involved in the regulation of emotion, but the critical pathway that influences heart rate is from the limbic system to the cardio-inhibitory center.

    The cardio-accelerating center within the medulla oblongata of the brain is stimulated by many factors, including pain sensations from the skin and anticipation of exercise. Efferent neurons from the cardio-accelerating center terminate in the heart muscles themselves, rather than in the sinoatrial node. When stimulated, these neurons release a neurotransmitter (norepinephrine) that increases both the heart rate and the stroke volume (amount of blood pumped with each contraction).

    The heart rate is also affected by hormones. Thyroxine, the hormone secreted by the thyroid gland, increases the heart rate. Epinephrine, a hormone secreted by the adrenal medullas, increases both the rate and the stroke volume.

39.41   What regulates the rate at which blood flows through the circulatory system?

    Animals must be able to adjust the rate of blood flow in response to changing conditions. When cellular activity is low, as during sleep, the rate of blood flow is lowered to conserve energy. During strenuous activity, the rate of blood flow must be rapid enough to meet the increased demand for exchange of materials between the blood and the more active cells.

The cardiac output, or quantity of blood the heart pumps per minute, is about 5 liters in a resting human. Cardiac output is the product of two factors: (1) the heart rate (number of contractions per minute) and (2) the stroke volume (amount of blood ejected from the heart during each contraction).

Heart rate is controlled primarily by the sinoatrial node, but also by the cardio-inhibitory and cardio-accelerating centers within the medulla oblongata of the brain and by hormones secreted by the thyroid and adrenal glands (see Question 39.40).

Stroke volume is controlled by artery diameter. Because the vessels and the heart form a closed circulatory system, the volume of blood expelled from the heart during each contraction can only be increased if the rate at which blood is returned to the heart undergoes a corresponding increase. As the volume of blood returning per minute to the heart increases, the muscle contractions that force blood through the heart become stronger. Blood is returned to the heart more rapidly when the blood pressure is higher, i.e., when the arteries are more constricted.

Artery diameter is controlled by *vasomotor centers* in the medulla oblongata in response to carbon dioxide levels in the blood and by brain centers that control emotions. High concentrations of carbon dioxide, a waste product of cellular respiration, reflect high levels of cellular activity. The amount of carbon dioxide in the blood is detected by neurons in two vasomotor centers, one on each side of the medulla oblongata, which send electro-chemical impulses along vasomotor nerves to the muscles of the arteries. High levels of carbon dioxide cause constriction of the arterial walls, and thus an increase in blood pressure and a more rapid flow of blood through the circulatory system. Low levels of carbon dioxide produce the opposite effect: the arteries become dilated, blood pressure drops, and blood flow becomes slower.

Finally, blood flow is controlled by the brain centers that control the emotions, including the *cerebral cortex* and the *limbic system*, which emit electrochemical impulses that travel to the vasomotor centers of the medulla oblongata. Certain emotional states can accelerate the heart rate and constrict the arteries; other emotional states can inhibit the heart rate and dilate the arteries to the point that the individual faints. Information is transmitted from the vasomotor centers to the arterial walls, which either constricts or dilates the vessels.

BLOOD

39.42 About how much blood is in the circulatory system of an average person?

(*a*) 1 liter; (*b*) 2 liters; (*c*) 5 liters; (*d*) 10 liters

39.43 A mature mammalian erythrocyte (red blood cell) is unusual in that it has

(*a*) a cell wall. (*b*) no nucleus. (*c*) no continuous plasma membrane. (*d*) plastids.

39.44 Both erythrocytes and leukocytes form in the

(*a*) bone marrow. (*b*) thymus. (*c*) arterial walls. (*d*) lymph nodes.

39.45 An erythrocyte lives for approximately

(*a*) one week. (*b*) one month. (*c*) three months. (*d*) one year.

39.46 The difference between plasma and serum is that _____ is blood without its clotting materials and _____ is blood without its cells.

39.47 The main function of erythrocytes is to _____, for which they contain a special protein, called _____.

39.48 The general function of leukocytes is to _____. One type of leukocyte synthesizes _____, which are the proteins that clump microbes.

39.49 A blood clot forms when a plasma protein called _____, normally present in the blood, is converted to _____, which forms the threads of a clot.

39.50 What are the materials carried by the blood of a vertebrate animal?

⊛   The function of blood is to maintain the composition of interstitial fluid so that materials needed by cells are available and waste materials are removed. To perform this function, the blood of a vertebrate animal transports:

1. Oxygen from the lungs or gills to all parts of the body
2. Carbon dioxide from the cells to the lungs or gills
3. Food monomers from the digestive tract to various parts of the body, where they are used or stored
4. Waste products from the cells to the kidneys
5. Heat from the deeper parts of the body to the surface, where it can be dissipated
6. Cells and molecules of the immune system, which fight invasions of bacteria, viruses, and other foreign organisms
7. Materials that repair vessel damage
8. Special molecules, such as hormones, that are formed in one part of the body and used in other parts

GAS EXCHANGE

39.51 The gas-exchange surfaces of most larger aquatic animals are

(*a*) tracheae. (*b*) Malpighian tubules. (*c*) gills. (*d*) book lungs.

39.52 An advantage of gas exchange in aquatic habitats, as compared with terrestrial habitats, is that it is easier to keep the gas-exchange surfaces

(*a*) wet. (*b*) ventilated. (*c*) free of injury. (*d*) saturated with oxygen.

39.53 A disadvantage of gas exchange in aquatic habitats, as compared with terrestrial habitats, is that

(*a*) gas-exchange surfaces tend to collapse in water. (*b*) water currents are too slow for most types of surfaces. (*c*) oxygen concentration in water is much lower than in air. (*d*) carbon dioxide concentration in water is much lower than in air.

39.54 An animal must have some way of moving air or water across its gas-exchange surfaces, a process known as

(*a*) countercurrent exchange. (*b*) ventilation. (*c*) facilitated diffusion. (*d*) active respiration.

39.55 Gas exchange in the gills of a fish is enhanced by having the blood flow in a direction opposite to the direction of water flow, a process known as

(*a*) countercurrent exchange. (*b*) ventilation. (*c*) facilitated diffusion. (*d*) active respiration.

39.56 A grasshopper ventilates its gas-exchange surfaces by

(*a*) moving its diaphragm. (*b*) moving its rib cage. (*c*) the beating of millions of cilia. (*d*) rhythmic body movements.

39.57 The surface area of a human lung is made larger by alveoli and is approximately the size of a

(*a*) dinner plate. (*b*) table. (*c*) four-person tent. (*d*) tennis court.

39.58 Breathing rate in mammals is controlled by a part of the brain called the

(*a*) thalamus. (*b*) hypothalamus. (*c*) medulla oblongata. (*d*) cerebellum.

39.59 The breathing center in the brain responds to changes in the

(*a*) oxygen concentration of the blood. (*b*) carbon dioxide concentration of the blood. (*c*) glucose in the mitochondria. (*d*) acetyl coenzyme A in the mitochondria.

39.60 Gases move across membranes by _____. To move in this way, the membranes must be _____.

39.61 It is _____ difficult to ventilate in water than air. A fish spends _____ energy in ventilation than a lizard.

39.62 The countercurrent exchange in a fish gill increases the rate of _____ between water and blood.

39.63 The gas-exchange surface of an earthworm is _____; of a crayfish, _____; of a clam, _____; of a beetle, _____; of a land snail, _____; of a spider, _____; of a snake, _____; of a hawk, _____; of a seal, _____.

39.64 Surface tension holds two wet membranes tightly together. It holds the outer surfaces of the lungs to the wall of the chest but is greatly weakened on the inner surfaces of the lungs by a chemical that acts as a _____, in order to prevent these surfaces from sticking together.

39.65 A mammal ventilates its lungs by moving its _____ and its _____. A reptile ventilates its lungs by moving its _____. An amphibian ventilates its lungs by _____ air.

39.66 At a particular barometric pressure (e.g., at sea level), the partial pressure of a gas reflects its _____, whether in air or dissolved in water. When blood from the right atrium reaches the lung, it has a _____ partial pressure of oxygen and a _____ partial pressure of carbon dioxide than air in the alveoli. Cellular respiration _____ the partial pressure of oxygen and _____ the partial pressure of carbon dioxide, so a cell has a _____ partial pressure of oxygen and a _____ partial pressure of carbon dioxide than blood coming from the left ventricle.

39.67 Each hemoglobin molecule can carry _____ molecules of oxygen, one in each _____. After the first molecule of oxygen is bound, the affinity of hemoglobin for others is _____. Likewise, after the first molecule of oxygen is unloaded, the affinity of hemoglobin for others is _____. The oxygen dissociation curve (percent saturation of hemoglobin as a function of the partial pressure of oxygen) has a sigmoid shape, because at the intermediate partial pressures of tissues, a slight change in partial pressure causes a _____ change in percent saturation; hemoglobin rapidly _____ and _____ oxygen once the first _____ has been transferred.

39.68 Most carbon dioxide is transported in the blood in the form of _____ ions. Hydrogen ions formed when carbon dioxide enters the blood become attached to _____, so that the addition of carbon dioxide causes only a small decrease in blood pH.

39.69 What are the necessary features of a gas-exchange surface?

⚛ Gas exchange between the body of an organism and its external environment may take place over the entire outer body surface or over only portions of that surface. The particular arrangement of cells that form a gas-exchange surface and the position of these cells on the body vary greatly among different types of organisms. However, any surface that promotes the diffusion of gases must have four basic features, as described below.

  1. The surface area must be relatively large; diffusion is a slow process, and the larger the area, the more diffusion that can be achieved. Large surface areas usually contain extensive tissue projections and foldings to conserve space.
  2. The surface must be moist at all times, because oxygen and carbon dioxide must be dissolved in water to diffuse across cell membranes. Aquatic organisms easily meet this requirement, but it is difficult for organisms living on land to maintain a moist surface. Many adaptations in terrestrial organisms minimize, but can never totally prevent, water loss during respiration.
  3. A surface for gas exchange must be close to the active cells of the body or to the fluid that transports gases between these cells and the surface. Diffusion is too slow to carry gases very deeply into the body of an organism.
  4. Air or water must be moved over the gas-exchange surface. If the environment adjacent to the surface remained motionless, the concentration of oxygen would soon become too low and the concentration of carbon dioxide too high for effective diffusion to continue in that area. The body of the organism must move through the environment, or the environment must be moved across the gas-exchange surface. The various methods of moving water or air across a gas exchange surface are called *ventilation mechanisms*.

39.70 How is breathing rate adjusted for different levels of activity?

⚛ A resting mammal inhales and exhales at regular intervals. This rhythm of breathing originates in neurons within two special respiratory centers on either side of the medulla oblongata of the brain. Breathing is an involuntary action—we do not have to remember to inhale and exhale, although we control it when we speak and during a variety of other activities.

Impulses transmitted to the muscles of the rib cage and the diaphragm from the respiratory centers direct the expansion and contraction of the chest cavity, and so also the lungs, which adhere to the inner wall of the chest. The depth of quiet breathing is governed by stretch receptors located in the lung tissues. The stimulation of these receptors by expansion of the lungs during inhalation sends impulses to the respiratory centers, which cause inhalation to stop. During quiet breathing, exhalation automatically follows the cessation of inhalation; it involves a relaxation of the muscles and no special stimulus is needed.

In addition to establishing a basic rhythm of exhalation and inhalation, the respiratory centers adjust the breathing rate in response to bodily requirements for gas exchange. Breathing slows during sleep and increases dramatically during vigorous exercise, fever, and emotional upset. Breathing can be altered by inputs to the respiratory centers from a variety of chemical and neural sources. Within the normal ranges of physical activity, the respiratory centers respond to the concentration of carbon dioxide in the blood. The rate of cellular respiration increases when cells become more active, and so carbon dioxide, a waste product of the reaction, is a sensitive indicator of the body's activity level and its oxygen requirements. An increase in carbon dioxide in the blood causes an increase in the breathing rate, and vice versa.

Other neural mechanisms are activated during very labored breathing. When the lungs are in a deflated condition, deflation receptors in the lungs transmit impulses to the respiratory centers, which initiate a rapid and forced inspiration (a gasp for breath). An area within the *pons* of the hindbrain also communicates information to the respiratory centers during extremely labored breathing.

Answers to Objective Questions

39.1 c
39.2 a
39.3 d
39.4 b
39.5 c
39.6 hearts; vessels; movements
39.7 enters; leaves; ostia; valves
39.8 gastrovascular cavity; gastrovascular cavity; open; open; closed; open; closed; closed
39.9 oxygen
39.11 d
39.12 b
39.13 b
39.14 b
39.15 atria; veins; ventricles; arteries
39.16 one; one; gills; other tissues
39.17 two; one; lungs; skin
39.18 two; one; lungs; ventricle; oxygen-rich; oxygen-poor
39.19 two; two; oxygen-rich; lungs; oxygen-poor
39.21 d
39.22 a
39.23 c
39.24 a
39.25 c

39.26 d
39.27 c
39.28 c
39.29 a
39.30 ventricles; atria; pulmonary artery; aorta; ventricles
39.31 right atrium; right ventricle; pulmonary; pulmonary; left atrium; left ventricle; aorta; lungs
39.32 systole; diastole; systolic; diastolic
39.33 body size
39.34 heart rate; stroke volume; arteries
39.35 connective tissue; smooth muscle; endothelium; endothelium
39.36 skeletal; breathing
39.37 edema; lymph vessels
39.38 valves
39.39 coronary artery; artery; brain; thrombus; embolus; atherosclerosis
39.42 c
39.43 b
39.44 a
39.45 c
39.46 serum; plasma

39.47 transport oxygen; hemoglobin
39.48 kill microbes; antibodies
39.49 fibrinogen; fibrin
39.51 c
39.52 a
39.53 c
39.54 b
39.55 a
39.56 d
39.57 d
39.58 c
39.59 b
39.60 diffusion; wet
39.61 more; more
39.62 diffusion
39.63 skin; gills; gills; tracheae; book (or diffusion) lungs; book (or diffusion) lungs; lungs; lungs; lungs
39.64 surfactant
39.65 rib cage; diaphragm; rib cage; "swallowing"
39.66 concentration; lower; higher; lowers; raises; lower; higher
39.67 four; polypeptide; increased; decreased; large; loads; unloads; molecule
39.68 bicarbonate; hemoglobin

CHAPTER 40
Nutrition and Digestion

NUTRITIONAL REQUIREMENTS*

40.1 Which of the following molecules can be used by an animal as a source of energy?

(*a*) Carbohydrates only;   (*b*) Fats only;   (*c*) Carbohydrates or fats;   (*d*) Carbohydrates, fats, or proteins

40.2 The molecule used by most animals for long-term energy storage is

(*a*) glycogen.   (*b*) starch.   (*c*) fat.   (*d*) cholesterol.

40.3 Energy is stored in the liver and muscles as

(*a*) glycogen.   (*b*) starch.   (*c*) fat.   (*d*) cholesterol.

40.4 An animal with a diet deficient in at least one essential nutrient is said to be

(*a*) starving.   (*b*) undernourished.   (*c*) malnourished.   (*d*) suffering from kwashiorkor disease.

40.5 How many of the 20 amino acids are essential amino acids for an adult human?

(*a*) 6;   (*b*) 8;   (*c*) 11;   (*d*) 14

40.6 Which of the following vegetarian meals will supply all essential amino acids in about the correct proportions for synthesizing human proteins?

(*a*) Spinach and beans;   (*b*) Corn and rice;   (*c*) Beans and rice;   (*d*) Peas and beans

40.7 Most vitamins function as

(*a*) lubricants for active transport.   (*b*) a foundation for building bone.   (*c*) transport molecules within plasma membranes.   (*d*) coenzymes.

40.8 A mineral is an atom that can be used by an animal in a form that is

(*a*) an organic molecule.   (*b*) an inorganic molecule or ion.   (*c*) bonded to a vitamin.   (*d*) bonded to several water molecules.

40.9 The oxidation of fat releases about _____ kilocalories per gram, whereas the oxidation of carbohydrates or proteins releases about _____ to _____ kilocalories per gram.

40.10 The number of kilocalories a resting animal requires to maintain itself is called the _____ metabolic rate. The two classes of vertebrates with the highest resting requirements for energy are _____ and _____, because they are _____.

40.11 When we compare all mammals, we find that the caloric requirement to support each gram of body weight is inversely related to _____.

40.12 After fat reserves have been depleted during starvation, the body's _____ are used as sources of energy.

40.13 The four types of essential nutrients are: _____; _____; _____; and _____.

---

* Answers to Chapter 40 objective questions appear on page 285.

40.14   What determines the essential nutrients of an animal?

@   The diet of each type of animal must include a specific group of essential nutrients—essential amino acids, essential fatty acids, vitamins, and minerals—to provide the raw materials needed to synthesize the different kinds of organic molecules the animal must have to sustain life. The essential nutrients are materials the animal must have but cannot synthesize in its cells. The nutrients that are essential differ for each type of animal because the ability to synthesize particular molecules is a genetic trait acquired through natural selection and because each type of animal has a unique evolutionary history.

In general, the more simple and primitive animals are able to synthesize more of the materials they require than can the more complex and advanced animals. The ability to construct many materials was lost during the evolution of more complex animals because these materials became so commonly available in the diet that the enzymes required to synthesize them were no longer necessary and were lost from the genetic repertoire.

For example, most vertebrate animals are able to synthesize vitamin C in their cells, but this ability has been lost in guinea pigs, fruit-eating bats, a few types of birds, humans, and some other primates. All animals require vitamin C, for it is essential in the construction and maintenance of substances that bind cells together, especially in skin, bone, and muscle. The only animals that require vitamin C in their diets, however, are those with ancestors that regularly consumed an adequate supply of vitamin C and gradually lost the enzymes necessary for its synthesis.

40.15   Why do malnourished children usually have enlarged abdomens?

@   A swollen abdomen and legs are symptomatic of severe protein deficiency. In such cases, the blood does not contain enough plasma proteins to hold water in the blood vessels, and water seeps out of the capillaries and accumulates in the interstitial fluids between cells, especially in the abdominal cavity and legs. This condition also produces low blood pressure and causes the problems associated with poor blood circulation.

In parts of Africa, a child with an enlarged abdomen is said to be kwashiorkor, which means "the rejected one," because protein deficiency begins when a child is weaned after a younger sibling is born. Without the protein-rich milk from its mother, a child in a poverty-stricken area is likely to suffer from an inadequate protein intake.

DIGESTION: GENERAL PROPERTIES

40.16   Another term for digestion is

(**a**) dehydration synthesis.   (**b**) hydrolysis.   (**c**) absorption.   (**d**) monomer interchange.

40.17   Digestion is brought about by

(**a**) acids.   (**b**) alkaline solutions.   (**c**) enzymes.   (**d**) vitamins and minerals.

40.18   Digestion in a hydra or planarian takes place within its

(**a**) mouth.   (**b**) gastrovascular cavity.   (**c**) digestive tract.   (**d**) coelom.

40.19   Digestion in an earthworm or snail takes place within its

(**a**) mouth.   (**b**) gastrovascular cavity.   (**c**) digestive tract.   (**d**) coelom.

40.20   Digestion within a digestive tract is

(**a**) incomplete.   (**b**) extracellular.   (**c**) the same as absorption.   (**d**) an irreversible process.

40.21   In the process of digestion, carbohydrates are converted to _____, proteins to _____, fats to _____ and _____, and nucleic acids to _____.

40.22   A disadvantage of digestion within a gastrovascular cavity is that _____ cannot be taken in at the same time that _____ leave, because a single opening serves as both _____ and _____.

40.23   Food and wastes move through a digestive tract by means of _____ of the tract's _____. Each segment of the tract can be temporarily closed off by ringlike muscles called _____.

40.24   The digestive tract of a bird has three chambers between its esophagus and intestine: a _____ and _____ for storage of food, and a _____ for grinding of food.

40.25 What is the advantage of a digestive tract as compared with a digestive cavity?

✎ A digestive *cavity*, or incomplete digestive system, has only one opening to the outside environment. A digestive *tract*, or complete digestive system, has two openings, one for food intake and the other for waste removal. Cnidarians, flatworms, and other acoelomates have digestive cavities (the gastrovascular cavity). Advanced animals, including both pseudocoelomates and coelomates, have digestive tracts.

Food enters a digestive cavity by way of the single opening, which is often fringed with special structures to poison the prey and so keep it from struggling and injuring tissue inside the cavity. The food then moves into the cavity, where it is digested. The portions of food that cannot be digested are moved out of the body through the same opening in the form of feces. Because the digestive cavity has a single opening, food entering the cavity cannot be separated from the feces leaving the cavity. To prevent food and feces from mixing, food is not taken in at the same time that feces leave—a restriction that limits the rate of food intake.

A digestive tract, found in most animals, is a muscular tube with two openings—one for food intake (the mouth) and the other for feces removal (the anus). This one-way system permits food to be ingested and held while fecal material is collected and expelled at the same time. The one-way flow also enables each segment of the tract to be specialized for performing a particular function, so food passes through a sort of assembly line from mouth to anus. The degree of this specialization is greatest in the vertebrate digestive tract, which consists of specific regions for different functions: initial preparation of food, storage, digestion, absorption, and formation and removal of feces. Each region is separated from the others by special circular muscles, called *sphincters*, that can contract to close off that region of the tract.

THE MAMMALIAN DIGESTIVE TRACT

40.26 Among mammals, an herbivore has

(*a*) more teeth than a carnivore. (*b*) fewer teeth than a carnivore. (*c*) flatter teeth than a carnivore. (*d*) teeth that are more pointed than a carnivore's.

40.27 With regard to natural eating habits, a human is

(*a*) an herbivore. (*b*) a carnivore. (*c*) an omnivore. (*d*) a granivore.

40.28 The main function of prolonged chewing is to rupture

(*a*) membranes. (*b*) cell walls. (*c*) muscle bundles. (*d*) connective tissue.

40.29 A digestive enzyme, salivary amylase, in the saliva begins digestion of

(*a*) carbohydrates. (*b*) proteins. (*c*) fats. (*d*) nucleic acids.

40.30 A lubricant, mucin, in saliva is made of

(*a*) polyunsaturated fats. (*b*) actin and myosin. (*c*) glycoproteins. (*d*) phospholipids.

40.31 About how much saliva does a person produce each day?

(*a*) 100 mL; (*b*) 250 mL; (*c*) 500 mL; (*d*) 1 L

40.32 The original function of the vertebrate stomach was

(*a*) storage. (*b*) digestion. (*c*) absorption. (*d*) enzyme secretion.

40.33 Gastric juice has a pH of about

(*a*) 1. (*b*) 2. (*c*) 6. (*d*) 10.

40.34 A digestive enzyme, pepsin, in the gastric juice begins digestion of

(*a*) carbohydrates. (*b*) proteins. (*c*) fats. (*d*) nucleic acids.

40.35 Inactive enzyme precursors, such as pepsinogen for pepsin, are called

(*a*) polyglycoids. (*b*) cholenzymes. (*c*) activases. (*d*) zymogens.

40.36 Most digestion and all absorption of food take place in the

(*a*) stomach. (*b*) small intestine. (*c*) cecum. (*d*) large intestine.

40.37   The first 25 cm of the human small intestine is the

(a) duodenum.   (b) jejunum.   (c) ileum.   (d) small colon.

40.38   The many projections on the wall of the small intestine function to

(a) secrete digestive enzymes.   (b) increase the surface area for absorption.   (c) hold products of digestion, so they do not enter the large intestine.   (d) hold mucus, so ulcers do not form.

40.39   In a villus, some of the glycerol and fatty acids are combined to form fats, coated with proteins, and then transported as chylomicrons to the

(a) lacteals.   (b) capillaries.   (c) lumen of the small intestine.   (d) lumen of the large intestine.

40.40   In a villus, some of the glycerol and fatty acids are bound to carrier proteins and transported as lipoproteins to the

(a) lacteals.   (b) capillaries.   (c) lumen of the small intestine.   (d) lumen of the large intestine.

40.41   One material absorbed in large quantities by the walls of the large intestine is

(a) glucose.   (b) alcohol.   (c) water.   (d) vitamin C.

40.42   Intestinal gas is the product of

(a) irritated intestinal cells.   (b) intestinal bacteria.   (c) undigested meat.   (d) vitamin fermentation.

40.43   The reddish-brown color of normal feces is caused by

(a) undigested plant materials.   (b) dead bacteria.   (c) hemoglobin from degraded red blood cells. (d) sloughed-off cells from the digestive tract.

40.44   A human is an omnivore with 32 teeth: eight bladelike _____ for biting; four pointed _____ for tearing; eight _____ for grinding; and twelve _____ (including four "wisdom" teeth) for crushing.

40.45   The structure in the mouth that prevents food from entering the nasal cavities is the _____.

40.46   The biologic term for throat is _____, an area that leads to two channels—the _____ for transport of food and the _____ for transport of air. A structure called the _____ closes the air channel when food is being swallowed.

40.47   The stomach is located on the _____ side of the abdomen, just below (or posterior to) the _____.

40.48   The stomach of a nonruminant herbivore comprises a _____ proportion of the digestive tract than the stomach of a carnivore. The small intestine of a nonruminant herbivore comprises a _____ proportion of the digestive tract than the small intestine of a carnivore.

40.49   The stomach functions to _____, _____, and _____ food.

40.50   The lining of the small intestine is folded, ridged, and covered with small fingerlike projections called _____, which in turn are covered with a brush border composed of closely packed, cylindrical _____.

40.51   Materials released into the lumen of the duodenum include: digestive enzymes, which are synthesized in the _____ and the _____; bicarbonate ions, which neutralize the stomach acids and are released from the _____; and bile, which is made in the _____ and stored in the _____.

40.52   Bile consists of _____, which aid digestion and absorption of _____; pigments, which are waste products from the degradation of _____; and _____, which is the most common constituent of gallstones.

40.53 Three hormones stimulate release of digestive materials: _____ stimulates release of gastric juices; _____ stimulates release of bicarbonate ions; and _____ stimulates release of bile and pancreatic enzymes.

40.54 Bicarbonate ions, essential for neutralizing acids in the duodenum, travel from the _____, where they are produced, to the duodenum by way of the _____.

40.55 In the lumen of the small intestine, pancreatic amylase converts _____ to _____, lipase converts _____ to _____ and _____, nucleases convert _____ to _____, trypsin and chymotrypsin convert _____ to _____, aminopeptidase and carbopeptidase convert _____ to _____, and bile salts _____ fat.

40.56 In the brush border of the small intestine, maltase, sucrase, and lactase convert _____ to _____, and peptidases convert _____ to _____.

40.57 Products of digestion that enter the capillaries of villi are transported via the _____ vein to the _____. Products of digestion that enter the lacteals of villi are transported via the _____ to the _____.

40.58 Many humans develop intestinal gas and diarrhea from consuming milk and milk products, because they lack the enzyme for digesting the _____ in milk.

40.59 The cecum of herbivorous mammals contains bacteria that digest _____. Since products of this digestion are not released where they can be maximally absorbed (the first parts of the small intestine), a rabbit _____ some of its feces.

40.60 When peristalsis in the large intestine is too slow, a condition known as _____ develops. If persistent, it may lead to a weakening and outpocketing of the intestinal walls, known as a _____, or as left-side appendicitis. When peristalsis in the large intestine is too fast, a condition known as _____ develops.

40.61 The main function of the rectum is to _____ feces.

40.62 How do the digestive tracts of carnivores differ from those of herbivores?

⚜   Animal meat requires more storage and less processing than plant materials. The teeth of a carnivore are pointed and sharp for killing its prey and tearing it into pieces small enough to swallow. Animal meat does not require chewing. The teeth of an herbivore, by contrast, are flat for crushing and grinding plant materials. A mammal cannot digest cellulose and so derives no nutrients from plant materials unless the cell walls are ruptured by chewing. A carnivore has a large stomach for food storage, since it eats large and infrequent meals. The stomach of a dog or cat makes up 70% of its digestive tract. An herbivore has a smaller stomach, because it eats smaller amounts of food more frequently. The stomach of a horse makes up only about 8% of its digestive tract. (A ruminant, however, has an enormous stomach, with several chambers, for digestion of cellulose by bacteria and protozoa.) Most digestion and all absorption of food take place in the small intestine, and a carnivore, whose food requires less processing, has a shorter small intestine than an herbivore, whose food requires extensive processing.

40.63 What prevents the walls of the digestive tract from being digested?

⚜   Both the stomach and small intestine contain enzymes that can digest their own muscular walls. Yet this rarely happens, because the protein-digesting enzymes are not active until released into the lumen of the stomach or small intestine, and the inner walls of these structures are covered with a protective coat of mucus.

Digestive glands in the pancreas and walls of the stomach secrete proteolytic enzymes (pepsin, trypsin, and chymotrypsin) as inactive enzyme precursors, known generally as *zymogens*; the enzymes do not become active until they reach the lumen of the stomach or small intestine. Thus, protein digestion does not occur in the glands, ducts, or walls of the digestive system.

Active protein-digesting enzymes in the lumen of the digestive tract cannot digest the walls of the tract, because the walls are lined with a protective film of mucus that cannot be digested by enzymes. Occasionally, however, the protective layer of mucus breaks down, and the walls of the stomach or small intestine are digested. Two materials known to remove mucus are alcohol and aspirin. Emotional stress also leads to ulcers, usually duodenal ulcers, when the acidic gastric juices are not immediately neutralized by bicarbonates as the juices enter the duodenum.

40.64   Why does a cow have so many stomachs?

☚   A cow has four stomachs: *rumen*, *reticulum*, *omasum*, and *abomasum* (Fig. 40.1). The first three stomachs are pouches derived from the esophagus, and the abomasum is the true stomach. This unusual arrangement of the mammalian digestive tract, found only in ruminants (cud-chewing, hoofed mammals such as cows, sheep, and deer), is an adaptation for digesting the cellulose within plant cells. Cellulose is a polymer of glucose and an excellent source of energy. No mammal is able to synthesize an enzyme that digests cellulose, but ruminants digest it by harboring cellulose-digesting bacteria and protozoa within their stomachs.

The cellulose-digesting microorganisms live in the rumen and reticulum of a cow. Swallowed food enters first the rumen and then the reticulum, where the microbes digest and ferment the liberated glucose, since conditions inside the stomachs are anaerobic. From the reticulum, the coarser plant materials are regurgitated for rechewing and then swallowed again for further enzymatic action. The microorganisms use the products of their digestion and release fatty acids, which move to the omasum, along with some of the bacteria and protozoa. There the material is concentrated by reabsorption of water through the omasum walls and then is moved to the abomasum, where acids kill the microbes. In the small intestine, the microbes are digested and their amino acids, glucose, and other monomers, together with the fatty acids released earlier, are absorbed into the bloodstream of the cow.

The four stomachs of a ruminant enable parts of the digestive tract to be more specialized than the digestive tracts of other herbivores for digestion of cellulose (the rumen and reticulum), for absorption and recycling of water (the omasum) from the enormous quantity of saliva used in digestion by the microorganisms, and for killing of the microorganisms by acids (the abomasum).

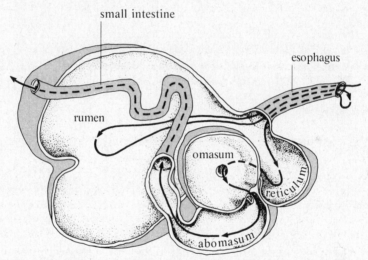

Fig. 40.1. The four stomachs of a cow. The first three chambers—rumen, reticulum, and omasum—are enlargements of the esophagus, and the fourth chamber—the abomasum—is the true stomach. The rumen and reticulum are specialized for microbial digestion of plant material. The omasum is specialized for absorbing water from the enormous amounts of saliva used in microbial digestion. The abomasum is specialized for killing, with acids, the bacteria to prevent further population growth and to prepare the bacteria for breakdown by digestive enzymes in the small intestine.

40.65   Why do we have an appendix?

☚   An appendix is found only in humans, a few species of great apes, and the wombat (a marsupial). About 6 cm long and 1 cm in diameter, it is a hollow organ that dangles from the cecum. The walls of the appendix are muscular and lined first with a layer of lymph tissue and then an innermost layer of epithelium. It is structurally similar to the colon and is also capable of peristalsis. The appendix has no known function; we do not know why humans have one. Since it vaguely resembles a lymph node, the appendix may function to prevent intestinal infections.

Appendicitis, or inflammation of the appendix, is the most common cause of emergency surgery today. The appendix becomes a liability when its lumen becomes blocked by fecal material or by swelling of the lymph tissue in reaction to an infection. Fluids secreted by the appendix then accumulate and become infected by intestinal bacteria; the area then becomes inflamed, swollen, and painful. If not removed, the appendix may burst and spread its infection throughout the abdominal cavity.

THE LIVER AND PANCREAS

40.66 Digestive enzymes are released by the pancreas, and bile is released by the liver, in response to the hormone

(*a*) insulin. (*b*) zymogen. (*c*) cholecystokinin. (*d*) secretin.

40.67 Which of the following animals has no need for a gallbladder?

(*a*) Horse; (*b*) Human; (*c*) Lion; (*d*) Dog

40.68 A disease caused by insufficient amounts of insulin is

(*a*) jaundice. (*b*) elephantiasis. (*c*) diabetes insipidus. (*d*) diabetes mellitus.

40.69 Pancreatic enzymes reach the duodenum via the

(*a*) blood. (*b*) lymph. (*c*) pancreatic duct. (*d*) cystic duct.

40.70 Insulin and glucagon, synthesized by the islets of Langerhans in the pancreas, reach their target cells via the

(*a*) blood. (*b*) lymph. (*c*) pancreatic duct. (*d*) cystic duct.

40.71 Four important functions of the liver are to: (1) produce a fluid, called _____, that emulsifies _____; (2) convert the end products of _____ into other molecular forms; (3) regulate components of the _____; and (4) convert _____ substances into compounds that can be safely excreted by the kidneys.

40.72 Four important functions of the pancreas are to: (1) produce _____, which neutralizes acids in the _____; (2) produce _____ enzymes and release them into the _____; (3) produce _____, which controls cellular uptake of glucose and its conversion into _____; and (4) produce _____, which stimulates the conversion of glycogen into _____.

40.73 The blood-sugar level is controlled by two organs: the _____, which releases glucose into the blood, and the _____, which releases the hormone _____ that allows glucose to move from the blood to the interiors of cells.

40.74 The liver converts the toxic substance _____, which is a waste product of amino acid metabolism, to the less toxic compound _____, which is then excreted by the kidneys.

40.75 What types of food monomers can be converted into other types by the mammalian liver?

☞ The liver has a remarkable capacity to convert molecules from one form to another, a capacity that permits mammals to utilize a variety of foods. If the diet includes the essential amino acids, essential fatty acids, vitamins, and minerals, then the liver cells can construct most of the molecules needed to maintain life (Fig. 40.2). Amino acids can be synthesized into the particular proteins carried by the blood, converted into nonessential amino acids, converted into glucose and stored as glycogen or fat, or converted into glucose and released into the blood for immediate use. Triglycerides can be used in the construction of specific lipids, such as phospholipids, or transported to fat cells for energy storage. The glycerol portion of a triglyceride can be converted into glycogen for energy storage. Glycogen obtained from these sources can be broken down into glucose and released directly into the bloodstream or converted into fat.

Liver cells also render potentially harmful materials nontoxic so they can be removed by the kidneys. The liver's conversion of ammonia—the toxic waste product from the breakdown of amino acids—into its less toxic form, urea, is a critical bodily function.

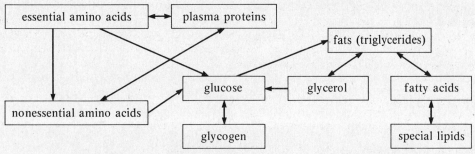

Fig. 40.2. Some of the conversions of food monomers carried out by the liver.

Answers to Objective Questions

40.1 *d*

40.2 *c*

40.3 *a*

40.4 *c*

40.5 *b*

40.6 *c*

40.7 *d*

40.8 *b*

40.9 9.5; 4.3; 5.3

40.10 basal; Aves; Mammalia; endotherms

40.11 body size

40.12 muscles

40.13 essential amino acids; essential fatty acids; vitamins; minerals

40.16 *b*

40.17 *c*

40.18 *b*

40.19 *c*

40.20 *b*

40.21 monosaccharides; amino acids; fatty acids; glycerol; nucleotides

40.22 food; feces; mouth; anus

40.23 peristalsis; walls; sphincters

40.24 crop; stomach; gizzard

40.26 *c*

40.27 *c*

40.28 *b*

40.29 *a*

40.30 *c*

40.31 *d*

40.32 *a*

40.33 *b*

40.34 *b*

40.35 *d*

40.36 *b*

40.37 *a*

40.38 *b*

40.39 *a*

40.40 *b*

40.41 *c*

40.42 *b*

40.43 *c*

40.44 incisors; canines; premolars; molars

40.45 soft palate (or uvula)

40.46 pharynx; esophagus; trachea; epiglottis

40.47 left; diaphragm

40.48 smaller; larger

40.49 store; churn; digest

40.50 villi; microvilli

40.51 pancreas; walls of the small intestine; pancreas; liver; gall bladder

40.52 bile salts; fats; red blood cells; cholesterol

40.53 gastrin; secretin; cholecystokinin

40.54 pancreas; pancreatic duct

40.55 polysaccharides; maltose; fat; fatty acids; glycerol;

nucleic acids; nucleotides; polypeptides; smaller polypeptides; smaller polypeptides; amino acids; emulsify

40.56 disaccharides; monosaccharides; di- and tripeptides; amino acids

40.57 hepatic portal; liver; lymphatic vessels; blood (specifically, the left jugular vein)

40.58 lactose

40.59 cellulose; eats

40.60 constipation; diverticulum; diarrhea

40.61 store

40.66 *c*

40.67 *a*

40.68 *d*

40.69 *c*

40.70 *a*

40.71 bile; fats; digestion; blood; toxic

40.72 bicarbonate ions; duodenum; digestive; duodenum; insulin; glycogen; glucagon; glucose

40.73 liver; pancreas; insulin

40.74 ammonia; urea

CHAPTER 41
Excretion

OSMOREGULATION*

41.1 Osmoregulation is control over the

(**a**) removal of nitrogen from the body. (**b**) pH of the blood. (**c**) concentrations of salt and water in the body. (**d**) osmotic properties of cell membranes.

41.2 A marine bony fish must continuously

(**a**) acquire water and get rid of salt. (**b**) get rid of both water and salt. (**c**) get rid of water and acquire salt. (**d**) acquire both water and salt.

41.3 A freshwater fish must continuously

(**a**) acquire water and get rid of salt. (**b**) get rid of both water and salt. (**c**) get rid of water and acquire salt. (**d**) acquire both water and salt.

41.4 A terrestrial animal must be able to

(**a**) actively pump salts out through its skin. (**b**) excrete large amounts of salt in its urine. (**c**) excrete large amounts of water in its urine. (**d**) conserve water.

41.5 The osmoregulatory tissue in all animals is

(**a**) epithelial. (**b**) connective. (**c**) nervous. (**d**) muscle.

41.6 Osmoregulation is control over the amounts of _____ and _____ in the body. An animal cell swells and bursts if too much _____ is taken up, which can happen when there is a higher concentration of _____ inside the cell than outside the cell.

41.7 An animal is not an osmoregulator if its fluids are _____ with its surroundings. An animal in a _____ environment must continually take in water. An animal in a _____ environment must continually remove water from its body.

41.8 Most marine invertebrates have body fluids that are _____ to their environment. Marine bony fishes have body fluids that are _____ to their environment. Freshwater fishes have body fluids that are _____ to their environment. Bony fishes evolved in _____ environments, and some of them later colonized _____ environments.

41.9 Osmoregulation in all animals involves transport epithelium. This tissue is characterized by intercellular junctions that are _____ junctions, which form a continuous barrier, thus ensuring that all solutes entering and leaving the area must pass through _____.

41.10 How does a fish control the water and salt concentrations within its body?

The osmoregulatory problems of freshwater fishes are different from those of marine fishes. The body fluids of a bony fish have salt concentrations intermediate between seawater and fresh water, so a marine fish is hypotonic and a freshwater fish is hypertonic to its environment. The invertebrate ancestors of fishes evolved in the oceans and had body fluids that were isotonic to seawater. Bony fishes, however, evolved in lakes and rivers and so developed body fluids that are less salty than those of their invertebrate ancestors but are more salty than fresh water. Some of these bony fishes then returned to oceanic habitats.

Cartilaginous fishes, such as sharks and rays, never lived in fresh water and so retained body fluids that are approximately isotonic to seawater. The higher solute concentration of their body fluids is achieved, in part, by retaining urea rather than by maintaining high salt concentrations.

* Answers to Chapter 41 objective questions appear on page 293.

A freshwater fish prevents excess water intake in three ways. First, it avoids swallowing the surrounding water, although some water is unavoidably consumed during feeding. Second, it has a waterproof skin that prevents entry of water through most of its surface. Third, the large quantities of water that do enter the body across exposed gill surfaces are removed by the kidneys, which produce enormous quantities of very dilute urine. Ions are inevitably lost with the urine, and to compensate for this loss, a freshwater fish has transport epithelium in its gills that actively transports sodium and chloride ions from the surrounding water into the body.

A marine bony fish prevents water loss by producing very little urine, which contains high concentrations of ions and relatively little water, and by having a waterproof skin. Nevertheless, it loses a great deal of water through its gills. This water is replaced by consuming enormous amounts of seawater and removing salts from it by active transport through the transport epithelium of the gills and by excretion through the kidneys.

INVERTEBRATE EXCRETORY SYSTEMS

41.11 In the flame-cell system of a planarian, materials are drained directly from the

(*a*) blood. (*b*) lymph. (*c*) interstitial fluid. (*d*) coelom.

41.12 The flame-cell system functions mostly to

(*a*) remove ammonium ions. (*b*) remove urea. (*c*) regulate pH. (*d*) osmoregulate.

41.13 In insects, Malpighian tubules drain materials directly from the

(*a*) gut. (*b*) hemocoel. (*c*) blood. (*d*) lymph.

41.14 A Malpighian tubule empties urine into the

(*a*) gut. (*b*) coelom. (*c*) ureters. (*d*) lymph.

41.15 A nephridium of an earthworm drains materials directly from the

(*a*) gut. (*b*) coelom. (*c*) blood. (*d*) lymph.

41.16 The simplest tubular excretory system is the _____ system found in the phylum _____.

41.17 The Malpighian tubules of insects remove _____ from the _____ and function in _____.

41.18 A Malpighian tubule is an outpocketing of the _____. Much of the water it accumulates is reabsorbed into the body across the epithelium of the _____.

41.19 As fluid moves through a nephridium in an earthworm, the transport epithelium pumps _____ out of the tubules so that they can be absorbed into the _____. An earthworm's urine is _____ to its body fluids, which compensates for the _____ of water, by osmosis, through its _____.

41.20 In what ways do the tubular excretory systems of invertebrates differ from one another?

🐚 There are three main forms of tubular excretory systems in invertebrates: the *flame-cell system* of flatworms; the *Malpighian tubules* of insects; and the *nephridia* of earthworms. They differ because of the different anatomies of these animals: a flatworm has neither a coelom nor a circulatory system; an insect has a small coelom, a large hemocoel, and an open circulatory system; and an earthworm has a coelom and a closed circulatory system.

A flame-cell system, shown in Fig. 41.1*a*, drains materials directly from the interstitial fluid, across the plasma membrane of its terminal flame cell and into the tubular cavity. Cilia that extend from the flame cell create currents that transport fluids down the tube to an excretory pore. A flame-cell system functions mainly in osmoregulation, since cellular wastes move into the gastrovascular cavity and out of the body by way of the mouth.

A Malpighian tubule, shown in Fig. 41.1*b*, is an elongated outpocket between the midgut and hindgut of the digestive tract. Materials from the blood-filled sinuses of the hemocoel enter the tubule's closed end across the plasma membranes of terminal cells. The materials are transported along the tubule to the gut for removal from the body along with the feces. Most of the water and ions in the fluid are absorbed from the wall of the rectum back into the blood. A Malpighian tubule functions both to remove nitrogenous wastes and to osmoregulate.

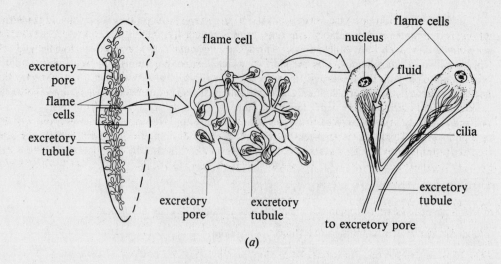

(a)

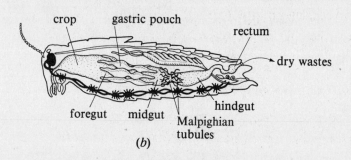

(b)

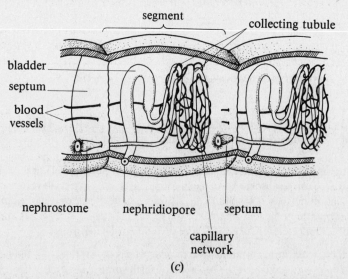

(c)

Fig. 41.1. Excretory systems of invertebrates. (a) The flame-cell system of a flatworm (complementary structure on animal's right-hand side has been omitted) drains materials from the interstitial fluid to the outside of the body. Fluid enters the tubule through a flame cell, which has cilia that move the fluid, and leaves the tubule through an excretory pore. (b) The Malpighian tubule of an insect drains fluid from the blood-filled hemocoel to the hindgut. When the fluid reaches the rectum, almost all of the water and ions are removed and returned to the blood. (c) The nephridium of an earthworm is open at both ends. Each segment of the worm has a nephridium, which drains fluid through a nephrostome from the coelom of another segment. As fluid moves through the tubule, it exchanges materials with the blood in surrounding capillaries. The tubule is enlarged to form a bladder for storage of urine prior to its exiting through the nephridiopore.

A nephridium, unlike the other two forms of excretory tubules, is open at both ends, as shown in Fig. 41.1c. At one end, a funnel-shaped, ciliated cell called a *nephrostome* (probably homologous to the flame cell) is immersed in coelomic fluid, and at the other end, the tubule opens to the outside of the body. Each nephridium is surrounded by capillaries, so that as fluid moves along it, materials can be exchanged between the fluid in the tubule and the blood in the capillaries; this arrangement permits fine adjustments to be made with regard to what is excreted and what is retained in the body fluids. A nephridium functions both to remove nitrogenous wastes and to osmoregulate.

During the evolution of invertebrate animals, the nephridium seems to have evolved from the flame-cell system; it takes advantage of the closed circulatory system for direct exchange of materials between the blood and the urine as the urine forms. The Malpighian tubule apparently did not evolve from either the flame-cell system or the nephridium but had a separate origin associated with the hemocoel and open circulatory system of insects.

VERTEBRATE KIDNEYS

41.21 The basic unit of a vertebrate kidney is the

(a) ureter. (b) nephron. (c) Malpighian tubule. (d) islets of Langerhans.

41.22 A fish excretes nitrogen in the form of

(a) ammonium ions. (b) amino acids. (c) urea. (d) uric acid.

41.23 A bird or terrestrial reptile excretes nitrogen in the form of

(a) ammonium ions. (b) amino acids. (c) urea. (d) uric acid.

41.24 A mammal excretes nitrogen in the form of

(a) ammonium ions. (b) amino acids. (c) urea. (d) uric acid.

41.25 The nephron of a freshwater fish, which represents the first vertebrate nephron to evolve, has six segments: (1) a Bowman's capsule for _____ of fluid from the blood; (2) a narrow neck with _____ to speed the flow; (3) a proximal segment for _____ of glucose, small proteins, and _____ ions from the _____ to the _____; (4) an intermediate segment covered with _____ to speed the flow; (5) a distal segment for _____ of _____ ions from the _____ to the _____; and (6) a _____ duct to carry urine out of the nephron.

41.26 The nephron of a marine fish has been altered during its evolution in seawater. It lacks the two _____ segments, because the filtrate must move slowly in order to maximize reabsorption of _____. Its proximal segment actively transports ions from the _____ to the _____. Its distal segment transports _____ from the filtrate to the blood.

41.27 The amphibian nephron is identical to the nephron of a _____.

41.28 A marine reptile has a nephron similar to the one of _____ fishes. It excretes excess _____ through glands near the nose or eye.

41.29 The nephron of a bird or mammal is specialized, compared with the nephrons of other vertebrates, for _____ of water; it uses a(n) _____ gradient to move water from one place to another.

41.30 What determines the form in which nitrogen is eliminated?

⚗ Whenever a cell converts amino acids or nucleotides into carbohydrates or fats, nitrogen becomes a waste product that must be removed from the body. Excess nitrogen may be excreted in any of three forms—ammonia, urea, or uric acid—depending on how much water the animal has available for diluting its nitrogenous waste and whether its embryos develop within an impermeable envelope.

Ammonia is the simplest form of nitrogenous waste; nitrogen is already in this form when it is removed from an amino acid. However, ammonia is highly toxic to cells when present above a certain concentration, because it is a base that makes fluids too alkaline. Thus, nitrogen can be eliminated as ammonia (or ammonium ions, when in fluids) only if the animal has plenty of water to flush it out of the body. Invertebrate animals (except insects and some land snails), freshwater fishes, and aquatic forms of amphibians excrete nitrogen as ammonium ions. Substantial amounts leave through their gills, and the rest is excreted in the enormous amounts of dilute urine that these animals produce.

An animal without a lot of water available for diluting ammonium ions excretes nitrogen in the form of urea or uric acid, depending on where the embryo develops. Urea is soluble in water, whereas uric acid is virtually insoluble. An embryo developing within an impermeable membrane or shell would be poisoned by its own wastes if they were in a soluble form, so its excess nitrogen is placed within molecules of uric acid, synthesized within the liver from ammonia and glutamate. Uric acid is a purine that, when present in high concentrations, forms insoluble crystals. Since uric acid does not mix with fluids, it does not poison the shell-enclosed embryo. This form of nitrogenous waste product continues to be synthesized by the animal throughout its life. Terrestrial reptiles, birds, insects, and land snails eliminate nitrogen as uric acid. In birds and reptiles, the uric acid excreted by the kidneys mixes with feces in the cloaca to form a semisolid, gray paste.

Mammals, marine fishes, and most adult amphibians exrete excess nitrogen as urea, which is soluble in water and 100,000 times less toxic than ammonium ions. None of these animals has access to large amounts of water or lays eggs (or is in an egg) with impermeable coverings. Urea is formed in the liver by combining two molecules of ammonia with one molecule of carbon dioxide.

$$2NH_3 + CO_2 \longrightarrow \begin{array}{c} H \\ \diagdown \\ N-C-N \\ \diagup \qquad\quad \diagdown \\ N \qquad\qquad\quad H \end{array} \overset{\overset{\textstyle O}{\|}}{} \begin{array}{c} H \\ \diagup \\ \end{array} + H_2O$$

From the liver it is carried by the blood to the kidneys for excretion.

THE MAMMALIAN KIDNEY

41.31   About how many nephrons are there in each kidney of a human?

(a) 16;   (b) 200;   (c) 1000;   (d) 1,000,000

41.32   The force that moves fluid from the blood through the walls of a capillary and Bowman's capsule of a nephron is

(a) the beating of cilia.   (b) blood pressure.   (c) peristalsis of the capsule.   (d) gravity.

41.33   Which of the following components of the blood does *not* enter the nephron?

(a) Ions;   (b) Glucose;   (c) Plasma proteins;   (d) Urea

41.34   The Bowman's capsule functions as a

(a) filter.   (b) bellows.   (c) suction pump.   (d) sponge.

41.35   Which of the following is *not* reabsorbed from the filtrate to the blood at the proximal tubule?

(a) Glucose;   (b) Na$^+$;   (c) Plasma proteins;   (d) Water

41.36   Which of the following materials is removed from the filtrate at the loop of Henle?

(a) Glucose;   (b) Water;   (c) Ammonia;   (d) Mg^{2+}

41.37   The loop of Henle is most highly developed in

(a) freshwater fishes.   (b) salamanders.   (c) desert lizards.   (d) mammals.

41.38   Which of the following parts of the nephron is *least* permeable to water?

(a) Proximal tubule;   (b) Descending limb of the loop of Henle;   (c) Ascending limb of the loop of Henle;
(d) Collecting duct

41.39   Fluid within the loop of Henle is most concentrated in the

(a) ascending limb.   (b) descending limb.   (c) hairpin bend.   (d) bend between the ascending limb and the distal tubule.

41.40   Each kidney releases urine into a _____, which is a muscular tube that connects the kidney to the _____, which in turn empties into the _____, which carries urine to the outside of the body.

41.41 Blood enters the kidney via a vessel called the _____. Each branch of that vessel forms two capillary beds before blood is returned to the heart: one bed forms the _____ within the _____ of the nephron, and the other bed surrounds the _____ of the _____. Such an arrangement of two capillary beds in tandem is called a _____ system.

41.42 Refer to Fig. 41.2, and identify the parts of a kidney indicated.

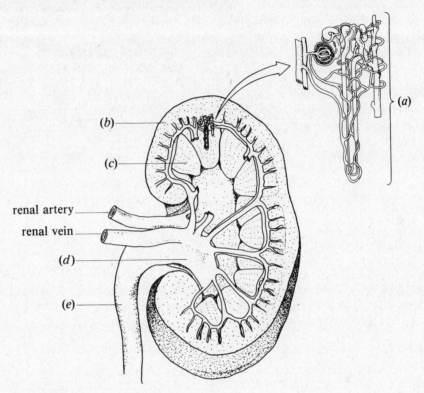

Fig. 41.2

41.43 Refer to Fig. 41.3, and identify the parts of a nephron indicated.

41.44 When the pH of the blood is too low, _____ are secreted into the nephron from the surrounding capillaries. At the same time, _____, which promote formation of hydroxyl ions from water, and _____, which bind the hydrogen ions released when hydroxyl ions form from water, are transported from the nephron into the capillaries.

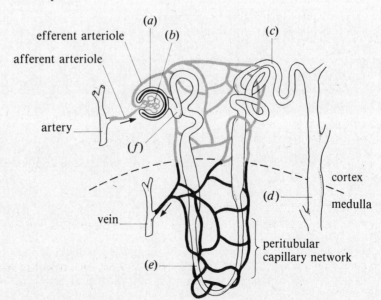

Fig. 41.3

41.45 Water is moved from the loop of Henle to the interstitial fluid around it by active transport of _____ and _____ out of the filtrate at the _____ limb of the loop and diffusion of _____ out of the urine at the collecting duct. These changes draw water out of the filtrate, by osmosis, from the _____ limb of the loop of Henle.

41.46 Adjustments in sodium concentration occur at the _____ of the nephron. Reabsorption of sodium ions is controlled by the hormone _____, which is produced by the adrenal cortex.

41.47 Permeability of the collecting duct to water is controlled by the _____ hormone, which is released by the _____. When this hormone is abundant, the permeability of the duct to water is _____ and a more _____ urine is released. Large quantities of _____ urine form when a lot of alcohol or caffeine has been consumed, because these drugs _____ release of the hormone.

41.48 Desert mammals are adapted to water shortage by having nephrons with longer _____.

41.49 How do the kidneys contribute to homeostasis?

❧ The kidneys are vitally important in maintaining the appropriate body chemistry. The liver and the kidneys regulate the compositions of the blood and interstitial fluids, which in turn determine the materials within the cells. The kidneys:

1. Remove wastes that form during cellular metabolism as well as toxic substances and excess nontoxic materials from the body
2. Maintain appropriate concentrations of water and ions, especially sodium, potassium, chloride, calcium, magnesium, sulfate, and phosphate ions
3. Regulate the volume of blood and interstitial fluids by controlling ion excretion
4. Ensure an appropriate balance of hydrogen ions (H^+) and hydroxyl ions (OH^-), so that the pH of the body fluids is optimal for chemical reactions

41.50 How do the kidneys function as osmoregulators?

❧ Most osmoregulation takes place as the filtrate passes through the distal tubule and collecting duct of the mammalian nephron. Sensory cells in the brain, the walls of the circulatory system, and the kidney detect deviations in ion concentrations and in blood pressure. They then initiate homeostatic adjustments through hormonal actions.

The presence of two hormones, aldosterone and antidiuretic hormone (ADH), dictates which one of four adjustments—the removal of (1) ions, (2) water, (3) both ions and water, or (4) neither ions nor water—will be made in the fluid as it passes through the distal tubules and collecting ducts of the nephrons.

Many different kinds of ions may be pumped out of the distal tubule and returned to the blood. This activity is governed by aldosterone—a hormone secreted by the adrenal cortex in response to low blood pressure. When more of this hormone is present, more ions are returned to the blood from the nephron. If the walls of the collecting duct are permeable to water, then water is also drawn out of the nephrons and into the blood, increasing the blood pressure. The secretion of aldosterone is controlled by the vessels of the kidneys. Specialized cells lining the interior of small arteries around the nephrons produce a hormone, angiotensin, that causes the arteries to constrict and stimulates the adrenal cortex to release aldosterone. As blood volume drops, more angiotensin is produced, the vessels become smaller, and more aldosterone is released. When more ions and water are returned to the blood, the blood volume is restored and the production of angiotensin decreases.

The second hormone, antidiuretic hormone (ADH), controls the amount of water in the urine. This hormone, produced in the hypothalamus and stored in the posterior pituitary gland, determines the permeability of the collecting duct to water. The ratio of water to solutes in the blood is monitored by neurons within the hypothalamus. When the water content is low in relation to solutes, the hypothalamus commands the pituitary gland to release more ADH, which makes the collecting duct more permeable to water, and water moves out of the nephron by osmosis. (In this segment of the nephron, the urine contains relatively low concentrations of solutes compared with the surrounding interstitial fluid, which has a high solute concentration due to the active transport of sodium and chloride ions by the ascending limb of the loop of Henle and to the diffusion of urea out of the collecting duct.)

Even more water is drawn out of the collecting duct when both aldosterone and ADH are present. Ions pumped out of the distal tubule draw more water, by osmosis, out of the collecting duct, and the urine becomes extremely concentrated and reduced in volume. More ADH is released in response to low blood pressure, because blood pressure is monitored by special receptors in the left atrium of the heart; these receptors send information to the hypothalamus, which, in turn, controls release of ADH by the pituitary gland.

Both alcohol and caffeine suppress the release of ADH. When either of these drugs is consumed in large amounts, copious amounts of dilute urine are formed and the body becomes dehydrated.

Answers to Objective Questions

41.1 c
41.2 a
41.3 c
41.4 d
41.5 a
41.6 salt; water; water; solutes
41.7 isotonic; hypertonic; hypotonic
41.8 isotonic; hypotonic; hypertonic; freshwater; marine
41.9 tight; plasma membranes
41.11 c
41.12 d
41.13 b
41.14 a
41.15 b
41.16 flame cell; Platyhelminthes
41.17 nitrogenous wastes; hemocoel; osmoregulation
41.18 gut; rectum
41.19 ions; blood; hypotonic; uptake; skin

41.21 b
41.22 a
41.23 d
41.24 c
41.25 filtration; cilia; active transport; divalent; filtrate; blood; cilia; active transport; monovalent; filtrate; blood; collecting
41.26 ciliated; water; blood; filtrate; water
41.27 freshwater fish
41.28 freshwater; ions (or salts)
41.29 reabsorption (or conservation); osmotic
41.31 d
41.32 b
41.33 c
41.34 a
41.35 c
41.36 b
41.37 d
41.38 c

41.39 c
41.40 ureter; urinary bladder; urethra
41.41 renal artery; glomerulus; Bowman's capsule; tubular portions; nephron; portal
41.42 (a) nephron; (b) cortex; (c) medulla; (d) pelvis; (e) ureter
41.43 (a) Bowman's capsule; (b) glomerulus; (c) distal tubule; (d) collecting duct; (e) loop of Henle; (f) proximal tubule
41.44 H^+ (or NH_4^+) ions; Na^+ ions; HCO_3^- ions
41.45 Na^+; Cl^-; ascending; urea; descending
41.46 distal tubule; aldosterone
41.47 antidiuretic; posterior pituitary; increased; concentrated; dilute; suppress
41.48 loops of Henle

CHAPTER 42
Temperature Control

TRANSFER OF HEAT: PHYSICAL PRINCIPLES*

42.1 Where the foot of an arctic fox contacts the cold ground, it loses heat by

   (*a*) conduction. (*b*) convection. (*c*) radiation. (*d*) evaporation.

42.2 An overheated wood stork urinates on its legs in order to lose heat by

   (*a*) conduction. (*b*) convection. (*c*) radiation. (*d*) evaporation.

42.3 A lizard basks in the sun in order to acquire heat by

   (*a*) conduction. (*b*) convection. (*c*) radiation. (*d*) evaporation.

42.4 On a hot day when the temperature is 35 °C (95 °F), a roadrunner (a bird) moves from the desert floor, where the air is still, to the top of a shrub, where there is a breeze, in order to lose heat by

   (*a*) conduction. (*b*) convection. (*c*) radiation. (*d*) evaporation.

42.5 A chuckwalla (a lizard) spreads out on a cool rock in order to lose heat by

   (*a*) conduction. (*b*) convection. (*c*) radiation. (*d*) evaporation.

42.6 In general, for every 10 °C rise in cellular temperature, the rate of biochemical reactions _____. When cellular temperatures reach about 50 °C, chemical reactions cease because the _____ no longer function. When cellular temperatures drop below 0 °C, chemical reactions cease because _____ of the cell are damaged by _____.

42.7 Thermal energy moves between an organism and its environment by four physical processes: _____, which is direct transfer of molecular movement between two solids; _____, which is the movement of heat by currents of air or water; _____, which is the emission of electromagnetic waves; and _____, which is the removal of heat by converting a surface liquid to a gas.

42.8 An organism has two main sources of heat: the _____ and its own _____.

42.9 Heat transfer by conduction is slower through some materials, called _____, than through other materials. Within an animal, heat moves most slowly through tissues made chiefly of _____ molecules.

42.10 Heat moves from warmer to cooler places. How then can an animal lose body heat when its environment is warmer than its body?

   The only way to remove heat from a body when the air temperature exceeds body temperature is by evaporative cooling, in which water is transformed from a liquid to a gas by absorbing heat from a surface. Animals promote evaporative heat loss by sweating, salivating, and licking their body surfaces. When exposed to intense solar heat, an animal that keeps its body surface wet can maintain a body temperature as much as 30 °C cooler than if its surface were dry.

   Few organisms, however, have access to large quantities of water and so limit their evaporative cooling to short periods of dangerously high temperatures. Desert animals, for example, rarely cool off in this way. Instead, they seek shade and avoid activity during the day.

   An animal immersed in water cannot lose heat by evaporative cooling. It cannot lower its body temperature below that of the surrounding water.

* Answers to Chapter 42 objective questions appear on page 297.

TEMPERATURE REGULATION IN ECTOTHERMS

42.11 An animal whose body temperature fluctuates with the temperature of its environment is

(*a*) a poikilotherm. (*b*) a homeotherm. (*c*) an ectotherm. (*d*) an endotherm.

42.12 An animal that warms its body mainly by absorbing heat from its surroundings is

(*a*) a poikilotherm. (*b*) a homeotherm. (*c*) an ectotherm. (*d*) an endotherm.

42.13 Which of the following is primarily an ectotherm?

(*a*) Hawk; (*b*) Shrew; (*c*) Elephant; (*d*) Lizard

42.14 Which of the following is more of a poikilotherm than the others?

(*a*) Fish; (*b*) Grasshopper; (*c*) Frog; (*d*) Snake

42.15 The body temperature of a small desert insect is always about the same as the air temperature, because almost all of its heat transfer is by

(*a*) conduction. (*b*) convection. (*c*) radiation. (*d*) evaporation.

42.16 When external temperatures are cool, an ectotherm cannot raise its body temperature by metabolic processes, because the rate of its metabolism is always _____ to its body temperature. A decrease in body temperature _____ the rate of chemical activity and so _____ the rate of heat production.

42.17 A reptile regulates its body temperature chiefly by _____ adaptations, whereas a bird regulates its body temperature chiefly by _____ adaptations. In addition, all terrestrial organisms have _____ adaptations that help determine whether heat will be gained or lost.

42.18 A moth or bee can warm itself by repeated contractions of its wing muscles, during which heat is generated from _____.

42.19 Honey bees warm their hive by physical movements, which generate heat from _____, and by huddling together, which decreases heat loss by decreasing their _____. They cool the hive by bringing water into it, thereby promoting heat loss by _____.

42.20 Without physiological control of its metabolic rate, how can an ectotherm regulate its body temperature?

🐚 An ectotherm is unable to control its own heat production; it acquires heat mainly from its environment. Most terrestrial ectotherms nevertheless maintain fairly constant body temperatures by means of behavioral adjustments.

Environmental temperatures vary substantially from place to place within even a small area of land. Thus, a terrestrial animal can raise its body temperature by moving into the warm sun and cool it by seeking shade or burrowing beneath the ground. Both the color of an animal and its posture greatly influence the amount of heat it can acquire by basking in the sun. Terrestrial vertebrates also lose heat by evaporative cooling. A lizard, for example, makes rapid breathing movements similar to panting in order to circulate air over the moist surfaces of its mouth, which increases air convection and so also increases evaporative heat loss.

The body temperature of an aquatic animal, other than a bird or mammal, is closely correlated with the temperature of the surrounding water. Water is an excellent conductor of heat, so any localized area of warmer temperature, such as an animal's body, quickly loses heat until it reaches the same temperature as its surroundings. Conduction also makes the temperature of water more similar, from place to place within a small area, than the temperature of air. Aquatic invertebrates and fishes are basically *poikilotherms*, with very little control over their own body temperatures.

TEMPERATURE REGULATION IN ENDOTHERMS

42.21 An animal whose body temperature remains almost constant, in spite of fluctuations in the environmental temperature, is

(*a*) a poikilotherm. (*b*) a homeotherm. (*c*) an ectotherm. (*d*) an endotherm.

42.22 An animal that warms its body mainly by the heat of cellular respiration is

(*a*) a poikilotherm. (*b*) a homeotherm. (*c*) an ectotherm. (*d*) an endotherm.

42.23 Which of the following helps an animal get rid of body heat?

(*a*) Long ears; (*b*) Light-colored hair or feathers; (*c*) Subcutaneous fat; (*d*) Large body

42.24 A camel is able to tolerate the heat of a desert by

(*a*) storing water in its hump. (*b*) shunting blood into its hump. (*c*) allowing its body temperature to drop at night. (*d*) having a small ratio of surface area to volume.

42.25 A small rise in the body temperature of a human is corrected mainly by

(*a*) constricting the skin arteries. (*b*) dilating the skin arteries. (*c*) sweating. (*d*) increased tension of muscles in the skin.

42.26 A large rise in the body temperature of a human is corrected mainly by

(*a*) constricting the skin arteries and sweating. (*b*) constricting the skin arteries and shivering. (*c*) dilating the skin arteries and sweating. (*d*) dilating the skin arteries and shivering.

42.27 A small drop in the body temperature of a human is corrected mainly by

(*a*) constricting the skin arteries. (*b*) dilating the skin arteries. (*c*) sweating. (*d*) increased tension of muscles in the skin.

42.28 A large drop in the body temperature of a human is corrected mainly by

(*a*) constricting the skin arteries and sweating. (*b*) constricting the skin arteries and shivering. (*c*) dilating the skin arteries and sweating. (*d*) dilating the skin arteries and shivering.

42.29 The "thermostat" of a bird or mammal is in its

(*a*) cerebral cortex. (*b*) spinal cord near the skull. (*c*) medulla oblongata. (*d*) hypothalamus.

42.30 Endothermy evolved in response to life on land, where environmental temperatures _____ more than in water. In general, a bird or mammal is _____ than the temperature of its environment.

42.31 Each species of bird or mammal maintains its own particular body temperature, which is around _____ °C. A human maintains a slightly lower body temperature, which on the average is _____ °C.

42.32 A mammal insulates its body core against heat loss by _____ and _____. A bird insulates its body core against heat loss by _____ and _____.

42.33 The amount of heat that moves into or out of a body is proportional to the body's _____. The amount of heat produced by an endotherm is proportional to its _____. One way to adapt to a cold climate is to have a _____ body, which provides a smaller ratio of _____ to _____.

42.34 A marine mammal, such as a seal or whale, conserves body heat in cold water by _____ and by countercurrent exchange of heat from the _____ to the _____ of its extremities.

42.35 The hypothalamus of a mammal receives information about body temperature from the _____ and the _____.

42.36 Two hormones contribute to thermoregulation in mammals: _____, which increases cellular respiration throughout the body (except the brain) and adjusts an animal to the cold season; and _____, which increases cellular respiration during stress.

42.37 The thermostat of a hibernating animal is set at about 5 °C so as to lower the _____ rate, because of insufficient _____. A mammal generates heat to come out of hibernation by increased cellular respiration in its _____ in response to neural stimulation.

42.38 How does an endotherm lower its body temperature when it is too high?

⚜ Sensitive feedback systems maintain the internal temperatures of birds and mammals within a few degrees of their optimal body temperatures. The mechanisms involved in temperature regulation are integrated by two neural centers within the hypothalamus of the brain: one initiates heat loss from the body; the other governs the production and conservation of heat.

A small rise in body temperature is detected by sensory receptors in the skin and by special neurons, which monitor blood temperature, in the hypothalamus itself. When the neural center of the hypothalamus involved in lowering body temperature receives information that body temperature is too high, it commands the arteries of the skin to dilate so that more blood, and therefore more heat, reaches the surface where heat can be lost.

A large rise in body temperature causes the hypothalamus to command both an extreme dilation in the arteries of the skin (as much as 12% of the total cardiac output) and the release of water to the body surfaces. In humans, water for cooling the body is released through about 2.5 million sweat glands distributed over the surface of the body. They can produce up to 4 L of sweat per hour. Sweat contains water, ions, and a chemical that promotes further dilation of the small arteries in the skin. Heat from the blood moves into the sweat, and the water evaporates into the environment, taking the heat with it. Sweat effectively prevents an increase in body temperature, but the lost water and ions must be completely replenished by drinking fluids. Other mammals may produce sweat in more localized areas, such as the pads of the feet, or copious amounts of saliva, which evaporates from the mouth and tongue, especially when the animal pants (rapid, shallow breathing). Some animals spread saliva over their body surfaces by licking, and its evaporation removes heat from the body. A bird loses heat chiefly by evaporation of fluids from its mouth and, if it is very hot, will increase the rate of evaporation by a behavior, called gular fluttering, that resembles the rapid panting of a dog or cat.

42.39 How does an endotherm raise its body temperature when it is too low?

⚜ A lower than normal body temperature is detected by sensory receptors in the skin and by special neurons, which measure blood temperature, in the hypothalamus. This information is relayed to the neural center in the hypothalamus that controls the production and conservation of heat.

A small drop in body temperature causes the hypothalamus to command constrictions of the arteries in the skin, thereby reducing blood flow to the surface of the body, where some of the heat it carries could be lost. The body temperature is raised by greater conservation, rather than production, of heat.

A large drop in body temperature causes the hypothalamus to command both extreme constrictions of the skin arteries and increased heat production. Cellular respiration is increased by greater muscle tension if the temperature is only a few degrees below normal and by muscle shivering if a profound drop in temperature has occurred. During the muscle contractions of tension and shivering, no work is done and most of the energy from cellular respiration becomes heat. The rate at which heat is produced by the body may be increased fourfold by shivering.

42.40 What happens to temperature regulation in an endotherm during hypothermia?

⚜ Prolonged exposure to cold causes such extensive shivering that glycogen reserves in the muscles and liver become depleted. Consequently, the body can no longer generate much heat, and its temperature continues to drop. When the body temperature reaches 35 °C, the brain and muscles no longer function at optimal levels and the animal becomes disoriented, irritable, and clumsy in movement. When the body temperature reaches 32 °C, collapse occurs and death is probable; even the intake of energy foods will not raise the body temperature at this point, because the hypothalamus is no longer controlling the internal temperature. Nor will covering the animal with blankets raise its body temperature, since the endothermic animal has, in essence, become an ectothermic animal and no amount of insulation can cause it to increase its heat production. The affected animal can only be revived by administering warmth from an external source, such as a fire, warm bath, or body heat of another animal.

Answers to Objective Questions

42.1 *a*

42.2 *d*

42.3 *c*

42.4 *b* (The roadrunner is able to lose heat by convection because the ambient temperature is lower than the roadrunner's body temperature.)

42.5 *a*

42.6 doubles; enzymes; membranes; ice

42.7 conduction; convection; radiation; evaporation

42.8 sun; metabolism

42.9 insulators; lipid

42.11 *a*

42.12 *c*

42.13 *d*

42.14 *a*

42.15 *b*

42.16 proportional; decreases; decreases

42.17 behavioral; physiological; physical

42.18 cellular respiration

42.19 cellular respiration; surface area; evaporation

42.21 *b*

42.22 *d*

42.23 *a*

42.24 *c*

42.25 *b*

42.26 *c*

42.27 *a*

42.28 *b*

42.29 *d*

42.30 fluctuate; warmer

42.31 40; 37

42.32 subcutaneous fat; hair; subcutaneous fat; feathers

42.33 surface area; volume; larger; surface area; volume

42.34 subcutaneous fat (blubber); arteries; veins

42.35 skin; blood

42.36 thyroxin; epinephrine

42.37 metabolic; food; brown fat

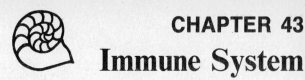

CHAPTER 43
Immune System

NONSPECIFIC DEFENSES*

43.1 Perspiration, saliva, and tears contain an enzyme, lysozyme, that kills

(*a*) virus-infected cells. (*b*) protozoa. (*c*) bacteria. (*d*) viruses.

43.2 Lysozyme kills by destroying

(*a*) cell walls. (*b*) mitochondrial enzymes. (*c*) lipid bilayers. (*d*) the machinery for DNA replication.

43.3 Most bacteria ingested with food are killed by

(*a*) cilia and mucus on the linings of the tract. (*b*) stomach acids. (*c*) the intrinsic factor in the stomach. (*d*) bile in the small intestine.

43.4 White blood cells that are nonspecific killers of microbes are

(*a*) B cells. (*b*) phagocytes. (*c*) killer T cells. (*d*) helper T cells.

43.5 Blood vessels near a wound dilate and become more permeable in response to which material released from damaged cells?

(*a*) Pyrogens; (*b*) Antibodies; (*c*) Histamine; (*d*) Interferons

43.6 Secretions from oil glands and sweat glands in the skin _____ its _____, which interferes with the activities of most bacteria.

43.7 An infected area becomes swollen because its arteries become _____; its veins become _____; and its capillaries become _____, causing fluids to move from the blood into the interstitial fluid.

43.8 White blood cells called phagocytes move from place to place by _____ and kill microbes by first _____ them and then _____ them.

43.9 What prevents all the disease-causing microorganisms on one's skin and tracts from invading the inner tissues?

The skin and linings of the tracts are the first line of defense against disease-causing microbes. The infectious microbes on the body surfaces rarely penetrate these tough outer layers. The body is vulnerable to invasion by these routes only if these tissues are broken, for example, by a cut or an insect bite.

Individual microorganisms that could cause disease do not live long on unbroken skin or internal linings, because the microbes that normally inhabit these areas create a hostile environment. Some beneficial microorganisms consume the invading microbes directly; others produce chemicals that interfere with their activities.

The body itself produces many materials that prevent growth of foreign microbial populations. Perspiration, saliva, and tears contain an enzyme, *lysozyme*, that digests bacterial cells walls, thereby causing the bacteria to burst from excessive intake of water. Oil glands and sweat glands secrete fluids with a pH of between 3 and 5 to create an environment that interferes with most bacterial activity. The membranes lining the respiratory, digestive, urinary, and genital tracts are covered with hairlike projections (*cilia*) and a layer of sticky fluid (*mucus*) that work together to trap microbes and move them out of the body. The stomach and vagina are so acidic that few microbes can pass through these areas.

43.10 Why does a cut in the skin become red, swollen, warm, and painful?

Substances released from cells damaged by invading microbes trigger an *inflammatory response*, which manifests itself as redness, swelling, heat, and pain in the infected region. Some of the chemicals released by injured cells cause the veins in the area to constrict and the arteries to dilate; others (especially histamine) increase the per-

* Answers to Chapter 43 objective questions appear on page 305.

299

meability of the capillaries, so that fluid leaks from the blood into the infected area. One chemical causes the materials in the area to clot, thereby walling off the infection so that disease-causing microbes cannot flow into uninfected areas. The chemicals released from damaged cells and the pressure of the accumulating fluid stimulate the nerves to produce the sensation of pain, which serves to protect the infected area; the individual is reluctant to touch or move a swollen and painful area of infection. At this stage, the symptoms of the disease primarily result from the body's defense system rather than from the cell damage caused by foreign microbes.

Of all the materials of the body's defense system, special white blood cells—called *neutrophils* and *monocytes* or, more simply, just *phagocytes*—reach the infected area first. These cells move continuously through the body and are capable of directed locomotion toward the site of microbial invasion. The first thing they do at the site is form a barricade that prevents the microbes from invading other parts of the body. Then they engulf (by phagocytosis) and digest the microbes, a procedure that, in turn, usually destroys many of the responding white cells. The dead white cells, microbes, and fragments of damaged body cells accumulate during this process and form the whitish fluid, pus, that eventually oozes from an infected area.

THE HUMORAL IMMUNE SYSTEM

43.11   The term *humor* refers to

(*a*) bone marrow.   (*b*) plasma and lymph.   (*c*) all internal tissues.   (*d*) all subcutaneous tissues.

43.12   The humoral immune system defends mostly against bacteria and viruses in the

(*a*) body fluids.   (*b*) digestive tract.   (*c*) internal organs.   (*d*) regions beneath the skin.

43.13   The term *immunity* refers to

(*a*) the combined actions of all white blood cells.   (*b*) events that occur within the lymphatic system. (*c*) general defenses against all microorganisms.   (*d*) specific defenses against microbes encountered during an earlier exposure.

43.14   Artificial immunity can be acquired from a

(*a*) serious illness.   (*b*) vaccination.   (*c*) repeated exposure to the same microbe.   (*d*) treatment with penicillin.

43.15   Antibodies are synthesized by

(*a*) B lymphocytes.   (*b*) phagocytes.   (*c*) helper T lymphocytes.   (*d*) killer T lymphocytes.

43.16   The regions of an antibody that make it distinct from all other kinds of antibodies are its

(*a*) variable (V) regions.   (*b*) constant (C) regions.   (*c*) mutated (M) regions.   (*d*) bifurcated (B) regions.

43.17   The regions of an antibody that determine its general role, or effector function, are its

(*a*) variable (V) regions.   (*b*) constant (C) regions.   (*c*) mutated (M) regions.   (*d*) bifurcated (B) regions.

43.18   Microbes have specific markers on their surfaces; these markers, called _____, are macromolecules that the host's body recognizes as being foreign. The immune system responds to microbial surface markers by producing specific proteins, called _____, that combat microorganisms having those particular macromolecules on their surfaces. For every foreign macromolecule, a specific form of _____ can be made by a specific type of _____ cell.

43.19   Every antibody has the ability to _____ and _____ an antigen, as well as an effector mechanism, such as complement, to assist in _____ the microbe.

43.20   An antibody is a Y-shaped _____ molecule consisting of two identical _____ chains of _____ and two identical _____ chains of _____ bound together by disulfide bridges. The antigen-binding sites lie within the _____ regions of both chains, at the ends of the two arms.

43.21   Each antibody has _____ antigen-binding sites. It combines with _____ foreign microbes, causing them to _____.

43.22 Once the microbes have been acted upon by antibodies, they may be inactivated by the _____, consumed by _____, or lysed by materials of the _____ system, which is a group of at least 11 proteins that make holes in the membranes of microbes by digestion.

43.23 Monoclonal antibodies are groups of _____ antibodies, synthesized by cells formed from fusing _____ and _____.

43.24 How does the structure of an antibody give it specificity of function?

🐚 An antibody is a globular protein constructed of four polypeptide chains: two identical heavy chains, with more than 400 amino acids each, and two identical light chains, with about 200 amino acids each. Along half the molecule, carbohydrate groups are attached and the two heavy chains are held closely together by a series of disulfide bonds. Along the other half, the chains are aligned in two pairs, with one heavy and one light chain in each pair. The entire molecule is shaped like a Y (Fig. 43.1). Each antibody molecule has two functions: (1) an effector function, or type of action taken to eliminate the antigen, and (2) a specific antigen-binding function.

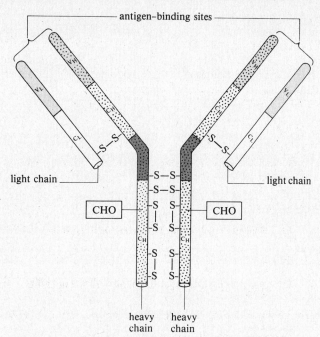

Fig. 43.1. Structure of an antibody molecule. Each antibody consists of four polypeptides: two heavy chains and two light chains. Each kind of antibody has unique sequences of amino acids in its variable regions, labeled V_L (variable light chain) and V_H (variable heavy chain) in the diagram. These unique sequences determine the molecule's ability to bind with a specific antigen. Other regions of the molecule, the so-called constant regions (C_L and C_H), give the molecule one of five known effector functions; the constant regions control how the molecule interacts with such effectors as phagocytes and complement.

There are five groups of mammalian antibodies, which are classified according to their effector function—IgG, IgM, IgA, IgD, and IgE. (Ig stands for *immunoglobin*, the term for all proteins with antibody function.) IgG antibodies are the gamma globulins that circulate in the blood and attack both bacteria and viruses. Other groups attach to the plasma membranes of B cells, activate complement, enhance phagocyte activity, and play various other roles in fighting disease-causing microbes. The five groups are distinguished from one another by the amino acid sequences in their constant (C) regions, with all molecules in a group having the same sequence. Additionally, the attached carbohydrate groups help determine the particular effector function of the antibody.

There must be millions of different kinds of antibodies with regard to specific antigen-binding capacity, since one kind exists for almost every kind of foreign macromolecule. The specificity of an antibody for an antigen lies in its sequence of amino acids within the two "arms" of the molecule. These so-called variable (V) regions form the active sites, where the molecule binds to specific antigens. Both arms have the same amino acid sequence and so bind the same kind of antigen. Thus, each antibody can join two antigens, and many antibodies working together can clump, or *agglutinate*, many antigens for more efficient elimination by the different effectors.

43.25   What are monoclonal antibodies?

⊛   Monoclonal antibodies are identical antibodies formed by a clone of identical B cells. They are made naturally in the body but are virtually impossible to isolate from all other antibodies produced there. Monoclonal antibodies used in medicine and research are made in large quantities in laboratories by means of an unusual tissue-culture technique.

The technique for getting millions of identical antibodies was developed by Cesar Milstein and Georges Köhler in the late 1970s. They fused B cells, which do not multiply in tissue culture, with tumor cells, which multiply rapidly in tissue culture. The fused cells synthesized antibodies and proliferated under laboratory conditions. It then became easy to develop a clone of cells, all identical to the original cell and all synthesizing the same antibody.

Why is this such an exciting achievement? Large numbers of identical antibodies can be used to: (1) fight an infection that has overwhelmed an individual's immune system; (2) detect the presence of a particular antigen in the body; (3) detect the presence of hormones released early in pregnancy; (4) detect the presence of a particular kind of cancer, such as colon cancer, and its precise location (by labeling the antibody with radioactive tracers); and (5) study the chemistry of the antibodies themselves.

Monoclonal antibodies have been called magic bullets, since they go directly to their target antigen when injected into the body. Medical researchers are now working on ways to attach drugs to the antibodies as a way of efficiently bringing drugs and diseased cells together.

CELL-MEDIATED IMMUNITY

43.26   T cells of the cell-mediated immune system make specific proteins, similar to antibodies, that become

(**a**) embedded within membranes of lymph nodes.   (**b**) receptors on the plasma membrane of the T cell.
(**c**) embedded in interstitial fluid.   (**d**) linked to antibodies by disulfide bridges.

43.27   When a T cell recognizes an antigen, it

(**a**) multiplies.   (**b**) moves from the thymus to the spleen.   (**c**) releases interferons.   (**d**) releases antibodies.

43.28   Messenger molecules, secreted by helper T cells, that recruit other white blood cells are called

(**a**) interferons.   (**b**) antibiotics.   (**c**) cytotoxins.   (**d**) lymphokines.

43.29   Messenger molecules, released by virus-infected cells, that bind to the surfaces of healthy cells and stimulate them to synthesize proteins that prevent viral reproduction are called

(**a**) interferons.   (**b**) antibiotics.   (**c**) cytotoxins.   (**d**) lymphokines.

43.30   Lymphocytes that cause the formation of holes in plasma membranes are

(**a**) B cells.   (**b**) killer (or cytotoxic) T cells.   (**c**) suppressor T cells.   (**d**) helper T cells.

43.31   Lymphocytes that activate B cells and T cells are

(**a**) activator B cells.   (**b**) cytotoxic T cells.   (**c**) macrophages.   (**d**) helper T cells.

43.32   Lymphocytes that inhibit the development and proliferation of T and B cells are

(**a**) suppressor B cells.   (**b**) suppressor T cells.   (**c**) macrophages.   (**d**) neutrophils.

43.33   The constant regions of a T-cell receptor _____ the receptor in the _____. The variable regions of a T-cell receptor serve to _____ antigens.

43.34   The three different classes of differentiated T cells are: _____ T cells, which kill target cells by causing their lysis; _____ T cells, which assist B cells and other T cells; and _____ T cells, which cause B cells and other T cells to be less active.

43.35   Antibodies produced by B cells are primarily active against _____ and _____. T cells are primarily active against _____. A virus multiplying in a body cell, for example, is

_____ by a T cell, and the exposed viruses are then attacked by _____. A T cell recognizes a virus-infected cell by new _____ that appear on the cell's _____.

43.36 A T cell first forms, as a stem cell, in the _____ and then matures in the _____. A B cell first forms, as a stem cell, in the _____; its site of maturation remains unknown. Once mature, the T and B cells migrate to the _____ and _____.

43.37 Each B and T cell has receptor proteins on its _____ that recognize _____. All receptors of each cell are _____ in their ability to recognize _____. Thus, there must be at least one B cell and one T cell for every possible type of foreign _____.

43.38 An initial encounter with a microbe causes each T cell and B cell that reacts with one of its antigens to _____ and _____ to form a _____. Some of these B and T cells are short-lived; they fight the infection and are called _____ cells. Others are long-lived; they become _____ cells and are stored in the _____ and _____. A second encounter with that same type of microbe usually produces no symptoms of illness, because of the _____ of specific B and T cells, each derived from the same _____ cell. This series of events, which provides immunity, is known as _____.

43.39 How do the different kinds of T cells develop?

🐚   The source of all blood cells, including white cells, is the bone marrow. However, this tissue produces only *stem cells*—primitive, immature lymphocytes that migrate to other parts of the body for development into mature, functional cells. Most immature lymphocytes are formed during fetal life (prior to birth).

About half the lymphocytes that leave the bone marrow pass through the *thymus*—a mass of tissue located within the chest cavity just below the neck. The thymus is quite large during infancy but shrinks to a very small size in early childhood and remains small throughout life. Cells that pass through this organ before entering the circulatory system develop into T cells. They are especially effective in detecting and destroying eukaryotic cells with foreign antigens on their surfaces, such as those that have become cancerous or infected with viruses.

The plasma membrane of a T cell contains receptor proteins that recognize one particular antigen. When the cell contacts this antigen, it differentiates into one of three types of T cells—cytotoxic, helper, or suppressor. Cytotoxic (or killer) T cells destroy their target cells by releasing a substance that dissolves holes in its plasma membrane, causing the target cell to lyse. Helper T cells stimulate B cells to make antibodies and facilitate the actions of other T cells. Some helper cells secrete *lymphokines* or *interleukins*, which are messenger molecules that recruit other white blood cells to the battle site. Suppressor T cells cause both B cells and other T cells to become less active.

43.40 Why is it unusual to get the same infectious disease more than once?

🐚   Future attacks by the same type of microbe are prevented by the T and B lymphocytes. An animal has millions of different kinds of T and B cells, each specialized in fighting one particular kind of disease-causing microbe. Until the invading microbe contacts these cells, each type of lymphocyte exists in very low numbers and in an immature state. The population of a particular T cell or B cell rapidly increases and matures when its foreign antigen is detected. Some of the newly formed T and B cells become active in the body's fight against the microbe with that antigen. They are called *plasma cells*. Others, called *memory cells*, are stored in the spleen and lymph nodes, where they remain until the next invasion by that microbe. Then the memory cells rapidly activate the immune system so that the invading microbe has little chance of getting established. This protection, by already differentiated and abundant B and T cells, against a second invasion by the same microbe is known as *immunity*.

DISTINGUISHING BETWEEN SELF AND NONSELF

43.41 The major histocompatibility complex is a

(**a**) series of complement-enhanced reactions to antigens.   (**b**) group of antigens, coded by a family of genes, on the surfaces of body cells.   (**c**) form of autoimmunity.   (**d**) the major cause of cancer.

43.42 Which of the following blood groups enables a person to give blood to any other person?

(**a**) A;   (**b**) B;   (**c**) AB;   (**d**) 0

43.43 What happens to a person who receives the wrong type of blood?

(a) All the arteries dilate. (b) All the arteries constrict. (c) The red blood cells agglutinate. (d) The spleen and lymph nodes deteriorate.

43.44 An example of an autoimmune disease is

(a) asthma. (b) cancer. (c) systemic lupus erythematosus. (d) erythroblastosis fetalis.

43.45 Which of the following diseases is common among individuals with deficient immune systems?

(a) Asthma; (b) Cancer; (c) Systemic lupus erythematosus; (d) Erythroblastosis fetalis

43.46 The Rh factor causes erythroblastosis fetalis when a woman who is Rh _____ develops _____ against her fetus, which is Rh _____ because of inheritance of this cell-surface antigen from its _____, who is Rh _____. Symptoms of the disease are caused by _____ of the baby's _____.

43.47 Transplanted tissues and organs are rejected when the host's _____ cells attack antigens on the _____ of the transplant. This set of antigens, unique to each genotype, is known as the _____ complex.

43.48 If one needed an organ transplant, the best donor would be _____, if such a person existed. The next-best donor would be a _____ or _____, because on the average one shares _____ percent of the same genes with these people.

43.49 According to the immune surveillance theory, cancer cells develop all the time in everyone, but they do not form _____ because they are _____ as _____ and destroyed by the body's _____ cells.

43.50 Why is it so difficult to successfully transplant tissues and organs?

🐚 Except in the case of identical siblings, each individual carries a unique set of genes that directs the cells to synthesize a unique collection of molecules. Some of the molecules on cell surfaces form the major histocompatibility complex and are recognized as foreign by the T cells of another individual. When tissues or organs are transferred from one person to another, the host's immune system is likely to attack the transplant. Modern transplant techniques include close matching of the major histocompatibility complexes of donor and recipient and the use of drugs to suppress the recipient's immune system.

IMMUNE DISORDERS

43.51 An allergic reaction is initiated by antibodies of the

(a) IgG group. (b) IgM group. (c) IgA group. (d) IgE group.

43.52 The symptoms of an allergic reaction develop in response to

(a) interferons. (b) interleukins. (c) histamine. (d) complement.

43.53 Someone with severe combined immunodeficiency has no

(a) interferons. (b) macrophages. (c) T or B cells. (d) functioning lymph nodes.

43.54 Untreated victims of severe combined immunodeficiency usually die from

(a) infections that in other people are minor. (b) anaphylactic shock. (c) congested lungs. (d) unusually high fever.

43.55 The virus that causes acquired immune deficiency syndrome (AIDS) parasitizes

(a) B cells. (b) cytotoxic T cells. (c) helper T cells. (d) the membranes of lymph nodes.

43.56 An allergic reaction is an overreaction of the _____ to an environmental _____.

43.57 In a severe allergic reaction, called _____ shock, all of the _____ become
_____ in response to unusually large amounts of _____ released by mast cells in the
body. This type of reaction can be fatal, because of the sudden drop in _____.

43.58 Victims of acquired immune deficiency syndrome (AIDS) usually die of _____ or _____,
because they do not have enough _____. The AIDS virus is found only in the _____
of the body. Exposure to the AIDS virus is determined by testing the _____ for the presence
of _____.

43.59 The AIDS virus is especially difficult to treat, because it is a(n) _____-virus and its genes remain for
long periods of time attached to the cell's _____.

43.60 What causes an allergic reaction?

The immune system responds to a variety of noninfectious foreign materials, including pollen, drugs,
certain foods, bee or wasp stings, and the chemicals in such plants as poison oak and poison ivy.

An *allergy* (literally "altered reaction") is an inappropriate, overreaction of the immune system. Common
allergies are hives, hay fever, asthma, and eczema. Antibodies belonging to the IgE class trigger the reaction by
combining with both the antigen and the surfaces of *mast cells*, which are noncirculating cells that form part of
connective tissue, to cause the release of large amounts of histamine into the bloodstream. Histamine, a normal
initiator of the inflammatory response, stimulates the dilation of arteries and increased permeability of capillaries
that result in fluid buildup in the interstitial areas of the affected tissues. Sneezing, coughing, itching, difficulty in
breathing, and rashes are all symptoms of an inflammatory response in a particular region of the body.

A severe allergic reaction, called *anaphylactic shock*, occurs when large amounts of histamine are suddenly
released by the mast cells. All the peripheral arteries dilate at once, causing a precipitous drop in blood pressure,
or shock. It is fatal if not immediately treated.

Allergies are treated with drugs that cause vasoconstriction—antihistamines in the case of normal allergic
reactions and epinephrine in the case of anaphylactic shock.

Answers to Objective Questions

43.1 c
43.2 a
43.3 b
43.4 b
43.5 c
43.6 lower; pH
43.7 dilated; constricted; more permeable
43.8 amoeboid projections; engulfing; digesting
43.11 b
43.12 a
43.13 d
43.14 b
43.15 a
43.16 a
43.17 b
43.18 antigens; antibodies; antibody; B
43.19 recognize; bind with; killing
43.20 protein; heavy; polypeptides; light; polypeptides; variable
43.21 two; two; agglutinate
43.22 antibodies; phagocytes; complement
43.23 identical; B cells; tumor cells

43.26 b
43.27 a
43.28 d
43.29 a
43.30 b
43.31 d
43.32 b
43.33 anchor; plasma membrane; recognize
43.34 cytotoxic (or killer); helper; suppressor
43.35 viruses; bacteria; eukaryotic cells; lysed; antibodies; antigens; plasma membrane
43.36 bone marrow; thymus; bone marrow; spleen; lymph nodes
43.37 plasma membrane; antigens; identical; antigens; macromolecule
43.38 differentiate; multiply; clone; plasma; memory; spleen; lymph nodes; abundance; parental; clonal selection
43.41 b
43.42 d

43.43 c
43.44 c
43.45 b
43.46 negative; antibodies; positive; father; positive; agglutination; red blood cells
43.47 T cells; cell surfaces; major histocompatibility
43.48 an identical sibling; sibling; parent; 50
43.49 tumors; recognized; foreign; T
43.51 d
43.52 c
43.53 c
43.54 a
43.55 c
43.56 immune system; antigen
43.57 anaphylactic; peripheral arteries; dilated; histamine; blood pressure
43.58 infections; cancer; helper T cells; fluids; blood; antibodies
43.59 retro; chromosomes

CHAPTER 44
Neurons and Neurotransmitters

NEURONS AND GLIAL CELLS*

44.1   The parts of neurons that perform basic cellular functions, such as protein synthesis, are the

(*a*) somas.   (*b*) axons.   (*c*) dendrites.   (*d*) synaptic knobs.

44.2   The parts of neurons that receive neurotransmitters and pass on graded electrotonic potentials toward the soma are the

(*a*) myelin sheaths.   (*b*) axons.   (*c*) axon hillocks.   (*d*) dendrites.

44.3   The dendrites of a typical vertebrate motor neuron, compared to the neuron's axon, are generally

(*a*) longer.   (*b*) larger in diameter.   (*c*) more myelinated.   (*d*) more branched.

44.4   Which of the following is *not* done by glial cells?

(*a*) Receiving and conducting electrochemical signals;   (*b*) Giving metabolic support to neurons;   (*c*) Producing insulating sheaths around axons;   (*d*) Removing debris after the death of a neuron

44.5   The glial cells that form the blood-brain barrier by lining brain capillaries are the

(*a*) oligodendroglial cells.   (*b*) astrocytes.   (*c*) Schwann cells.   (*d*) Ranvier cells.

44.6   The fundamental information-processing unit in all neural control systems is the _____ or _____, which has the specialized properties of _____ and _____.

44.7   The three classes of neurons in vertebrates and complex invertebrates are: _____, which receive information from sensory receptors and transmit it to the central nervous system; _____, which transmit messages to the effectors (_____ and _____); and, _____, which transmit messages between the other two types of neurons.

44.8   Identify the lettered parts of the typical vertebrate motor neuron shown in Fig. 44.1.

44.9   In a vertebrate motor neuron, the parts of the cell that can have specialized receptor areas for incoming electrochemical messages are the _____, _____, and _____. Outgoing signals are conducted along the _____ to the _____, where the signals then pass across a _____ to other nerve cells or effectors.

44.10   When a motor neuron carries signals (neural impulses) to an effector, the neuron is said to _____ the effector.

44.11   _____ is a process in which glial (also called neuroglial) cells wrap their _____ around an axon. The gaps between glial cells are called _____. In the vertebrate central nervous system (_____ and _____), the glial cells that myelinate axons are the _____; in the peripheral nervous system, the myelinating glial cells are the _____.

44.12   What is the difference between a neuron and a glial cell?

   Neurons and glial cells are the basic components of neural control systems. The neuron, or nerve cell (see Fig. 44.1), is the fundamental information-processing unit, receiving and integrating information from external and internal environments, and using this information to control effectors (muscles and glands). The neuron has two specialized properties for this task: irritability (or excitability) and conductivity. Irritability—a property found to some degree in all cells—is the capacity to respond to environmental stimuli. For a neuron, these

* Answers to Chapter 44 objective questions appear on page 313.

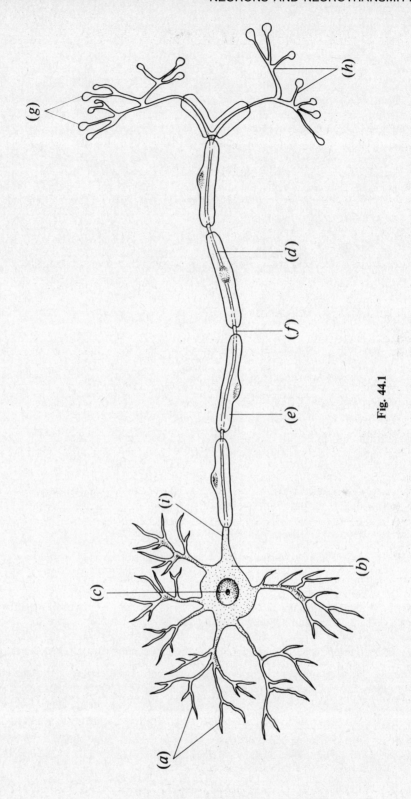

Fig. 44.1

stimuli are coded messages in the form of electrochemical impulses coming to it from sensory receptors and other neurons. The neuron responds to these stimuli by passing on its own flow of coded electrochemical impulses. The term *conductivity*, when used with a wire in an electric circuit, refers to the wire's ability to carry or conduct an electric current. With a neuron, conductivity is the ability to conduct a "current" of electrochemical impulses along its own length and then to transmit it to the next neuron or effector.

The other basic components of neural control systems, the *glial* (or *neuroglial*) cells, as their name implies, "glue" the neural systems together. Because glial cells surround the neurons, they are able to insulate neurons from the rest of the body and provide them with many life-support services. Glial cells bring neurons the substances for metabolism, remove metabolic wastes and debris from damaged or dead neurons, regulate the chemistry of the fluids bathing the neurons, insulate the neurons from each other to prevent interference between the electrochemical message channels, and provide myelin sheaths for saltatory conduction (discussed in Question 44.39). There are many types of glial cells: *astrocytes*, which form the blood-brain barrier by lining brain capillaries; *oligodendroglial cells*, which are the glial support cells for the vertebrate central nervous system (brain and spinal cord); and *Schwann cells*, which perform the latter function in the vertebrate peripheral nervous system.

RESTING AND ACTION POTENTIALS

44.13 If two electrodes attached to a voltmeter are placed on both sides of an axon's plasma membrane (one in the cytoplasm and the other on the membrane's outer surface) and the membrane is in its "resting state," then the voltmeter will typically give a reading of

(*a*) +30 millivolts.   (*b*) −7 millivolts.   (*c*) −50 millivolts.   (*d*) −70 millivolts.

44.14 The sodium-potassium pump

(*a*) transports Na^+ and K^+ out of the neuron.   (*b*) transports Na^+ into the neuron and K^+ out.
(*c*) transports K^+ into the neuron and Na^+ out.   (*d*) transports Na^+ and K^+ into the neuron.

44.15 When a neuron shows a stable resting potential, the concentration of Na^+ is

(*a*) 10 times higher inside the cell than outside.   (*b*) 10 times higher outside the cell than inside.
(*c*) 30 times higher inside the cell than outside.   (*d*) 30 times higher outside the cell than inside.

44.16 In the resting state of the neural membrane, diffusion due to concentration gradients, if allowed, would drive

(*a*) Na^+ into the cell.   (*b*) Na^+ out of the cell.   (*c*) K^+ into the cell.   (*d*) K^+ and Na^+ out of the cell.

44.17 At the nerve cell membrane, the equilibrium potential for potassium is

(*a*) +65 millivolts.   (*b*) +35 millivolts.   (*c*) −70 millivolts.   (*d*) −90 millivolts.

44.18 An action potential, for a given axon, is

(*a*) different in size each time it occurs.   (*b*) always the same size.   (*c*) larger when information has to be conveyed faster.   (*d*) smaller when information goes to a gland rather than a muscle.

44.19 Which of the following increases when an action potential is initiated?

(*a*) Diffusion of sodium ions into the neuron;   (*b*) Diffusion of sodium ions out of the neuron;   (*c*) Diffusion of potassium ions out of the neuron;   (*d*) Diffusion of potassium ions into the neuron

44.20 When an action potential abruptly drops from positive to negative, this is because

(*a*) potassium gates are inactivated and sodium gates are opened.   (*b*) sodium gates are inactivated and potassium gates are opened.   (*c*) both potassium and sodium gates are inactivated.   (*d*) both potassium and sodium gates are opened.

44.21 The "spike" phase of the action potential lasts for roughly

(*a*) 2 milliseconds.   (*b*) 20 milliseconds.   (*c*) 200 milliseconds.   (*d*) 2000 milliseconds.

44.22 The speed at which impulses are conducted increases with

(*a*) increasing diameter of the soma.   (*b*) increasing diameter of the axon.   (*c*) increasing number of dendrites.
(*d*) increasing branching of the dendrites.

44.23 The primary function of the myelin sheaths around a vertebrate axon is to

(*a*) regulate the sodium-potassium pumps. (*b*) increase the size of the action potentials. (*c*) increase the speed of conduction of the impulse. (*d*) deactivate used neurotransmitters.

44.24 The axons of invertebrate animals have no myelin sheaths. This lack is compensated for by having

(*a*) very long axons. (*b*) very short axons. (*c*) axons of very large diameter. (*d*) axons of very small diameter.

44.25 A membrane's excitability is a function of two properties: _____, the concentration of oppositely charged ions across the membrane, and _____, the permeability of the membrane to ionic currents.

44.26 In the resting state of the axon, the steady voltage difference across the plasma membrane, called the _____, is typically _____.

44.27 When an axon membrane shows a steady resting potential, there are _____ times more potassium ions inside the axon than outside, and _____ times more sodium ions outside the axon than inside. In this state, the axon membrane is 10 times more permeable to _____ than it is to _____.

44.28 In the resting state, the axon membrane is _____, with more _____ charged ions outside than inside. This unequal distribution of ions is due to: (1) the selective permeability of the membrane, which forms an almost impenetrable barrier to _____, and (2) the action of the _____, which pumps _____ Na^+ out of the neuron for every _____ K^+ brought in.

44.29 Typically, it takes many simultaneous _____ electrotonic potentials to initiate an _____ potential.

44.30 An action potential is initiated each time the membrane potential is raised to _____ potential. Because action potentials never occur below this potential and upon occurring are always the same _____, action potentials are called _____ events.

44.31 The positive phase of an action potential is initiated when a stimulus _____ the membrane to _____ potential and the voltage-sensitive _____ gates open. The membrane potential returns to negative, i.e., is _____, when the _____ gates _____ and the voltage-sensitive _____ gates open.

44.32 When action potentials are conducted along an axon, each successive action potential rises to the same characteristic positive membrane potential. In many neurons, this peak is roughly at _____. This behavior is called the _____ law of neural conduction.

44.33 Action potentials travel in one direction only along an axon because behind the potential, the membrane is in a brief _____ when it is insensitive to new stimulation.

44.34 Action potentials are conducted by lateral currents of _____ that _____ adjacent sections of the membrane to _____.

44.35 In the vertebrate axon, the action potential moves between _____, in what is called _____ conduction.

44.36 What is the resting membrane potential of an axon, and how is it maintained?

🐚 A neural membrane, like the plasma membrane of any cell, is selectively permeable; certain atoms and molecules are kept inside the cell, others enter and leave freely, and still others are allowed to move in only one direction. Because many of these particles are ions, this selective permeability produces a forced separation of charges between the inside and outside of the membrane. A *membrane potential* is a measure (in millivolts) of the charge inside the membrane relative to the charge outside. The *resting membrane potential* of the axon of a neuron is this potential difference between inside and outside when the axon is "resting," i.e., not actively conducting impulses. In this state, if one of the two electrodes connected to a voltmeter is inserted in the axon's cytoplasm while the other is placed nearby on the external surface of the membrane, the voltmeter will typically show a potential of −70 millivolts (mV). This means that the interior of the axon is 70 mV more negative than the exterior.

Three types of ions play significant roles in determining resting potentials: sodium (Na^+), potassium (K^+), and large negatively charged organic molecules (amino acids and proteins). The inside of the resting axon contains approximately 30 times more potassium ions and about 10 times fewer sodium ions than the external fluids. All of the large negatively charged organic molecules are located inside the axon. The different concentrations of these three types of ions are maintained by an interplay of several factors: diffusion; electrical attractions and repulsions; active transport across the cell membrane; and selective permeability of the axon membrane to these three ions.

Channels in the axon membrane permit some movement of these ions through the membrane. The sodium ions move through a specific channel with a gate that is sensitive to the electrical state of the membrane. At the resting membrane potential, these voltage-sensitive gates are essentially closed, although some sodium ions leak inward down their concentration gradients. The potassium ions move through two types of channels—one that is permanently open and another, comparable to the sodium channel, that has a voltage-sensitive gate. In the resting state, the voltage-sensitive gate is closed, but the potassium ions can still move freely out of the cell along the permanently open channels. The negatively charged organic molecules, the third type of ion, are too large to fit through the membrane channels and always remain inside the axon.

The potassium ions tend to diffuse out of the axon slowly and continuously, but their movement is opposed by both attraction to the negatively charged organic molecules and their repulsion by the positively charged sodium ions outside the membrane. Nevertheless, potassium diffusion outward is more rapid than sodium diffusion inward. If there were no other mechanism operating during the resting phase, the interior of the axon would not be at a constant −70 mV but would instead become increasingly negative. However, an active-transport mechanism called the *sodium-potassium pump* is continuously moving sodium out of the cell and returning potassium to the interior. This pump, a protein molecule within the membrane, operates from energy stored in ATP molecules; it moves three sodium ions out for every two potassium ions that it moves to the interior.

44.37 What is an action potential?

⚙ An action potential is a very rapid change in the axon membrane potential from the negative resting potential (−70 mV) to a positive peak (typically, +40 mV) and then back to the resting potential. This change, if it occurs at all, always occurs in exactly the same pattern (Fig. 44.2), which is why it is called an all-or-none event.

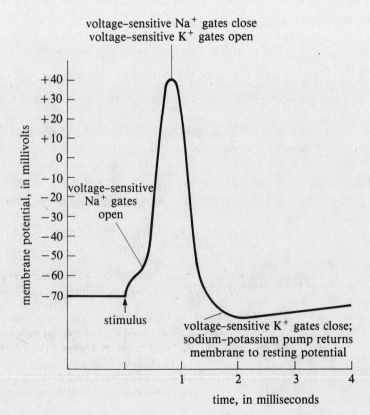

Fig. 44.2. An action potential as displayed on the screen of a cathode-ray oscilloscope. The stages of the action potential are shown, along with the changes in membrane gates that produce these stages.

The action potential is always preceded by a gradual decrease in the axon's negativity toward a *threshold of excitation* (or *threshold potential*) of roughly −60 mV. This slow decrease is due to the summation of excitatory inputs from other neurons (see Question 44.60). At threshold, some voltage-sensitive sodium gates open, allowing an increase in the inward diffusion of sodium ions. This "depolarization" of the membrane triggers more sodium gates to open, until the membrane potential reaches roughly +40 mV. At this point, the sodium gates close (inactivate) and the voltage-sensitive potassium gates open. So much potassium now flows out that the cell is briefly "hyperpolarized" (the membrane potential is more negative than −70 mV). During this phase, the membrane is said to be in a *refractory period* because it cannot respond to another stimulus. The voltage-sensitive potassium gates then close, and the sodium-potassium pump restores the resting potential.

44.38   What is the all-or-none law of neural conduction?

🐚   The action potential that rises and falls in a limited area of the axon membrane is only one stage in a neuron's reception, conduction, and transmission of electrochemical impulse messages. The next stage in this process—the movement of a sequence of action potentials along the axon from the axon hillock to the terminal knobs—is called *conduction* of the impulse. Just as the action potential is an all-or-none event, so also the entire conduction process follows an all-or-none law: The action potential as it is conducted along the axon is always the same size; it doesn't increase or decrease.

The action potential moves along the axon because each successive action potential produces a flow of positive ions into the next section of the membrane, depolarizing that section and producing a new and equal action potential. This sequence continues to the synaptic knobs.

This conduction sequence goes only in one direction for two reasons: First, the neural systems are so connected that input signals travel only toward the axon's synaptic knobs; and second, the area directly behind the last action potential is in a refractory period, so the signal cannot retrace its path.

44.39   What is the function of myelination in saltatory conduction?

🐚   The axons of vertebrate neurons are myelinated, and thereby insulated, by glial cells that have their plasma membranes wrapped tightly around the axons. However, the *nodes of Ranvier*—each located at the junction of two glial cells—are exposed. With the axon insulated by myelination except at the nodes of Ranvier, the action potential jumps from node to node instead of moving continuously along the axon. It jumps in this way because the lateral flow of Na^+ ions from each action potential can only depolarize adjacent membrane at the uninsulated nodes. This movement from node to node is called *saltatory conduction* (from the Latin *saltare* = to leap), and it is much faster and more energy-efficient than conduction in unmyelinated axons of the same diameter.

SYNAPSES AND NEUROTRANSMITTERS

44.40   An electrical synapse differs from a chemical synapse in that the electrical synapse

(*a*) has wider clefts between the presynaptic and postsynaptic membranes.   (*b*) has more varied signals crossing the synapse.   (*c*) is found only in vertebrates.   (*d*) is much faster, having essentially instantaneous transmission.

44.41   When a membrane potential known as an EPSP develops in the postsynaptic membrane, it

(*a*) increases the likelihood of an action potential in the postsynaptic neuron.   (*b*) decreases the likelihood of an action potential in the postsynaptic neuron.   (*c*) has no effect on an action potential in the postsynaptic neuron.   (*d*) decreases the likelihood of an action potential in the presynaptic neuron.

44.42   The neurotransmitter released into the synapse between neurons and muscle cells that produces an EPSP in skeletal muscle cells is

(*a*) gamma-amino butyric acid (GABA).   (*b*) acetylcholine (ACh).   (*c*) norepinephrine.   (*d*) epinephrine.

44.43   The drug curare causes paralysis by preventing a specific neurotransmitter molecule from binding with its receptor protein. Which neurotransmitter is so affected?

(*a*) Serotonin;   (*b*) Dopamine;   (*c*) Glutamic acid;   (*d*) Acetylcholine

44.44   The benzodiazepine drug known as Valium produces relaxation by aiding the binding to receptor proteins of the inhibitory neurotransmitter

(*a*) ACh.   (*b*) GABA.   (*c*) dopamine.   (*d*) glycine.

44.45   Parkinson's disease, which is characterized by tremors and progressive rigidity of the limbs, is caused by a degeneration of brain neurons involved in movement control that use the neurotransmitter

(*a*) ACh.   (*b*) aspartic acid.   (*c*) dopamine.   (*d*) GABA.

44.46   The euphoric condition achieved by joggers called "runner's high" is thought to be produced by a high concentration in the blood of

(*a*) endorphins.   (*b*) ACh.   (*c*) norepinephrine.   (*d*) dopamine.

44.47   The hormone adrenalin is the same as the neurotransmitter

(*a*) epinephrine.   (*b*) norepinephrine.   (*c*) GABA.   (*d*) ACh.

44.48   Identify the lettered parts of the typical vertebrate chemical synapse shown in Fig. 44.3.

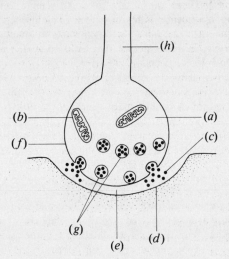

Fig. 44.3

44.49   When an action potential reaches a vertebrate chemical synapse, it opens _____ gates in the plasma membrane of the synaptic knob, permitting this ion to diffuse into the knob. This in turn causes _____-containing neurotransmitters to fuse with the _____ and release the neurotransmitters into the _____. The neurotransmitters then diffuse over to the _____, where they interact with _____ proteins; this interaction produces either an _____ or an _____.

44.50   In an electrical synapse between neurons, the action potential flows from cell to cell through intercellular channels called _____.

44.51   The constant competition at a synapse between EPSPs and IPSPs is called _____. Whether or not an action potential results is determined by a process called _____ at the axon hillock.

44.52   When a neurotransmitter produces a graded electrotonic potential in the postsynaptic membrane that makes the membrane potential more negative, that graded potential is called an _____ or _____.

44.53   Vertebrates have a chemical synapse, called a _____, that lies between a motor neuron and a muscle cell; in this synapse, the axon terminals of the motor neurons are in grooves in the muscle-cell membrane called _____. The neurotransmitter _____ is released at this synapse when an action potential arrives.

44.54   The disease _____ occurs when the bacterium *Clostridium tetani* enters the body through a puncture wound and produces a neurotoxin that interferes with _____ synapses of motor neurons. This produces excessive contractions and spastic paralysis.

44.55   After receptor proteins at the neuromuscular junction release the neurotransmitter _____, which has crossed the neuron-to-muscle synapse, this neurotransmitter is degraded by the enzyme _____ into _____ and _____.

44.56   The neurotransmitter _____, which is critical to the production and regulation of sleep, is derived from the amino acid _____.

44.57   Certain neuropeptides, _____ and _____, are produced by the nervous system, but act like derivatives of the drug opium (e.g., morphine). They have a variety of physiological and emotional effects such as depressed respiration and euphoria.

44.58   Molecules that are not neurotransmitters but that bind to postsynaptic receptor proteins and influence the cell's response to neurotransmitters are called _____.

44.59   What are the differences between electrical and chemical synapses?

     Action-potential messages are transmitted from neuron to neuron, or neuron to effector cell, across a synapse. The synapse comprises the junction between two cells formed by two membranes, one from each cell, and the fluid-filled space between the membranes. Because neural messages travel in only one direction, the membrane of the sending cell is called the *presynaptic membrane* and the membrane of the receiving cell is called the *postsynaptic membrane*. The fluid-filled gap is called the *synaptic cleft*.

     There are two types of synapses: electrical and chemical. In an electrical synapse, action potentials move from presynaptic to postsynaptic membranes in a fashion similar to the conduction of the impulse along an axon. In such a junction, the synaptic cleft is so narrow that electric currents generated by the action potentials in the presynaptic membrane flow across the gap (through a gap junction) to the postsynaptic membrane, where they affect voltage-sensitive ion channels and produce action potentials. Such synapses are found in invertebrates and vertebrates, but chemical synapses are more prevalent in vertebrates.

     In chemical synapses (see Fig. 44.3), the synaptic cleft is too wide for electric currents to pass directly between the membranes. Instead, the action potential message is transmitted to the postsynaptic membrane by a variety of neurotransmitter molecules that diffuse across the cleft. Action potentials arriving at the synaptic knobs of the axons increase the permeability of the knob membrane to calcium ions (Ca^{2+}). This, in turn, causes neurotransmitter-filled vesicles stored in the knobs to fuse with the presynaptic membrane and release their neurotransmitter molecules into the cleft. These molecules then diffuse across the cleft to the postsynaptic membrane, where they become attached to receptor molecules. The bonding of neurotransmitters with receptor molecules triggers changes in the permeability of the postsynaptic membrane that, in turn, produce changes in the postsynaptic membrane potential. These changes, called *postsynaptic potentials*, can be excitatory or inhibitory, depending on the type of neurotransmitter-receptor connection.

     An *excitatory postsynaptic potential* (EPSP) is a decrease in the internal negativity of the postsynaptic membrane; it increases the probability that the receiving neuron will generate an action potential. Such EPSPs are due principally to an increased diffusion of sodium ions into the postsynaptic membrane. The other type of postsynaptic potential, the *inhibitory postsynaptic potential* (IPSP), is an increase in the internal negativity of the postsynaptic membrane; it decreases the probability of an action potential in the receiving neuron. It is thought that IPSPs are due to a brief opening in voltage-sensitive gates that either allow an outward diffusion of K^+ or an inward diffusion of Cl^-. How EPSPs and IPSPs are integrated in the receiving neuron is discussed in Question 44.60.

     Immediately after an EPSP or IPSP has occurred, neurotransmitter molecules are released from the receptor proteins on the postsynaptic membrane and are then either broken down by specific enzymes into nonfunctional components, diffuse away through the synaptic cleft, or are transported back into the synaptic knobs for reuse.

44.60   Discuss the process of summation at the axon hillock.

     At any given moment, a neuron is receiving messages from many synapses. Each neuron of the human brain is estimated to have typically 1000–10,000 synapses; in some brain areas responsible for the coordination of movement, a single neuron may have as many as 70,000 synapses. Not all of these are releasing neurotransmitters at any given moment, but the synapses that are produce a great many simultaneous small EPSPs and IPSPs in the receptor neuron's postsynaptic membranes, most of which are located on the dendrites and soma. All of these changes in potential generate ionic currents that flow along the membranes of the dendrites and soma toward the axon hillock (see Fig. 44.1), where action potentials are generated. If at any given moment the axon-hillock membrane is in an excitable state and the sum of all the currents reaching it from the receptor surfaces is sufficient to decrease the negativity of the membrane potential to threshold, then the receiving neuron will generate and conduct action potentials. This process of integration of ionic currents at the axon hillock is called *summation*.

Answers to Objective Questions

44.1   *a*

44.2   *d*

44.3   *d*

44.4   *a*

44.5   *b*

44.6   nerve cell; neuron; irritability; conductivity

44.7   sensory neurons; motor neurons; muscles; glands; interneurons

44.8   (*a*) dendrites; (*b*) soma (or cell body); (*c*) nucleus; (*d*) axon; (*e*) myelin sheath; (*f*) node of Ranvier; (*g*) synaptic knobs;

(*h*) terminal branches;
(*i*) axon hillock

44.9 dendrites; soma; axon; axon; synaptic knobs; synapse

44.10 innervate

44.11 myelination; plasma membranes; nodes of Ranvier; brain; spinal cord; oligodendroglial cells; Schwann cells

44.13 *d*

44.14 *c*

44.15 *b*

44.16 *a*

44.17 *d*

44.18 *b*

44.19 *a*

44.20 *b*

44.21 *a*

44.22 *b*

44.23 *c*

44.24 *c*

44.25 capacitance; conductance

44.26 resting membrane potential; −70 millivolts

44.27 30; 10; K$^+$; Na$^+$

44.28 polarized; positively; Na$^+$; sodium-potassium pump; three; two

44.29 graded; action

44.30 threshold; size; all-or-none

44.31 depolarizes; threshold; Na$^+$; repolarized; Na$^+$; inactivate; K$^+$

44.32 +40 millivolts; all-or-none

44.33 refractory period

44.34 Na$^+$; depolarize; threshold

44.35 nodes of Ranvier; saltatory

44.40 *d*

44.41 *a*

44.42 *b*

44.43 *d*

44.44 *b*

44.45 *c*

44.46 *a*

44.47 *a*

44.48 (*a*) synaptic knob; (*b*) mitochondrion; (*c*) neurotransmitter

molecules; (*d*) postsynaptic membrane; (*e*) synaptic cleft; (*f*) presynaptic membrane; (*g*) synaptic vesicles; (*h*) axon-terminal branch

44.49 Ca^{2+}; synaptic vesicles; presynaptic membrane; synaptic cleft; postsynaptic membrane; receptor; EPSP; IPSP

44.50 gap junctions

44.51 synaptic integration; summation

44.52 inhibitory postsynaptic potential; IPSP

44.53 neuromuscular junction; motor end plates; acetylcholine

44.54 tetanus; inhibitory

44.55 acetylcholine; acetylcholinesterase; acetic acid; choline

44.56 serotonin; tryptophan

44.57 endorphins; enkephalins

44.58 neuromodulators

CHAPTER 45

Neural Control Systems

EVOLUTION OF NERVOUS SYSTEMS*

45.1 The trend in evolution toward an increasing concentration of sensory receptors and neural control centers in the anterior end of an animal is called

(*a*) segmentation. (*b*) cephalization. (*c*) anteriorization. (*d*) centralization.

45.2 The first animals to have neurons were probably similar to modern

(*a*) sponges. (*b*) flatworms. (*c*) annelid worms. (*d*) cnidarians.

45.3 Which of the following animals can be said to have a "brain"?

(*a*) Planarian; (*b*) Sea anemone; (*c*) Jellyfish; (*d*) Starfish

45.4 The simplest form of nervous system that integrates body activities is found in cnidarians and is called a

(*a*) nerve-trunk system. (*b*) ladder system. (*c*) nerve-net system. (*d*) nerve-cord system.

45.5 Three typical circuits in nervous systems are: _____ circuits, in which information from several pathways is fed into one pathway; _____ circuits, in which information from one pathway spreads out over several pathways; and _____ circuits, in which information travels within a closed circular pathway.

45.6 In general, for invertebrates, when somas (nerve cell bodies) and synapses are grouped together these groupings are called _____. For vertebrates, such groupings *outside* the central nervous system are called _____, but those situated *within* the central nervous system are typically called _____.

45.7 Nervous systems have two main functions: to initiate and coordinate responses to the _____, and to maintain _____.

45.8 _____, the most primitive animals to show a true central nervous system, have a _____ and one or more nerve _____. When there are two parallel nerve _____ joined by connecting nerves, this is called a _____ type nervous system. In annelids and arthropods these separated parallel nerve _____ tend to be closer together or fuse, and there are _____ in each segment.

45.9 Three major trends that affected the evolution of nervous systems are: centralization, the change from radial to bilateral symmetry, and cephalization. What are these trends, and how did they affect this evolution?

Because neural tissues are rarely preserved in fossils, scientists have had to piece together the early evolution of nervous systems from stages seen in living representatives of early animals. Of these, it now seems that modern cnidarians (sea anemones, *Hydra*, jellyfish) are most similar to the first animals to have neurons and nervous systems.

The modern cnidarians are *radially symmetrical*: there is no front and back, or right and left sides; instead, the body parts are organized circularly, like spokes radiating from the center of a wheel. The cnidarians have the simplest known forms of nervous systems. In *Hydra*, for example, there is a *nerve-net system*, in which essentially identical neurons interconnected by synapses crisscross the body. The net transmits information from sensory receptor cells to musclelike effector cells. When the sensory cells react to chemical or mechanical stimuli, the neural message radiates outward along the net in all directions, producing contractions in large numbers of effector cells. This allows some degree of coordination of localized responses, such as the movement of a tentacle.

Also seen in a modern cnidarian, the jellyfish, is a somewhat more advanced nervous system that shows the first evidence of *centralization*: the gathering together of neurons to form control centers. In the jellyfish, this

* Answers to Chapter 45 objective questions appear on page 326.

takes the form of a ring of neurons around its bell-shaped body; the ring produces coordinated whole-body swimming movements.

A major advancement in the evolution of nervous systems accompanied the appearance of animals with *bilaterally symmetrical* bodies, which are organized on a longitudinal axis with right and left sides that are mirror images of each other. This type of body has a distinct *anterior* (front) end, *posterior* (rear) end, *dorsal* (top) surface, and *ventral* (bottom) surface.

The first and simplest animals to exhibit this type of organization were the flatworms, represented today by such forms as the planarian. This animal shows an increase in centralization, with neurons gathered together to form pathways and control centers. Bundles containing the somas and fibers of neurons form two parallel nerve cords that extend the full length of the body. In the anterior end, or head, the nerve cords fuse to form a *ganglion* (collection of somas and synapses). This accumulation of neural tissue in the head end is thought to represent the first example of an evolutionary trend called *cephalization*. Although this planarian cephalic (situated in the head) ganglion is quite primitive, it has been called the first "brain."

Increasing centralization and cephalization occurred in the evolution of the bilateral nervous system, in both higher invertebrates (annelids, mollusks, cephalopods, arthropods) and vertebrates. In many advanced invertebrates, there is a central nervous system consisting of paired, solid ventral nerve cords with ganglia in each segment of the body and a dominant ganglion (brain) in the head. In vertebrates, the central nervous system is a single, hollow, dorsal nerve cord (the *spinal cord*) with no conspicuous segmental ganglia and with a large dominant brain in the head.

THE VERTEBRATE NERVOUS SYSTEM

45.10   Within the vertebrate peripheral nervous system, the efferent division that deals with "voluntary" activity, in which impulses are carried to the skeletal muscles, is the

(*a*) autonomic system.   (*b*) visceral system.   (*c*) somatic system.   (*d*) parasympathetic system.

45.11   The human cranial nerves that send parasympathetic stimulation to, among other organs, the heart, stomach, and liver are the

(*a*) trigeminal nerves.   (*b*) abducens nerves.   (*c*) vagus nerves.   (*d*) glossopharyngeal nerves.

45.12   There are how many pairs of spinal nerves in a human?

(*a*) 8;   (*b*) 12;   (*c*) 25;   (*d*) 31

45.13   There are how many pairs of cranial nerves in a human?

(*a*) 8;   (*b*) 12;   (*c*) 25;   (*d*) 31

45.14   Which of the following is *not* an effect produced by parasympathetic stimulation?

(*a*) Dilation of the pupils;   (*b*) Increased saliva production;   (*c*) Increased stomach activity;   (*d*) Constriction of the bronchi

45.15   Which of the following is *not* a characteristic of the human sympathetic nervous system?

(*a*) Prepares the person for "fight or flight";   (*b*) Has ganglia near the spinal cord;   (*c*) Increases heart rate;   (*d*) Is a craniosacral division of the autonomic nervous system

45.16   Which of the following is true of vertebrate sympathetic and parasympathetic systems?

(*a*) Both systems are continually active;   (*b*) Both systems innervate all body organs;   (*c*) When one system is active the other is not;   (*d*) One system increases organ activity, while the other system inhibits such activity

45.17   Which of the following human parasympathetic functions is *not* under the contral of a cranial nerve?

(*a*) Constriction of the pupil;   (*b*) Contraction of the bladder;   (*c*) Increase of salivation;   (*d*) Stimulation of gallbladder activity

45.18   Axons of preganglionic neurons in the human sympathetic nervous system emerge from which regions of the spinal cord?

(*a*) Cranial and sacral;   (*b*) Thoracic and lumbar;   (*c*) Cranial and thoracic;   (*d*) Lumbar and sacral

45.19 Preganglionic fibers in both divisions of the autonomic nervous system are said to be cholinergic because they all secrete which transmitter from their synaptic knobs?

(*a*) Gamma-amino butyric acid;   (*b*) Serotonin;   (*c*) Acetylcholine;   (*d*) Norepinephrine

45.20 Which of the following structures, in the evolution of the vertebrate brain, has shown the greatest size increase relative to the rest of the brain?

(*a*) Forebrain;   (*b*) Midbrain;   (*c*) Hindbrain;   (*d*) Rhombencephalon

45.21 Cell bodies of neurons bringing afferent information into the spinal cord are located in

(*a*) dorsal root ganglia.   (*b*) ventral root ganglia.   (*c*) the gray matter of the spinal cord.   (*d*) the white matter of the spinal cord.

45.22 Which of the following has the largest percentage of its brain devoted to prosencephalon?

(*a*) Fish;   (*b*) Frog;   (*c*) Bird;   (*d*) Cat

45.23 In the vertebrate somatic nervous system, axons run directly from somas in the central nervous system to skeletal muscles. In the autonomic nervous system, on the other hand, there are two neurons from the central nervous system to the innervated organ: The _____ neuron, with its cell body in the central nervous system, synapses with a _____ neuron that innervates the organ.

45.24 A stereotyped movement or glandular secretion in response to a sensory stimulus is called a _____. In vertebrates, the neural circuits for such stereotyped responses are called _____, and these include a sensory neuron, one or more interneurons in the central nervous system, and one or two efferent neurons.

45.25 Bundles of parallel neural fibers (axons) that connect the nervous system to other body organs, and the central nervous system to the peripheral nervous system, are called _____. If the bundle consists only of fibers that innervate effectors, it is a _____; if the bundle consists only of fibers that carry afferent information, it is a _____; and if the bundle consists of fibers that carry both afferent and efferent information, it is a _____.

45.26 Vertebrate nervous systems are divided into two major divisions: the central nervous system, which includes the _____ and _____; and the _____ nervous system, which includes all neurons and parts of neurons other than those in the _____ and _____.

45.27 The nerves carrying impulse messages from the central nervous system to the effectors are called _____, while those carrying sensory messages to the central nervous system are called _____.

45.28 In vertebrate evolution, a dorsal, tubular _____ became expanded and was modified into a spinal cord and brain. The central canal of the spinal cord extends into the brain, where it expands into the _____ that are filled with _____.

45.29 The five groups of human spinal nerves, listed from head (anterior) end downward along the spine are: _____ pairs of _____ nerves; _____ pairs of _____ nerves; _____ pairs of _____ nerves; _____ pairs of _____ nerves; and _____ pair of _____ nerves.

45.30 In the vertebrate autonomic nervous system, most ganglia of the _____ system are in a chain of ganglia near the spinal cord, while ganglia in the _____ system are close to the innervated organs.

45.31 Identify the lettered components of the schematic drawing of a knee-jerk reflex shown in Fig. 45.1.

45.32 In a visceral reflex arc, the _____ neuron synapses with the _____ neuron outside the central nervous system.

45.33 The _____ matter of the vertebrate spinal cord consists primarily of cell bodies, dendrites, and synapses. The _____ matter of the cord consists primarily of _____ and gets its name from their coating of _____.

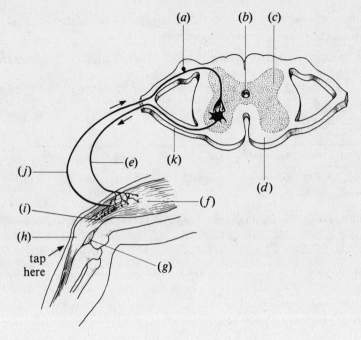

Fig. 45.1

45.34 In general, the parasympathetic system acts to conserve and restore _____, while the sympathetic system prepares the body for increased _____ expenditure.

45.35 The vertebrate central nervous system is protected by three layers of connective tissue called _____. The outer layer is the _____, the middle layer is the _____ membrane, and the inner layer is the _____.

45.36 While in the human cerebrum the outer layer, or _____, is _____ matter and the interior is _____ matter, in the spinal cord the relationship is reversed.

45.37 Identify the lettered structures in the generalized diagram of the principal divisions of the vertebrate brain shown in Fig. 45.2.

45.38 The three main divisions of all vertebrate brains are: hindbrain, or _____; midbrain, or _____; and forebrain, or _____. The brainstem includes all parts of the midbrain and hindbrain except the _____.

45.39 What is a reflex arc?

ⓒ A stereotyped response to a sensory stimulus, a fixed movement pattern or a glandular secretion, is a reflex. All vertebrates, even humans with their immense capacity for learning and intelligence, have a large variety of fixed circuits built into their nervous systems. These circuits are called reflex arcs, and there are two types: *somatic*,

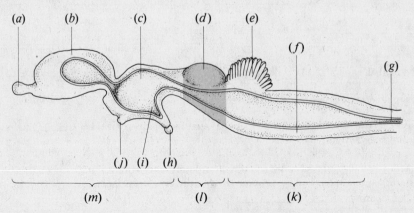

Fig. 45.2

involving somatic nervous system control of skeletal muscles, and *visceral* (or *autonomic*), involving autonomic nervous system control of internal organs.

In humans the simplest example of a somatic reflex arc is the knee-jerk reflex, which is shown in Fig. 45.1. Checking this reflex is a routine part of every physical examination; the doctor taps the tendon of a knee, and there is a reflex, forward jerk of the lower leg. What happens is: stretch receptors in the quadriceps muscle of the thigh respond to the stretching of the tendon; this stimulates action potentials, which travel from the stretch receptor along a sensory neuron, through a dorsal root, and into the gray matter of the spinal cord; here the sensory neuron synapses with a motor neuron that runs out a ventral root back to the quadriceps muscle, where it commands the muscle to contract; this jerks the lower leg forward. A comparable *monosynaptic* (one synapse between sensory and motor neurons) somatic reflex arc in humans is the quick removal of a hand from heat. Most human somatic reflex arcs, however, are *polysynaptic*, with one or more interneurons within the central nervous system between the sensory and motor neurons.

Visceral reflex arcs occur in the two divisions of the autonomic nervous system, the sympathetic and parasympathetic systems (see Question 45.40). A major difference in the neural circuitry between somatic and visceral reflex arcs is that while the motor neuron in a somatic reflex arc goes directly from the central nervous system to the skeletal muscle being innervated, in a visceral reflex arc there are always two efferent neurons from the central nervous system to the innervated organ: a *preganglionic* neuron that goes from the central nervous system to an autonomic ganglion, where it synapses with a second neuron—the *postganglionic* neuron—that then runs to the innervated organ.

45.40 You are watching a horror movie, and you notice that your heart is beating fast, your mouth is dry, and you are breathing rapidly. What is this response called, and what division of the nervous system is responsible for it?

🐌 You are experiencing some of the more noticeable components of the "fight-or-flight" response, produced by the sympathetic division of the autonomic nervous system. In general, the sympathetic system prepares an animal to respond to an emergency, to be able to fight it or flee from it, while the other autonomic division, the parasympathetic system, works to restore and conserve energy.

The two systems and many of their effects are diagramed in Fig. 45.3. It is seen there that most, but not all, body organs are innervated by both systems, and often they have opposite (antagonistic) effects on the same organ. Other major differences between the systems are: while the parasympathetic exits the central nervous system in cranial and sacral nerves, the sympathetic exits through thoracic and lumbar nerves; while preganglionic sympathetic neurons synapse with postganglionic fibers in a chain of sympathetic ganglia near and on both sides of the spinal cord, in the parasympathetic system the synapse between preganglionic and postganglionic fibers takes place near the innervated organ.

45.41 Discuss the evolution of the cerebrum from fish to mammal.

🐌 A schematic, generalized version of the component structures in the vertebrate brain is shown in Fig. 45.2. Some idea of how these structures, particularly the cerebrum, changed in evolution may be gained from Fig. 45.4, where representative brains are shown for a modern fish (Fig. 45.4a) and a modern mammal (Fig. 45.4b). It is immediately apparent from Fig. 45.4 that between fish and mammal a massive increase has occurred in the percentage of the brain devoted to the cerebrum.

In a fish, the midbrain contains the primary centers for integration of sensory information and control of behavior. The midbrain receives information about the internal environment from the spinal cord, and its optic lobes receive information about vision directly from the eyes. The olfactory bulbs receive information about odors from olfactory receptors in the nose, organize this information, and pass it on to the cerebrum. The cerebrum of a fish consists of a pair of smooth-surfaced lobes that further integrate and organize the olfactory information and then transmit it to control centers in the midbrain. This form of cerebrum is referred to as a "smell brain."

In the evolution from fish to amphibian to reptile to mammal, there was a steady decrease in the relative size and importance of the midbrain, as the expanding forebrain acquired an increasing number of information-processing and control functions. The cerebrum of an amphibian is also a smell brain, but it has an additional structure. In the evolution from fish to amphibian, the somas of the neurons migrated from the interior of the cerebrum to form a thin outer covering, or *cortex*. This aggregation of somas (and unmyelinated axonal and dendritic endings) is called *gray matter*. The interior of the cerebrum consists principally of myelinated axons, which, because of their white color, are collectively called *white matter*.

The cerebrum of the early reptiles remained essentially unchanged from the amphibian cerebrum, but the cortex changed significantly in the mammal-like reptiles. The forward, upper part of the cortex received and processed other kinds of information in addition to olfactory information. During the evolution of mammals, this new cortex, or *neocortex*, changed profoundly, greatly increasing in size until it covered the ancestral smell brain completely. In more advanced mammals, the surface of the neocortex is deeply folded and convoluted (Fig. 45.4b). How the cortex functions in humans is discussed in Questions 45.68 to 45.70.

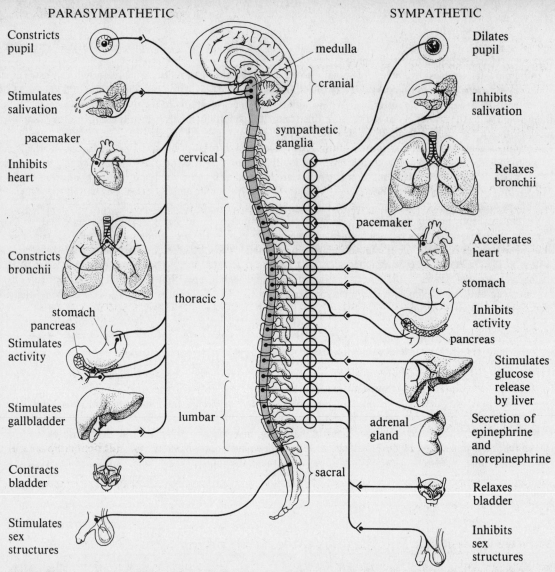

PARASYMPATHETIC

Constricts pupil

Stimulates salivation

pacemaker

Inhibits heart

Constricts bronchii

stomach pancreas

Stimulates activity

Stimulates gallbladder

Contracts bladder

Stimulates sex structures

medulla

cranial

sympathetic ganglia

cervical

thoracic

lumbar

sacral

SYMPATHETIC

Dilates pupil

Inhibits salivation

Relaxes bronchii

pacemaker

Accelerates heart

stomach

Inhibits activity

pancreas

Stimulates glucose release by liver

adrenal gland

Secretion of epinephrine and norepinephrine

Relaxes bladder

Inhibits sex structures

Fig. 45.3. The parasympathetic and sympathetic divisions of the autonomic nervous system. The parasympathetic neurons exit the central nervous system in cranial and sacral nerves, while the sympathetic neurons exit in thoracic and lumbar nerves. These nerves exit in pairs, one member of each pair on either side of the central nervous system, but only one nerve of each pair is shown. The sympathetic preganglionic neuron synapses with a postganglionic neuron in the sympathetic ganglia near and on both sides of the spinal cord, while a parasympathetic neuron synapses near the innervated organ.

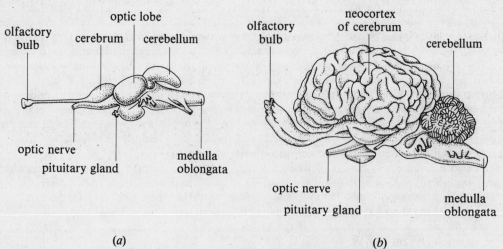

olfactory bulb

cerebrum

optic lobe

cerebellum

optic nerve

pituitary gland

medulla oblongata

olfactory bulb

neocortex of cerebrum

cerebellum

optic nerve

pituitary gland

medulla oblongata

(a)

(b)

Fig. 45.4. Comparison of two vertebrate brains. Left-side views of the brains of (a) a fish (codfish) and (b) a mammal (horse).

THE HUMAN BRAIN

45.42   Which of the following is not a structure in the hindbrain?

(*a*) Medulla oblongata;   (*b*) Thalamus;   (*c*) Cerebellum;   (*d*) Pons

45.43   Which of the following structures is in the diencephalon?

(*a*) Cerebral cortex;   (*b*) Olfactory bulbs;   (*c*) Hypothalamus;   (*d*) Basal ganglia

45.44   Which of the following brain structures is *not* considered to be part of the limbic system?

(*a*) Amygdaloid nucleus;   (*b*) Hippocampus;   (*c*) Corpora quadrigemina;   (*d*) Fornix

45.45   The part of the hindbrain that is responsible for hand-eye coordination is the

(*a*) pons.   (*b*) hippocampus.   (*c*) medulla oblongata.   (*d*) cerebellum.

45.46   Paralysis of both lower limbs but not the upper limbs, due to spinal cord damage, is called

(*a*) hemiplegia.   (*b*) quadriplegia.   (*c*) posterioplegia.   (*d*) paraplegia.

45.47   Which of the following is a structure in the mesencephalon?

(*a*) Inferior colliculus;   (*b*) Cerebellum;   (*c*) Thalamus;   (*d*) Mammillary body

45.48   A touch on the right hand stimulates neurons in the

(*a*) left somatic sensory area.   (*b*) left occipital lobe.   (*c*) right somatic sensory area.   (*d*) right occipital lobe.

45.49   The most dorsal (topmost) regions of the human primary motor areas on both hemispheres control movement of the

(*a*) hands.   (*b*) legs.   (*c*) lips.   (*d*) tongue.

45.50   In humans, the cerebral cortex is roughly what percent of the total brain mass?

(*a*) 30%;   (*b*) 50%;   (*c*) 65%;   (*d*) 80%

45.51   All auditory (hearing) information passing on its way to the cortex goes through which midbrain relay centers?

(*a*) Inferior colliculi;   (*b*) Superior colliculi;   (*c*) Thalamus;   (*d*) Temporal lobes

45.52   In the "split-brain" operation for epilepsy, the nerve tract (or *commissure*) that allows communication between the two hemispheres is cut. This nerve tract is the

(*a*) fissure of Rolando.   (*b*) corpus callosum.   (*c*) fornix.   (*d*) hippocampal gyrus.

45.53   For most people, dreaming occurs during which stage of sleep?

(*a*) Deep sleep;   (*b*) REM sleep;   (*c*) Alpha sleep;   (*d*) Slow-wave sleep

45.54   When a person is alert, with eyes open, actively trying to solve complex problems, the EEG shows

(*a*) alpha waves.   (*b*) beta waves.   (*c*) delta waves.   (*d*) gamma waves.

45.55 Match each of the following structures in the human brain with its function.

(*a*)	amygdaloid nucleus	(1) _____ Fiber tract connecting and coordinating activities in the two hemispheres
(*b*)	basal ganglia	(2) _____ Structures in the telencephalon that are involved in controlling skeletal
(*c*)	cerebellum	muscles
(*d*)	corpus callosum	(3) _____ Part of the limbic system that is involved in controlling emotional
(*e*)	hypothalamus	behavior
(*f*)	limbic system	(4) _____ Set of some 90 nuclei that regulate brain alertness
(*g*)	pons	(5) _____ Forebrain network of structures that maintains homeostasis and
(*h*)	reticular formation	controls emotional responses
(*i*)	superior colliculi	(6) _____ Regulator of eating and drinking, and controller of the "master" endo-
(*j*)	thalamus	crine gland (the pituitary gland)
		(7) _____ Major sensory relay station in the diencephalon for messages to the
		cortex
		(8) _____ Adjuster of posture and coordinator of refined limb movements
		(9) _____ Hindbrain structure that has nuclei that control the rate of breathing
		(10) _____ Midbrain relay centers for visual information going to the cortex

45.56 The left primary motor area of the cortex controls voluntary contractions of the _____ muscles of the _____ side of the body.

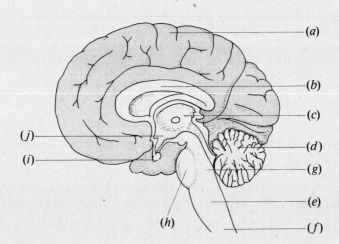

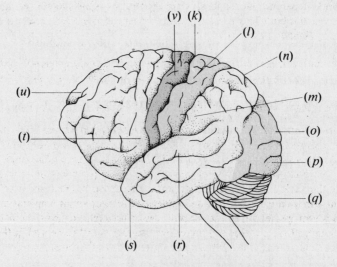

Fig. 45.5

45.57   Identify the lettered parts in the two views of the human brain shown in Fig. 45.5. *Top*: A midline (midsagittal) view of the right hemisphere. *Bottom*: A side (lateral) view of the left hemisphere.

45.58   Match each of the following structures in the human cortex with its function.

(*a*)	Broca's area	(1) _____	Responsible for understanding spoken or written language
(*b*)	frontal lobes	(2) _____	Coordinates muscles used in speech production
(*c*)	occipital lobes	(3) _____	Contain primary visual cortex
(*d*)	parietal lobes	(4) _____	Control voluntary contractions of skeletal muscles
(*e*)	primary motor areas	(5) _____	Contain somatic sensory areas
(*f*)	somatic sensory areas	(6) _____	Receive afferent messages from skin and body surfaces
(*g*)	temporal lobes	(7) _____	Involved in planning and decision making
(*h*)	Wernicke's area	(8) _____	Contain primary auditory area

45.59   In the motor cortex, there are _____ neurons devoted to controlling facial than to controlling genital muscles. The map of the neurons of the motor cortex, an upside-down representation of the human body, is called a _____.

45.60   The cerebral cortex of each hemisphere is divided into five lobes: four visible from the outside (_____, _____, _____, _____); and one seen only in midsagittal view (_____). The convolutions of the cortex consist of deep grooves called _____, shallow grooves called _____, and bulges between the grooves called _____.

45.61   Units of information are stored in the brain as _____. There are two stages in this storage: _____ memory that lasts a few minutes; and _____ memory that is essentially permanent.

54.62   For most people, the cortical areas responsible for understanding language and producing speech are in the _____ hemisphere.

45.63   The American pyschologist who won the Nobel Prize in 1981 for his research on human "split-brain" patients is _____.

45.64   Human states of consciousness can be monitored from the outside surface of the head by recording electrical brain waves with an _____ or _____. For someone who is conscious, relaxed, with eyes closed, the typical pattern is an _____ cycles-per-second _____.

45.65   Periodically during sleep (roughly every _____ minutes), the sleeper shows signs of agitation such as irregular breathing, increased heart rate, twitching fingers, and irregular low-amplitude brain waves. These periodic episodes are called _____ sleep, _____ sleep, or _____ sleep.

45.66   As a person goes from consciousness into deep sleep, the EEG shows increasing _____, changing from _____ amplitude, _____ frequency waves, to _____ amplitude, _____ frequency waves.

45.67   The reticular formation, a core of neural tissue within the brainstem, extends from the _____ to the _____ and is responsible for awakening the brain from sleep and maintaining _____.

45.68   Discuss how the somatic sensory areas and the primary motor areas were mapped on the human cortex.

Ⓢ   It has been determined for humans, and a variety of other mammals, that there are localized functions in the cerebral cortex, that is, certain specific areas of cortex (sensory areas) have responsibilities for receiving and processing each type of sensory information, that other areas (motor areas) have responsibility for the control of movement, and that still other areas (association areas) integrate and use the information in the control of behavior. Several known areas in the human cortex and their functions are given in Questions 45.57 and 45.58.

In humans, information from the skin and internal structures about temperature, touch, pressure, and proprioception is sent (projected) to the *somatic sensory area* (also called the *primary sensory area* or *primary somatosensory area*), which is a thin strip of cortex running dorsal to ventral in the parietal lobes of both hemispheres just behind the central sulcus (also called *fissure of Rolando*). In other animals, such a somatic

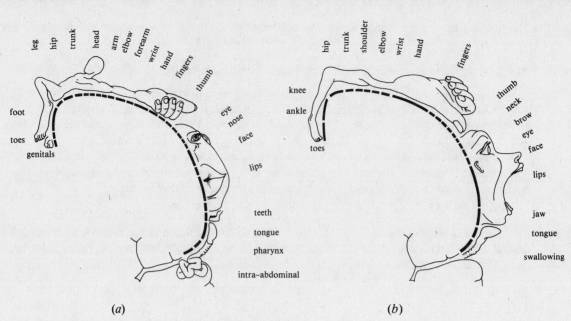

Fig. 45.6. Maps of (*a*) somatic sensory area and (*b*) primary motor area in the cortex of the right hemisphere of a human brain.

sensory area is "mapped" by naturally or artificially (i.e., with electric currents) stimulating the relevant sense organs and recording the resulting electrical activity (evoked potentials) on the cortex. In humans, all such mapping has been done as part of brain surgery performed to deal with brain disease or damage. A summary of what is known is shown in Fig. 45.6*a*. The drawings represent the body parts sending sensory information, and the size of each body part shows the relative amount of neural tissue devoted to receiving information from that body part. Note that the face and hands are predominant and that the map is essentially an upside-down version of the human body called a *sensory homunculus*. The somatic sensory area on the left hemisphere receives information principally from the right side of the body, and the somatic area on the right hemisphere receives information principally from the left side.

In humans, the primary motor area (or motor cortex) is located on both hemispheres in the frontal lobes just in front of the *central sulcus*, running dorsal to ventral in parallel with the somatic sensory area. These motor areas control conscious and voluntary movement of the skeletal muscles, with the left motor area controlling the right side of the body and the right area controlling the left side. In other mammals these areas are mapped by systematically investigating which body muscles respond to electrical stimulation of areas of the cortex; in humans the mapping is again dependent on correlation with brain damage and disease and clinical procedures done to deal with these problems. A summary of what is known is shown in Fig. 45.6*b*, where again the drawing represents the body area controlled and the relative amount of cortex devoted to that control. Again hands and face predominate, and again there is an upside-down representation of the human body (a *motor homunculus*).

45.69 You are reading a book out loud. Trace the path through the brain that the information takes from the printed to the spoken words.

☙   Visual information, here what you see on the printed page, travels along the neural pathways, shown in simplified form in Fig. 45.7. In essence, what is seen by the left side of each eye, travels (is projected) to the visual cortex in the occipital lobe (see Fig. 45.5) of the left hemisphere, and what is seen by the right side of each eye is projected to the right visual cortex.

Although the neurally coded images of the lines of print on the page would go to both hemispheres, the understanding and use of such language information occurs only in the left hemisphere for roughly 97% of humans. The coded information, then, travels from the left visual cortex first to Wernicke's area (see Fig. 45.5), where language is "understood," and then the phrases to be spoken are transmitted along the left hemisphere through a fiber pathway (the *arcuate fasciculus*) to Broca's area located in the frontal lobe (see Fig. 45.5), which controls the production of speech by the mouth regions of the nearby motor cortex.

45.70 A male patient with severe epilepsy is treated with the surgical procedure known as the "split-brain" operation. After recovery from the operation, he is tested with an apparatus that can simultaneously project different visual

visual field

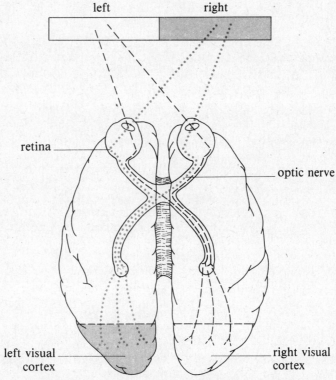

Fig. 45.7. Simplified pathways of visual information from the eyes
to the visual cortex, showing that information from the right side
of the eyes goes to the right visual cortex, and information from
the left side of the eyes goes to the left visual cortex.

information to each hemisphere. He is shown the word TEACUP in such a way that the right visual cortex receives
the word TEA and the left visual cortex receives the word CUP. When asked, what word does the patient say he
sees and why?

🐚 In a "split-brain" operation, a cut is made through the *corpus callosum*—the main communication channel
between the left and right hemispheres (see Fig. 45.5). This operation is only performed on patients with severe
and long-lasting epilepsy, a disease of the cortex in a small area of tissue in one hemisphere that stimulates
abnormal electrical activity that spreads over that hemisphere and, often, across the corpus callosum to the
other hemisphere. This spreading activity can produce muscle convulsions and unconsciousness. The split-brain
operation does not cure epilepsy, but by preventing an attack in one hemisphere from crossing to the other
hemisphere, it can greatly reduce the severity of the symptoms.

At first, aside from this decrease in the symptoms of epilepsy, split-brain patients were believed to retain the
same personalities and intellectual functions that they had prior to the operation. However, when these patients
were given sophisticated tests by the American psychologist Roger Sperry and his colleagues, a remarkable
discovery was made: the operation had created two separate and not identical human minds within each patient.
The left mind (or left hemisphere) had language (reading, writing, speaking) and was capable of abstract and logical
thought. The right mind (or right hemisphere) specialized in nonverbal spatial capabilities, such as understanding
relationships in three-dimensional space, recognizing faces, perceiving some aspects of music, and some understanding
of simple language (but not speaking or writing). For this amazing discovery, Sperry received the Nobel prize in 1981.

In the test described in the question, the word TEA is shown only to the right side of each eye and the word
CUP only to the left side of each eye. Thus (see Fig. 45.7) only the word CUP is projected to the left visual
cortex and only the word TEA is projected to the right visual cortex. As the left, or speaking cortex (see
Question 45.69) sees only CUP and cannot be informed of the word TEA by the right cortex because of the cut
in the corpus callosum, the patient reports that he sees the word CUP.

Answers to Objective Questions

45.1 *b*

45.2 *d*

45.3 *a*

45.4 *c*

45.5 convergent; divergent; reverberating

45.6 ganglia; ganglia; nuclei

45.7 external environment; internal homeostasis

45.8 flatworms; brain; cords; cords; ladder; cords; ganglia

45.10 *c*

45.11 *c*

45.12 *d*

45.13 *b*

45.14 *a*

45.15 *d*

45.16 *a*

45.17 *b*

45.18 *b*

45.19 *c*

45.20 *a*

45.21 *a*

45.22 *d*

45.23 preganglionic; postganglionic

45.24 reflex; reflex arcs

45.25 nerves; motor nerve; sensory nerve; mixed nerve

45.26 brain; spinal cord; peripheral; brain; spinal cord

45.27 efferent; afferent

45.28 nerve cord; ventricles; cerebrospinal fluid

45.29 8; cervical; 12; thoracic; 5; lumbar; 5; sacral; 1; coccygeal

45.30 sympathetic; parasympathetic

45.31 (*a*) dorsal root ganglion; (*b*) central canal; (*c*) gray matter; (*d*) white matter; (*e*) motor neuron; (*f*) quadriceps muscle; (*g*) patella; (*h*) tendon; (*i*) stretch receptor; (*j*) sensory neuron; (*k*) ventral root

45.32 preganglionic; postganglionic

45.33 gray; white; axons; myelin sheaths

45.34 energy; energy

45.35 meninges; dura mater; arachnoid; pia mater

45.36 cortex; gray; white

45.37 (*a*) olfactory bulb; (*b*) cerebrum; (*c*) thalamus; (*d*) optic lobe; (*e*) cerebellum; (*f*) medulla; (*g*) spinal cord; (*h*) pituitary; (*i*) hypothalamus; (*j*) optic chiasm; (*k*) hindbrain; (*l*) midbrain; (*m*) forebrain

45.38 rhombencephalon; mesencephalon; prosencephalon; cerebellum

45.42 *b*

45.43 *c*

45.44 *c*

45.45 *d*

45.46 *d*

45.47 *a*

45.48 *a*

45.49 *b*

45.50 *d*

45.51 *a*

45.52 *b*

45.53 *b*

45.54 *b*

45.55 (1) *d*; (2) *b*; (3) *a*; (4) *h*; (5) *f*; (6) *e*; (7) *j*; (8) *c*; (9) *g*; (10) *i*

45.56 skeletal; right

45.57 (*a*) neocortex; (*b*) corpus callosum; (*c*) thalamus; (*d*) cerebellum; (*e*) medulla oblongata; (*f*) spinal cord; (*g*) reticular formation; (*h*) pons; (*i*) pituitary gland; (*j*) hypothalamus; (*k*) central sulcus; (*l*) somatic sensory area; (*m*) Wernicke's area; (*n*) parietal lobe; (*o*) occipital lobe; (*p*) visual cortex; (*q*) cerebellum; (*r*) primary auditory area; (*s*) temporal lobe; (*t*) Broca's area; (*u*) frontal lobe; (*v*) primary motor area

45.58 (1) *h*; (2) *a*; (3) *c*; (4) *e*; (5) *d*; (6) *f*; (7) *b*; (8) *g*

45.59 more; homunculus

45.60 frontal; parietal; temporal; occipital; limbic; fissures; sulci; gyri

45.61 memory traces; short-term; long-term

45.62 left

45.63 Roger Sperry

45.64 electroencephalogram; EEG; 8 to 13; alpha wave

45.65 90; rapid eye movement; REM; paradoxical

45.66 synchronization; low; high; high; low

45.67 medulla oblongata; hypothalamus; alertness

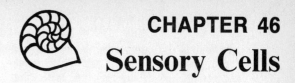

CHAPTER 46
Sensory Cells

RECEPTOR FUNCTION*

46.1   Most sensory cells respond to

(*a*) environmental electricity.   (*b*) pressure.   (*c*) changes in energy.   (*d*) threshold levels of energy.

46.2   Before environmental information can be transmitted to the brain, it must always be

(*a*) transduced.   (*b*) integrated.   (*c*) amplified.   (*d*) modulated.

46.3   A role of accessory structures, such as the bones of the middle ear, in a sense organ is to

(*a*) transduce the stimulus.   (*b*) integrate the response.   (*c*) amplify the stimulus.   (*d*) amplify the response.

46.4   The strength of a generator potential in a sensory neuron (or primary receptor) or of a receptor potential in a receptor cell (or secondary receptor) of a sense organ is

(*a*) always -70 mV.   (*b*) always -60 mV.   (*c*) almost always $+40$ mV.   (*d*) variable.

46.5   A generator potential or receptor potential usually modulates the
(*a*) frequency of spontaneous action potentials in a sensory neuron.   (*b*) transduction of energy.   (*c*) amplification of electricity.   (*d*) synthesis of neurotransmitters.

46.6   Reception of a stimulus by a receptor cell occurs when it _____ energy. Each type of receptor cell responds to a different form of _____ .

46.7   The conversion of environmental energy into the electrochemical energy of neurons is called sensory _____ . It is performed by a _____ or by the _____ of a sense organ.

46.8   Transmission of environmental information to the central nervous system occurs when a sensory neuron develops a _____ or a receptor cell develops a _____ , which happens when the _____ of the _____ is altered by the stimulus.

46.9   The five kinds of sensory receptors are: _____ , which respond to physical deformations of tissues; _____ , which respond to certain molecules dissolved in solution; _____ , which respond to heat; _____ , which respond to excess heat, pressure, or certain chemicals; and _____ , which respond to energy of different wavelengths. Sensory receptors can also be categorized as _____ , which receive information from the external environment; _____ , which receive information from the internal environment; and _____ , which receive information about the body's orientation in space.

46.10   How does environmental information reach the central nervous system?

An animal's response to a change in its external or internal environment is coordinated by its central nervous system. Environmental information must therefore be converted into neural messages before a response can take place. An environmental change usually involves some form of energy. The conversion of environmental energy into the electrochemical energy of neurons is called *transduction* and is performed by sensory cells.

Transduction and the transmission of transduced information along afferent neural pathways may be performed by a single sensory cell or by a group of sensory cells organized into a sensory organ.

When a single sensory cell both transduces and transmits information, it is called a *sensory neuron*. The cell membrane enclosing a dendrite of the neuron responds to a particular form of environmental energy by altering its permeability to ions, which causes a change in the membrane potential. The new potential is the *generator*

---

* Answers to Chapter 46 objective questions appear on page 334.

potential of the sensory neuron and, if large enough, initiates an action potential in the axon that travels to the central nervous system. Generator potentials vary greatly in value; they can be larger or smaller than action potentials, which always have the same value.

When a sensory organ performs both transduction and transmission, some of the cells are involved in transduction, some are accessory structures, and others are sensory neurons that transmit the information to the central nervous system. Accessory structures focus, amplify, or localize the environmental energy before it is transduced. (The lens of a vertebrate eye, for example, bends the light so that it converges onto the retina.) The energy is then transduced by receptor cells when the permeability of their membranes is so altered that ionic flow changes the membrane potential. The altered potential in a receptor cell is called a *receptor potential* (rather than a generator potential, as it is called in sensory neurons). Like the generator potential, the receptor potential may be smaller or larger than an action potential. If large enough, the receptor potential alters the membrane potential in the sensory neuron to which it is connected by a synapse. This change may initiate an action potential in the axon of the sensory neuron; the nerve impulse (i.e., a sequence of action potentials) is then conveyed along the afferent pathway to the central nervous system.

All detection by an animal of the environment external to the animal's nervous system is accomplished by its sensory cells. Each type of sensory cell is sensitive to a certain form of energy, such as heat, light, or sound. An animal can receive information only if it has sensory cells that are capable of transducing the form of energy accompanying the environmental event. An animal's sensory cells result from natural selection and vary for different species. Humans lack suitable sensory cells for many forms of energy, including x-rays, radar, and radio or television waves; we detect such phenomena only after they have been converted by mechanical devices into forms of energy that our sensory cells can recognize. Many animals can detect environmental phenomena that we cannot. Bees see ultraviolet radiation, bats and porpoises hear very high-pitched sounds, snakes locate prey by sensing the heat emanating from their prey's bodies, and some fishes detect prey and mates by means of electric currents. Most animals have sensory cells that respond to mechanical, chemical, thermal, pain, and electromagnetic stimuli.

VISION

46.11   The eye cup of a planarian

(*a*) forms only black and white images.   (*b*) forms colored images.   (*c*) detects only the intensity and direction of light.   (*d*) detects only infrared light.

46.12   The compound eye of an insect

(*a*) forms only black and white images.   (*b*) forms colored images.   (*c*) detects only the intensity and direction of light.   (*d*) detects only infrared light.

46.13   The camera eye of an octopus is most similar to the eye of a

(*a*) planarian.   (*b*) snail.   (*c*) butterfly.   (*d*) fish.

46.14   The rods and cones of a vertebrate retina function to

(*a*) focus light.   (*b*) amplify light.   (*c*) transduce light.   (*d*) filter light.

46.15   The sensory neurons of a vertebrate retina are its

(*a*) rods and cones.   (*b*) ganglion cells.   (*c*) amacrine cells.   (*d*) bipolar cells.

46.16   The compound eye of an insect or crustacean is formed by many subunits, called _____, each with its own cornea, lens, and photoreceptors. Pigment cells, which line the sides of each subunit, absorb all light entering from a(n) _____ so that the _____ receive only light from a single point in the environment. This arrangement makes the compound eye especially good at detecting _____.

46.17   Identify the lettered structures in the vertebrate eye diagramed in Fig. 46.1.

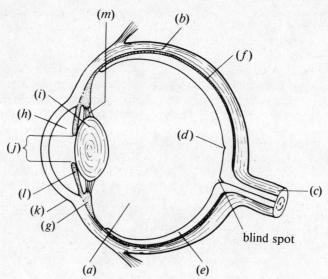

Fig. 46.1. The vertebrate eye.

46.18 Match the following structures of the vertebrate eye with their respective functions.

(a)	cornea	(1) _____	Provides opening for light to enter
(b)	fovea	(2) _____	Transduces blue, green, and red light
(c)	iris	(3) _____	Transduces all waves of light
(d)	lens	(4) _____	Controls the amount of light that enters
(e)	optic nerve	(5) _____	Alters the shape of the lens
(f)	pupil	(6) _____	Transmits information to the CNS
(g)	periphery of retina	(7) _____	Focuses light directly on retina
(h)	ciliary muscle	(8) _____	Bends light and protects inner eye

46.19 The vertebrate eye has two major functions: to form a light image on the _____ and then to convert that image into _____ in the _____, which carries the information to the visual cortex of the brain.

46.20 Transduction of light is performed by the _____ and the _____ in the _____ of the vertebrate eye. During this transduction, light energy causes a change in the _____ of a pigment molecule known as _____ and then breakdown of the molecule into _____ and _____. These changes in the molecule initiate a _____ potential in the photoreceptor cell. Part of the pigment molecule is a derivative of vitamin _____.

46.21 Identify the lettered structures in the diagram of a vertebrate retina shown in Fig. 46.2.

46.22 Match the following retinal cells with their respective functions.

(a)	amacrine cell	(1) _____	Absorbs all wavelengths of light not captured by photoreceptors
(b)	bipolar cell	(2) _____	Carries signals from one photoreceptor to another and to several bipolar cells
(c)	cone		
(d)	ganglion cell	(3) _____	Carries signals from one bipolar cell to another and to several ganglion cells
(e)	horizontal cell	(4) _____	Controls frequency of action potentials in the optic nerve
(f)	pigmented epithelial cell	(5) _____	Modifies output from the photoreceptors
(g)	rod	(6) _____	Transduces blue, green, or red light
		(7) _____	Transduces almost all wavelengths of light

46.23 A human retina has both rods, which provide night vision, and cones, which provide color vision. The rods are found in greatest density in the _____ of the retina, and the cones are found in greatest density in the _____. The retinas of some nocturnal mammals, such as mice and bats, have only _____ as photoreceptors, and the retinas of some diurnal mammals, such as squirrels, have only _____ as photoreceptors.

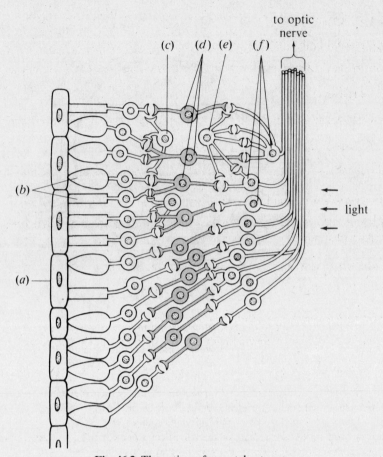

Fig. 46.2. The retina of a vertebrate eye.

46.24   How is light focused on the retina of a vertebrate eye?

🐚   Light reaches the eye in rays that range from an almost parallel to a diverging alignment. The image is focused when the light rays are bent to converge precisely on the retina. The *cornea* and *lens* are two accessory structures of the vertebrate eye that bend incoming light.

The curved shape of the cornea bends light so the rays converge toward the retina. The shape of the cornea, however, is not adjustable; it cannot accommodate for the distance of an object from the eye.

The lens is a convex, elastic structure that changes shape in accordance with how far the object being viewed is from the eye. In all vertebrates except fishes and amphibians, the lens is connected, via *suspensory ligaments*, to *ciliary muscles* that contract to flatten the lens and relax to make the lens more convex. The farther the object is from the eye, the more parallel the light rays coming from it, and the less bending required to focus the image on the retina. Thus, the ciliary muscles contract more to give the lens a flatter shape. Conversely, the closer the object, the more divergent are its light rays and the more they need to be bent. Thus, the ciliary muscles relax and the lens returns, by its own elastic recoil, to its more natural convex shape.

46.25   How do the rods and cones of a human retina differ in terms of the images they produce?

🐚   The eye contains two basic types of photoreceptor cells—rods and cones. The rods are so sensitive to light that they can detect a single photon, but they cannot distinguish fine details or colors except shades of gray. Rods play a particularly important role in dim light. Color vision is provided by sensory information from combinations of three types of cones; each cone is sensitive to only blue, green, or red light. Cones distinguish fine detail because only one or a few cones connect to each sensory neuron; each cone provides the brain with a distinct piece of information. Rods do not distinguish fine detail because many rods connect with each sensory neuron. Most cones are located in an area in the center of the retina called the *fovea*, so that detailed color vision is most acute when the eye looks directly at an object. Most rods are positioned away from the fovea, so that in dim light vision is better on the periphery of the retina, or "out of the corner of the eye."

HEARING AND BALANCE

46.26   The receptor cells for both hearing and balance are

(**a**) mechanoreceptors.   (**b**) chemoreceptors.   (**c**) thermoreceptors.   (**d**) electromagnetic receptors.

46.27   Sound is amplified by the

(**a**) pinna.   (**b**) tympanic membrane.   (**c**) malleus, incus, and stapes.   (**d**) round window.

46.28   The part of the ear where sound is transduced is the

(**a**) tympanic membrane.   (**b**) malleus, incus, and stapes.   (**c**) semicircular canals.   (**d**) cochlea.

46.29   The sensory receptors that respond to sound develop receptor potentials when their

(**a**) hairs are bent.   (**b**) pigments absorb pressure.   (**c**) surface proteins are altered by a change in pH.
(**d**) sodium-potassium pumps become deactivated.

46.30   The structures in a human that provide balance are located in the

(**a**) outer ear.   (**b**) middle ear.   (**c**) inner ear.   (**d**) eustachian tubes.

46.31   Receptor cells for balance and equilibrium in mammals are the

(**a**) malleus, incus, and stapes.   (**b**) hair cells.   (**c**) statoliths.   (**d**) horizontal cells.

46.32   Lateral lines, which contain mechanoreceptors that perceive movement of the body and surrounding water, are found in

(**a**) squid.   (**b**) snails.   (**c**) fishes.   (**d**) water snakes.

46.33   Sound moves through an ear when pressure waves in the _____ cause vibrations of the _____ membrane, which sets up vibrations in first the _____, then the _____, and finally the _____ of the middle ear. Sound travels from the middle ear to the _____ of the inner ear through the _____.

46.34   Sound reaches mechanoreceptors of the inner ear when pressure waves in the _____ of the _____ cause vibrations of the _____ membrane. This vibrating membrane rubs the mechanoreceptors, which are _____ cells, against the stationary _____ membrane to cause distortions of the plasma membranes of the mechanoreceptors. Sodium gates in the plasma membranes open, and a _____ potential is produced.

46.35   Identify the lettered structures in the drawing of a mammalian ear in Fig. 46.3.

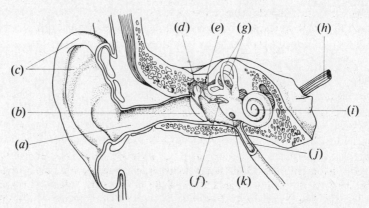

Fig. 46.3. The mammalian ear.

46.36 Match the following structures of the ear with their respective functions.

(*a*)	auditory canal	(1) _____	Channels pressure waves of air into the middle ear
(*b*)	auditory (eustachian) tube	(2) _____	Collects pressure waves of air
(*c*)	auditory nerve	(3) _____	Converts pressure waves of air into vibrations of bones
(*d*)	incus	(4) _____	Dissipates sound waves
(*e*)	malleus	(5) _____	Equalizes pressure between the middle ear and the atmosphere
(*f*)	oval window	(6) _____	Provide information about the spatial orientation of the head
(*g*)	pinna	(7) _____	Transfers vibrations from a bone to a fluid
(*h*)	round window	(8) _____	Transfers vibrations from a bone to a membrane
(*i*)	semicircular canals	(9) _____	Transfers vibrations from a bone to a bone
(*j*)	stapes	(10) _____	Transfers vibrations from a membrane to a bone
(*k*)	tympanic membrane	(11) _____	Transmits action potentials to the auditory cortex

46.37 In a mammal, changes in position of the head, with respect to gravity, are detected by _____ cells in response to fluid movements in the _____ and _____ of the inner ear. Rotation of the head is detected by _____ cells in response to fluid movements in the _____ of the inner ear.

46.38 In an invertebrate animal, body position is detected by _____, in which the sensory receptor is a _____ that responds to pressure from grains of sand or other dense granules known collectively as _____.

46.39 Why are the sound receptor cells of the ear called mechanoreceptors?

⚫ A mechanoreceptor responds to a mechanical stimulus that stretches or presses on its cell membrane. The distortion of the membrane alters its permeability, producing a change in membrane potential. Mechanoreceptors transduce sound, touch, pressure, and movement of the body into neural messages.

Sound is the rearrangement of a random distribution of air molecules into areas of compression, where the molecules are densely packed, and areas of rarefaction, where the molecules are far apart. These two areas move away from the source of the disturbance in alternating waves. Although these air molecules do not themselves travel far, they generate new waves by disturbing nearby molecules. As the frequency of the waves increases, the pitch of the sound increases; as the difference in the density of air molecules between the areas of compression and rarefaction becomes greater, the sound becomes louder. The sound dies out when so much energy has been dissipated that a wave of compressed molecules can no longer disturb the surrounding air molecules. Sound traveling through water exhibits the same characteristics, except that water molecules are displaced rather than air molecules.

Sound receptors of the ear are *hair cells* (so called because they have long projections, or cilia, resembling hairs) attached to the *basilar membrane* on one end and in contact with the *tectorial membrane* on the other end (Fig. 46.4). Most of the mechanical energy in the vibrations of the oval window is transferred via the fluid to the basilar membrane, which vibrates up and down. When the hair cells on the basilar membrane move up, they press against the virtually stationary tectorial membrane. The membranes of the hair cells stretch and bend, creating receptor potentials that may intitiate action potentials in associated sensory neurons. High-frequency vibrations displace the region of the basilar membrane nearest the oval window, whereas vibrations of lower frequencies displace portions of the membrane farther from the oval window. Thus, a different set of hair cells is affected by each type of sound.

46.40 How are position and movement of the body detected even in the absence of visual clues, e.g., in the dark or with the eyes closed?

⚫ The inner ear contains receptors that respond to gravity and to changes in the rotation of the head. Movement of the head in relation to gravity is detected by hair cells in the *vestibular sacs*—two fluid-filled, interconnected cavities, called the *utricle* and *saccule*, which lie just above the cochlea. The cilia that project from the hair cells lining these sacs are embedded in a gelatinous material containing small crystals of calcium carbonate. The crystals are heavy enough to be moved by gravity, so when the head tilts, the gelatin shifts position and pulls on the cilia. As a result of the displacement of the cilia, the cell membranes of the hair cells become distorted, thereby creating receptor potentials.

Rotation of the head is detected by receptor cells in the three *semicircular canals* at the top of the inner ear. Each canal is oriented along one of the three planes of space—forward-backward, up-down, and left-right. The canals are filled with fluid, and one end of each canal consists of a small chamber lined with hair cells.

When the canal rotates, the fluid tends to remain stationary. The movement of the canal against the stationary fluid distorts the membranes of the hair cells and causes receptor potentials.

Mechanoreceptors inside the body respond to changes in the length of muscles and to forces exerted on tendons and ligaments. *Kinesthesia*, or movement sensation, is produced by sensory neurons in the skeletal muscles, tendons, and joints. They produce generator potentials which may become action potentials in their axons and provide information about the position of the limbs.

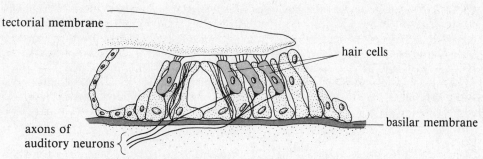

Fig. 46.4. Sound receptors of the inner ear. Waves in the fluid of the cochlea cause movements of the basilar membrane and its attached hair cells, which are the receptor cells for sound. As a hair cell moves up and down, its cilia press repeatedly against the almost stationary tectorial membrane and distortions develop in the plasma membrane around the cilia. The distortions alter the membrane's permeability to ions and initiate a receptor potential that, if strong enough, stimulates an action potential in the auditory neuron to which the hair cell is connected by a synapse.

TASTE AND SMELL

46.41 A molecule cannot be tasted or smelled until it has been

(*a*) converted into a protein.   (*b*) converted into a neurotransmitter.
(*c*) grouped into a multimolecular complex.   (*d*) dissolved in a liquid.

46.42 The receptors for both taste and smell are

(*a*) mechanoreceptors.   (*b*) chemoreceptors.   (*c*) thermoreceptors.   (*d*) electromagnetic receptors.

46.43 The taste receptors of a bottom-feeding fish are located

(*a*) all over its body surface.   (*b*) within taste buds near its fins.   (*c*) within taste buds on its gills.
(*d*) within its mouth.

46.44 The taste receptors of all terrestrial vertebrates are located

(*a*) all over the body surface.   (*b*) within taste buds in the trachea.   (*c*) within the nasal cavity.
(*d*) within taste buds in the mouth.

46.45 Most of what we "taste" in food is actually

(*a*) imagined by our cerebral cortex.   (*b*) a memory from childhood, when we had more taste receptors.
(*c*) odors.   (*d*) normal components of saliva.

46.46 The sensory cell for taste is a _____, whereas for smell it is a _____.

46.47 A human recognizes four primary tastes: _____, _____, _____, and _____. Each primary taste is detected by particular regions of the _____.

46.48 The taste receptors of terrestrial vertebrates are arranged, along with accessory structures, in sense organs called _____.

46.49 Most mammals have much keener senses of smell than we do, because they are mainly active during the
_____ and are _____-dwelling animals, whereas our primate ancestors were mainly
active during the _____ and were _____-dwelling animals, which selected for keen
_____ rather than smell. Smell also plays a larger role in the behavior of other mammals than it
does in humans. Many mammals, for example, mark their territories with _____ to establish odor
signals recognized by others of their species.

46.50 How is the presence of chemicals, such as those in food, detected by the central nervous system?

◉   The capacity to respond to chemical changes is a fundamental property of cells. It is not known how the presence of particular molecules is transduced into action potentials. Most likely, the molecules become attached to surface proteins on sensory cells and in this way alter the permeability of the plasma membranes to ions.

Sensory cells for taste are receptor cells within taste buds located in the mouth, primarily on the upper surface and edges of the tongue. Taste receptors provide four primary tastes—sweet, bitter, sour, and salty—as well as various combinations of the primary tastes. (Most complex taste sensations depend also on odor.) The tongue is covered with small protuberances, called *papillae*, which are surrounded by trenches that trap saliva. Chemically sensitive cilia extend from receptor cells within the papillae into these trenches, where they make contact with dissolved materials.

Sensory cells for smell are sensory neurons located in a small area of the membrane on top of the nasal cavity. They respond to molecules carried in the air that become dissolved in the fluid that coats the nasal membranes. Sniffing forces more air onto the area where cilia of the receptors are located. The olfactory receptors of a human can detect thousands of different odors.

Chemoreceptors inside the body monitor internal chemical events and provide feedback to neural control centers. Receptors sensitive to carbon dioxide are located in the medulla oblongata of the brain and in some arteries. Chemoreceptors in the hypothalamus respond to changes in concentrations of water, glucose, salt, and other materials in the blood. As with other chemoreceptors, these cells presumably respond when specific molecules to which they are sensitive attach to proteins on their plasma membranes, thereby causing a change in membrane permeability.

Answers to Objective Questions

46.1 *c*

46.2 *a*

46.3 *c*

46.4 *d*

46.5 *a*

46.6 absorbs; energy

46.7 transduction; sensory neuron (or primary receptor); receptor cells (or secondary receptors)

46.8 generator potential; receptor potential; permeability; plasma membrane

46.9 mechanoreceptors; chemoreceptors; thermoreceptors; pain receptors; electromagnetic receptors; exteroceptors; interoceptors; proprioceptors

46.11 *c*

46.12 *b*

46.13 *d*

46.14 *c*

46.15 *b*

46.16 ommatidia; angle; photoreceptors; movement

46.17 (*a*) vitreous humor; (*b*) sclera; (*c*) optic nerve; (*d*) fovea; (*e*) retina; (*f*) choroid coat; (*g*) ciliary body and muscle; (*h*) aqueous humor; (*i*) lens; (*j*) pupil; (*k*) cornea; (*l*) iris; (*m*) suspensory ligament

46.18 (1) *f*; (2) *b*; (3) *g*; (4) *c*; (5) *h*; (6) *e*; (7) *d*; (8) *a*

46.19 retina; action potentials; optic nerve

46.20 rods; cones; retina; shape; rhodopsin; opsin; retinal; receptor; A

46.21 (*a*) epithelium; (*b*) photoreceptors (rods and cones); (*c*) horizontal cell; (*d*) bipolar cells; (*e*) amacrine cell; (*f*) ganglion cells

46.22 (1) *f*; (2) *e*; (3) *a*; (4) *d*; (5) *b*; (6) *c*; (7) *g*

46.23 periphery; fovea; rods; cones

46.26 *a*

46.27 *c*

46.28 *d*

46.29 *a*

46.30 *c*

46.31 *b*

46.32 *c*

46.33 air; tympanic; malleus; incus; stapes; fluid; oval window

46.34 fluid; cochlea; basilar; hair; tectorial; receptor

46.35 (*a*) auditory canal; (*b*) tympanic membrane; (*c*) pinna; (*d*) malleus; (*e*) incus; (*f*) stapes and oval window; (*g*) semicircular canals; (*h*) auditory nerve; (*i*) cochlea; (*j*) auditory (eustachian) tube; (*k*) round window

46.36 (1) *a*; (2) *g*; (3) *k*; (4) *h*; (5) *b*; (6) *i*; (7) *f*; (8) *j*; (9) *d*; (10) *e*; (11) *c*

46.37 hair; utricle; saccule; hair; semicircular canals

46.38 statocysts; hair cell; statoliths

46.41 *d*

46.42 *b*

46.43 *a*

46.44 *d*

46.45 *c*

46.46 receptor cell; sensory neuron

46.47 sweet; bitter; sour; salty; tongue

46.48 taste buds

46.49 night; ground; day; tree; vision; urine

CHAPTER 47

Hormonal Control Systems

HORMONES*

47.1   Broadly defined, a hormone is a molecule that

(*a*) moves through the bloodstream.   (*b*) influences development.   (*c*) alters the activity of certain nonadjacent cells.   (*d*) has the same chemical activity in a variety of organisms.

47.2   The target cells of a hormone always have

(*a*) special receptors to which the hormone binds.   (*b*) special channels through which the hormone moves. (*c*) large amounts of the hormone stored within vesicles.   (*d*) undifferentiated cytoplasm.

47.3   Which of the following hormones is a steroid?

(*a*) Prostaglandin;   (*b*) Estrogen;   (*c*) Epinephrine;   (*d*) Thyroxin

47.4   A steroid hormone typically alters the activity of its target cells by

(*a*) digesting holes in the cell's plasma membrane.   (*b*) entering the cell and altering gene expression. (*c*) passing its message to an intracellular messenger.   (*d*) digesting holes in the cell's lysosomes.

47.5   Which of the following hormones is a modified amino acid?

(*a*) Prostaglandin;   (*b*) Estrogen;   (*c*) Epinephrine;   (*d*) Progesterone

47.6   A peptide hormone typically alters the activity of its target cells by

(*a*) digesting holes in the cell's plasma membrane.   (*b*) entering the cell and altering gene expression. (*c*) passing its message to an intracellular messenger.   (*d*) digesting holes in the cell's lysosomes.

47.7   Animal tissues that synthesize hormones are closely associated with, and sometimes resemble, cells of the

(*a*) immune system.   (*b*) embryonic mesoderm.   (*c*) circulatory system.   (*d*) nervous system.

47.8   An exocrine gland releases its secretions into a _____. An endocrine gland releases its secretions into a _____. Hormones are secreted by _____ glands and by other specialized secretory cells. The study of hormones and hormone-secreting glands is called _____.

47.9   A steroid hormone typically binds to a _____ in the _____ of its target cell. The complex then enters the nucleus and binds with a special receptor on the _____. This binding controls _____ at that site.

47.10   A hormone that influences its target cell without entering the cell does so either by activating a _____ or by altering the _____ of the plasma membrane to _____.

47.11   A peptide hormone does not enter its target cell. Instead, its attachment to a receptor in the cell activates a membrane-bound enzyme, typically adenylate cyclase, which causes conversion of _____ to _____. This product then alters the activities of enzymes in the cytoplasm. The first messenger in the system is the _____, and the second messenger is _____. The particular effect of the second messenger depends on the _____ present in the target cell.

47.12   How do hormones alter activities in their target cells?

Most hormones command their target cells to do more or less of what the cells normally do. They do this by altering enzyme activity, either directly by taking control of enzyme synthesis or indirectly by initiating

---

* Answers to Chapter 47 objective questions appear on page 341.

a series of reactions catalyzed by enzymes already present in the cytoplasm. Additionally, almost all vertebrate hormones have some effect on the permeability of the plasma membrane to ions and other dissolved substances.

Hormones control cellular activities either by entering the cell and influencing activities directly or by transferring commands to specific chemical messengers within the cell. Whether a hormone enters a cell or initiates changes from outside the cell depends on its chemical nature.

Steroid hormones are small lipid molecules that move freely through the lipid bilayer of a plasma membrane. Only their target cells, however, contain the specific receptor molecules (large proteins) that allow the hormones to regulate cellular activities. Each type of hormone interacts with a different type of receptor molecule, and each target cell contains only receptors that interact with the hormones to which the cell is sensitive. The hormone and the receptor form a complex that moves from the cytoplasm into the nucleus, where it attaches to a specific site on a chromosome. The hormone-receptor complex exerts an influence on gene activity at the site by triggering or suppressing transcription of the genetic code into messenger RNA.

Nonsteroid hormones, which are usually derived from proteins, exert control over their target cells by attaching themselves to receptor sites on the plasma membrane. The binding of a hormone to its receptor typically activates the enzyme adenylate cyclase, which is always present within the membrane. Once activated, this enzyme promotes the synthesis of cyclic adenosine monophosphate (cyclic AMP) from adenosine triphosphate (ATP). The hormone is released rapidly after it is bound to the receptor and is quickly destroyed by enzymes. The cyclic AMP that is synthesized in response to the hormone initiates a series of chemical reactions within the cell that influence the activity of the genes in the nucleus. The particular effect of cyclic AMP depends on the particular kinds of enzymes present in the cytoplasm. The series of enzyme-catalyzed reactions it initiates is known as an enzyme cascade. Because command information is relayed in this type of hormonal action, the nonsteroid hormone is called the first messenger and the cyclic AMP is called the second messenger.

INVERTEBRATE HORMONES

47.13 Which of the following groups of Arthropoda has well-developed endocrine systems?

(a) Arachnida; (b) Crustacea; (c) Insecta; (d) All classes of Arthropoda

47.14 The molt of an insect is triggered by

(a) thyroxine. (b) ecdysone. (c) juvenile hormone. (d) a pheromone.

47.15 The development of adult characteristics in a molting insect is promoted by

(a) thyroxine. (b) ecdysone. (c) juvenile hormone. (d) a pheromone.

47.16 The retention of larval characteristics in a molting insect is promoted by

(a) thyroxine. (b) ecdysone. (c) juvenile hormone. (d) a pheromone.

47.17 A male moth finds a mate by means of her

(a) thyroxine. (b) ecdysone. (c) brain hormone. (d) pheromone.

47.18 The British biologist V. B. Wigglesworth discovered, in the 1930s, two hormones that regulate development in insects. One is _____, which promotes growth, molting, and the development of adult traits. It is produced by the _____ glands in the head or thorax. The other hormone is _____, which promotes retention of larval characteristics. It is produced by the _____ glands in the head.

47.19 Of the two insect hormones discovered by Wigglesworth, _____ has no role in the adult insect, whereas _____ promotes the development of eggs and sperm.

47.20 Why are the chemical control systems of insects often referred to as neuroendocrine systems?

☙ The chemical and neural control systems in insects are not completely separated into endocrine and neural structures. In addition to the separate endocrine glands that secrete hormones, the brain and other aggregations of nerve cells throughout the insect's central nervous system produce a variety of chemical messengers, all apparently proteins, that function in a manner similar to hormones.

THE VERTEBRATE NEUROENDOCRINE CONTROL CENTER

47.21 The part of the brain with the greatest influence over the endocrine system is the

(a) hypothalamus. (b) amygdala. (c) cerebral cortex. (d) medulla oblongata.

47.22 Hormone-secreting cells, called neurosecretory cells, are abundant in the

(*a*) hypothalamus.   (*b*) amygdala.   (*c*) cerebral cortex.   (*d*) medulla oblongata.

47.23 Oxytocin and antidiuretic hormone reach the posterior pituitary by way of

(*a*) the anterior pituitary gland.   (*b*) lymphatic vessels.   (*c*) blood vessels.   (*d*) axons.

47.24 Oxytocin and antidiuretic hormone reach their target cells by way of

(*a*) the anterior pituitary gland.   (*b*) lymphatic vessels.   (*c*) blood vessels.   (*d*) axons.

47.25 Hypothalamic releasing hormones reach the anterior pituitary gland by way of

(*a*) the posterior pituitary gland.   (*b*) lymphatic vessels.   (*c*) blood vessels.   (*d*) axons.

47.26 Excessive production of growth hormone during adulthood can lead to

(*a*) a pituitary giant.   (*b*) a pituitary dwarf.   (*c*) disproportionately large hands, feet, and jaw.
(*d*) deterioration of the bones.

47.27 In mammals, prolactin stimulates the production of

(*a*) progesterones.   (*b*) mucus in the digestive tract.   (*c*) digestive enzymes in the small intestine.   (*d*) milk.

47.28 The hypothalamus contains two sets of neurosecretory cells. One set produces the hormones secreted by the
_____ and the other produces _____ hormones that regulate the _____
pituitary.

47.29 The pituitary gland is controlled by the _____. The posterior pituitary develops as an outgrowth of
the _____ and secretes two hormones made in the _____. These two hormones are
_____, which stimulates labor in a pregnant female and milk production by mammary glands, and
_____, which promotes the reabsorption of water from the nephrons. The anterior pituitary, by
contrast, develops as an outgrowth of the _____ and synthesizes the hormones it secretes.

47.30 The anterior pituitary secretes four tropic (i.e., stimulatory) hormones: (1) thyroid-stimulating hormone (TSH),
which stimulates the release of _____, triiodothyronine, and _____ from the
_____ gland; (2) adrenocorticotropin (ACTH), which stimulates the release of _____
from the _____; (3) follicle-stimulating hormone (FSH), which stimulates the release of
_____ from the _____; and (4) luteinizing hormone, which stimulates release of
_____ and _____ from the _____.

47.31 All the pituitary hormones are molecules made chiefly of monomers of _____.

47.32 The anterior pituitary has been called the master gland, because of the tropic hormones it releases. The real
master "gland," however, is the _____, because its _____ hormones regulate the
secretory activity of the anterior pituitary.

47.33 Most birds begin reproductive activities in response to increasing day length. The factors listed below connect
the environmental information—day length—to the behavioral response—mating. List these factors in the sequence
that they occur by numbering them from 1 to 10.

(*a*) _____ anterior pituitary   (*f*) _____ gonadotropic releasing hormone
(*b*) _____ mating behavior   (*g*) _____ gonads
(*c*) _____ day length   (*h*) _____ hypothalamus
(*d*) _____ eyes   (*i*) _____ pineal gland
(*e*) _____ gonadotropic hormones   (*j*) _____ sex hormones

47.34 How are the activities of the many glands of a vertebrate animal regulated?

🕮   *Tropic hormones* regulate activities within the vertebrate endocrine system. A tropic hormone is produced
by one endocrine structure and affects the activities of other endocrine structures. The anterior pituitary gland
produces four tropic hormones: thyroid-stimulating hormone (TSH), which controls the secretion of hormones

by the thyroid gland; adrenocorticotropic hormone (ACTH), which stimulates hormone secretion by the cortex of the adrenal gland; and two gonadotropic hormones, follicle-stimulating hormone (FSH) and luteinizing hormone (LH), which influence the secretion of sex hormones by the gonads.

Because the tropic hormones released by the anterior pituitary gland regulate so many other glands, it has been called the master gland of vertebrate animals. However, the real master "gland" is the hypothalamus of the brain, which lies above the pituitary gland and controls the activities of the anterior pituitary by means of chemical messengers, called *releasing hormones* and *release-inhibiting hormones*, that are transported by the bloodstream. Although the hypothalamus secretes hormones, it is composed entirely of nerve cells and forms a direct link between the nervous system and the endocrine system.

47.35   What roles do hormones play in homeostasis?

❀   Regulatory hormones adjust and control cellular activities to maintain normal homeostatic conditions in the internal body fluids, temporarily shift these conditions to abnormal emergency states in response to stress, and regulate the daily and seasonal rhythms and cycles of vertebrate life.

An example of the hormonal regulation of homeostasis is the effect of antidiuretic hormone (ADH) on the concentration of water in the blood. A control center in the hypothalamus is sensitive to changes in the concentration of water in the blood. Whenever the cells in this center sense a concentration below normal, they transmit a neural message to the posterior pituitary gland, which releases ADH into the bloodstream. The ADH travels throughout the body but only affects target cells in the collecting ducts of the kidney, instructing them to become permeable to water. Water that would have formed part of the urine is then removed from the nephrons and returned to the blood. ADH continues to be released until an optimal concentration of water in the blood is restored. When the hypothalamic control center senses that the blood is too dilute, it signals the posterior pituitary gland to stop secreting ADH so that more water is excreted in the urine.

The hypothalamic-pituitary control of water concentration in the blood is but one example of how synchronized activities of neural and endocrine control systems maintain homeostasis. Hormones are involved in regulating essentially all aspects of vertebrate physiology and behavior. Through the continual adjustment of cellular activities, a stable internal environment is maintained despite external changes.

VERTEBRATE ADRENAL GLANDS

47.36   The adrenal glands are located adjacent to the

(*a*) larynx.   (*b*) urinary bladder.   (*c*) kidneys.   (*d*) gonads.

47.37   The fight-or-flight response is developed by hormones of the

(*a*) hypothalamus.   (*b*) adrenal medulla.   (*c*) adrenal cortex.   (*d*) adrenal-pancreatic complex.

47.38   The main function of norepinephrine is to increase

(*a*) blood pressure.   (*b*) urine production.   (*c*) cellular respiration.   (*d*) the release of epinephrine.

47.39   Epinephrine and norepinephrine function as both hormones and

(*a*) fuel for cellular respiration.   (*b*) neurotransmitters.   (*c*) ions to promote action potentials.
(*d*) solutes to promote osmotic flow.

47.40   All the hormones of the adrenal cortex are synthesized from

(*a*) tyrosine.   (*b*) glycoproteins.   (*c*) cholesterol.   (*d*) fats.

47.41   The mammalian adrenal gland is really two glands: an outer _____ and an inner _____. The _____ is essential to life, whereas one can live without the _____.

47.42   Epinephrine and norepinephrine are small molecules, called catecholamines, synthesized from _____.

47.43   The adrenal medulla secretes _____ and _____ in response to commands from the _____ division of the _____ nervous system.

47.44   The adrenal cortex secretes a family of similar molecules, called _____ and steroids. The adrenal cortex of a human produces three main types of these hormones. One type, the _____, elevate blood-sugar levels and suppress the inflammatory response. They are released during stress in response to commands by _____. A second type, the _____, control salt and water balance. Hormones of the third type—the steroids—are similar, structurally and functionally, to the _____ hormones produced by the _____.

47.45   How do the adrenal hormones help adjust the body to stress?

     Vertebrate regulatory hormones play a critically important role in mobilizing the body to respond to emergencies. Many neural and endocrine systems, but especially the hormones secreted by the adrenal glands, participate in these responses.

     In humans, the hormone *cortisol*, or *hydrocortisone*, is secreted into the blood by the adrenal cortex whenever the individual is stressed because of illness or injury, extreme physical effort, pain, radical changes in body temperature, or intense emotion. Cortisol stimulates the breakdown of body proteins into sugars to provide energy, liberates vital amino acids for use in tissue repair, combats inflammatory reactions that accompany injuries, increases the capacity of muscles to remain contracted, and is involved in a variety of other life-protecting functions.

     Another reaction to stress is the fight-or-flight response, in which more sugar is released into the blood; blood pressure, breathing rate, and heart rate are increased; blood is shunted from the digestive tract to the skeletal muscles; blood-clotting time is reduced; and a variety of other changes occur that prepare the animal for extreme effort. All of these responses are initiated by the nervous system and sustained by *epinephrine* and *norepinephrine* from the adrenal medulla. The secretion of these two hormones is stimulated by the sympathetic division of the autonomic nervous system in response to intense physical exertion, pain, fear, anger, or other heightened emotional states. They prepare the body for fighting or for running away from an environmental threat.

OTHER VERTEBRATE GLANDS

47.46   The first hormone to be isolated (in 1902) was

     (*a*) thyroxine.   (*b*) testosterone.   (*c*) epinephrine.   (*d*) secretin.

47.47   The mammalian thyroid gland is located adjacent to the

     (*a*) adenoids.   (*b*) trachea.   (*c*) kidneys.   (*d*) pancreas.

47.48   Thyroxine and triiodothyronine, produced by the thyroid gland, are synthesized from iodine and

     (*a*) phenylalanine.   (*b*) cholesterol.   (*c*) glycoproteins.   (*d*) tyrosine.

47.49   The parathyroid glands are located adjacent to the

     (*a*) adenoids.   (*b*) thyroid gland.   (*c*) adrenal glands.   (*d*) pancreas.

47.50   A person with diabetes mellitus does not secrete enough

     (*a*) sugar.   (*b*) insulin.   (*c*) glucagon.   (*d*) epinephrine.

47.51   The neurons of a person with diabetes mellitus do not produce sufficient

     (*a*) ATP.   (*b*) fatty acids.   (*c*) enzymes.   (*d*) steroids.

47.52   The pineal gland is located

     (*a*) on the kidneys.   (*b*) in the brain.   (*c*) beneath the thymus gland.   (*d*) beneath the thyroid gland.

47.53   Thyroxine controls _____ in frogs and the development of _____ and _____ during embryonic development of other vertebrates. In an adult endotherm, it controls the _____ rate.

47.54   Both the thyroid and parathyroid glands secrete hormones that control the concentration of _____ ions in the blood. The amount of this ion is increased by _____ and decreased by _____.

47.55   The concentration of glucose in the blood is controlled by two hormones produced by the _____. One of the hormones, _____, causes the removal of glucose from the blood and the other,

_____, causes the addition of glucose to the blood. Secretion of each of these hormones is controlled by the _____.

47.56 The gonads produce sex hormones. The testes synthesizes mainly _____, of which the most common form is _____. The ovary synthesizes _____ and _____. All three hormones are _____ molecules synthesized from _____.

47.57 The thymus gland secretes thymosin, which stimulates the development and differentiation of _____.

47.58 The pineal gland secretes _____, which regulates functions related to the duration of _____ in the environment. Most of these functions involve rhythms associated with _____.

47.59 How do hormones regulate cycles of activity?

⚗ Most vertebrates exhibit daily physiological and behavioral patterns of activity called *circadian rhythms* (*circa* = about; *dian* = a day), which are regulated by coordinated neural and endocrine activities. Human body temperature, for example, is not maintained at a perfectly constant 37 °C, but varies $\pm 1°$ in a consistent and predictable cycle each day. Body temperature is usually lowest in the early morning and peaks sometime between midday and late afternoon. Each individual has a unique daily rhythm of body temperature as well as of heart rate, blood pressure, blood-sugar concentration, and many other bodily functions.

The mechanisms that regulate vertebrate circadian rhythms are not fully understood. These rhythms are correlated in part with the external rhythms of light and dark; however, they continue after an animal has been placed in continuous light or dark, indicating that some internal clock must maintain these rhythms in the absence of external cues. In vertebrates, the mechanism may be located in the pineal gland. This small gland within the brain receives information about external light conditions through the eyes and, in some species, directly through the skull. The pineal gland secretes a hormone, *melatonin*, in daily cycles that are synchronized with the external light cycles. Melatonin, in turn, stimulates the release of hormones by the hypothalamus and other neural and endocrine control centers.

Many seasonal cycles in vertebrate life are also regulated by hormones. Reproductive activities, especially, are initiated in response to increases in levels of sex hormones brought about in response to elevated levels of melatonin from the pineal gland. In the case of seasonal cycles, the pineal gland is in some way recording the change in day length with season and altering its melatonin secretion in response to this change.

47.60 Are prostaglandins and histamine hormones?

⚗ In vertebrate biology, the term *hormone* is usually reserved to describe chemical messengers that are secreted by components of the neuroendocrine system. However, research over the past several decades has shown that most types of body cells will synthesize and secrete hormonelike messengers if appropriately stimulated. Like hormones, these messengers move through body fluids and affect cellular activities. Unlike hormones, these messengers are released by cells that are not specialized secretory cells. Two hormonelike substances of current interest are the prostaglandins and histamine.

Prostaglandins were first discovered in human semen and were so named because they were believed to be secreted only by the prostate gland. It is now known that although semen does contain the highest concentrations of these substances, virtually all mammalian cells have the capacity to secrete prostaglandins. There are at least 16 different molecular forms of prostaglandins, and each one performs a unique function.

Prostaglandins stimulate a variety of responses. Certain ones produce contractions in the smooth muscles of the uterus, some relieve asthma by relaxing the smooth muscles of the respiratory passages, and still others allow ulcers to heal by reducing the secretions of gastric juices into the stomach. One type of prostaglandin raises blood pressure; another type lowers blood pressure. One type inhibits the formation of blood clots; another type increases the probability of blood-clot formation. Some contribute to the development of fevers, headaches, and inflamed joints.

Prostaglandins are modified fatty acid molecules synthesized from phospholipids in the plasma membrane. They are the only known regulatory chemicals formed of fatty acids. Almost any type of perturbation of the plasma membrane initiates the synthesis of prostaglandins, including the reception of a nonsteroid hormone, ultraviolet radiation, a bee sting, or even mechanical stimulation of the membrane. The exact mechanisms by which prostaglandins achieve their effects are not known, but some evidence suggests that they may control the production of cyclic AMP.

Another important hormonelike messenger, *histamine*, is a small molecule synthesized from common amino acids. It is produced and secreted by any type of cell when it is injured. Histamine aids in the repair of damaged cells by relaxing muscles in the walls of arterioles to permit more blood flow to the injured area. It also increases the permeability of the capillaries to antibodies and white blood cells—specific materials that combat illness and injury.

Histamine probably produces the symptoms of the common cold, asthma, and allergic reactions. For example, the presence of plant pollen in the nose of someone who suffers from hay fever stimulates the secretion of histamine. These molecules then facilitate the influx of body fluids and defense materials into the localized area to produce the allergic reaction—congestion, inflammation, runny nose and eyes, and so on. Prostaglandins probably act to enhance the effects of histamine during this reaction. Antihistamines and the hormones secreted by the adrenal cortex counteract the effects of histamine.

Answers to Objective Questions

47.1 *c*

47.2 *a*

47.3 *b*

47.4 *b*

47.5 *c*

47.6 *c*

47.7 *d*

47.8 duct; blood vessel; endocrine; endocrinology

47.9 receptor; cytoplasm; chromosome; transcription

47.10 second messenger; permeability; ions

47.11 ATP; cyclic AMP; hormone; cyclic AMP; enzymes

47.13 *d*

47.14 *b*

47.15 *b*

47.16 *c*

47.17 *d*

47.18 ecdysone; prothoracic; juvenile hormone; corpora allata

47.19 ecdysone; juvenile hormone

47.21 *a*

47.22 *a*

47.23 *d*

47.24 *c*

47.25 *c*

47.26 *c*

47.27 *d*

47.28 posterior pituitary; releasing; anterior

47.29 hypothalamus; brain; hypothalamus; oxytocin; antidiuretic hormone (ADH; also called vasopressin); mouth

47.30 thyroxine; calcitonin; thyroid; corticosteroids; adrenal cortex; estrogens; ovarian follicle; estrogens; progesterone; ovarian corpus luteum

47.31 amino acids

47.32 hypothalamus; releasing

47.33 (a) 6; (b) 10; (c) 1; (d) 2; (e) 7; (f) 5; (g) 8; (h) 4; (i) 3; (j) 9

47.36 *c*

47.37 *b*

47.38 *a*

47.39 *b*

47.40 *c*

47.41 cortex; medulla; cortex; medulla

47.42 tyrosine

47.43 epinephrine; norepinephrine; sympathetic; autonomic

47.44 corticosteroids; glucocorticoids; ACTH; mineralocorticoids; sex; gonads

47.46 *d*

47.47 *b*

47.48 *d*

47.49 *b*

47.50 *b*

47.51 *a*

47.52 *b*

47.53 metamorphosis; bones; nervous systems; basal metabolic

47.54 calcium; parathyroid hormone; calcitonin

47.55 pancreas; insulin; glucagon; blood-sugar level

47.56 androgens; testosterone; estrogens; progesterone; steroid; cholesterol

47.57 T lymphocytes

47.58 melatonin; light; reproduction

CHAPTER 48
Muscles and Movement

TYPES OF MOVEMENT*

48.1   Cytoplasmic streaming, a characteristic of plant cells, amoebas, and vertebrate white blood cells, is caused by

(*a*) sliding microtubules.   (*b*) contracting microfilaments.   (*c*) elongating cell walls.   (*d*) changes in turgor pressure.

48.2   Amoeboid movement, a characteristic of amoebas and human macrophages, occurs when ectoplasm contracts to move endoplasm into a pseudopodium. Contraction of the ectoplasm appears to be caused by

(*a*) sliding microtubules.   (*b*) contracting microfilaments.   (*c*) elongating cell walls.   (*d*) changes in turgor pressure.

48.3   The to-and-fro movements of cilia and flagella are caused by

(*a*) sliding microtubules.   (*b*) contracting microfilaments.   (*c*) elongating cell walls.   (*d*) changes in turgor pressure.

48.4   Tiny animals, such as the larvae of cnidarians, move from place to place chiefly by

(*a*) cytoplasmic streaming.   (*b*) amoeboid movement.   (*c*) contractions of muscle cells.   (*d*) the beating movements of cilia.

48.5   An earthworm moves from place to place by

(*a*) rolling movements caused by statocysts.   (*b*) many small pseudopodia, called setae.   (*c*) peristaltic waves of contractions of circular and longitudinal muscles.   (*d*) to-and-fro movements of many tiny legs.

48.6   A grasshopper moves from place to place when its muscles

(*a*) pull its bones.   (*b*) push its bones.   (*c*) pull its external plates.   (*d*) push its external plates.

48.7   All animal movement is based on two contractile systems: _____, which are chains of _____ molecules, and _____, which are organelles made of _____ molecules.

48.8   All eukaryotic cells have microfilaments formed of _____ molecules. A muscle cell has microfilaments made of both _____ and _____ molecules.

48.9   A cilium bends when the two _____ of a doublet slide past each other. Each cilium has _____ such doublets, as well as _____ central singlets. This system of movement resembles the _____ system of skeletal muscles. The similarity between these two systems appears to be a product of _____ evolution.

48.10   All multicellular animals except _____ have muscle cells specialized for _____. At first muscle cells were used only for moving body parts, such as tentacles. As animals evolved, muscles replaced _____ as the main effectors of locomotion.

48.11   Locomotion in an earthworm is accomplished by peristaltic waves of contractions of _____ and _____ muscles. Contractions of the _____ muscles elongate the worm, because they contract against the incompressible _____, which forms what is called a _____ skeleton.

48.12   An insect skeleton cannot grow, because it is made of _____ materials. A vertebrate skeleton can grow, because it is made of _____ materials. Vertebrate skeletons are formed of two tissue types: _____ and _____.

* Answers to Chapter 48 objective questions appear on page 347.

48.13 Vertebrate muscles are of three basic types: _____ muscles, which are innervated by the _____ nervous system and effect locomotion; _____ muscles, which are innervated by the _____ nervous system and effect movements of vessels and internal organs; and _____ muscles, which are innervated by the _____ nervous system and pump blood. Both _____ and _____ muscles are striated, whereas _____ muscles are not. A muscle cell of both _____ and _____ muscles contains just a single nucleus, whereas a cell of _____ muscles contains more than one nucleus.

48.14 What causes amoeboid movement?

🐚 Amoeboid movement is named after the amoeba, a unicellular organism that moves by forming a projection of its cell, called a *pseudopodium* ("false foot"), into which the rest of the cell then flows by cytoplasmic streaming. The cell re-forms as a rounded structure in this new position. Another pseudopodium then forms, and the process is repeated. A series of these tiny movements enables the entire cell to travel a few centimeters an hour. Other types of protists, as well as human white blood cells and cancer cells, use this same method of creeping locomotion.

An amoeboid cell contains highly viscous peripheral cytoplasm, called *ectoplasm*, and less viscous central cytoplasm, called *endoplasm*. Locomotion begins when a pseudopodium attaches firmly to the substrate in front of the cell and establishes what will become the new position of the cell. Ectoplasm in the posterior part of the cell is then converted into endoplasm, which streams forward into the pseudopodium; there it spreads peripherally and forms a rounded cell where once only the pseudopodium was positioned. The endoplasm is then converted back into the more rigid ectoplasm before the next amoeboid movement occurs.

Microfilaments of both actin and myosin occur in the ectoplasm and are known to play some role in cytoplasmic streaming. When actin filaments exist by themselves, they form a gel that contracts when it contacts myosin filaments. Two current hypotheses about the role of microfilaments in amoeboid movements are: (1) the endoplasm is pulled forward by contractions of microfilaments in the leading end of the pseudopodium, and (2) the endoplasm is pushed forward by contractions of microfilaments in the trailing end of the cell. Support for the second hypothesis comes from the much greater abundance of actin microfilaments in the trailing end of the cell.

48.15 How does an earthworm, which has muscles but no skeleton, obtain support for locomotion?

🐚 An earthworm is constructed of a series of body segments, each with two sets of muscles—one encircling the segment and the other extending the length of the segment. When the circular muscles contract, the segment becomes not only narrower, but also longer and fairly rigid, because of pressure from the coelomic fluid within the segment. This type of support, from bodily fluids, is known as a *hydrostatic skeleton*. Thus, to move forward, the worm needs only to squeeze some of its anterior segments while at the same time holding posterior ones stationary, which it does by grasping the substrate with protruding bristles called *setae*. The elongating segments can only move forward, and when they have done so, their setae grasp the substrate beneath them and the more posterior segments are pulled forward by contractions of the longitudinal muscles. Segments of the worm alternately elongate and shorten as peristaltic waves of muscle contractions move, from anterior to posterior, through the body of the worm.

THE VERTEBRATE MUSCULOSKELETAL SYSTEM

48.16 The original function, in the first vertebrates, of the skeleton was to provide

(*a*) support for locomotion. (*b*) protection from enemies and osmosis. (*c*) minerals. (*d*) blood cells.

48.17 This original function is still performed today by bones of the

(*a*) jaw. (*b*) skull and rib cage. (*c*) pelvis. (*d*) thigh.

48.18 Which of the following is likely to have the strongest leg bones?

(*a*) Jockey; (*b*) Swimmer; (*c*) Weight lifter; (*d*) Golfer

48.19 Which of the following connects a muscle to a bone?

(*a*) Cartilage; (*b*) Ligament; (*c*) Tendon; (*d*) Disc

48.20 Which of the following connects a bone to a bone?

(*a*) Cartilage; (*b*) Ligament; (*c*) Tendon; (*d*) Disc

48.21 Which of the following acts as a shock absorber to cushion the tibia and the femur where they come together?

(*a*) Cartilage; (*b*) Ligament; (*c*) Tendon; (*d*) Disc

48.22 A muscle cell is a muscle

(*a*) bundle. (*b*) fiber. (*c*) fibril. (*d*) filament.

48.23 Materials stored in bones include the minerals _____ and _____ and the organic macromolecule _____ .

48.24 The vertebrate skeleton is made of living, dynamic tissue. Most of it is formed of _____ during early development and, in most vertebrates, this tissue is later converted to _____ by the deposition of _____ around the collagen fibers of the matrix. In either form of connective tissue, the matrix is made from secretions of cells located within _____ , which surround the _____ canals that contain _____ and _____ .

48.25 A vertebrate skeleton can be divided into two subskeletons: the _____ skeleton made of the skull and vertebral column and the _____ skeleton made of the limb bones and their girdles.

48.26 The vertebral column is made of _____ bones, called _____ , which are separated from one another by _____ .

48.27 The four types of tissue involved in movement are: _____ , which provides support; _____ , which joins support tissues _____ , which contracts to move support tissues; and _____ , which connects contractile tissue to support tissue. All of these tissues gain strength from the same type of protein, _____ .

48.28 The biceps muscle of the arm is made of many muscle _____ , which in turn are made of hundreds of thousands of long, cylindrical cells called _____ . Each cell is made of hundreds of long, cylindrical _____ , which have banding patterns caused by the overlapping of _____ and _____ molecules.

48.29 What are the functions of bones?

☘ Bones not only provide support for locomotion but also protect the body from injury. In vertebrate animals, all bones were initially on the outside of the body, where they provided protection against predators and the physical environment. An internal skeleton developed only in the more advanced fishes. A remnant of the primitive external skeleton remains today in the form of the skull, which surrounds and protects the vulnerable soft tissues of the brain. The bones of the rib cage also serve to protect vulnerable tissues, in this case the lungs and heart.

Several types of materials are stored in the bones. Calcium and phosphorus, as well as smaller amounts of other minerals, are stored in bones when excess amounts are ingested in the diet. When insufficient amounts of these minerals are available, the stores in the bones are released to be used in cellular activities. Some fat is also stored in the yellow marrow of long bones and can be used as a source of energy.

All types of blood cells are made in the bones. This vital function takes place in the red marrow of such flat bones as the ribs, skull, pelvis, and vertebrae.

48.30 Why are some tendons long and others short?

☘ Every skeletal muscle is attached to at least two bones in such a way that changes in the length of the muscle alter the positions of the bones relative to one another. Muscles are attached to bones by *tendons*, which are tough cords similar to ligaments. Of the four structures involved in movement—bones, muscles, ligaments, and tendons—the tendons are the strongest and the least likely to break.

Some tendons are very short; others are quite long. Long tendons allow the muscles to be located far from the bones they move. For example, the muscles that raise the fingers are located in the forearm and are connected to the finger bones by long tendons that lie along the tops of the hand and fingers. If these muscles were near the bones they move, the fingers and hand would be considerably more bulky and less useful in grasping and manipulating objects.

A particularly long tendon, commonly referred to as the Achilles tendon, connects the gastrocnemius, or calf, muscle to the bone of the heel. This long connection between muscle and bone frees the ankle of muscle so that it is light in weight. In some swift-running mammals, such as deer and horses, this tendon extends from the heel all the way up to the back of the upper leg and the gastrocnemius muscle is eliminated completely; the lower legs of these mammals are slim and light so that they can run faster for longer periods of time.

MUSCLE PHYSIOLOGY

48.31 The fundamental, repeating unit of a skeletal myofibril is the

(*a*) sarcoplasmic reticulum. (*b*) myosin cross bridge. (*c*) sarcomere. (*d*) motor unit.

48.32 According to the now-established sliding-filament model of muscle contraction, the molecules that move to shorten a muscle are

(*a*) actin. (*b*) collagen. (*c*) myosin. (*d*) creatine phosphate.

48.33 Cross bridges, which connect the two molecules of a fibril during a muscle contraction, are made of

(*a*) actin. (*b*) collagen. (*c*) myosin. (*d*) creatine phosphate.

48.34 The ion that must be present for binding of the cross bridges is

(*a*) calcium. (*b*) sodium. (*c*) iron. (*d*) potassium.

48.35 The neurotransmitter between a motor neuron and a muscle cell is

(*a*) serotonin. (*b*) endorphin. (*c*) dopamine. (*d*) acetylcholine.

48.36 The all-or-none phenomenon of muscle contraction refers to a maximum contraction or no contraction of a

(*a*) muscle. (*b*) muscle bundle. (*c*) muscle fiber. (*d*) muscle fibril.

48.37 An oxygen debt develops during

(*a*) tetanus. (*b*) sarcoplasmic release. (*c*) anaerobic work. (*d*) aerobic work.

48.38 Anaerobic work becomes painful because of an accumulation of

(*a*) calcium ions. (*b*) myosin. (*c*) lactic acid. (*d*) creatine phosphate.

48.39 An all-out sprint cannot continue for more than about 45 seconds because the muscles

(*a*) run out of glycogen. (*b*) run out of oxygen. (*c*) accumulate too much creatine phosphate.
(*d*) accumulate acetylcholine on their plasma membranes.

48.40 When a muscle contracts, _____ energy within _____ is converted to the _____ energy of movement.

48.41 The sarcomere of a skeletal muscle exhibits two dark bands: an I band near the edge has only filaments that are _____, and an A band in the broad central regions has some filaments that are _____ and others that are _____. We now know that the I band contains only molecules of _____ and the A band contains molecules of both _____ and _____.

48.42 When a muscle is at rest, the myosin-binding sites on the actin molecules are blocked by a strand of _____ and by the _____ complex. These proteins are removed and the muscle can contract when _____ bind to _____.

48.43 The ions that stimulate muscle contraction are stored within the _____, a special form of _____. They are released into the cytoplasm in response to _____ in the plasma membrane.

48.44 The strength of a contraction is varied by varying the number of _____ that are active and the rate at which _____ occur in each of them.

48.45   A slow-twitch fiber is specialized for _____ cellular respiration; it has _____ capillaries around it, a _____ amount of myoglobin, _____ mitochondria, and uses both _____ and _____ as fuels. A fast-twitch fiber is specialized for _____ cellular respiration; it has _____ capillaries around it, a _____ amount of myoglobin, _____ mitochondria, and uses only _____ as fuel.

48.46   Energy released from aerobic cellular respiration in a muscle cell is temporarily stored as _____, which can be used directly to activate myosin, and _____, which has to be converted to _____ before it can be used.

48.47   Muscle cells do not undergo cell division. Muscles made largely of fast-twitch fibers thicken with anaerobic work by increasing their numbers of _____. Muscles made largely of slow-twitch fibers thicken, albeit slightly, with aerobic work by increasing their numbers of _____.

48.48   What causes the shortening of a muscle?

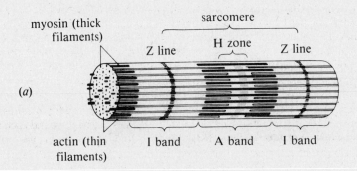

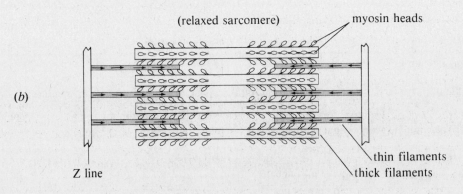

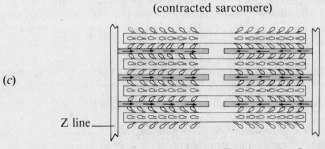

Fig. 48.1. Structure of a myofibril. (*a*) Each fibril is made of repeating units called sarcomeres. (*b*) A sarcomere is made of two sets of thin actin filaments and a set of thick myosin filaments. (*c*) A fibril shortens when the myosin filaments pull the two sets of actin filaments closer together.

🐌 The repeating units, or *sarcomeres*, of a myofibril are made of two types of protein—actin and myosin. *Actin* molecules are globular proteins that form long chains, or thin filaments. *Myosin* molecules are long polypeptides, wound around each other, with globular protrusions called *cross bridges*; myosin forms thick filaments. A fibril shortens during a muscle contraction when the myosin filaments of each sarcomere pull two sets of actin filaments closer together (Fig. 48.1). The myosin cross bridges repeatedly attach themselves to the actin filaments and, by pulling and letting go, slide the actin across the myosin. The attachment is a chemical bond, in which the actin is briefly bound to the cross bridge and then released. This description is the *sliding-filament model* of muscle contraction. The mechanics of its actions are well established, but the chemical nature is not completely understood.

The immediate source of energy for muscle contraction is adenosine triphosphate (ATP) formed during cellular respiration. Another molecule, creatine phosphate, is used to temporarily store energy from cellular respiration but has to be converted to ATP prior to use.

48.49 How is a skeletal muscle stimulated to contract?

🐌 Even the simplest movement of the skeleton is a highly complex process during which many muscles contract, relax, or maintain steady tension. The activities of these muscle groups must be coordinated if movement is to be smooth and efficient. This important function is performed by the central nervous system, especially by the cerebellum and the motor cortex.

Motor neurons carry the stimulus from the central nervous system to the muscles. Each motor neuron is connected by synapses to more than one muscle fiber and, when stimulated, causes all fibers that it innervates to contract. A motor neuron and the fibers it controls constitute a *motor unit*. Some motor units have hundreds of fibers, others only a few. The dexterity of the muscular movement diminishes as the number of fibers that a neuron stimulates increases. One neuron is connected to only five fibers in the eye, because eye movement requires fine adjustments. At the opposite extreme, one neuron may control several thousand different fibers in a thigh muscle.

The neurotransmitter of the neuromuscular junction, where a motor neuron and muscle fiber come together, is acetylcholine. It generates action potentials in the plasma membrane of the fiber, and they are carried throughout the cell interior by means of deep infoldings of the plasma membrane. The action potentials are passed to membranes of the *sarcoplasmic reticulum* (a form of endoplasmic reticulum), which surround each fibril, and cause the release of calcium ions stored within the sarcoplasmic reticulum. Calcium ions then cause the myosin cross bridges to (1) temporarily act as enzymes that release energy from ATP and (2) have access to the actin. The active sites on the actin filaments of a resting fibril are covered with long protein molecules, called *tropomyosin*, and a series of globular proteins, called *troponin complexes*. When calcium ions are present, they bind to troponin and, in doing so, remove both the troponin complex and the tropomyosin, thereby exposing the binding sites on the actin filament. Cross bridges can then attach and slide the actin filaments closer together. After the fibrils have contracted, the calcium ions are returned by active transport to the membranes of the sarcoplasmic reticulum.

48.50 What causes muscle fatigue?

🐌 The cause of muscle fatigue depends on whether the work being done is mainly anaerobic or mainly aerobic. During anaerobic work, glucose is catabolized in the absence of oxygen into two molecules of lactic acid and two molecules of ATP; only about 2% of the energy of glucose is transferred to ATP (see Question 7.19). During aerobic work, glucose or fatty acid is combined with oxygen and catabolized to carbon dioxide and water. Approximately 36 molecules of ATP are produced, which is 40% of the available energy within a glucose or fatty acid molecule (see Questions 7.61 and 7.67).

Anaerobic exercise cannot continue for long because: (1) lactic acid accumulates in the muscles and gradually lowers the pH, which causes pain and interferes with normal chemical activities; and (2) the inefficient use of glucose causes the muscle glycogen to be used up rapidly. In an all-out sprint, for example, the glycogen reserves are depleted in approximately 45 seconds.

Aerobic exercise can continue for long periods of time because it uses, efficiently, two fuels—glucose and fatty acids. Although glucose reserves are always limited, an average-sized person has enough stored fat to walk 1000 miles! Exercise more rapid than a slow walk uses both glucose and fatty acids. Fatigue develops when glycogen reserves are depleted, and the more rapid the pace of the exercise, the sooner depletion occurs. Other causes of fatigue from aerobic exercise include dehydration, mental fatigue, and synapse fatigue.

Answers to Objective Questions

48.1 *b*	**48.4** *d*	**48.7** microfilaments; protein; microtubules; protein
48.2 *b*	**48.5** *c*	
48.3 *a*	**48.6** *c*	**48.8** actin; actin; myosin

48.9 microtubules; nine; two; sliding filament; convergent
48.10 sponges; contractions; cilia
48.11 circular; longitudinal; circular; coelomic fluid; hydrostatic
48.12 noncellular; cellular; cartilage; bone
48.13 skeletal; somatic; smooth; autonomic; cardiac; autonomic; skeletal; cardiac; smooth; cardiac; smooth; skeletal
48.16 *b*
48.17 *b*
48.18 *c*
48.19 *c*
48.20 *b*
48.21 *a*

48.22 *b*
48.23 calcium; phosphorus; fat
48.24 cartilage; bone; minerals; lacunae; Haversian; blood vessels; nerves
48.25 axial; appendicular
48.26 26; vertebrae; discs
48.27 bone (or cartilage); ligament; muscle; tendon; collagen
48.28 bundles; fibers; fibrils; actin; myosin
48.31 *d*
48.32 *a*
48.33 *c*
48.34 *a*
48.35 *d*
48.36 *c*
48.37 *c*

48.38 *c*
48.39 *a*
48.40 chemical; ATP; mechanical
48.41 thin; thin; thick; actin; actin; myosin
48.42 tropomyosin; troponin; calcium ions; troponin
48.43 sarcoplasmic reticulum; endoplasmic reticulum; action potentials
48.44 motor units; action potentials
48.45 aerobic; many; large; many; glucose; fatty acids; anaerobic; few; small; few; glucose
48.46 ATP; creatine phosphate
48.47 fibrils; capillaries

CHAPTER 49
Animal Reproduction and Development

MODES OF REPRODUCTION*

49.1   Which of the following is a hermaphrodite?

(*a*) Ant;   (*b*) Earthworm;   (*c*) Aphid;   (*d*) Trout

49.2   The limited period of sexual receptivity that occurs around the time of ovulation in all female mammals except humans is called

(*a*) menstruation.   (*b*) luteinization.   (*c*) oogenesis.   (*d*) estrus.

49.3   External fertilization occurs almost exclusively in habitats that are

(*a*) tropical.   (*b*) moist.   (*c*) warm.   (*d*) crowded.

49.4   In most nonmammalian vertebrates, the reproductive products (i.e., sperm, eggs, embryos) leave the body by way of a

(*a*) reproductive pore.   (*b*) genital duct.   (*c*) cloaca.   (*d*) ejaculatory opening.

49.5   Most ungulates (i.e., hoofed animals) of temperate latitudes mate in the _____ so that young are present in the _____ when _____ is plentiful.

49.6   Male and female reproductive cycles must be synchronous; they are controlled internally by _____ in response to environmental cues, of which the most common and influential is _____.

49.7   An aphid has two modes of reproduction: a _____ mode when it is crowded and its food supply is dwindling, and a _____ mode when it is uncrowded and has plenty of food.

49.8   In fishes and amphibians with external fertilization, the probability that the sperm of one male will fertilize the eggs of a particular female is increased by _____ behavior, which triggers simultaneous _____ of the _____.

49.9   External fertilization generally produces _____ zygotes, each with a _____ probability of survival. Internal fertilization generally produces _____ zygotes, each with a _____ probability of survival. The probability of an embryo surviving to become an independent individual is increased by having an egg that is _____ to the harsh environment, by _____ development, and by _____ care.

49.10   Why is reproduction a seasonal event for most animals?

  Large amounts of energy and nutrients are needed to form and nourish offspring, which is why organisms typically bear their young during the season of the year when food sources are most abundant. When the seasonal availability of resources determines the time of reproduction, mating is also seasonal since a specific time interval elapses between mating and the appearance of young in most organisms. In temperate environments, most plants grow and reproduce only between late spring and early fall. Consequently, animals that feed on plant material bear their young in the spring, when vegetation is plentiful, and rear their young during the summer. Predators of herbivorous animals also produce their young in the spring and early summer so that large populations of prey will be available when their offspring are growing.

  Competition from other organisms also affects resource availability, particularly in tropical environments, where physical conditions do not change dramatically during the year. Tropical animal species that compete for food usually reproduce at different times of the year, so that the demand for resources is staggered.

  When mates are difficult to find, organisms must congregate at specific places during specific times for purposes of mating. Mating in some ants, for example, occurs only at certain times of the day on a few

* Answers to Chapter 49 objective questions appear on page 359.

349

consecutive days of the year. During these few hours, each colony releases winged males and females that form huge mating swarms above the highest point in the area. Every colony in the population must recognize and respond to the same environmental cues in order for mating between colonies to take place.

An even more remarkable example of mating synchrony is provided by the periodical cicadas. The adult forms of these insects appear and mate above ground only during a few weeks every 13 or 17 years, depending on the species. This extreme reproductive cycle is believed to be a way of avoiding heavy predation. Because these insects appear so infrequently, their potential predators are unable to rely on them as a food source and so have not evolved adaptations for capturing them. Only a small percentage of the adult population is lost to predators with generalized feeding habits, because the cicadas appear suddenly in very large numbers. The relatively low densities of predators that are present when the adults appear are simply unable to eat the cicadas fast enough to significantly affect this insect population.

REPRODUCTIVE ANATOMY OF A MAMMAL

49.11 Sperm are produced in the

(a) seminiferous tubules. (b) interstitial cells. (c) vas deferens. (d) prostate gland.

49.12 Testosterone, the male sex hormone, is synthesized in the

(a) seminiferous tubules. (b) interstitial cells. (c) vas deferens. (d) prostate gland.

49.13 Mature sperm are stored in the

(a) seminiferous tubules. (b) vas deferens. (c) epididymis. (d) seminal vesicles.

49.14 How many mature eggs are typically produced by each ovary of a nonpregnant woman each year?

(a) 6; (b) 12; (c) 24; (d) 52

49.15 When a mature egg leaves the ovary, it enters the

(a) follicle. (b) endometrium. (c) interstitial cells. (d) oviduct.

49.16 Fertilization takes place in the

(a) follicle. (b) oviduct. (c) uterus. (d) vagina.

49.17 The female equivalent of the glans of the penis is the

(a) vestibule. (b) hymen. (c) baculum. (d) clitoris.

49.18 The male gonads are the _____, which are suspended from the body wall within the _____. They have two functions: to produce _____ and _____.

49.19 Sperm travel during an ejaculation from the _____, where they are stored, to the _____, where they are transported to the ejaculatory duct and then to the _____, which carries both reproductive and excretory fluids. A vasectomy is a surgical procedure, for contraceptive purposes, in which the _____ is cut and blocked so as to prevent sperm from being present in the semen.

49.20 Semen consists of sperm and materials from three types of glands: the _____, which contribute mucus, amino acids, and fructose; the _____, which surrounds the urethra and contributes an alkaline solution; and the _____, which secrete the clear, viscous fluid ejected just prior to the rest of the semen. The penis becomes rigid and erect, because it is filled with _____.

49.21 The female gonads are the _____, located within the _____. They have two functions: to produce _____ and _____.

49.22 An egg travels from a _____ of an _____ to an _____, where it is fertilized, and then to the _____, where it develops. At birth, the young mammal moves from its site of development to the outside environment by way of the _____.

49.23 Where are the eggs of a mammal produced, and how do they get to the place where sperm can fertilize them?

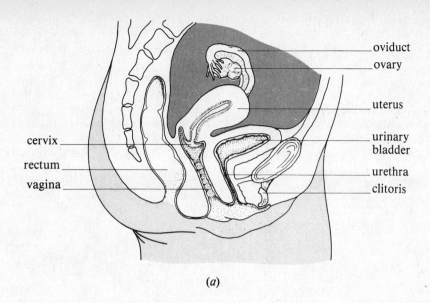

(a)

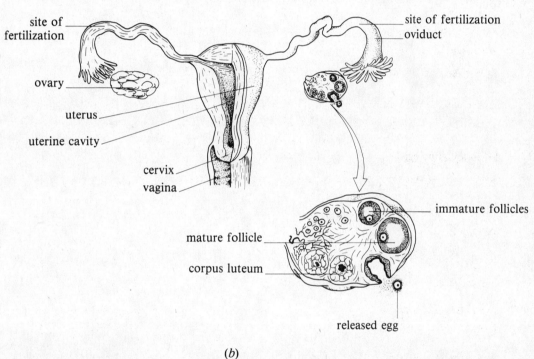

(b)

Fig. 49.1. The reproductive system of a woman. (a) Side view; (b) front view, with one side (on the left) cut away to show internal structures and the one ovary (on the right) enlarged to show developing follicles and corpus luteum.

The female mammal has two ovaries located in the lower abdominal cavity. They develop mature eggs in alternate months (only one egg normally matures each month). Inside an ovary, each egg resides within its own individual sac, or *follicle*, until it matures. Mature eggs are fairly large (about 1 mm in diameter) and contain sufficient materials to nourish the first cells of the embryo.

A mature egg is released each month from an ovary into one of the two *oviducts* leading to the *uterus*. The oviducts are tubes that are not directly connected to the ovaries, so the egg must pass briefly through an open space between the organs of the abdominal cavity. The opening to each oviduct is expanded into a funnel that captures almost every egg released from an ovary. Fertilization of an egg by a sperm occurs in the segment of the oviduct closest to the funnel, as shown in Fig. 49.1.

49.24   Where are sperm produced in a mammal, and how do they get to the place where they can fertilize an egg?

Sperm are produced in the *testes*, which are a pair of glands suspended outside the abdominal cavity in a male mammal. Sperm move from each testis into a network of long, coiled tubes called the *epididymis*, which

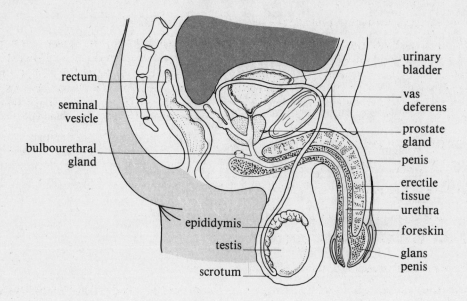

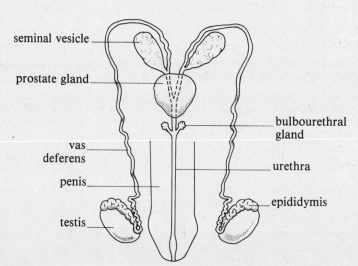

Fig. 49.2. The reproductive system of a man. (*a*) Side view; (*b*) front view.

lies within the scrotum just outside each testis (Fig. 49.2). The sperm undergo their final stage of maturation in the epididymis and are stored there until ejaculation. Just prior to ejaculation, mature sperm move into the *vas deferens*—a long tube that extends from each epididymis up into the abdominal cavity. Inside the body cavity, each vas deferens circles around the urinary bladder and connects with the single *urethra*, as shown in Fig. 49.2. The urethra serves the dual function of transporting urine from the bladder and conducting sperm to the tip of the penis.

When stimulated by copulation or masturbation, or during spontaneous emission, the muscles in the walls of the vas deferens contract strongly to force the sperm rapidly through the vas deferens. Fluids from the *seminal vesicles*, the *prostate gland*, and the *bulbourethral glands* are added to the sperm to form the semen.

Sperm ejaculated into a woman's vagina travel through the uterus and enter the oviducts, a journey that can take 30 minutes to 3 hours. Movement of the sperm into the uterus is chiefly dependent on the activity of the sperm themselves. Movement from the uterus to the oviducts is aided by the muscular contractions of the female reproductive tract caused by prostaglandins in the semen. Female orgasm—a poorly understood aspect of reproduction—is not essential to fertilization but contributes to sperm movement.

Approximately 400 million sperm are deposited in the vagina during an ejaculation, but rarely do more than a few hundred reach the site of fertilization. Once the sperm reach the outer third of the oviduct, where the egg is located, they must depend only on their swimming movements to reach the egg.

49.25 Why are the testes of most mammals located outside the body cavity?

🐌 In the male embryo, the testes develop in the abdominal cavity near the kidneys and migrate to the *scrotum* shortly before or at the time of birth. Unlike the rest of the abdominal area, the scrotum has little or no fatty insulation. Sperm development occurs optimally at temperatures a few degree below the normal body temperature of 37 °C. A suitable temperature is maintained inside the testes by involuntary movements of the muscles that connect the scrotum to the body wall. The muscles contract or relax, moving the scrotum nearer to or farther away from the heat of the body when environmental temperatures are cold or warm, respectively.

GAMETE FORMATION IN A MAMMAL

49.26 Spermatogenesis requires the presence of

(*a*) fructose. (*b*) progesterone. (*c*) testosterone. (*d*) thyroxine.

49.27 Each ejaculate of a man contains about how many sperm?

(*a*) 400; (*b*) 4000; (*c*) 400,000; (*d*) 400,000,000

49.28 During oogenesis, each diploid cell produces

(*a*) four functional eggs. (*b*) two functional eggs and two polar bodies. (*c*) one functional egg and three polar bodies. (*d*) four functional polar bodies.

49.29 The female hormone that causes deposition of fat in the breasts and hips, as well as growth of pubic hair, during puberty is

(*a*) luteinizing hormone. (*b*) follicle-stimulating hormone. (*c*) estrogen. (*d*) progesterone.

49.30 The female hormone that causes an increase in blood vessels in the uterus and development of milk glands in the breasts is

(*a*) luteinizing hormone. (*b*) follicle-stimulating hormone. (*c*) estrogen. (*d*) progesterone.

49.31 Menstruation is triggered by an abrupt decline in the amount of

(*a*) luteinizing hormone. (*b*) follicle-stimulating hormone. (*c*) estrogen. (*d*) progesterone.

49.32 A sperm has two functions: to carry _____ to the egg and to _____ the egg.

49.33 A sperm consists of three sections: a head, which carries the _____ and is capped with an egg-penetrating _____; a middle piece, which is rich in _____; and a tail, which is really a single _____ used for locomotion.

49.34 Oogenesis of a woman begins when she is an _____ and is completed at the same time she produces an egg and it is _____.

49.35 The females of many primates, including humans, have _____ cycles, in which the _____ is shed, whereas other mammals have _____ cycles, in which it is reabsorbed.

49.36 During the first 14 days of the menstrual cycle, growth of the follicle is promoted by _____, which is released from the anterior pituitary. As the follicle grows, it secretes _____. Ovulation occurs in response to a small peak in _____ concentration and a large peak in _____ concentration in the blood. After ovulation, the anterior pituitary stops secreting _____ but continues to secrete _____, which converts the ruptured follicle into a _____, and this structure synthesizes both _____ and _____.

49.37 What is the function of testosterone?

🐌 The structure and function of the entire male reproductive system depend on testosterone. It is necessary for sperm production and is responsible for erection, ejaculation, and sex behaviors that result in delivery of sperm into the female reproductive tract. A deficiency of this hormone leads to sterility.

Virtually all of the characteristics associated with being a human male are testosterone-dependent, including depth of voice and the amount and distribution of body hair, muscle, and fat. Although the concentration of testosterone in the blood of a man remains fairly constant, small increases may occur during sexual excitement, as evidenced by an increase in beard growth during such times. Testosterone controls male traits in other species as well, including the growth and shedding of antlers in male deer, the brilliant plumage of many male birds, the characteristic marking odor of tomcats, and even a male dog's habit of lifting his leg to urinate.

49.38 How is the menstrual cycle regulated?

🐤 Five hormones regulate a woman's menstrual cycle: gonadotropin-releasing hormone (GnRH), follicle-stimulating hormone (FSH), luteinizing hormone (LH), estrogens, and progesterone. These hormones form a hierarchy of control. GnRH is synthesized in the hypothalamus and controls the release of both FSH and LH from the anterior pituitary gland, where they are produced. FSH causes the ovarian follicle and its egg to mature, and the maturing follicle synthesizes and releases estrogens. LH stimulates conversion of a ruptured follicle into another gland, the *corpus luteum*, which synthesizes and releases both estrogens and progesterone. The presence of progesterone in the blood inhibits release of GnRH from the hypothalamus, and so inhibits release of both FSH and LH.

The menstrual cycle begins, after menstruation has removed the endometrium, when GnRH stimulates release of FSH, which causes an ovarian follicle to grow and mature. The estrogens it releases stimulate cell division in the endometrium to repair the damage caused by menstruation and to increase the thickness of the tissue. High concentrations of estrogens released into the bloodstream from the mature follicle stimulate the anterior pituitary gland to release a brief spurt of FSH and a large amount of LH on about day 14 of the cycle. This sudden increase in FSH and LH causes ovulation, in which the mature egg breaks out of the follicle and moves into the oviduct.

After ovulation, the anterior pituitary gland stops producing FSH but continues to release LH, which causes conversion of the ruptured follicle into a corpus luteum. The estrogens and progesterone released from the corpus luteum act together to prepare the reproductive organs for pregnancy and stimulate the endometrium to become soft, moist, and thick. Progesterone increases the volume of muscles and blood vessels in the walls of the uterus, stimulates activity of mucous glands in the endometrium, and causes milk glands to develop in the breasts.

In the absence of pregnancy, the corpus luteum degenerates as the cycle nears 28 days in length, and the estrogen and progesterone levels decline. Without hormonal support to the endometrium, the arteries to this area constrict and the tissues are deprived of nutrients and sloughed off. Menstruation occurs, marking the end of one menstrual cycle and the beginning of another. The low level of progesterone no longer inhibits production of FSH and this hormone increases in concentration, causing the development of a new egg and follicle.

49.39 How do the sex hormones work to maintain pregnancy?

🐤 If the egg becomes fertilized and pregnancy develops, the membranes around the implanted embryo secrete a hormone, chorionic gonadotropin, on approximately the sixth day after ovulation (20th day of the cycle). This hormone suppresses menstruation by maintaining the corpus luteum as a functioning gland. Its hormones keep the endometrium soft, moist, thick, and engorged with blood, a condition suitable for maintaining pregnancy. The presence of estrogens and progesterone also inhibits production of FSH by the anterior pituitary gland, so no new follicles and eggs mature during pregnancy.

Five days after implantation (the 25th day of the cycle), the embryo becomes deeply embedded in the inner lining of the uterus and begins to receive nutrients by diffusion from the endometrium. Extraembryonic membranes form, and the *amniotic sac* becomes filled with fluid to cushion the embryo during its development. By the age of 2 or 3 weeks, the embryo begins to receive maternal nutrients through the *placenta*—a system of blood vessels that develops between the embryo and the maternal circulatory system. This organ also serves as a gland and produces hormones that stimulate the corpus luteum to continue to produce estrogens and progesterone. These hormones help maintain the uterus in a suitable condition for embryonic development. During the third month of pregnancy, the placenta itself begins to produce estrogens and progesterone and the corpus luteum gradually degenerates.

49.40 What causes the birth of more than one offspring at a time?

🐤 A rare occurrence in humans but common in other mammals is the release of more than one egg into one or both oviducts at the same time. If all of these eggs are fertilized, they develop simultaneously and produce more than one infant. These *fraternal* siblings (twins, triplets, etc.) in humans or litter mates in other mammals are as genetically similar as siblings from single births of the same parents; each offspring develops from a different fertilized egg.

Litter size in mammals is a species-specific trait, modified to some extent by environmental conditions. The normal litter size for humans is one, and the tendency in some family lines to produce twins is a genetic trait in women of those families.

Identical siblings are formed from a *single* fertilized egg in which the developing embryo divides into two or more separate parts sometime during the first 2 weeks of development. The occurrence of identical siblings is an accident of development rather than an inherited trait.

FERTILIZATION

49.41   The acrosome of a sperm contains

(*a*) hydrolytic enzymes.   (*b*) DNA.   (*c*) mitochondria.   (*d*) fructose.

49.42   The function of bindin (a protein) in the acrosomal process is to

(*a*) prevent more than one sperm from entering the egg.   (*b*) digest the vitelline layer.   (*c*) ensure that the egg is being fertilized by a sperm of the same species.   (*d*) sever the sperm's tail.

49.43   The fertilization cone, which pulls the sperm into the egg, is formed from the

(*a*) acrosome of the sperm.   (*b*) acrosomal process of the sperm.   (*c*) vitelline layer of the egg.   (*d*) plasma membrane of the egg.

49.44   The fast block to polyspermy develops in response to the

(*a*) opening of sodium gates in the plasma membrane.   (*b*) release of bindin.   (*c*) spreading of the fertilization cone around the egg.   (*d*) formation of the fertilization membrane.

49.45   The slow block to polyspermy develops in response to the

(*a*) opening of sodium gates in the plasma membrane.   (*b*) release of bindin.   (*c*) spreading of the fertilization cone around the egg.   (*d*) formation of the fertilization membrane.

49.46   On its route into an egg, a sperm _____ its way through the surrounding gel, attaches its _____ proteins to special receptor molecules on the _____, and moves (probably by hydrolyzing this material) to the _____ of the egg, which forms a fertilization cone.   Then the two _____ fuse, and the sperm _____ is drawn into the egg.

49.47   Cortical granules, which are vesicles in the egg cortex, respond to increased concentrations of _____ by secreting materials that elevate the _____ and cause it to form the _____, which prevents the entry of additional sperm.

49.48   A fertilized egg increases its rate of cellular respiration and protein synthesis in response to _____ ions.   The ions indirectly activate the egg by causing an increase in the cell's _____.

49.49   An enucleated egg can be artificially activated (by injecting it with calcium ions or pricking it with a needle) to increase its protein synthesis, which means that _____ must have been made prior to fertilization and stored in the cytoplasm.

49.50   What prevents more than one sperm from entering an egg?

⊕   An egg reacts rapidly to the entry of a sperm.   The plasma membrane is altered immediately to make it impossible for another sperm to penetrate.   The *fast block* to polyspermy, which occurs instantly, develops when sodium gates in the egg's plasma membrane open in response to fusion of this membrane with the sperm's plasma membrane.   Sodium ions rush into the egg and cause a change in membrane potential that in some way blocks the entry of additional sperm.   This barrier, however, is only temporary because the egg cannot function with an unchecked inflow of sodium ions.

A *slow block* to polyspermy develops within a minute after the fast block.   Calcium ions released from storage areas within the endoplasmic reticulum, in response to the change in membrane potential, cause small vesicles (called *cortical granules*) in the cortex of the cytoplasm to release their contents into the space between the plasma membrane and the vitelline layer.   These materials include enzymes and solutes.   One of the enzymes loosens the material between the membrane and vitelline layer.   The solutes cause an osmotic flow of water into the area, which swells and elevates the vitelline layer.   Another enzyme causes the outer part of the swollen vitelline layer to harden into a *fertilization membrane*, which forms a barrier to penetration by sperm.

EARLY STAGES OF DEVELOPMENT

49.51   Cleavage is a unique form of mitotic cell division in that

(*a*) the nucleus does not participate.   (*b*) there is no growth of the cells.   (*c*) no spindle develops to guide the chromosomes.   (*d*) the plasma membranes of daughter cells do not separate.

49.52 A cell formed from cleavage is called a

(*a*) blastomere. (*b*) morula. (*c*) blastula. (*d*) blastopore.

49.53 The solid ball of cells formed from cleavage is called the

(*a*) blastomere. (*b*) morula. (*c*) blastula. (*d*) blastopore.

49.54 The hollow ball of cells formed from cleavage is called the

(*a*) blastomere. (*b*) morula. (*c*) blastula. (*d*) blastocoel.

49.55 Which of the following organs develops first?

(*a*) Liver; (*b*) Heart; (*c*) Notochord; (*d*) Kidneys

49.56 Gastrulation converts a _____ into a _____ having three primary germ layers: an outermost layer of _____, a middle layer of _____, and an inner layer of _____. Gastrulation is brought about by an _____ of cells in the hollow-ball stage.

49.57 A gastrula has a new cavity (instead of a blastocoel) called the _____, which will eventually form the animal's _____. The opening of this cavity to the outside is the _____.

49.58 During organogenesis, the notochord forms from dorsal _____; the neural tube from dorsal _____; the muscles, skeleton, kidneys, and gonads from _____; the lungs, liver, pancreas, and lining of the digestive tract from _____; and the inner ear and eye lens from _____.

49.59 If amphibians, birds, and mammals are ranked in order of increasing proportion of yolk in their eggs, _____, which have the least yolk, come first, followed by _____, and then come _____, which have the most yolk.

49.60 Why does the pattern of early development vary so from one type of vertebrate to another?

🐚 Cleavage is a series of mitotic cell divisions that increases the number of cells but does not change the size of the original mass. The large zygote is therefore subdivided into a mass of smaller cells. As the mass becomes organized into smaller and smaller units, the particular developmental pattern that emerges is influenced by the amount of yolk, or nutrients, stored in the original zygote. The amount is identical for all individuals of a species but varies greatly among different species. Developing birds and reptiles require large quantities of stored nutrients because they have no access to other resources while they are enclosed in their shells. In contrast, mammals require very little yolk because they establish a connection with their mother's circulatory system and begin to receive nutrients from her blood early in their development. The zygotes of fishes and amphibians contain just enough yolk to carry them through the early stages of their development until they become self-feeding larvae.

The yolk is heavier than the rest of the material in the zygote and is concentrated in the lower part of the zygote. The rate at which cleavage occurs is always slower in areas where the concentration of yolk is high. Eggs with little yolk have *holoblastic cleavage*, in which the entire zygote or embryo divides with each cleavage. Eggs with large amounts of yolk have *meroblastic cleavage*, in which only the areas with little yolk participate in each cleavage.

Holoblastic cleavage in placental mammals produces *blastomeres* of equal size, which eventually form a *blastocyst* that implants in the wall of the uterus. Meroblastic cleavage in birds and reptiles is restricted to a tiny area that contains little yolk; it never extends throughout the entire egg. Many cleavages produce a flat disk of small cells, which float on the large volume of yolk below. Cleavage in fishes and amphibians is holoblastic but produces an asymmetrical blastula, because cleavage occurs more slowly in areas with more yolk. The blastula consists of tiny cells in the top half and larger cells in the bottom half.

MECHANISMS OF DEVELOPMENT

49.61 All three axes (left-right, dorsal-ventral, and anterior-posterior) of a frog egg are defined prior to cleavage. The first cleavage always bisects the gray crescent, which forms opposite the site of the

(*a*) blastopore. (*b*) opening into the neural tube. (*c*) point of sperm entry. (*d*) yolk plug.

49.62 In the 1920s, the German embryologist W. Vogt prepared a fate map of the amphibian embryo by dyeing different regions of the

(*a*) archenteron. (*b*) blastula. (*c*) fertilized egg. (*d*) gray crescent.

49.63 The process by which the developing notochord causes dorsal ectoderm above it to form a neural plate is known as

(*a*) induction.   (*b*) invagination.   (*c*) differentiation.   (*d*) morphogenesis.

49.64 A frog embryo separated into two parts after gastrulation develops into

(*a*) two unorganized masses of cells.   (*b*) one normal embryo and one undifferentiated mass.   (*c*) two normal embryos.   (*d*) two normal embryos and two undifferentiated masses.

49.65 The particular way that one cell of an embryo develops depends mostly on its _____. The ability of one group of cells to influence the development of another is called _____.

49.66 Cells of an embryo become specialized in structure and function by _____ different genes, i.e., by synthesizing different molecules of _____. This poorly understood process in eukaryotic cells is known as _____.

49.67 The German embryologists Hans Spemann and Hilde Mangold discovered, in the early 1900s, that the _____ of the _____ in an amphibian embryo induces the formation of the _____, which in turn induces development of the neural tube. They referred to this area as the primary _____ of the embryo.

49.68 If a two-celled frog embryo is separated along the line of its first cleavage, the two cells will form _____ embryo(s). If it is separated just prior to the two-celled stage, but along some other line, the two parts will form _____ embryo(s).

49.69 How do the genetically identical cells of an embryo become specialized in structure and function?

The process by which genetically identical cells of an embryo become specialized is known as *cellular differentiation*. In this process, only specific genes in each cell are "turned on," i.e., are transcribed into mRNA. Other genes, not needed for the cell's particular specialty, are "turned off" and not available for transcription. Once differentiation is accomplished, only certain genes within the cell continue to direct protein synthesis. For example, all of the cells in a vertebrate animal contain genes capable of directing the synthesis of actin and myosin and arranging these molecules into the structure of muscle fibrils; however, these genes are active only in the muscle cells.

It is not known how gene activity is regulated in animals, but the control systems are apparently passed on during cell division. When a differentiated cell divides, its descendants "inherit" the same capabilities for protein synthesis. Liver cells, for example, divide to form more liver cells; their structure and function are predetermined.

49.70 How was embryonic induction discovered?

The particular specialization that each cell acquires, or its pattern of differentiation, depends primarily on its location within the embryo. *Embryonic induction* is the process through which one group of cells influences the way in which another group of cells becomes differentiated.

The influence of developing cells on one another was first observed by a German experimental embryologist, Hans Spemann. Beginning in 1901, Spemann performed a variety of experiments on amphibian embryos in an attempt to determine which fragments of an embryo can produce all of the cell types necessary for the development of a complete individual. He found that if an embryo was separated into two parts prior to the gastrula stage, each part developed into a normal adult. If the embryo was divided after gastrulation, however, neither part developed normally. To determine at precisely what point during the formation of a gastrula the cells lost their ability to form individuals, Spemann divided embryos into fragments at various times during the process of gastrula formation and found that one part of a developing gastrula always produced a complete, normal individual and that the other parts yielded shapeless masses of cells. Further studies revealed that the part of the gastrula from which a normal individual developed always contained cells from the blastopore's *dorsal lip*—the indented area where the cells migrate inward.

As a demonstration of the special nature of the blastopore cells in directing differentiation, Spemann and his student, Hilde Mangold, removed cells from the dorsal lip of a salamander blastopore just prior to gastrulation and transplanted them onto another, normal salamander blastula. The host embryo, containing both its own blastopore and the foreign blastopore, developed into a sort of Siamese twin with two brains, spinal cords, and associated organs. Spemann and Mangold concluded that cells from the blastopore area cause other undifferentiated cells to begin the initial construction of an embryo. This phenomenon is now referred to as induction, and the dorsal lip of the blastopore is called the *primary organizer*, because it induces development of the notochord, which induces development of the neural tube, and so on.

HUMAN DEVELOPMENT

49.71 A human embryo begins to implant when it is a blastula, or has approximately 100 cells. How old is the embryo at this time?

(**a**) 12 hours;   (**b**) 2 days;   (**c**) 6 days;   (**d**) 2 weeks

49.72 What structure serves as a lung, digestive tract, and kidney for the developing embryo?

(**a**) Liver;   (**b**) Amnion;   (**c**) Placenta;   (**d**) Endometrium

49.73 How old is the embryo when most of its organs are formed?

(**a**) 2 months;   (**b**) 4 months;   (**c**) 6 months;   (**d**) 7 months

49.74 How old is the embryo when it becomes a fetus?

(**a**) 2 months;   (**b**) 4 months;   (**c**) 6 months;   (**d**) 7 months

49.75 The fluid released from the vagina just prior to childbirth is the

(**a**) baby's accumulated urine.   (**b**) amniotic fluid.   (**c**) mother's plasma from the umbilical cord.   (**d**) baby's plasma from its fetal circulation.

49.76 A placenta is made of _____ tissues, formed from the _____ of the blastocyst, and _____ tissues. It connects the embryo's _____ to the mother's _____ .

49.77 Of all the organ systems to develop, the _____ system is the first, appearing as early as the _____ week of development.

49.78 United States law defines a fetus as an individual when it is _____ old, because at that age it has a fair chance of surviving outside the womb.

49.79 A breech delivery, in which the _____ of the baby emerges last, may damage the baby because the _____ , which carries blood to the baby at that time, is squeezed between the baby's _____ and the mother's cervix. As a result, tissue damage, especially to the brain, may occur because of a lack of _____ during birth.

49.80 At what time during pregnancy are drugs most damaging to the developing child?

⚬   Drugs taken by the mother enter the baby's circulatory system by way of the *placenta*, a system of blood vessels that connects the embryonic and maternal circulatory systems. Not all materials can move freely between the bloodstreams of the mother and the embryo, however, because the connecting vessels are separated by membranes. Food molecules, oxygen, carbon dioxide, and embryonic waste materials, as well as some drugs, anesthetics, alcohol, antibodies, and certain viruses (including the virus that causes German measles) pass between the mother and the developing child. However, larger materials, such as red blood cells and most bacteria, cannot pass across these membranes, which also serve as a barrier to most maternal hormones and thereby protect male embryos from the influence of female hormones.

The major organs of the embryo form during the first 2 months of pregnancy. This is the most crucial period of development, when drugs can cause the most damage. Many women do not even know they are pregnant at this time and do not take the necessary precautions to ensure the normal formation of their child. Noxious chemicals, drugs, alcohol, irradiation, major viral infections, and certain other materials that the mother may be exposed to during this critical period can permanently deform the embryo. Although few of these substances have been definitely linked to the incidence of human birth defects, the effects of many chemicals on the developing embryo are now being studied. Even aspirin, which is readily available and massively consumed, has been associated with some developmental malformations. When narcotics are taken by the mother, the fetus is in danger of becoming addicted as well as deformed, and an addicted newborn will suffer severe withdrawal symptoms.

At least 20% of all pregnancies end in spontaneous abortions, or miscarriages, during the first 2 months of development. Most naturally aborted embryos have gross abnormalities caused by genetic defects or the introduction of damaging materials into the embryo from the mother's bloodstream.

Answers to Objective Questions

49.1 *b*
49.2 *d*
49.3 *b*
49.4 *c*
49.5 autumn; spring; food
49.6 hormones; day length
49.7 sexual; parthenogenic
49.8 courtship; release; gametes
49.9 many; small; few; high; resistant; internal; parental
49.11 *a*
49.12 *b*
49.13 *c*
49.14 *a*
49.15 *d*
49.16 *b*
49.17 *d*
49.18 testes; scrotum; sperm; testosterone
49.19 epididymis; vas deferens; urethra; vas deferens
49.20 seminal vesicles; prostate; bulbourethral glands; blood
49.21 ovaries; abdominal cavity; eggs; female sex hormones
49.22 follicle; ovary; oviduct; uterus; vagina
49.26 *c*
49.27 *d*
49.28 *c*
49.29 *c*
49.30 *d*
49.31 *d*

49.32 DNA; activate
49.33 DNA; acrosome; mitochondria; flagellum
49.34 embryo; fertilization
49.35 menstrual; endometrium; estrus
49.36 follicle-stimulating hormone; estrogens; follicle-stimulating hormone; luteinizing hormone; follicle-stimulating hormone; luteinizing hormone; corpus luteum; estrogens; progesterone
49.41 *a*
49.42 *c*
49.43 *d*
49.44 *a*
49.45 *d*
49.46 digests (or hydrolyzes); bindin; vitelline layer; plasma membrane; plasma membranes; nucleus
49.47 calcium ions; vitelline layer; fertilization membrane
49.48 calcium; pH
49.49 mRNA
49.51 *b*
49.52 *a*
49.53 *b*
49.54 *c*
49.55 *c*

49.56 blastula; gastrula; ectoderm; mesoderm; endoderm; invagination
49.57 archenteron; digestive tract; blastopore
49.58 mesoderm; ectoderm; mesoderm; endoderm; ectoderm
49.59 mammals; amphibians; birds
49.61 *c*
49.62 *b*
49.63 *a*
49.64 *a*
49.65 location; induction
49.66 expressing; mRNA; differentiation
49.67 dorsal lip; blastopore; notochord; organizer
49.68 two; one
49.71 *c*
49.72 *c*
49.73 *a*
49.74 *a*
49.75 *b*
49.76 embryonic; trophoblast; maternal; blood vessels; blood vessels
49.77 central nervous; third
49.78 7 months
49.79 head; umbilical cord; head; oxygen

CHAPTER 50
Adaptations to Climates

CLIMATES*

50.1   Macroclimate is controlled mostly by factors associated with

(*a*) vegetation.   (*b*) flatness of the terrain.   (*c*) latitude.   (*d*) longitude.

50.2   A microclimate is controlled mostly by irregularities in the land surface and by

(*a*) elevation.   (*b*) vegetation.   (*c*) latitude.   (*d*) cloud cover.

50.3   An organism's adaptations promote normal cellular activities within a restricted range of climatic conditions. This range is the organism's

(*a*) life span.   (*b*) reproductive stretch.   (*c*) range of latitude.   (*d*) tolerance range.

50.4   In which of the following habitats does the diurnal temperature of the soil surface vary most?

(*a*) Desert;   (*b*) Grassland;   (*c*) Shrubland;   (*d*) Forest

50.5   Which site in a forest has the lowest wind velocity?

(*a*) Above the canopy;   (*b*) In the canopy;   (*c*) Beneath the canopy but above the shrubs;   (*d*) Next to the ground

50.6   Which sites in a woodland receive the least precipitation?

(*a*) Areas between the canopies;   (*b*) Areas at the edge of a canopy;   (*c*) Areas halfway between the stem and the canopy edge;   (*d*) Areas next to the stem

50.7   An organism with a _____ tolerance range is restricted to specific microclimates. A prairie or tundra is a mosaic of different plant communities because there are slight variations in _____, which cause variations in the two products of climate: _____ and _____.

50.8   Vegetation influences microclimates by intercepting _____, _____, and _____.

50.9   The part of a plant that is most adapted to environmental temperatures is the _____. The part of an animal that is most adapted to environmental temperatures is the _____.

50.10   How does vegetation influence microclimates?

A *microclimate* is a local climate within a regional climate (or *macroclimate*). Irregularities of the land surface and the presence of vegetation are the main causes of microclimatic differences.

Vegetation influences microclimates by intercepting solar radiation, precipitation, and wind to modify the regional climate. A *closed canopy* causes vertical variations in light and temperature by forming a barrier to radiation. It shields the understory from incoming solar radiation in the daytime and traps outgoing heat radiation at night. An understory is cooler during the day and warmer during the night than the canopy above. A *discontinuous canopy*, as in a woodland, produces horizontal as well as vertical variations in light and temperature. The soil surface of an unshaded site accumulates more heat by day and loses more heat by night than the soil surface of a shaded site.

Vegetation intercepts precipitation to cause local variations in soil moisture. Rain or snow that accumulates on leaves evaporates and therefore provides no moisture for root uptake. Only when the leaf surfaces become saturated does water run off to the ground. As the total surface area of all leaves within a canopy is usually enormous, most of the water in precipitation evaporates rather than moistens the soil. The amount of precipi-

* Answers to Chapter 50 objective questions appear on page 364.

tation that reaches the ground increases with distance from the stem of a tree and often varies by as much as tenfold between stem and edge of the crown.

Vegetation deflects the wind so that the velocity of wind in a forest is about 20 to 60% of the velocity in open areas. Wind is most rapid above the canopy, less rapid within the canopy, and least rapid in the understory, especially right next to the ground. Wind is an important climatic variable, because by increasing convection, it increases the loss of heat and water from surfaces.

ADAPTATIONS TO WARM, WET CLIMATES

50.11 The leaves of plants in warm, wet, shaded microclimates are

(*a*) large and thin. (*b*) small and thin. (*c*) large and thick. (*d*) small and thick.

50.12 The leaves of rainforest trees get rid of heat mainly by

(*a*) radiation. (*b*) conduction. (*c*) convection. (*d*) evaporation.

50.13 A tropical vine, or liana, is a growth form adapted for gaining access to

(*a*) light. (*b*) pollinators. (*c*) water. (*d*) nutrients.

50.14 An epiphyte is a growth form adapted for gaining access to

(*a*) light. (*b*) pollinators. (*c*) water. (*d*) nutrients.

50.15 A class of animals that is well adapted to warm, wet climates but not well adapted to other types of climates is

(*a*) amphibians. (*b*) reptiles. (*c*) birds. (*d*) insects.

50.16 The particular form of a tree or vine in a tropical rainforest reflects the leaf's _____ position in the _____ .

50.17 The crown of a tropical rainforest tree is a dynamic structure; new leaves form in _____ areas and existing leaves are shed in _____ areas of the canopy.

50.18 Many epiphytes resemble desert plants, because their leaves are adapted to heat loss by _____ rather than by _____ .

50.19 Drip tips on leaves promote runoff of water from the leaf surface, a phenomenon known as _____ . Such removal of water is essential when the weather is _____ , for without it there would be no _____ and consequently no _____ .

50.20 How are plant leaves adapted to microclimates within a tropical rainforest?

🐚 Warm, wet climates yield such high densities of foliage that competition for light is a major selective force. Selection for access to light has led to the predominance of trees, vines, and epiphytes in tropical rainforests, because these growth forms have the ability to position their leaves above the leaves of other growth forms.

Trees and vines have their roots in the soil and their leaves in the canopy. The leaves absorb a lot of radiation and prevent overheating chiefly by evaporative cooling, since they have access to large amounts of soil water. Water evaporates from the stomata (i.e., by transpiration) as well as through the very thin cuticles of these leaves.

The size and shape of a leaf reflect its vertical position within the canopy. Leaves in the lower, shaded areas are large and thin with smooth margins; they maximize their surface areas for absorption of light and evaporation of water. Higher in the canopy, where direct solar radiation causes more overheating, the leaves are smaller with irregular margins, which are adaptations that increase convective heat loss. Emergent trees, with crowns above the canopy, have even smaller leaves with more irregular margins, since they absorb even more heat and are more exposed to air currents. Thus, the higher the position of the leaf in the canopy, the more heat it acquires and the more its form is adapted for convective heat loss. Nevertheless, all leaves of rainforest trees and vines lose most of their excess heat through evaporation.

Epiphytes are relatively small plants that position their leaves in the canopy by growing on the stems and branches of trees. They do not have access to soil water and must acquire it elsewhere. Many orchids have specialized root cells that act like sponges to absorb water from the tree bark. Bromeliads have leaves that fit closely together to form containers for collecting rainwater, which is then absorbed through leaf hairs and stored in the leaves. Some epiphytes have roots or leaves shaped as elaborate nets that accumulate debris, which holds moisture until it can be absorbed. Epiphytes with limited access to water have leaves adapted for heat loss by convection rather than by evaporation; many resemble the water-conserving leaves of desert plants.

ADAPTATIONS TO WARM, DRY CLIMATES

50.21 A leaf adapted to a warm, dry climate is

(**a**) large and thin. (**b**) small and thin. (**c**) large and thick. (**d**) small and thick.

50.22 The leaves of a desert plant get rid of excess heat mainly by

(**a**) radiation. (**b**) conduction. (**c**) convection. (**d**) evaporation.

50.23 The deep lobes or toothed margins of leaves function to increase the

(**a**) turbulence of air flow. (**b**) smoothness of air flow. (**c**) conduction of heat. (**d**) area for stomata.

50.24 Desert annuals survive outside the rainy season as

(**a**) leafless stems. (**b**) dormant roots. (**c**) seeds. (**d**) drought-resistant gametes.

50.25 The silvery hairs on the surfaces of the leaves of desert plants and the bodies of desert insects function to

(**a**) reflect solar radiation. (**b**) promote convection. (**c**) promote evaporation. (**d**) increase the ratio of surface area to volume for radiation.

50.26 A desert plant prevents overheating in one of three major ways: (1) by xeromorphic (drought-adapted) leaves that promote heat loss from _____; (2) by nonxeromorphic leaves that are _____ during very dry periods; (3) by being a _____ succulent.

50.27 The leaf of a creosote bush is small and deeply lobed. It maintains an internal temperature within a few degrees of the air temperature by losing heat through _____ at the same rate as it gains heat through _____. Evaporative heat loss is minimized by _____ its _____ during the heat of midday.

50.28 A kangaroo rat exists with no intake of free water, which is water already formed in food and drink. Its only source of water is from its _____. A kangaroo rat's kidneys are especially well adapted for _____ water.

50.29 How are the leaves of desert plants adapted to get rid of heat with minimal water loss?

✦ Most plants are killed by temperatures exceeding 50 °C, which are not at all uncommon temperatures on the surfaces of inanimate objects in the desert. Plants prevent such accumulation of heat by having: (1) *xeromorphic* (drought-adapted) leaves that promote convective heat loss; (2) *nonxeromorphic* leaves that are present only when or where water is plentiful (i.e., the plant is deciduous or has deep roots that tap a water table for water that can be used in evaporative heat loss); or (3) no leaves at all (e.g., a cactus).

Xeromorphic leaves are small with deeply lobed or toothed margins, a size and shape that increase turbulent air flow on the leaf surface and so promote convective heat loss. The leaf of a creosote bush, for example, loses heat by convection at about the same rate as it gains heat by radiation. Turbulent air flow, however, also increases evaporation from a surface, which these plants cannot afford. Evaporation is prevented by thick, waxy cuticles that cover the leaf surfaces. The loss of water is restricted to the stomata, which are kept closed during the scorching midday heat. While the stomata are closed, the leaves are positioned vertically, with only their thin margins facing the sun, or are rolled to form an even smaller surface and allow greater convective heat loss. The leaves of many desert plants are further covered with highly reflectant hairs or thorns that prevent some of the light from reaching their surfaces. Photosynthesis cannot take place when the stomata are closed, and many desert plants have either the C-4 photosynthetic pathway, which enables them to keep their stomata closed during about half the day, or the CAM pathway, which enables them to open their stomata only at night (see Questions 8.73 and 8.75).

50.30 How can a desert mammal survive without drinking water or eating succulent foods?

⚜ Most mammals need to drink water or to eat foods with high water content in order to maintain appropriate concentrations of water in their bodies. Some rodents, notably the kangaroo rat, some pocket mice, and the jerboa, are so adapted for conserving water that they can maintain a water balance by inputs from metabolic water alone. Metabolic water, in contrast with free water, is formed within cells as a waste product of cellular respiration, dehydration synthesis, and a variety of other reactions.

Desert rodents with only metabolic water as their water source eat dry seeds and do not produce unusually large amounts of water from metabolism. Nor are they any more tolerant of dehydration than other mammals. Instead, they are extraordinary in their ability to conserve the little water they do acquire. The kangaroo rat, for example, is nocturnal, produces very concentrated urine (has unusually long loops of Henle in its nephrons), has only a few sweat glands in its toe pads, is coprophagous (eats its own feces) in order to absorb more water, and cools its nasal passages by evaporation in such a way that the water vapor is condensed, and so conserved, prior to leaving the nose.

ADAPTATIONS TO COLD CLIMATES

50.31 By growing close to the ground, a tundra plant

(*a*) avoids the wind. (*b*) avoids herbivores. (*c*) attracts pollinators. (*d*) forms mutualistic relations with soil animals.

50.32 The leaves of a tundra plant resemble the leaves of a plant in a

(*a*) tropical rainforest. (*b*) temperate deciduous forest. (*c*) northern coniferous forest. (*d*) desert.

50.33 The function of red pigments in tundra plants is to

(*a*) expand the range of light used in photosynthesis. (*b*) warm the plants. (*c*) track the sun. (*d*) measure time.

50.34 Transparent hairs on catkins and caterpillars function to

(*a*) trap heat. (*b*) trap moisture. (*c*) reflect light. (*d*) collect dew.

50.35 An insect survives the cold of winter in a dormant stage by converting its glycogen to

(*a*) ATP. (*b*) alcohol. (*c*) lactic acid. (*d*) brown fat.

50.36 A woody plant becomes acclimatized, or "hardened," to the cold in preparation for winter. It lowers the freezing point of its cells and fluids by increasing the _____ of its _____.

50.37 A conifer needle promotes a _____ air flow, which reduces the loss of heat by _____ and the loss of water by _____.

50.38 Most tundra plants have a life span of _____ year(s).

50.39 Trees in cold climates survive the physiological drought of winter by having _____ leaves or by being _____.

50.40 How are the leaves of a conifer adapted to cold climates?

⚜ Plants of cold climates resemble those of deserts in that they are adapted to reduce transpiration during the dry season, which is winter in a cold climate. Thus, trees either shed their leaves in winter or have xeromorphic leaves that withstand the physiological drought when water is frozen and inaccessible.

Deciduous forests are found where winters are sufficiently short that a tree can grow and reproduce in spite of a dormant winter period. As the winter season becomes longer, the warm season becomes too short for a tree to remain dormant in winter and still photosynthesize enough sugars for growth and reproduction.

Evergreen conifers, with leaves adapted to cold and drought, prevail where the winters are long. The pyramidal crown of a conifer efficiently absorbs solar radiation at low sun angles, and its shorter branches increase its ability to shed snow from the leaves, making it possible to photosynthesize throughout the winter. A conifer needle promotes a streamlined flow of air, which reduces convection and transpiration. The dense clusters of short needles, especially in the spruce and fir trees that dominate the northern forests, absorb heat that has been radiated from adjacent needles and from the branch. They also form a barrier to wind flow so that heat and water vapor are held within the almost still air of the cluster. A waxy cuticle further reduces evaporation.

A conifer needle is also structured to absorb a great deal of solar radiation. It has a high ratio of surface area to volume as well as pigments that absorb more wavelengths of light than the pigments of other plants. Conifer leaves can photosynthesize whenever their internal temperatures exceed $-10\,°C$.

Answers to Objective Questions

50.1 *c*

50.2 *b*

50.3 *d*

50.4 *a*

50.5 *d*

50.6 *d*

50.7 narrow; elevation; soil moisture; temperature

50.8 solar radiation; precipitation; wind

50.9 leaf; body surface

50.11 *a*

50.12 *d*

50.13 *a*

50.14 *a*

50.15 *a*

50.16 vertical; canopy

50.17 unshaded; shaded

50.18 convection; evaporation

50.19 guttation; humid; transpiration; mineral uptake

50.21 *d*

50.22 *c*

50.23 *a*

50.24 *c*

50.25 *a*

50.26 convection; shed; leafless

50.27 convection; radiation; closing; stomata

50.28 metabolism; conserving

50.31 *a*

50.32 *d*

50.33 *b*

50.34 *a*

50.35 *b*

50.36 concentration; solutes

50.37 streamlined; convection; transpiration

50.38 many

50.39 xeromorphic; deciduous